DAV.

WD9

D1499527

basic
electricity

by VAN VALKENBURGH,
NOOGER & NEVILLE, INC.

VOL. 1

HAYDEN BOOK COMPANY, INC.
Rochelle Park, New Jersey

PREFACE

The texts of the entire Basic Electricity and Basic Electronics courses, as currently taught at Navy specialty schools, have now been released by the Navy for civilian use. This educational program has been an unqualified success. Since April, 1953, when it was first installed, over 25,000 Navy trainees have benefited by this instruction and the results have been outstanding.

The unique simplification of an ordinarily complex subject, the exceptional clarity of illustrations and text, and the plan of presenting one basic concept at a time, without involving complicated mathematics, all combine in making this course a better and quicker way to teach and learn basic electricity and electronics. The Basic Electronics portion of this course will be available as a separate series of volumes.

In releasing this material to the general public, the Navy hopes to provide the means for creating a nation-wide pool of pre-trained technicians, upon whom the Armed Forces could call in time of national emergency, without the need for precious weeks and months of schooling.

Perhaps of greater importance is the Navy's hope that through the release of this course, a direct contribution will be made toward increasing the technical knowledge of men and women throughout the country, as a step in making and keeping America strong.

Van Valkenburgh, Nooger and Neville, Inc.

New York, N. Y.
October, 1954

TABLE OF CONTENTS

Vol. 1 — Basic Electricity

The Electron Theory

All the effects of electricity take place because of the existence of a tiny particle called the "electron." Since no one actually has seen an electron, but only the effects it produces, we call the laws governing its behavior the "electron theory." The electron theory is not only the basis of design for all electrical and electronic equipment, it explains physical and chemical action and is helping scientists to probe into the very nature of the universe and life itself.

Since assuming that the electron exists has led to so many important discoveries in electricity, electronics, chemistry and atomic physics, we can safely assume that the electron really exists. All electrical and electronic equipment has been designed using the electron theory. Since the electron theory has always worked for everyone, it will always work for you.

Your entire study of electricity will be based upon the electron theory. The electron theory assumes that all electrical and electronic effects are due to the movement of electrons from place to place or that there are too many or too few electrons in a particular place.

When electrons move, THINGS HAPPEN!

The Electron Theory (continued)

According to the electron theory, all electrical and electronic effects are caused either by the movement of electrons from place to place or because there is an excess or lack of electrons at a particular place. Before working with electricity, you will want to know what an electron is and what causes it to move in a material.

All matter is composed of atoms of many different sizes and different complexities. But all atoms are alike in consisting of a nucleus surrounded by electrons that move about the nucleus. The nucleus and the number of electrons vary for each of the elements. The simplest element, hydrogen, has only one electron in orbit about the nucleus while some of the complex man-made heavy elements from atomic reactors can have more than 100 electrons in orbit around the nucleus. Because the electron is part of an atom, you will need to know something about the atomic structure of matter.

THE ELECTRON IS ELECTRICITY

WHAT ELECTRICITY IS

The Breakdown of Matter

You have heard that electrons are tiny particles of electricity, but you may not have a very clear idea of the part electrons play in making up all the materials around us. You can find out about the electron by carefully examining the composition of any ordinary material—say a drop of water.

If you take this drop of water and divide it into two drops, divide one of these two drops into two smaller drops and repeat this process a few thousand times, you will have a very tiny drop of water. This tiny drop will be so small that you will need the best microscope made today in order to see it.

DIVIDING A DROP OF WATER

IMAGE SEEN

This tiny drop of water will still have all the chemical characteristics of water. It can be examined by a chemist, and he will not be able to find any chemical difference between this microscopic drop and an ordinary glass of water.

The Breakdown of Matter (continued)

Now if you take this tiny drop of water and try to divide it in half any further, you will not be able to see it in your microscope. Imagine that you have available a super microscope which will magnify many times as much as any microscope presently existing. This microscope can give you any magnification you want, so you can put your tiny drop of water under it and proceed to divide it into smaller and smaller droplets.

As the droplet of water is divided into smaller and smaller droplets, these tiny droplets will still have all the chemical characteristics of water. However, you eventually will have a droplet so small that any further division will cause it to lose the chemical characteristics of water. This last bit of water is called a "molecule." If you examine the water molecule under high magnification, you will see that it is composed of three parts closely bonded together.

THIS IS WHAT HE SEES

The Structure of the Molecule

When you increase the magnifying power of the microscope, you will see that the water molecule is made up of two tiny structures that are the same and a larger structure that is different from the two. These tiny structures are called "atoms." The two tiny atoms which are the same are hydrogen atoms and the larger different one is an oxygen atom. When two atoms of hydrogen combine with one atom of oxygen, you have a molecule of water.

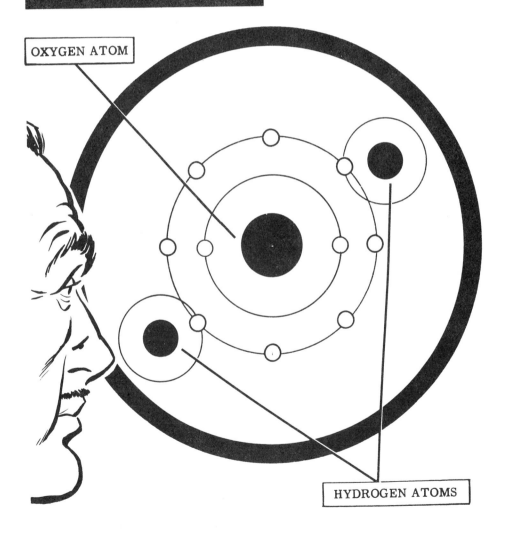

THE WATER MOLECULE

OXYGEN ATOM

HYDROGEN ATOMS

The Structure of the Molecule (continued)

While water is made up of only two kinds of atoms—oxygen and hydrogen —the molecules of many materials are more complex in structure. Cellulose molecules, the basic molecules of which wood is made, consist of three different kinds of atoms—carbon, hydrogen and oxygen. All materials are made up of different combinations of atoms to form molecules of the materials. There are only about 100 different kinds of atoms and these are known as elements: oxygen, carbon, hydrogen, iron, gold, nitrogen are all elements. The human body with all its complex tissues, bones, teeth, etc. is made up mainly of 15 elements, and only six of these are found in reasonable quantities.

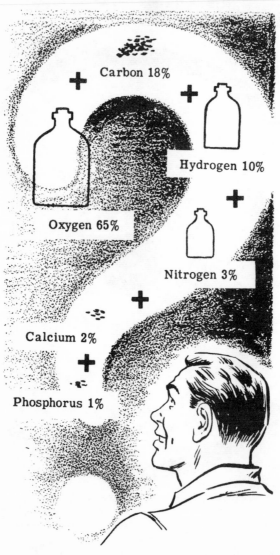

Carbon 18%

Hydrogen 10%

Oxygen 65%

Nitrogen 3%

Calcium 2%

Phosphorus 1%

The Structure of the Atom

Now that you know that all materials are made up of molecules which consist of various combinations of about only 100 different types of atoms, you will want to know what all this has to do with electricity. Increase the magnification of your imaginery super microscope still further and examine one of the atoms you find in the water molecule. Pick out the smallest atom you can see—the hydrogen atom—and examine it closely.

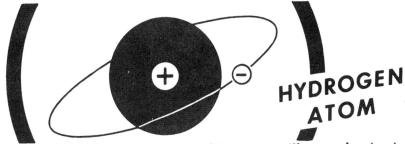

HYDROGEN ATOM

You see that the hydrogen atom is like a sun with one planet spinning around it. The planet is known as an "electron" and the sun is known as the "nucleus." The electron has a negative charge of electricity and the nucleus has a positive charge of electricity.

In an atom, the total number of negatively-charged electrons circling around the nucleus exactly equals the number of extra positive charges in the nucleus. The positive charges are called "protons." Besides the protons, the nucleus also contains electrically neutral particles called "neutrons," which are like a proton and an electron bonded together. Atoms of different elements contain different numbers of neutrons within the nucleus, but the number of electrons spinning about the nucleus always equals the number of free protons (or positive charges) within the nucleus.

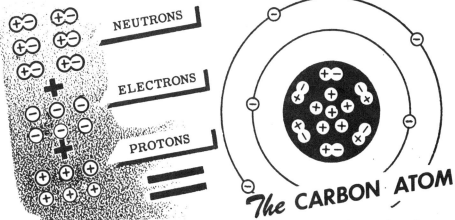

NEUTRONS

ELECTRONS

PROTONS

The CARBON ATOM

Electrons in the outer orbits of an atom are attracted to the nucleus by less force than electrons whose orbits are near the nucleus. These outer electrons are called "free" electrons and may be easily forced from their orbits, while electrons in the inner orbits are called "bound" electrons since they cannot be forced out of their orbits easily. It is the motion of the free electrons that makes up an electric current.

1-7

Review of Electricity—What It Is

Now let's stop and review what you have found out about electricity and the electron theory. Then you will be ready to study where electricity comes from.

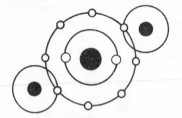

1. <u>MOLECULE</u>—The combination of two or more atoms.

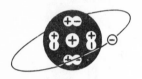

2. <u>ATOM</u>—The smallest physical particle into which an element can be divided.

3. <u>NUCLEUS</u>—The heavy positively-charged part of the atom which does not move.

4. <u>NEUTRON</u>—The heavy neutral particle in the nucleus consisting of a proton and an electron.

5. <u>PROTON</u>—The heavy positively-charged particle in the nucleus.

6. <u>ELECTRON</u>—The very small negatively-charged particle which is practically weightless and circles the nucleus.

7. BOUND ELECTRONS—Electrons in the inner orbits of an atom, which cannot easily be forced out of their orbits.

8. FREE ELECTRONS—Electrons that have left the orbit of an atom and are wandering freely through a material.

9. ELECTRICITY—The effect of electrons in moving from point to point, or the effect of too many (excess) or too few (lack of) electrons in a material.

HOW ELECTRICITY IS PRODUCED

The Six Sources of Electricity

To produce electricity, some form of energy must be used to bring about the action of electrons. The six basic sources of energy which can be used are FRICTION, PRESSURE, HEAT, LIGHT, MAGNETISM and CHEMICAL ACTION. Before getting into the study of these sources, you will first find out about electric charges.

FRICTION

CHEMICAL ACTION

PRESSURE

THE ELECTRON theory

MAGNETISM

HEAT

LIGHT

Electric Charges

You found that electrons travel around the nucleus of an atom and are held in their orbits by the attraction of the positive charge in the nucleus. If you could somehow force an electron out of its orbit, then the electron's action would become what is known as electricity.

Electrons which are forced out of their orbits in some way will leave a lack of electrons in the material which they leave and will cause an excess of electrons to exist at the point where they come to rest. This excess of electrons in one material is called a "negative" charge while the lack of electrons in the other material is called a "positive" charge. When these charges exist you have what is called "static" electricity.

To cause either a "positive" or "negative" charge, the electron must be moved while the positive charges in the nucleus do not move. Any material which has a "positive charge" will have its normal number of positive charges in the nucleus but will have electrons missing or lacking. However, a material which is negatively charged actually has an excess of electrons.

You are now ready to find out how friction can produce this excess or lack of electrons to cause static electricity.

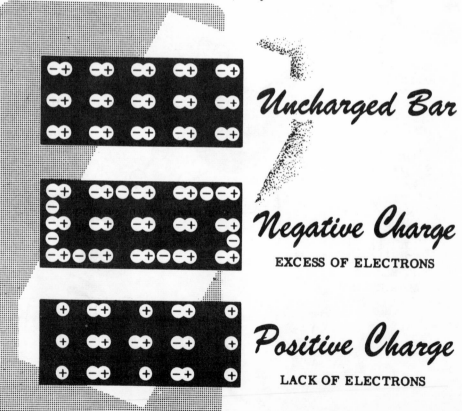

Uncharged Bar

Negative Charge
EXCESS OF ELECTRONS

Positive Charge
LACK OF ELECTRONS

Static Charges from Friction

You have studied the electron and the meaning of positive and negative charges, so that you are now ready to find out how these charges are produced. The main source of static electricity which you will use is friction. If you should rub two different materials together, electrons may be forced out of their orbits in one material and captured in the other. The material which captures electrons would then have a negative charge and the material which loses electrons would have a positive charge.

When two materials rub together, due to friction contact, some electron orbits of the materials cross each other and one material may give up electrons to the other. If this happens, static charges are built up in the two materials, and friction has thus been a source of electricity. The charge which you might cause to exist could be either positive or negative depending on which material gives up electrons more freely.

Some materials which easily build up static electricity are glass, amber, hard rubber, waxes, flannel, silk, rayon and nylon. When hard rubber is rubbed with fur, the fur loses electrons to the rod—the rod becomes negatively charged and the fur positively charged. When glass is rubbed with silk, the glass rod loses electrons—the rod becomes positively charged and the silk negatively charged. You will find out that a static charge may transfer from one material to another without friction, but the original source of these static charges is friction.

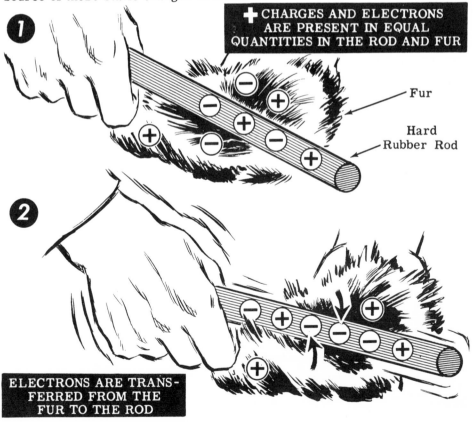

1

+ CHARGES AND ELECTRONS ARE PRESENT IN EQUAL QUANTITIES IN THE ROD AND FUR

Fur

Hard
Rubber Rod

2

ELECTRONS ARE TRANSFERRED FROM THE FUR TO THE ROD

Attraction and Repulsion of Charges

When materials are charged with static electricity they behave in a manner different from normal. For instance, if you place a positively charged ball near one which is charged negatively, the balls will attract each other. If the charges are great enough and the balls are light and free to move, they will come into contact. Whether they are free to move or not, a force of attraction always exists between unlike charges.

This attraction takes place because the excess electrons of a negative charge are trying to find a place where extra electrons are needed. If you bring two materials of opposite charges together, the excess electrons of the negative charge will transfer to the material having a lack of electrons. This transfer or crossing over of electrons from a negative to a positive charge is called "discharge."

Using two balls with the same type of charge, either positive or negative, you would find that they repel each other.

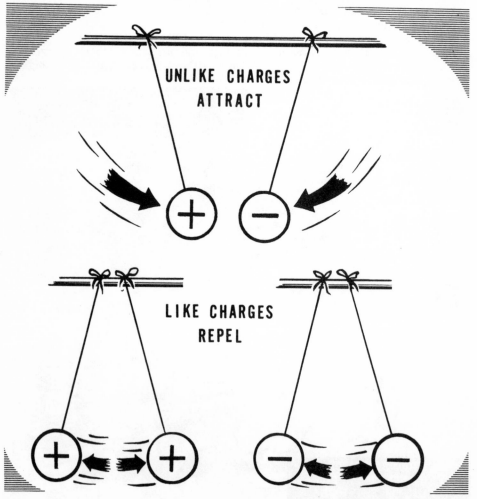

UNLIKE CHARGES
ATTRACT

LIKE CHARGES
REPEL

Transfer of Static Charges through Contact

While most static charges are due to friction, you will find that they may also be caused by other means. If an object has a static charge, it will influence all other nearby objects. This influence may be exerted through contact or induction.

Positive charges mean a lack of electrons and always attract electrons, while negative charges mean an excess of electrons and always repel electrons.

If you should touch a positively charged rod to an uncharged metal bar, it will attract electrons in the bar to the point of contact. Some of these electrons will leave the bar and enter the rod, causing the bar to become positively charged and decreasing the positive charge of the rod.

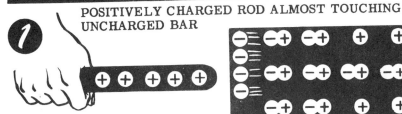

Giving a Bar a Positive Charge

POSITIVELY CHARGED ROD ALMOST TOUCHING UNCHARGED BAR

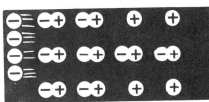

ELECTRONS ARE ATTRACTED BY POSITIVE CHARGE

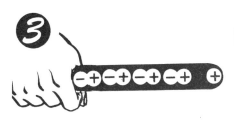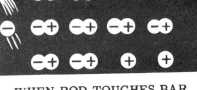

WHEN ROD TOUCHES BAR, ELECTRONS ENTER ROD

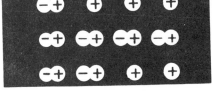

THE ROD IS NOW LESS POSITIVELY CHARGED

METAL BAR NOW HAS POSITIVE CHARGE

Transfer of Static Charges through Contact (continued)

By touching a negatively charged rod to the uncharged bar, you would cause the bar also to become negatively charged. As the negatively charged rod is brought near the uncharged bar, electrons in that portion of the bar nearest the rod would be repelled toward the side opposite the rod. The portion of the bar near the rod will then be charged positively and the opposite side will be charged negatively. As the rod is touched to the bar, some of the excess electrons in the negatively charged rod will flow into the bar to neutralize the positive charge in that portion of the bar but the opposite side of the bar retains its negative charge.

When the rod is lifted away from the bar, the negative charge remains in the bar and the rod is still negatively charged but has very few excess electrons. When a charged object touches an uncharged object, it loses some of its charge to the uncharged object until each has the same amount of charge.

Giving a Bar a Negative Charge

1 NEGATIVELY CHARGED ROD ALMOST TOUCHING

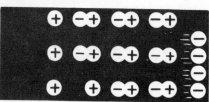

ELECTRONS IN BAR ARE
REPELLED BY NEGATIVE ROD

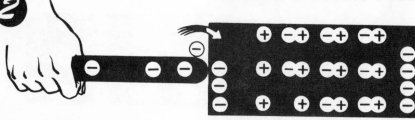

2

WHEN ROD TOUCHES BAR,
ELECTRONS JOIN POSITIVE CHARGES

3

ROD IS LESS
NEGATIVELY CHARGED

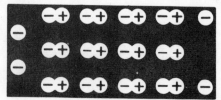

METAL BAR NOW HAS AN EXCESS
OF NEGATIVE CHARGES

Transfer of Static Charges through Induction

You have seen what happens when you touch a metal bar with a positively charged rod. Some of the charge on the rod is transferred and the bar becomes charged. Suppose that instead of touching the bar with the rod, you only bring the positively charged rod near to the bar. In that case, electrons in the bar would be attracted to the point nearest the rod, causing a negative charge at that point. The opposite side of the bar would again lack electrons and be charged positive. Three charges would then exist, the positive charge in the rod, the negative charge in the bar at the point nearest the rod and a positive charge in the bar on the side opposite the rod. By allowing electrons from an outside source (your finger, for instance) to enter the positive end of the bar, you can give the bar a negative charge.

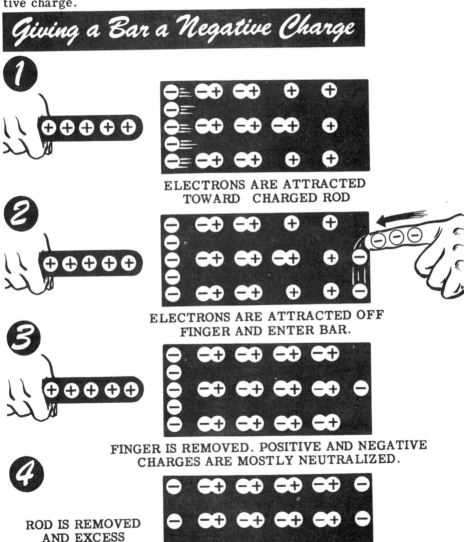

Giving a Bar a Negative Charge

1 ELECTRONS ARE ATTRACTED TOWARD CHARGED ROD

2 ELECTRONS ARE ATTRACTED OFF FINGER AND ENTER BAR.

3 FINGER IS REMOVED. POSITIVE AND NEGATIVE CHARGES ARE MOSTLY NEUTRALIZED.

4 ROD IS REMOVED AND EXCESS ELECTRONS REMAIN

Transfer of Static Charges through Induction (continued)

If the rod is negatively charged when brought near to the bar, it will induce a positive charge into that end of the bar which is near the rod.
Electrons in that portion of **the bar** will be repelled and will move to the
opposite end of the bar. The original negative charge of the rod then
causes two additional charges, one positive and one negative, in the bar.

Removing the rod will leave the bar uncharged since the excess electrons
in the negatively charged end will flow back to neutralize the bar. However, if before the rod is moved a path is provided for the electrons in
the negatively charged portion of the bar to flow out of the bar, the entire
bar will be positively charged when the rod is removed.

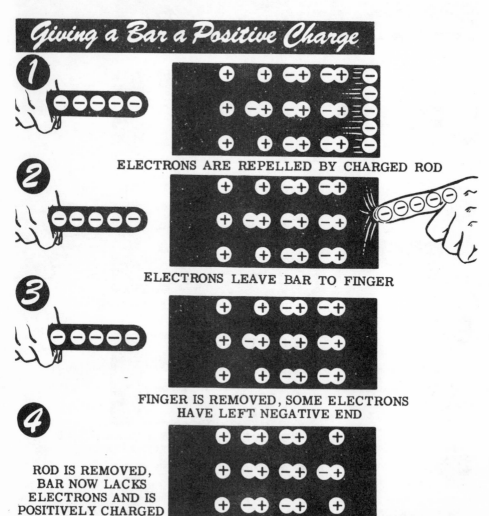

Giving a Bar a Positive Charge

1 ELECTRONS ARE REPELLED BY CHARGED ROD

2 ELECTRONS LEAVE BAR TO FINGER

3 FINGER IS REMOVED, SOME ELECTRONS
HAVE LEFT NEGATIVE END

4 ROD IS REMOVED,
BAR NOW LACKS
ELECTRONS AND IS
POSITIVELY CHARGED

You have discovered that static charges can be caused by friction and contact, or induction. Now you should see how the excess or lack of electrons
in the charged body may be neutralized, or discharged.

Discharge of Static Charges

Whenever two materials are charged with opposite charges and placed near one another, the excess electrons on the negatively charged material will be pulled toward the positively charged material. By connecting a wire from one material to the other, you would provide a path for the electrons of the negative charge to cross over to the positive charge, and the charges would thereby neutralize. Instead of connecting the materials with a wire, you might touch them together (contact) and again the charges would disappear.

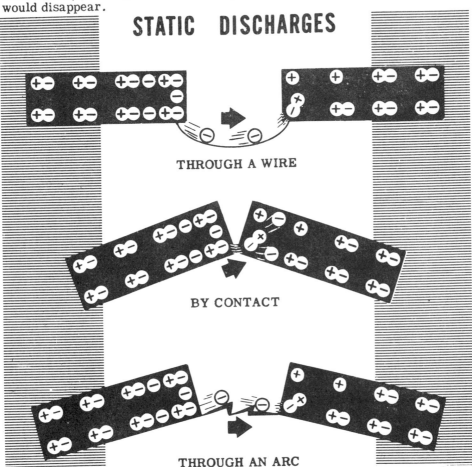

STATIC DISCHARGES

THROUGH A WIRE

BY CONTACT

THROUGH AN ARC

If you use materials with strong charges, the electrons may jump from the negative charge to the positive charge before the two materials are actually in contact. In that case, you would actually see the discharge in the form of an arc. With very strong charges, static electricity can discharge across large gaps, causing arcs many feet in length.

Lightning is an example of the discharge of static electricity resulting from the accumulation of a static charge in a cloud as it moves through the air. Natural static charges are built up wherever friction occurs between the air molecules, such as with moving clouds or high winds, and you will find that these charges are greatest in a very dry climate, or elsewhere when the humidity is low.

HOW FRICTION PRODUCES ELECTRICITY

Review of Friction and Static Electric Charges

You have now found out about friction as a source of electricity, and you have seen and participated in a demonstration of how static electric charges are produced and their effect on charged and uncharged materials. You have also seen how static charges can be transferred by contact or induction, and you have learned about some of the useful applications of static electricity.

Before going on to learn about the other basic sources of electricity, you should review those facts which you have already learned.

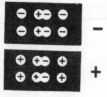

1. <u>NEGATIVE CHARGE</u> — An excess of electrons.

2. <u>POSITIVE CHARGE</u> — A lack of electrons.

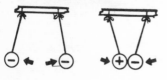

3. <u>REPULSION OF CHARGES</u> — Like charges repel each other.

4. <u>ATTRACTION OF CHARGES</u> — Unlike charges attract each other.

5. <u>STATIC ELECTRICITY</u> — Electric charges at rest.

6. <u>FRICTION CHARGE</u> — A charge caused by rubbing one material against another.

7. <u>CONTACT CHARGE</u> — Transfer of a charge from one material to another by direct contact.

8. <u>INDUCTION CHARGE</u> — Transfer of a charge from one material to another without actual contact.

9. <u>CONTACT DISCHARGE</u> — Electrons crossing over from a negative charge to positive through contact.

10. <u>ARC DISCHARGE</u> — Electrons crossing over from a negative charge to positive through an arc.

When you have completed your review of friction and static electric charges, you will go on to learn about <u>pressure</u> as a source of electricity.

HOW PRESSURE PRODUCES ELECTRICITY

Electric Charges from Pressure

Whenever you speak into a telephone, or other type of microphone, the pressure waves of the sound energy move a diaphragm. In some cases, the diaphragm moves a coil of wire past a magnet, generating electrical energy which is transmitted through wires to a receiver. Microphones used with public address systems and radio transmitters sometimes operate on this principle. Other microphones, however, convert the pressure waves of sound directly into electricity.

Crystals of certain materials will develop electrical charges if a pressure is exerted on them. Quartz, tourmaline, and Rochelle salts are materials which illustrate the principle of pressure as a source of electricity. If a crystal made of these materials is placed between two metal plates and a pressure is exerted on the plates, an electric charge will be developed. The size of the charge produced between the plates will depend on the amount of pressure exerted.

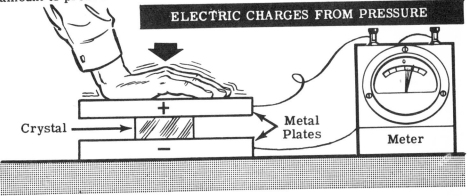

ELECTRIC CHARGES FROM PRESSURE

Crystal — Metal Plates — Meter

The crystal can be used to convert electrical energy to mechanical energy by placing a charge on the plates, since the crystal will expand or contract depending on the amount and type of the charge.

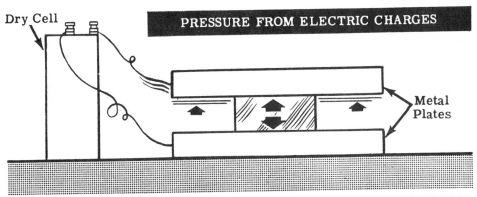

PRESSURE FROM ELECTRIC CHARGES

Dry Cell — Metal Plates

While the actual use of pressure as a source of electricity is limited to very low power applications, you will find it in many different kinds of equipment. Crystal microphones, crystal headphones, phonograph pickups and sonar equipment use crystals to generate electric charges from pressure.

HOW HEAT PRODUCES ELECTRICITY

Electric Charges from Heat

Another method of obtaining electricity is to convert heat into electricity directly, by heating a junction of two dissimilar metals. For example, if an iron wire and a copper wire are twisted together to form a junction, and the junction is heated, an electric charge will result. The amount of charge produced depends on the difference in temperature between the junction and the opposite ends of the two wires. A greater temperature difference results in a greater charge.

A junction of this type is called a thermo-couple and will produce electricity as long as heat is applied. While twisted wires may form a thermo-couple, more efficient thermo-couples are constructed of two pieces of dissimilar metal riveted or welded together.

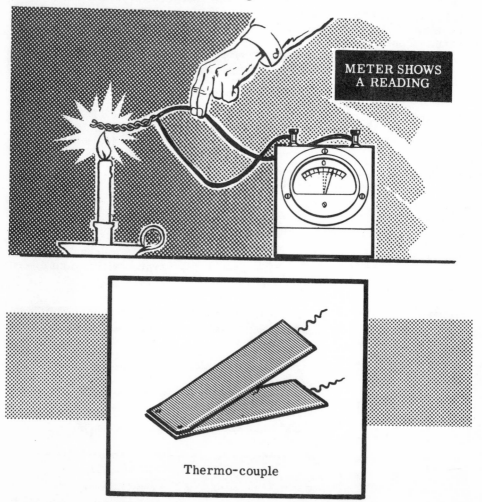

METER SHOWS
A READING

Thermo-couple

Thermo-couples do not furnish a large amount of charge and cannot be used to obtain electric power. They are normally used in connection with heat indicating devices to operate a meter directly marked in degrees of temperature.

HOW LIGHT PRODUCES ELECTRICITY

Electric Charges from Light—Photovoltaic Effects

Electricity may be produced by using light as the source of energy converted to electricity. When light strikes certain materials, they may conduct electric charges easier, develop an electric charge, emit free electrons or convert light to heat.

The most useful of these effects is the development of an electric charge by a photo cell when light strikes the photo-sensitive material in the cell.

A photo cell is a metallic "sandwich" or disc composed of three layers of material. One outside layer is made of iron. The other outside layer is a film of translucent or semitransparent material which permits light to pass through. The center layer of material is composed of selenium alloy. The two outside layers act like electrodes. When light is focused on the selenium alloy through the translucent material an electric charge is developed between the two outside layers. If a meter is attached across these layers the amount of charge can be measured. A direct use of this type of cell is the common light meter as used in photography for determining the amount of light which is present.

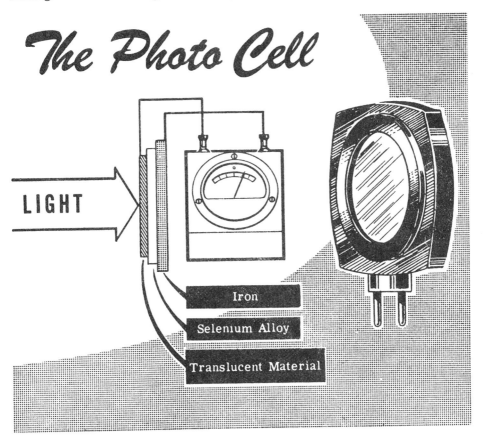

The Photo Cell

LIGHT

Iron

Selenium Alloy

Translucent Material

HOW LIGHT PRODUCES ELECTRICITY

Electric Charges from Light—Photo Electric Cell or Phototube

The photo electric cell, commonly called an "electric eye" or a "PE Cell," operates on the principle of the photo cell. The photo electric cell, however, depends upon a battery or some other source of electrical pressure in its operation of detecting changes in light. The photo cell has many uses, some of which are automatic headlight dimmers on automobiles, motion picture machines, automatic door openers and drinking fountains.

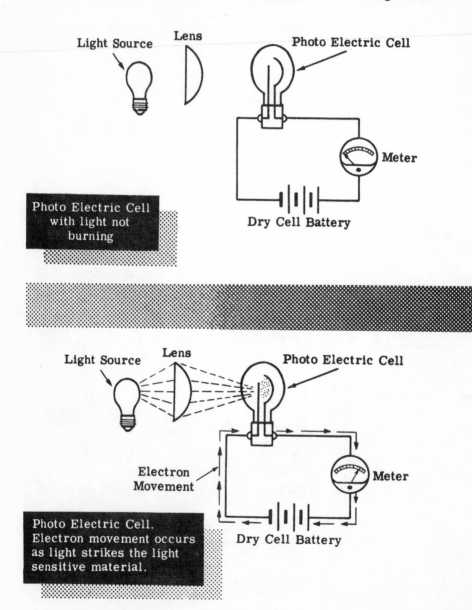

Light Source   Lens   Photo Electric Cell

Meter

Photo Electric Cell
with light not
burning

Dry Cell Battery

Light Source   Lens   Photo Electric Cell

Electron
Movement

Meter

Photo Electric Cell.
Electron movement occurs
as light strikes the light
sensitive material.

Dry Cell Battery

Electricity from Chemical Action

So far, you have discovered what electricity is and several sources of energy which may be used to produce it. Another source of electricity commonly used is the chemical action housed in electric cells and batteries.

Batteries are usually used for emergency and portable electric power. Whenever you use a flashlight emergency lantern or portable equipment, you will be using batteries. Batteries are the main source of power for present-day submarines. In addition, there is a wide variety of equipment which uses cells or batteries either as normal or emergency power. "Dead" batteries are a common type of equipment failure and such failures can be very serious.

Cells and batteries require more care and maintenance than most of the equipment on which you will work. Even though you may use only a few cells or batteries, if you find out how they work, where they are used and how to properly care for them, you will save time and in many cases a lot of hard work.

Now you will find out how chemical action produces electricity and the proper use and care of the cells and batteries that house this chemical action.

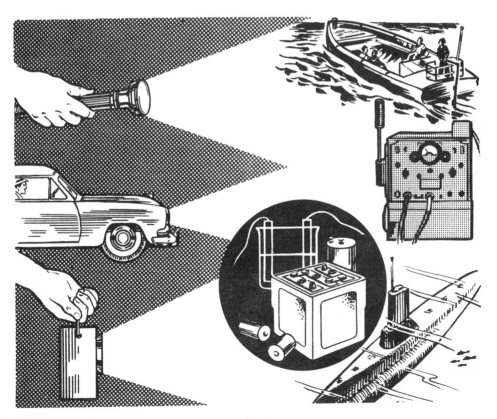

A Primary Cell—What It Is

To find out how the chemical action in batteries works, you might imagine that you can see electrons and what happens to them in a primary electric cell. The basic source of electricity produced by chemical action is the electric cell and, when two or more cells are combined, they form a battery.

Now if you could see the inner workings of one of these cells, what do you suppose you would see?

First you would notice the parts of the cell and their relation to each other. You would see a case or container in which two plates of different metals, separated from each other, are immersed in the liquid which fills the container.

Watching the parts of the cell and the electrons in the cell you would see that the liquid which is called the electrolyte is pushing electrons onto one of the plates and taking them off the other plate. This action results in an excess of electrons or a negative charge on one of the plates so that a wire attached to that plate is called the negative terminal. The other plate loses electrons and becomes positively charged so that a wire attached to it is called the positive terminal.

The action of the electrolyte in carrying electrons from one plate to the other is actually a chemical reaction between the electrolyte and the two plates. This action changes chemical energy into electrical charges on the cell plates and terminals.

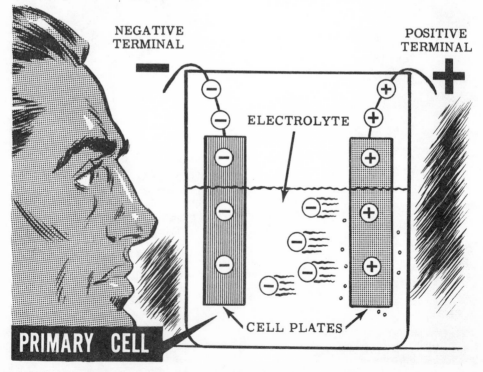

NEGATIVE
TERMINAL

POSITIVE
TERMINAL

ELECTROLYTE

PRIMARY CELL

CELL PLATES

Chemical Action in a Primary Cell

With nothing connected to the cell terminals, you would see that electrons are pushed onto the negative plate until there is room for no more. The electrolyte would take from the positive plate enough electrons to make up for those it pushed onto the negative plate. Both plates would then be fully charged and no electrons would be moving between the plates.

Now suppose you connected a wire between the negative and positive terminals of the cell. You would see the electrons on the negative terminal leave the terminal and travel through the wire to the positive terminal. Since there would now be more room on the negative terminal, the electrolyte would carry more electrons across from the positive plate to the negative plate. As long as electrons leave the negative terminal and travel to the positive terminal outside the cell, the electrolyte will carry electrons from the positive plate to the negative plate inside the cell.

While the electrolyte is carrying electrons, you would see that the negative plate is being used up and you would notice bubbles of gas at the positive terminal. Eventually the negative plate would be completely dissolved in the electrolyte by the chemical action, and the cell would be "dead," or unable to furnish a charge, until the negative plate is replaced. For that reason, this type of cell is called a primary cell—meaning that once it has completely discharged, it cannot be charged again except by using new materials.

For plates in a primary cell, carbon and most metals can be used, while acids or salt compounds can be used for the electrolyte. Dry cells such as those used in flashlights and lanterns are primary cells.

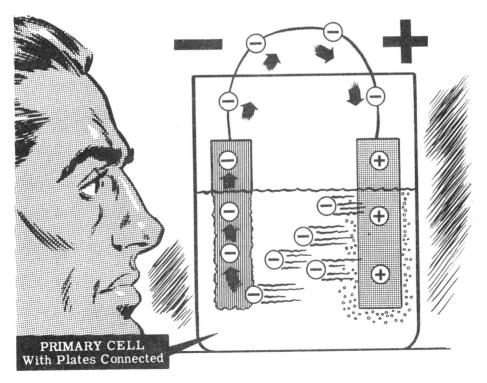

PRIMARY CELL
With Plates Connected

Dry Cells and Batteries

Almost any metals, acids and salts can be used in primary cells. There are many types of primary cells used in laboratories and for special applications, but the one which you have used and will be using most often is the dry cell. You will use the dry cell in many different sizes, shapes and weights—from the cell used in a pencil-size flashlight to the extra large dry cell used in emergency lanterns. Regardless of size, you will find that the material used and the operation of all dry cells is the same.

If you were to look inside a dry cell, you would find that it consists of a zinc case used as the negative plate, a carbon rod suspended in the center of the case for the positive plate, and a solution of ammonium chloride in paste form for the electrolyte. At the bottom of the zinc case you would see a tar paper washer used to keep the carbon rod from touching the zinc case. At the top, the casing would contain layers of sawdust, sand and pitch. These layers hold the carbon rod in position and prevent electrolyte leakage.

When a dry cell supplies electricity, the zinc case and the electrolyte are gradually used up. After the usable zinc and electrolyte are gone, the cell cannot supply a charge and must be replaced. Cells of this type are sealed and can be stored for a limited time without causing damage. When several such cells are connected together, they are called a dry battery. You cannot use dry cells to furnish large amounts of power so you will find them only where infrequent and emergency use is intended.

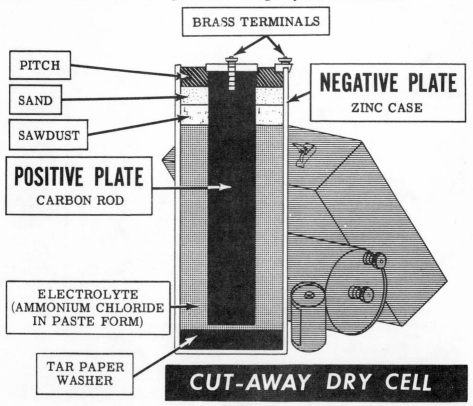

BRASS TERMINALS

PITCH

SAND

SAWDUST

NEGATIVE PLATE
ZINC CASE

POSITIVE PLATE
CARBON ROD

ELECTROLYTE
(AMMONIUM CHLORIDE
IN PASTE FORM)

TAR PAPER
WASHER

CUT-AWAY DRY CELL

A Secondary Cell—What It Is

In studying primary cells, you learned that chemical action is commonly used as a source of electric power for emergency or portable equipment. However, it will furnish only a small amount of power and cannot be recharged.

A storage battery of secondary cells can furnish large amounts of power for a short time and can be recharged. Batteries of this type require more maintenance and care than dry cell batteries but are used widely in equipment where large amounts of electricity are needed for short periods of time.

Secondary cells used in storage batteries are of the lead-acid type. In this cell the electrolyte is sulphuric acid while the positive plate is lead peroxide and the negative plate is lead. During discharge of the cell, the acid becomes weaker and both plates change chemically to lead sulfate.

The case of a lead-acid cell is made of hard rubber or glass, which prevents corrosion and acid leaks. A space at the bottom of the cell collects the sediment formed as the cell is used. The top of the case is removable and acts as the support for the plates.

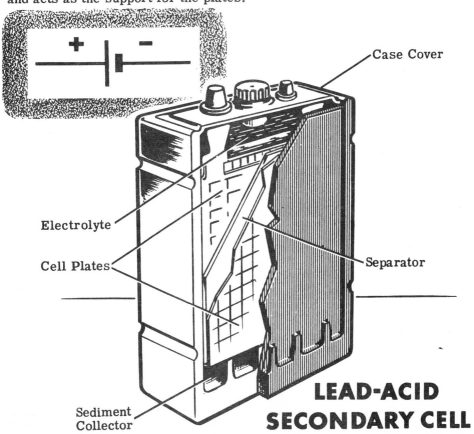

Case Cover

Electrolyte

Cell Plates

Separator

Sediment Collector

LEAD-ACID
SECONDARY CELL

A Secondary Cell—What It Is (continued)

Since the active materials are not rigid enough to be mounted independently, a special grid structure of inactive metal is used to hold them. For maximum chemical action, a large plate area is desired, so each positive plate is interlaced between two negative plates. In a typical cell, you might find seven positive plates attached to a common support interlaced with eight negative plates attached to a different support. Separators, made of wood or porous glass, hold each positive and negative plate apart but let the electrolyte pass through.

The positive and negative plates are fastened to the case cover which is held in place by a special acid-resistant tar. An opening in the cover allows water to be added to the electrolyte to replace water which evaporates. The cap for this opening has a vent to allow gas to escape since the cell in operation forms gas at the positive plate.

Since these cells furnish large amounts of electricity, they require larger terminals and leads. Connections and terminals are made of lead bars since other metals would corrode rapidly due to the acid electrolyte.

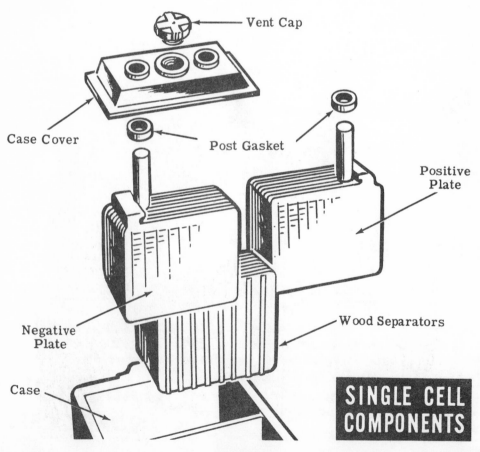

Vent Cap

Case Cover

Post Gasket

Positive Plate

Negative Plate

Wood Separators

Case

SINGLE CELL
COMPONENTS

Storage Batteries

When two or more secondary cells are connected together, they form a storage battery. This battery stores electricity and can be recharged after discharge.

Most storage batteries consist of three lead-acid cells in a common case permanently connected in series. Since each lead-acid cell is rated at about two volts, connecting three cells in series produces a battery voltage of six volts.

The symbol for a secondary cell is the same as that used for a primary cell and the storage battery symbol shows three cells connected in series. Storage batteries and secondary cells are not connected in parallel since a weaker cell would cause a stronger cell to discharge, thus lowering battery strength without the battery even being used.

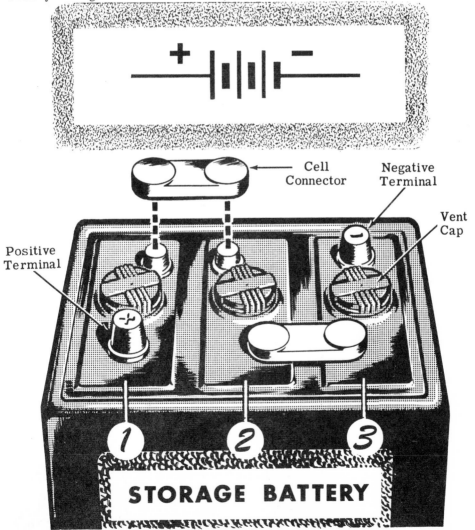

Electric Power from Magnetism

The most common method of producing electricity used for electric power is by the use of magnetism. The source of electricity must be able to maintain a large charge because the charge is being used to furnish electric power. While friction, pressure, heat and light are sources of electricity, you have found that their use is limited to special applications since they are not capable of maintaining a large enough charge for electric power.

All of the electric power used, except for emergency and portable equipment, originally comes from a generator in a power plant. The generator may be driven by water power, a steam turbine or an internal combustion engine. No matter how the generator is driven, the electric power it produces is the result of the action between the wires and the magnets inside the generator.

When wires move past a magnet or a magnet moves past wires, electricity is produced in the wires because of the magnetism in the magnetic material. Now you will find out what magnetism is and how it can be used to produce electricity.

Magnetism

Magnetism—What It Is

In ancient times, the Greeks discovered that a certain kind of rock, which they originally found near the city of Magnesia in Asia Minor, had the power to attract and pick up bits of iron. The rock which they discovered was actually a type of iron ore called "magnetite," and its power of attraction is called "magnetism." Rocks containing ore which has this power of attraction, are called natural magnets.

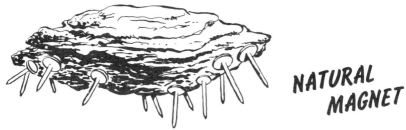

NATURAL MAGNET

Natural magnets were little used until it was discovered that a magnet mounted so that it could turn freely would always turn so that one side would point to the north. Bits of magnetite suspended on a string were called "lodestones," meaning a leading stone, and were used as crude compasses for desert travel by the Chinese more than 2,000 years ago. Crude mariner's compasses constructed of natural magnets were used by sailors in the early voyages of exploration.

The earth itself is a large natural magnet and the action of a natural magnet in turning toward the north is caused by the magnetism or force of attraction of the earth.

ANCIENT COMPASSES

Magnetism—What It Is (continued)

In using natural magnets, it was found that a piece of iron stroked with a natural magnet became magnetized to form an artificial magnet. Artificial magnets may also be made electrically and materials other than iron may be used to form stronger magnets. Steel alloys containing nickel and cobalt make the best magnets and are usually used in strong magnets.

Iron
Magnet

MAGNET STRENGTH

Steel
Alloy
Magnet

Iron becomes magnetized more easily than other materials but it also loses its magnetism easily so that magnets of soft iron are called temporary magnets. Magnets made of steel alloys hold their magnetism for a long period of time and are called permanent magnets.

Magnetism in a magnet is concentrated at two points, usually at the ends of the magnet. These points are called the "poles" of the magnet—one being called the "north pole," the other the "south pole." The north pole is at the end of the magnet which would point north if the magnet could swing freely, and the south pole is at the opposite end.

Magnets are made in various shapes, sizes and strengths. Permanent magnets are usually made of a bar of steel alloy, either straight with poles at the ends, or bent in the shape of the familiar horseshoe with poles on opposite sides of the opening.

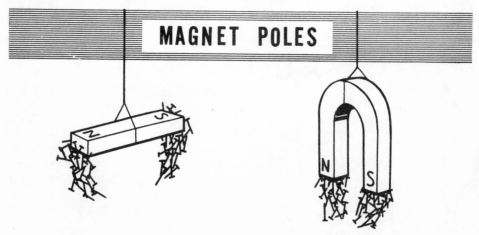

MAGNET POLES

Magnetism—What It Is (continued)

Magnetism is an invisible force and can be seen only in terms of the effect it produces. You know that the wind, for example, provides tremendous force, yet it is invisible. Similarly, magnetic force may be felt but not seen.

The magnetic field about a magnet can best be explained as invisible lines of force leaving the magnet at one point and entering it at another. These invisible lines of force are referred to as "flux lines" and the shape of the area they occupy is called the "flux pattern." The number of flux lines per square inch is called the "flux density." The points at which the flux lines leave or enter the magnet are called the "poles." The magnetic circuit is the path taken by the magnetic lines of force.

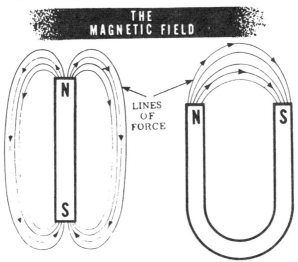

THE MAGNETIC FIELD

LINES OF FORCE

If you were to bring two magnets together with the north poles facing each other, you would feel a force of repulsion between the poles. Bringing the south poles together would also result in repulsion but, if a north pole is brought near a south pole, a force of attraction exists. In this respect, magnetic poles are very much like static charges. Like charges or poles repel each other and unlike charges or poles attract.

REPULSION

REPULSION

ATTRACTION

The action of the magnetic poles in attracting and repelling each other is due to the magnetic field around the magnet. As has already been explained, the invisible magnetic field is represented by lines of force which leave a magnet at the north pole and enter it at the south pole. Inside the magnet the lines travel from the south pole to the north pole so that a line of force is continuous and unbroken.

Magnetism—What It Is (continued)

One characteristic of magnetic lines of force is such that they repel each other, never crossing or uniting. If two magnetic fields are placed near each other, as illustrated by the placement of the two magnets, below, the magnetic fields will not combine but will reform in a distorted flux pattern. (Note that the flux lines do not cross each other.)

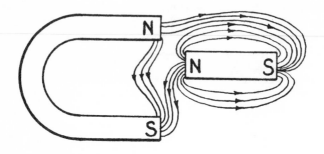

An Example of Bypassing Flux Lines

There is no known insulator for magnetic lines. It has been found that flux lines will pass through all materials. However, they will go through some materials more easily than others. This fact makes it possible to concentrate flux lines where they are used or to bypass them around an area or instrument.

MAGNETIC SCREEN

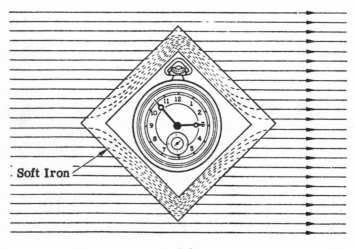

Soft Iron

Magnetism—What It Is (continued)

On the previous sheet you were told that magnetic lines of force will go through some materials more easily than through others. Those materials which will not pass flux lines so readily, or which seem to hinder the passage of the lines, are said to have a comparatively high "reluctance" to magnetic fields. Materials which pass, or do not hinder the "flow" of flux lines, are said to have a comparatively low reluctance to magnetic fields of force. Reluctance, with reference to a magnetic circuit, is roughly the equivalent of resistance, when an electric circuit is considered.

Magnetic lines of force take the path of least reluctance; for example, they travel more easily through iron than through the air. Since air has a greater reluctance than iron, the concentration of the magnetic field becomes greater in the iron (as compared to air) because the reluctance is decreased. In other words, the addition of iron to a magnetic circuit concentrates the magnetic field which is in use.

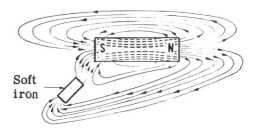

Soft
iron

| Effect of a soft iron bar in a magnetic field |

Magnetic lines of force act like stretched rubber bands. The figure below suggests why this characteristic exists, particularly near the air gap. Note that some lines of force curve outward across the gap in moving from the north pole to the south pole. This outward curve, or stretching effect, is caused by the repulsion of each magnetic line from its neighbor. However, the lines of force tend to resist the stretching effect and therefore resemble rubber bands under tension.

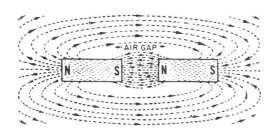

| Unlike poles attract |

Magnetism—What It Is (continued)

As has already been mentioned, magnetic lines of force tend to repel each other. By tracing the flux pattern of the two magnets with like poles together, in the diagram below, it can be seen why this characteristic exists.

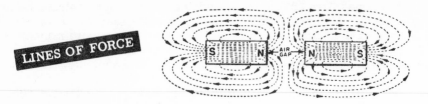

The reaction between the fields of the two magnets is caused by the fact that lines of force cannot cross each other. The lines, therefore, turn aside and travel in the same direction between the pole faces of the two magnets. Since lines of force which are moving in such a manner tend to push each other apart, the magnets mutually repel each other.

Only a certain number of magnetic lines can be crowded into a piece of material. This varies with each type of material but when the maximum number has been attained the material is said to be saturated. This phenomenon is made use of in many pieces of electrical equipment.

The property of magnetism may be induced, or introduced, in a piece of material which does not ordinarily have that characteristic. If a piece of unmagnetized soft iron is placed in the magnetic field of a permanent magnet the soft iron assumes the properties of a magnet; it becomes magnetized. This action, or process, is called magnetic induction and arises from the fact that magnetic lines of force tend to flow through a material which offers less reluctance than air to their passage.

When the lines of the magnetic field pass through the soft iron bar (see the diagram below), the molecules of the soft iron line up parallel with the lines of force, and with their north poles pointing in the direction that the lines of force are traveling through the iron. Magnetism then, is induced in the soft iron bar and in the polarity indicated.

If the permanent magnet is removed, the soft iron bar will lose a good deal of its magnetic quality. The amount of magnetism which remains is called residual magnetism. The term "residual magnetism" is encountered later in this course and in the study of DC generators.

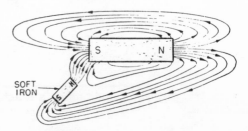

Demonstration—Magnetic Fields

To show that unlike magnetic poles attract each other, the instructor brings two bar magnets near each other with the north pole of one magnet approaching the south pole of the other. Notice that the magnets not only come together easily but attract each other strongly, showing that unlike poles attract. However, when the two magnets are brought together with similar poles opposing, it is difficult to force the magnets together, indicating that like poles repel each other. When the demonstration is repeated using horseshoe magnets, the results are the same—like poles repel, unlike poles attract.

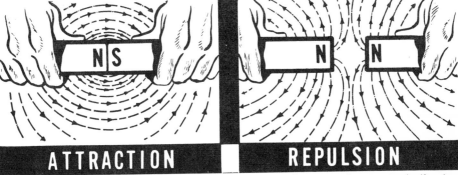

ATTRACTION · REPULSION

To show how lines of force form a magnetic field around a magnet, the instructor will use a bar magnet, a horseshoe magnet and iron filings to trace out a pattern of the magnetic field. He places a sheet of lucite over the magnet and then he sprinkles iron filings on the lucite. Observe that the iron filings do not evenly cover the sheet of lucite. Instead they arrange themselves in a definite pattern, with many more filings attracted to the magnet poles than to other places on the lucite. You also see that the filings arrange themselves in a series of lines around the poles, indicating the pattern of the magnetic lines of force which make up the magnetic field.

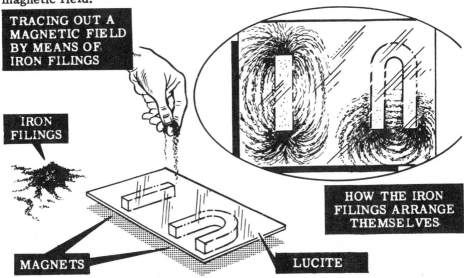

TRACING OUT A MAGNETIC FIELD BY MEANS OF IRON FILINGS

IRON FILINGS

HOW THE IRON FILINGS ARRANGE THEMSELVES

MAGNETS

LUCITE

Movement of a Magnet Past a Wire

One method by which magnetism produces electricity is through the movement of a magnet past a stationary wire. If you connect a very sensitive
meter across the ends of a stationary wire and then move a magnet past
the wire, the meter needle will deflect. This deflection indicates that
electricity is produced in the wire. Repeating the movement and observing the meter closely, you will see that the meter moves only while the
magnet is passing <u>near</u> the wire.

Placing the magnet near the wire and holding it at rest, you will observe
no deflection of the meter. Moving the magnet from this position, however,
does cause the meter to deflect and shows that, alone, the magnet and wire
are not able to produce electricity. In order to deflect the needle, movement of the magnet past the wire is necessary.

Movement is necessary because the magnetic field around a magnet produces an electric current in a wire only when the magnetic field is moved
across the wire. When the magnet and its field are stationary, the field
is not moving across the wire and will not produce a movement of electrons.

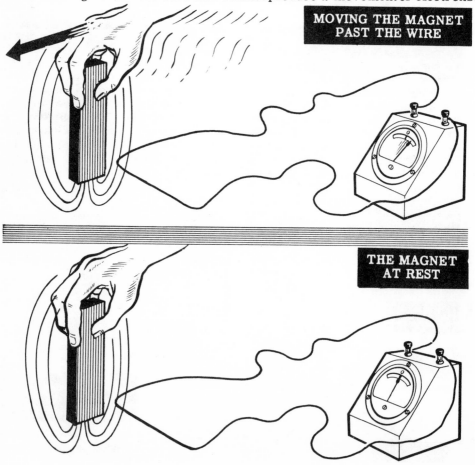

MOVING THE MAGNET PAST THE WIRE

THE MAGNET AT REST

HOW MAGNETISM PRODUCES ELECTRICITY

Movement of a Wire Past a Magnet

In studying the effect of moving a magnet past a wire, you discovered that electricity was produced only while the magnet and its field were actually moving past the wire. If you move the wire past a stationary magnet, you again will notice a deflection of the meter. This deflection will occur only while the wire is moving across the magnetic field.

To use magnetism to produce electricity, you may either move a magnetic field across a wire or move a wire across a magnetic field.

For a continuous source of electricity, however, you need to maintain a continuous motion of either the wire or the magnetic field.

To provide continuous motion, the wire or the magnet would need to move back and forth continuously. A more practical way is to cause the wire to travel in a circle through the magnetic field.

This method of producing electricity—that of the wire traveling in a circle past the magnets—is the principle of the electric generator and is the source of most electricity used for electric power.

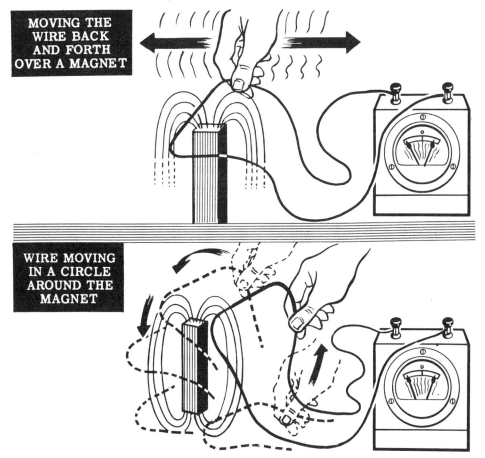

MOVING THE WIRE BACK AND FORTH OVER A MAGNET

WIRE MOVING IN A CIRCLE AROUND THE MAGNET

Movement of a Wire Past a Magnet (continued)

To increase the amount of electricity which can be produced by moving a wire past a magnet, you might increase the length of the wire that passes through the magnetic field, use a stronger magnet or move the wire faster. The length of the wire can be increased by winding it in several turns to form a coil. Moving the coil past the magnet will result in a much greater deflection of the meter than resulted with a single wire. Each additional coil turn will add an amount equal to that of one wire.

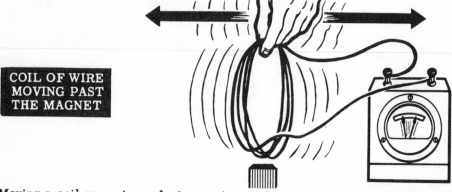

COIL OF WIRE
MOVING PAST
THE MAGNET

Moving a coil or a piece of wire past a weak magnet causes a weak flow of electrons. Moving the same coil or piece of wire at the same speed past a strong magnet will cause a stronger flow of electrons, as indicated by the meter deflection. Increasing the speed of the movement also results in a greater electron flow. In producing electric power, the output of an electric generator is usually controlled by changing either (1) the strength of the magnet or (2) the speed of rotation of the coil.

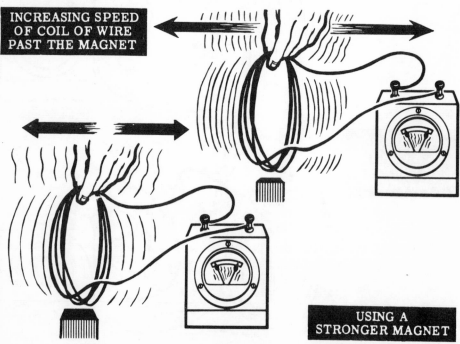

INCREASING SPEED
OF COIL OF WIRE
PAST THE MAGNET

USING A
STRONGER MAGNET

Review of Electricity and How It Is Produced

To conclude your study of how electricity is produced, suppose you review briefly what you have found out about electricity and where it comes from.

ELECTRICITY is the action of electrons which have been forced from their normal orbits around the nucleus of an atom. To force electrons out of their orbits, so they can become a source of electricity, some kind of energy is required.

Six kinds of energy can be used:

FRICTION — Electricity produced by rubbing two materials together.

PRESSURE — Electricity produced by applying pressure to a crystal of certain materials.

HEAT — Electricity produced by heating the junction of a thermo-couple.

LIGHT — Electricity produced by light striking photo-sensitive materials.

MAGNETISM — Electricity produced by relative movement of a magnet and a wire that results in the cutting of lines of force.

CHEMICAL ACTION — Electricity produced by chemical reaction in an electric cell.

Electrons in Motion

Electrons in the outer orbits of an atom are attracted to the nucleus by less force than electrons whose orbits are near the nucleus. These outer electrons may be easily forced from their orbits, while electrons in the inner orbits are called "bound" electrons since they cannot be forced out of their orbits.

Atoms and molecules in a material are in continuous random motion, the amount of this motion determined by the material, temperature and pressure. This random motion causes electrons in the outer rings to be forced from their orbits, becoming "free" electrons. "Free" electrons are attracted to other atoms which have lost electrons, resulting in a continuous passage of electrons from atom to atom within the material. All electrical effects make use of the "free" electrons forced out of the outer orbits. The atom itself is not affected by the loss of electrons, except that it becomes positively charged and will capture "free" electrons to replace those it has lost.

The random movement of the "free" electrons from atom to atom is normally equal in all directions so that electrons are not lost or gained by any particular part of the material. When most of the electron movement takes place in the same direction, so that one part of the material loses electrons while another part gains electrons, the net electron movement or flow is called current flow.

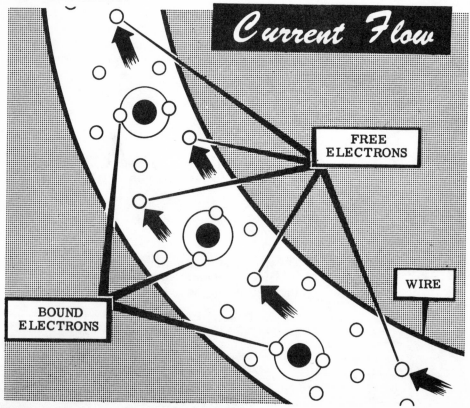

Electrons in Motion (continued)

Suppose you examine more closely what happens inside a material when an electron current begins to flow. You learned in Section II, Topic 1 that an atom is made up of a number of neutrons, protons and electrons. The protons have a positive charge, the electrons a negative charge, and the neutrons have no charge at all. The nucleus of the atom is made up of neutrons and protons and has a positive charge equal to the number of protons. Under normal conditions the number of electrons traveling around the nucleus equals the number of protons in the nucleus and the entire atom has no charge at all.

If an atom loses several of its free electrons, it then has a positive charge since there are more protons than electrons. From your work in Section II you know that like charges repel each other and unlike charges attract. About each positive or negative charge, unseen lines of force radiate in all directions and the area occupied by these lines is called an "electric field." Thus if a moving electron comes close to another electron, the second electron will be pushed away without the two electrons coming into contact.

Similarly, if an electron comes near a positive charge, the two fields reach out and attract each other even though there may be some distance between them. It is the attraction between the positive charge on the nucleus and the electrons in the outer orbit that determine the electrical characteristics of a material. If the atom of a particular material is so constructed that there is a very small attraction between the positive nucleus and the outer electrons, the outer electrons are free to leave the atom when they are under the influence of electric fields. Such a condition exists in metals; and silver, copper and aluminum have a very weak attractive force between the nucleus and the outer electrons. Substances such as glass, plastic, wood and baked clays have a very powerful bond between the nucleus and the outer electrons, and these electrons will not leave their atoms unless very strong electrical fields are applied.

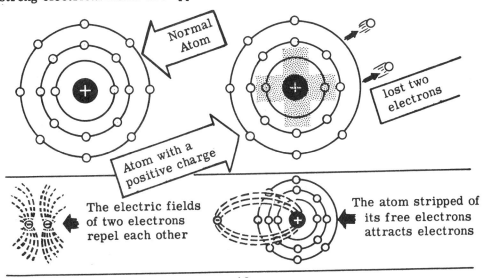

Normal Atom

lost two electrons

Atom with a positive charge

The electric fields of two electrons repel each other

The atom stripped of its free electrons attracts electrons

Electrons in Motion (continued)

You learned that a dry cell has the peculiar property of having an excess of electrons at its negative terminal and a shortage of electrons at its positive terminal. Suppose you examine just what happens when a metal wire is connected across the terminals of a dry cell.

The moment the wire is connected across the cell there will be an excess of electrons at the negative end and a shortage at the positive end. Remember that electrons repel each other and are attracted to places where there is a shortage of electrons. At the negative end of the cell the excess of electrons now have a place to go. The electric fields of these electrons push against the electrons in the atoms of the wire, and some of these outer electrons are pushed out of their atoms. These free electrons cannot remain where they are since their electric fields force them away from the piled up electrons at the negative terminal, so they are forced away from the negative terminal. When these newly freed electrons arrive at the next atom, they in turn force those outer electrons off their atoms and the process continues.

At the positive end of the wire there is a shortage of electrons, and therefore there is a strong attraction between the positive terminal and the outer electrons of the nearby atoms. These electric fields of the outer electrons are strongly pulled by the electric field of the positive terminal, and some of the electrons leave their atoms and move toward the positive end. When these electrons leave their atoms, the atoms become positively charged and electrons from the next atoms are attracted toward the positive end; and the process continues.

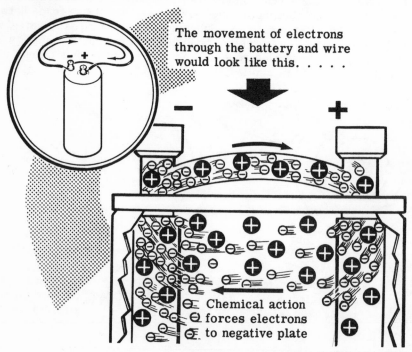

The movement of electrons through the battery and wire would look like this. . . . .

Chemical action forces electrons to negative plate

Electrons in Motion (continued)

If the excess and shortage of electrons at the two ends of the wire were fixed at a definite quantity, it would only be a very short time until all the excess electrons had traveled through the wire toward the positive end. The dry cell, however, continues to furnish excess electrons at one terminal and continues to remove electrons from the other terminal, so that the two terminals remain negative and positive for the life of the cell.

Under these conditions a constant stream of electrons begins to flow through the wire the instant the wire is connected to the cell. Electrons constantly arriving at the negative end keep applying a pushing force to the free electrons in the wire, and the constant removal of electrons from the positive end keeps applying a pulling force on the free electrons.

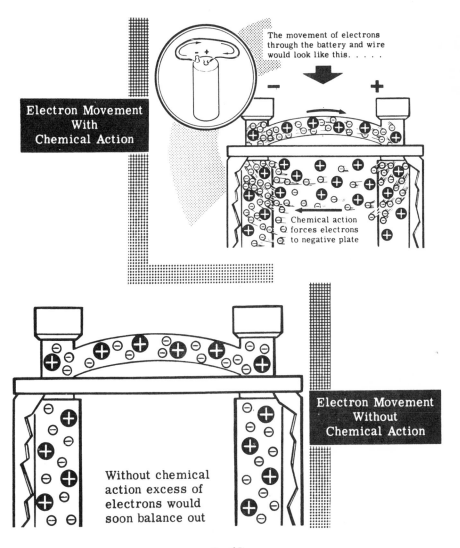

The movement of electrons through the battery and wire would look like this. . . . .

Electron Movement
With
Chemical Action

Chemical action
forces electrons
to negative plate

Electron Movement
Without
Chemical Action

Without chemical
action excess of
electrons would
soon balance out

Electrons In Motion (continued)

If you have any difficulty in picturing what is happening inside the wire, suppose you examine a similar situation which makes use of more familiar components. Imagine a large piece of drain pipe in which a large number of golf balls are suspended by means of wires. Each golf ball represents an atom with its bound electrons. Now fill all of the space between the golf balls with small metal balls the size of air rifle shot (BB shot). Each small ball represents a free electron. Now imagine an army of little men removing the BB's from one end of the pipe and ramming them back into the other end. This army represents the dry cell.

Since the pipe cannot be packed any more tightly, and since it is too strong to burst, all that can happen is that there will be a constant flow of small metal balls through the pipe. The faster the little men work and the harder they push, the greater will be the flow of BB shot. The flow begins at the instant the army begins to work, and continues at the same rate until the little men are too exhausted to move any more—the dry cell is then "dead."

A very similar situation exists between the drain pipe and a wire carrying an electric current. The main difference is that in the pipe, the metal balls press directly upon each other, while in the wire, the electrons themselves do not touch but their electric fields press against each other.

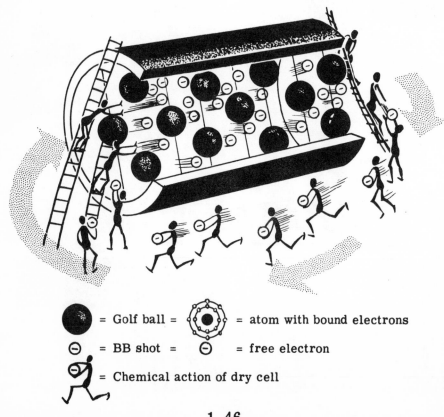

● = Golf ball = ⬤ = atom with bound electrons

⊖ = BB shot = ⊖ = free electron

= Chemical action of dry cell

Electrons in Motion (continued)

When current flow starts in a wire, electrons start to move throughout the wire at the same time, just as the cars of a long train start and stop together.

If one car of a train moves, it causes all the cars of the train to move by the same amount, and free electrons in a wire act in the same manner. Free electrons are always present throughout the wire, and as each electron moves slightly it exerts a force on the next electron, causing it to move slightly and in turn to exert a force on the next electron. This effect continues throughout the wire.

When electrons move away from one end of a wire it becomes positively charged, causing all the free electrons in the wire to move in that direction. This movement, taking place throughout the wire simultaneously, moves electrons away from the other end of the wire and allows more electrons to enter the wire at that point.

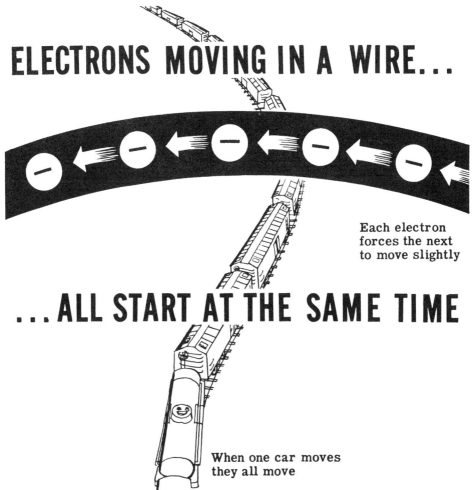

ELECTRONS MOVING IN A WIRE...

Each electron
forces the next
to move slightly

...ALL START AT THE SAME TIME

When one car moves
they all move

Electrons in Motion (continued)

Since electrons repel each other and are attracted by positive charges, they always tend to move from a point having an excess of electrons toward a point having a lack of electrons. Your study of the discharge of static charges showed that, when a positive charge is connected to a negative charge, the excess electrons of the negative charge move toward the positive charge.

If electrons are taken out of one end of a copper wire, a positive charge results, causing the free electrons in the wire to move toward that end. If electrons are furnished to the opposite end of the wire, causing it to be charged negatively, a continuous movement of electrons will take place from the negatively charged end of the wire toward the positively charged end. This movement of electrons is current flow and will continue as long as electrons are furnished to one end of the wire and removed at the other end.

Current flow can take place in any material where "free" electrons exist, although we are only interested in the current flow in metal wires.

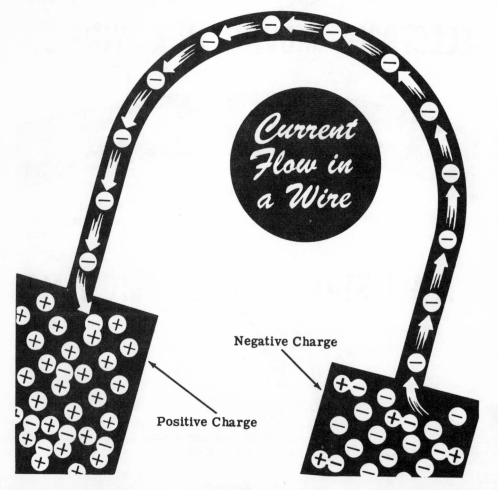

Direction of Current Flow

According to the electron theory; current flow is always from a (-) negative charge to a (+) positive charge. Thus, if a wire is connected between the terminals of a battery, current will flow from the (-) terminal to the (+) terminal.

Before the electron theory of matter had been worked out, electricity was in use to operate lights, motors, etc. Electricity had been harnessed but no one knew how or why it worked. It was believed that something moved in the wire from (+) to (-). This conception of current flow is called conventional current flow. Although the electron theory of current flow (-) to (+) is the accepted theory, you will find the conventional flow (+) to (-) is sometimes used in working with certain types of electrical equipment.

For your study of electricity, current flow is concluded to be the same as the electron flow—that is, from negative to positive.

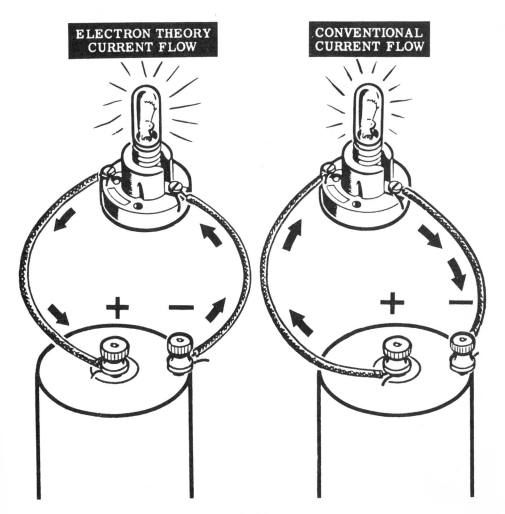

Review of Current Flow

Current flow does all the work involved in the operation of electrical equipment, whether it be a simple light bulb or some complicated electronic equipment such as a radio receiver or transmitter. In order for current to flow, a continuous path must be provided between the two terminals of a source of electric charges. Now suppose you review what you have found out about current flow.

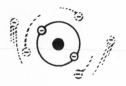

1. "BOUND" ELECTRONS — Electrons in the inner orbits of an atom which cannot easily be forced out of their orbits.

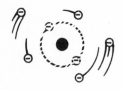

2. "FREE" ELECTRONS — Electrons in the outer orbits of an atom which can easily be forced out of their orbits.

3. CURRENT FLOW — Movement of "free" electrons in the same direction in a material.

4. ELECTRON CURRENT — Current flow from a negative charge to a positive charge.

5. CONVENTIONAL CURRENT — Current flow from a positive charge to a negative charge.

6. AMMETER — Meter used to measure current flow.

Electromagnetism

In the previous topic you learned the very important fact that an electric current can be caused to flow when you move a coil of wire so that it cuts through a magnetic field. You also learned that this is the most widespread manner in which electricity is generated for the home, for industry, and aboard ship.

Since magnetism can be made to generate electricity, it does not seem too great a jump for the imagination to wonder if electricity can generate a magnetic field. In this topic you will see for yourself that that is exactly what can be done.

In the last topic you made use of permanent magnets to cause an electric current to flow. You saw that more current could be generated as you increased the number of turns of wire, the speed of motion of the coil and the strength of the magnetic field. It is a simple matter to accomplish the first two of these in a practical electric generator, but it is very difficult to increase the strength of a permanent magnet beyond certain limits. In order to generate large amounts of electricity a much stronger magnetic field must be used. That is accomplished, as you will see in this topic, by means of an electromagnet. Electromagnets work on the simple principle that a magnetic field can be generated by passing an electric current through a coil of wire.

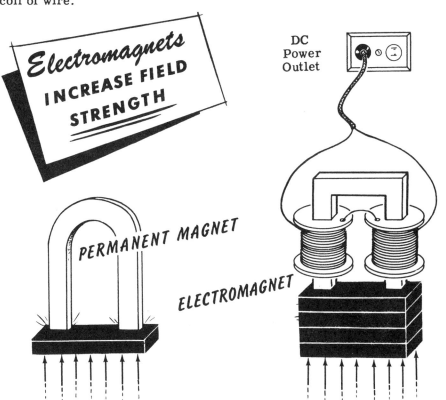

Electromagnets
INCREASE FIELD
STRENGTH

DC
Power
Outlet

PERMANENT MAGNET

ELECTROMAGNET

Electromagnetism (continued)

An electromagnetic field is a magnetic field caused by the current flow in a wire. Whenever electric current flows, a magnetic field exists around the conductor, and the direction of this magnetic field depends upon the direction of current flow. The illustration shows conductors carrying current in different directions. The direction of the magnetic field is counter-clockwise when current flows from left to right. If the direction of current flow reverses, the direction of the magnetic field also reverses, as shown. In the cross-sectional view of the magnetic field around the conductors, the dot in the center of the circle represents the current flowing out of the paper toward you, and the cross represents the current flowing into the paper away from you.

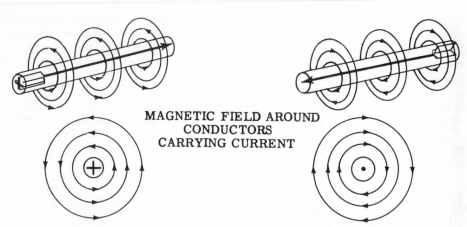

MAGNETIC FIELD AROUND
CONDUCTORS
CARRYING CURRENT

A definite relationship exists between the direction of current flow in a wire and the direction of the magnetic field around the conductor. This relationship can be shown by using the left-hand rule. This rule states that if a current-carrying conductor is grasped in the left hand with the thumb pointing in the direction of the electron current flow, the fingers, when wrapped around the conductor, will point in the direction of the magnetic lines of force. The illustration shows the application of the left-hand rule to determine the direction of the magnetic field about a conductor.

LEFT-HAND RULE FOR

A CONDUCTOR

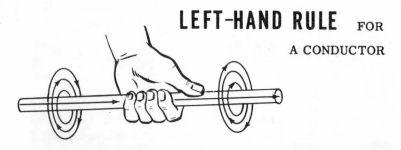

Remember that the left-hand rule is based on the electron theory of current flow (from negative to positive) and is used to determine the direction of the lines of force in an electromagnetic field.

Magnetic Field of a Loop or Coil

Here is a point that you will find very important in the near future—a coil of wire carrying a current acts as a magnet. If a length of wire carrying a current is bent to form a loop, the lines of force around the conductor all leave at one side of the loop and enter at the other side. Thus the loop of wire carrying a current will act as a weak magnet having a north pole and a south pole. The north pole is on the side at which lines of force leave the loop and the south pole on the side at which they enter the loop.

If you desire to make the magnetic field of the loop stronger, you can form the wire into a coil of many loops as shown. Now the individual fields of each loop are in series and form one strong magnetic field inside and outside the loop. In the spaces between the turns, the lines of force are in opposition and cancel each other out. The coil acts as a strong bar magnet with the north pole being the end from which the lines of force leave.

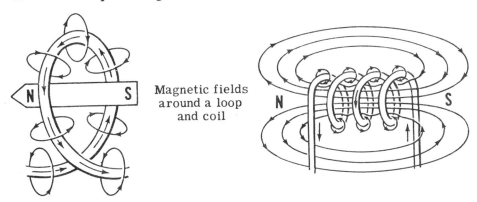

Magnetic fields around a loop and coil

A left-hand rule also exists for coils to determine the direction of the magnetic field. If the fingers of the left hand are wrapped around the coil in the direction of the current flow, the thumb will point toward the north pole end of the coil.

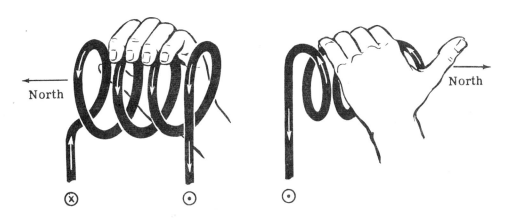

LEFT-HAND RULE FOR COILS

Electromagnets

Adding more turns to a current-carrying coil increases the number of lines of force, causing it to act as a stronger magnet. An increase in current also strengthens the magnetic field so that strong electromagnets have coils of many turns and carry as large a current as the wire size permits.

In comparing coils using the same core or similar cores, a unit called the ampere-turn is used. This unit is the product of the current in amperes and the number of turns of wire.

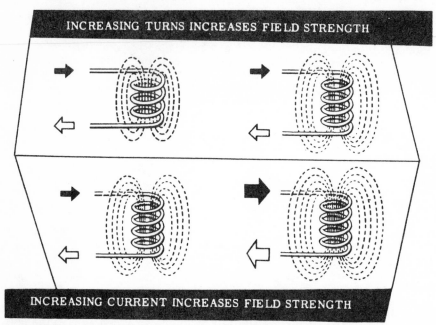

INCREASING TURNS INCREASES FIELD STRENGTH

INCREASING CURRENT INCREASES FIELD STRENGTH

Although the field strength of an electromagnet is increased both by using a large current flow and many turns to form the coil, these factors do not concentrate the field enough for use in a practical generator. To further increase the flux density, an iron core is inserted in the coil. Because the iron core offers much less reluctance (opposition) to lines of force than air, the flux density is greatly increased.

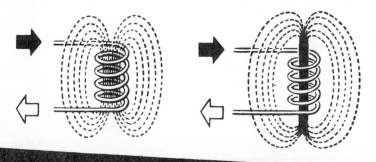

ADDING AN IRON CORE GREATLY INCREASES FLUX DENSITY

Electromagnets (continued)

If the iron core is bent to form a horseshoe and two coils are used, one on each
leg of the horseshoe-shaped core as illustrated, the lines of force travel around the
horseshoe and across the air gap, causing
a very concentrated field to exist across
the air gap. The shorter the air gap, the
greater the flux density between the poles.

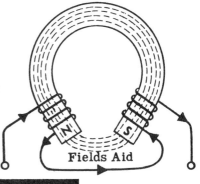

Fields Aid

**A HORSESHOE CORE
ELECTROMAGNET**

To cause such a field, the current flow in
the series connected coils must produce
two opposite magnetic poles at the ends of
the core. Reversing either coil would
cause the two fields to oppose each other,
cancelling out the field in the air gap.

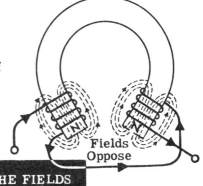

Fields
Oppose

REVERSING THE FIELDS

Electric meters make use of horseshoe-
type permanent magnets. Electric
motors and generators also make use of
a similar type of electromagnet. All of
these applications require the placement
of a number of loops of wire between the
poles of the magnet.

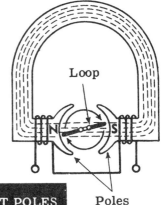

Loop

Poles

ELECTROMAGNET POLES

Demonstration—Magnetic Field Around a Conductor

To demonstrate that a magnetic field exists around a current-carrying conductor, the instructor connects a heavy copper wire in series with a switch across a dry cell battery. The copper wire is bent to support itself vertically and then inserted through a hole in the lucite sheet, which is held in a horizontal position. With the switch closed, iron filings—which have the property of aligning themselves along the lines of force in a magnetic field —are sprinkled on the lucite. The lucite is tapped lightly to make it easier for the iron filings to fall into position.

You see that the filings arrange themselves in concentric circles, showing that the magnetic lines of force form a circular pattern around the conductor. To show that the circular pattern is actually the result of the magnetic field, the instructor opens the switch and spreads the filings evenly over the cardboard, then repeats the demonstration. You see that, each time the circuit current flows, the filings arrange themselves to show the magnetic field.

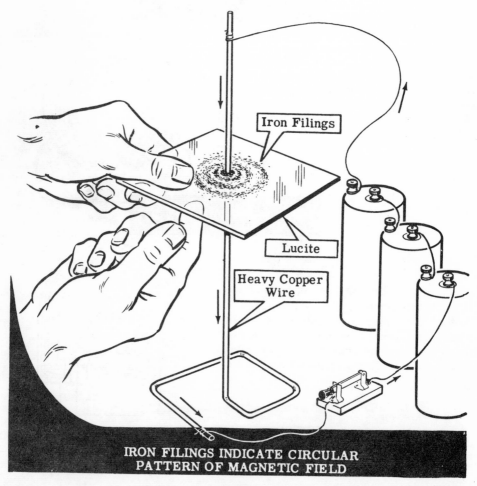

IRON FILINGS INDICATE CIRCULAR PATTERN OF MAGNETIC FIELD

Demonstration—Magnetic Field around a Conductor (continued)

To demonstrate the direction of the magnetic field around the current-carrying conductor, a compass needle is used.

A compass needle is nothing more than a small bar magnet which will line itself up with the lines of force in a magnetic field. You know from the previous demonstration that the magnetic field is circular. Therefore, the compass needle always will be positioned at right angles to the current-carrying conductor.

The iron filings are removed from the lucite, and the compass needle is placed on the lucite about 2 inches away from the conductor. With no current flowing, the north pole end of the compass needle will point to the earth's magnetic north pole. When current flows through the conductor, the compass needle lines itself up at right angles to a radius drawn from the conductor. As the compass needle is moved around the conductor, observe that the needle always maintains itself at right angles to it. This proves that the magnetic field around the conductor is circular.

Using the left-hand rule you can check the direction of the magnetic field which was indicated by the compass needle. The direction in which the fingers go around the conductor is the same as that of the north pole of the compass needle.

If the current through the conductor is reversed, the compass needle will point in the opposite direction, indicating that the direction of the magnetic field has reversed. Application of the left-hand rule will verify this observation.

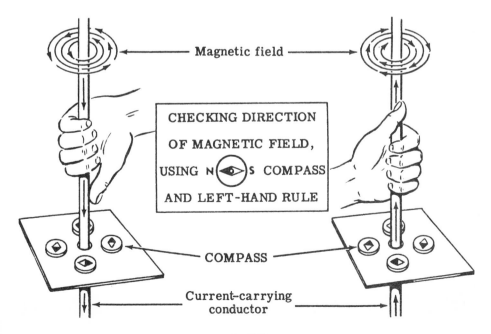

CHECKING DIRECTION OF MAGNETIC FIELD, USING N◆S COMPASS AND LEFT-HAND RULE

Magnetic field

COMPASS

Current-carrying conductor

Demonstration—Magnetic Fields Around a Coil

To demonstrate the magnetic field of a coil of wire, a lucite board is used with No. 10 wire threaded through it to form a coil as shown. The rest of the circuit is the same as for the previous part of the demonstration. Iron filings are sprinkled on the lucite and current is passed through the coil. Tapping the lucite will cause the iron filings to line up parallel to the lines of force. Observe that the iron filings have formed the same pattern of a magnetic field that existed around a bar magnet.

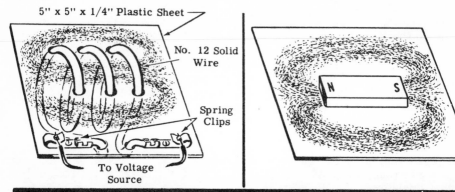

5" x 5" x 1/4" Plastic Sheet

No. 12 Solid Wire

Spring Clips

To Voltage Source

IRON FILINGS DEMONSTRATING MAGNETIC FIELD PATTERN AROUND A COIL

If the iron filings are removed, and the compass needle is placed inside the coil, the needle will line up along the axis of the coil with the north pole end of the compass pointing to the north pole end of the coil. Remember that the lines of force inside a magnet or coil flow from the south pole to the north pole. The north pole end of the coil can be verified by using the left-hand rule for coils. If the compass is placed outside the coil and moved from the north pole to the south pole, the compass needle will follow the direction of a line of force as it moves from the north pole to the south pole. When the current through the coil is reversed, the compass needle will also reverse its direction.

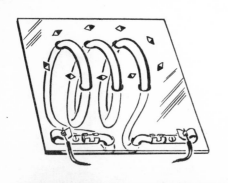
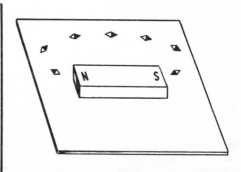

CHECKING DIRECTION OF MAGNETIC FIELD, USING COMPASS

Review of Electromagnetism

ELECTROMAGNETIC FIELD — Current flowing through a wire generates a magnetic field whose direction is determined by the direction of the current flow. The direction of the generated magnetic field is found by using the left-hand rule for a current-carrying conductor.

MAGNETIC FIELD OF A LOOP OR COIL — A loop generates a magnetic field exactly the same as a bar magnet. If many loops are added in series forming a coil, a stronger magnetic field is generated. The left-hand rule for a coil is used to determine the coil's magnetic polarity.

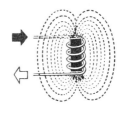

FIELD STRENGTH — Increasing the number of turns of a coil increases the field strength and increasing the coil current also increases the field strength. An iron core may be inserted to greatly concentrate the field (increase flux density) at the ends of the coil. The ampere-turn is the unit used in comparing the strength of magnetic fields.

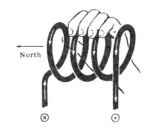

PERMANENT-MAGNET and ELECTROMAGNET FIELDS — Electromagnet fields are much stronger than the permanent magnet type, and are used in most practical electrical machinery. When electromagnets are used, the field strength can be varied by varying the amount of current flow through the field coils.

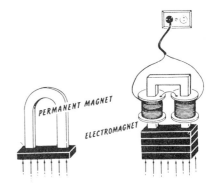

How Electric Charges Are Measured

In working with electric charges either standing still or in motion as current flow, you will need some unit for measuring the amount of electric charge. The basic unit of electrical charge is the electron but, since its charge is extremely small and the electron itself is so small that it cannot be seen, you will need to use a more practical unit of measurement.

You are familiar with the measurement of grain, for example. Each kernel of grain is much too small to be used as a practical unit of measurement; therefore the bushel, containing several million kernels, is the practical unit used. Similarly, water is not measured by counting drops of water. Instead, a unit called the quart is used. For measuring electric charges the unit used is the coulomb, which is approximately 6.28 million, million, million electrons.

The coulomb measures the quantity of electric charge or the number of electrons regardless of whether the charge is in motion or standing still.

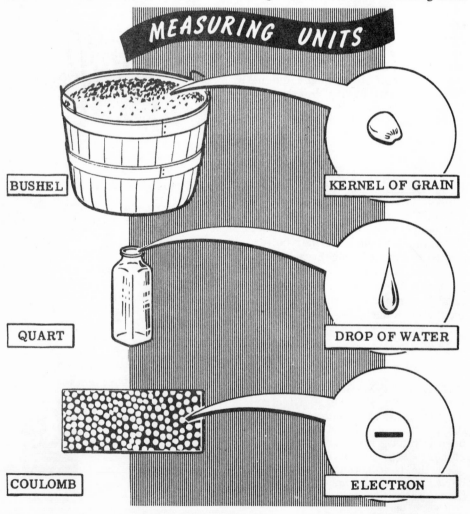

MEASURING UNITS

BUSHEL

KERNEL OF GRAIN

QUART

DROP OF WATER

COULOMB

ELECTRON

Units of Current Flow

Current flow is a measure of how many electrons are passing through a material in a given length of time. The coulomb is a measure of the number of electrons so that, by counting the coulombs which pass in a given amount of time, the current flow is measured. The unit of current flow is the ampere. One ampere of current is flowing when one coulomb of electrons passes through the material in one second, two amperes when two coulombs pass per second, etc.

Since amperes mean coulombs per second, the ampere is a measure of rate at which electrons are moving through a material. The coulomb, which represents the number of electrons in a charge, is a measure of quantity.

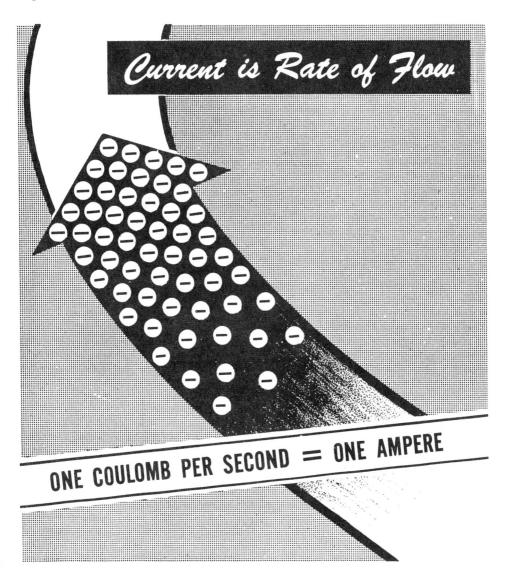

Measuring Units of Current Flow

In working with electricity, a means of measuring current flow through a material is necessary. An ammeter does this: it indicates in amperes the number of electrons passing per second.

When the amount of current flowing through a circuit is to be measured, the ammeter is always connected in series with the line that delivers current to the circuit; it will be damaged if it is connected in any other way. Because an ammeter indicates the rate of electron movement just as a meter in a water system shows the rate at which gallons of water are used, it follows that in order to show correctly the amount of current being used, the ammeter must be connected into the line (by breaking or opening the line to insert it).

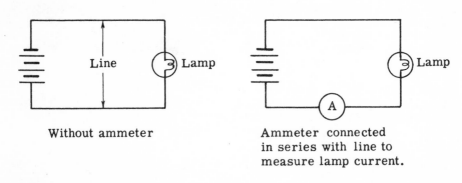

Without ammeter

Ammeter connected in series with line to measure lamp current.

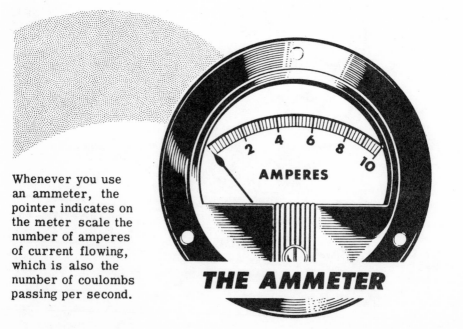

Whenever you use an ammeter, the pointer indicates on the meter scale the number of amperes of current flowing, which is also the number of coulombs passing per second.

THE AMMETER

How Small Currents Are Measured

While the ampere is the basic unit of measurement for current flow, it is not always a convenient unit to use. Current flows seldom exceed one thousand amperes but may often be as little as one one-thousandth of an ampere. For measuring currents of less than one ampere some other unit is needed. A cup of water is not measured in gallons, nor is the flow of water from a fire hydrant measured in cups. In any kind of measurement a usable unit of measurement is needed. Since current flow seldom exceeds one thousand amperes, the ampere can be used satisfactorily as the unit for currents in excess of one ampere. However, it is not convenient as the unit for currents of less than one ampere.

If the current flow is between one-thousandth of an ampere and one ampere, the unit of measure used is the milliampere (abbreviated ma.), which is equal to one-thousandth ampere. For current flow of less than one-thousandth ampere, the unit used is the microampere, which is equal to one-millionth ampere. Meters used for measuring milliamperes of current are called milliammeters, while meters used for measuring microamperes of current are called microammeters. Units of measurement are subdivided in such a way that a quantity expressed in one unit may be readily changed to another unit, either larger or smaller. For example, in volume measure one-half gallon equals two quarts, and four pints also equals two quarts. The relation between the different units of current is indicated below.

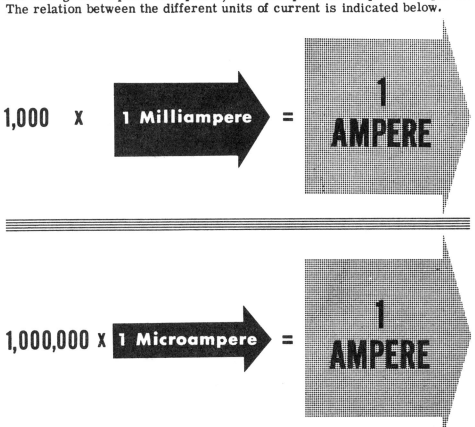

1,000 X 1 Milliampere = 1 AMPERE

1,000,000 X 1 Microampere = 1 AMPERE

How Units of Current Are Changed

In order to work with electricity, you must be able to change from one unit of current to another. Since a milliampere (ma.) is one-thousandth of an ampere, milliamperes can be changed to amperes by moving the decimal point three places to the left. For example, 35 milliamperes is equal to 0.035 ampere . There are two steps required in order to arrive at the correct answer. First, the original position of the decimal point must be located. The decimal is then moved three places to the left, changing the unit from milliamperes to amperes. If no decimal point is given with the number, it is always understood to follow the last number in the quantity. In the example given, the reference decimal point is after the number 5, and to change from milliamperes to amperes it must be moved three places to the left. Since there are only two whole numbers to the left of the decimal point, a zero must be added to the left of the number to provide for a third place as shown.

When changing amperes to milliamperes you move the decimal point to the right instead of the left. For example, 0.125 ampere equals 125 milliamperes and 16 amperes equals 16,000 milliamperes. In these examples, the decimal point is moved three places to the right of its reference position, with three zeros added in the second example to provide the necessary decimal places.

CHANGING MILLIAMPERES TO AMPERES

35 Milliamperes = ? Ampere

Move decimal point three places to the left.

35. MILLIAMPERES = **.035** AMPERE

REFERENCE POINT

CHANGING AMPERES TO MILLIAMPERES

.125 Ampere = ? Milliamperes

Move decimal point three places to the right.

.125 AMPERE = **125.** MILLIAMPERES

REFERENCE POINT

How Units of Current Are Changed (continued)

Suppose that you are working with a current of 125 microamperes and you need to express this current in amperes. If you are changing from a large unit to a small unit, the decimal point is moved to the right, while to change from a small unit to a large unit, the decimal point is moved to the left. Since a microampere is one-millionth ampere, the ampere is the larger unit. Then changing microamperes to amperes is a change from small to large units and the decimal point should be moved to the left. In order to change millionths to units, the decimal point must be moved six decimal places to the left so that 125 microamperes equals 0.000125 ampere . The reference point in 125 microamperes is after the 5, and in order to move the decimal point six places to the left you must add three zeros ahead of the number 125. When changing microamperes to milliamperes, the decimal point is moved only three places to the left, and thus 125 microamperes equals 0.125 milliampere .

If your original current is in amperes and you want to express it in microamperes, the decimal point should be moved six places to the right. For example, 3 amperes equals 3,000,000 microamperes, because the reference decimal point after the 3 is moved six places to the right with the six zeros added to provide the necessary places. To change milliamperes to microamperes the decimal point should be moved three places to the right. For example, 125 milliamperes equals 125,000 microamperes, with the three zeros added to provide the necessary decimal places.

CHANGING UNITS OF CURRENT

MICROAMPERES TO AMPERES

Move Decimal Point Six Places to the Left.

125. Microamperes **= .000125** Ampere

MICROAMPERES TO MILLIAMPERES

Move Decimal Point Three Places to the Left.

125. Microamperes **= .125** Milliampere

AMPERES TO MICROAMPERES

Move Decimal Point Six Places to the Right.

3. Amperes **= 3,000,000.** Microamperes

MILLIAMPERES TO MICROAMPERES

Move Decimal Point Three Places to the Right.

125. Milliamperes **= 125,000.** Microamperes

HOW CURRENT IS MEASURED

Milliammeters and Microammeters

An ammeter having a meter scale range of 0-1 ampere is actually a milliammeter with a range of 0-1000 milliamperes. Fractions are seldom used
in electricity so that, on the 0-1 ampere range, a meter reading of 1/2 ampere is given as 0.5 ampere or 500 milliamperes. For ranges less than
1 ampere, milliammeters and microammeters are used to measure current.

If you are using currents between 1 milliampere and 1000 milliamperes,
milliammeters are used to measure the amount of current. For currents
of less than 1 milliampere, microammeters of the correct range are used,
Very small currents of 1 microampere or less are measured on special
laboratory type instruments called galvanometers. You will not normally
use the galvanometer, since the currents used in electrical equipment are
between 100 microamperes and 100 amperes and thus can be measured
with a microammeter, milliammeter or ammeter of the correct range.
Meter scale ranges for milliammeters and microammeters, like ammeters,
are in multiples of 5 or 10 since these multiples are easily changed to other units.

In using a meter to measure current, the maximum reading of the meter
range should always be higher than the maximum current to be measured.
A safe method of current measurement is to start with a meter having a
range much greater than you expect to measure, in order to determine the
correct meter to use.

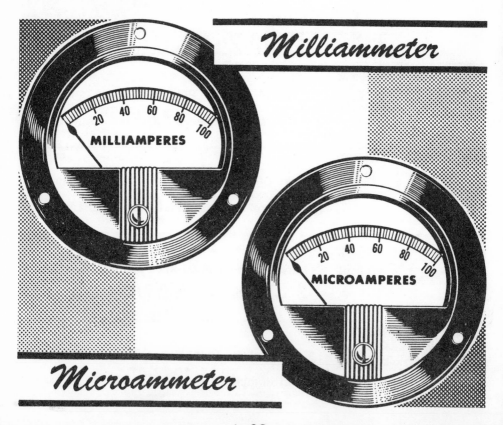

How Meter Scales Are Read

When you work with electricity it is necessary that you take accurate meter readings, to determine whether equipment is working properly, and to discover what is wrong with equipment which is not operating correctly. Many factors can cause meter readings to be inaccurate and it is necessary to keep them in mind whenever you use a meter. You will find the usable range of a meter scale does not include the extreme ends of the scale. For nearly all meters, the most accurate readings are those taken near the center of the scale. When current is measured with an ammeter, milliammeter or microammeter, the range of the meter used should be chosen to give a reading as near to mid-scale as possible.

All meters cannot be used in both horizontal and vertical positions. Due to the mechanical construction of many meters, the accuracy will vary considerably with the position of the meter. Normally, panel-mounting type meters are calibrated and adjusted for use in a vertical position. Meters used in many test sets and in some electrical equipment are made for use in a horizontal position.

A zero set adjustment on the front of the meter is used to set the meter needle at zero on the scale when no current is flowing. This adjustment is made with a small screwdriver and should be checked when using a meter, particularly if the vertical or horizontal position of the meter is changed.

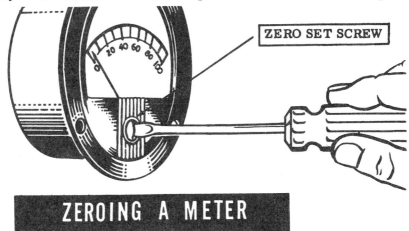

ZERO SET SCREW

ZEROING A METER

How Meter Scales Are Read (continued)

Meter scales used to measure current are divided into equal divisions, usually with a total of between thirty and fifty divisions. The meter should always be read from a position at right angles to the meter face. Since the meter divisions are small and the meter pointer is raised above the scale, reading the pointer position from an angle will result in an inaccurate reading, often as much as an entire scale division. This type of incorrect reading is called "parallax." Most meters are slightly inaccurate due to the meter construction, and additional error from a parallax reading may result in a very inaccurate reading.

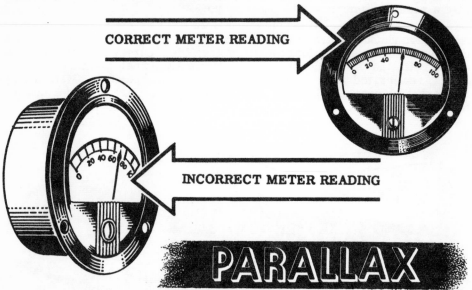

CORRECT METER READING

INCORRECT METER READING

PARALLAX

When the meter pointer reads a value of current between two divisions of the scale, usually the nearest division is used as the meter reading. However, if a more accurate reading is desired, the position of the pointer between the divisions is estimated, and the deflection between the scale divisions is added to the lower scale division. Estimating the pointer position is called "interpolation," and you will use this process in many other ways in working with electricity.

METER READING IS 23.6 AMPERES

Interpolation

Usable Meter Range

The range of an ammeter indicates the maximum current which can be measured with the meter. Current in excess of this value will cause serious damage to the meter. If an ammeter has a range of 0-15 amp, it will measure any current flow which does not exceed 15 amperes, but a current greater than 15 amperes will damage the meter.

While the meter scale may have a range of 0-15 amperes, its useful range for purposes of measurement will be from about 1 ampere to 14 amperes. When this meter scale indicates a current of 15 amperes, the actual current may be much greater but the meter can only indicate to its maximum range. For that reason the useful maximum range of any meter is slightly less than the maximum range of the meter scale. A current of 0.1 ampere on this meter scale would be very difficult to read since it would not cause the meter needle to move far enough from zero to obtain a definite reading.

Smaller currents such as 0.001 ampere would not cause the meter needle to move and thus could not be measured at all with this meter. The useful minimum range of a meter never extends down to zero, but extends instead only to the point at which the reading can be distinguished from zero.

Ammeter ranges are usually in multiples of 5 or 10 such as 0-5 amperes, 0-50 amperes, etc. Ranges above 0-100 amperes are not common since currents in excess of 100 amperes are seldom used.

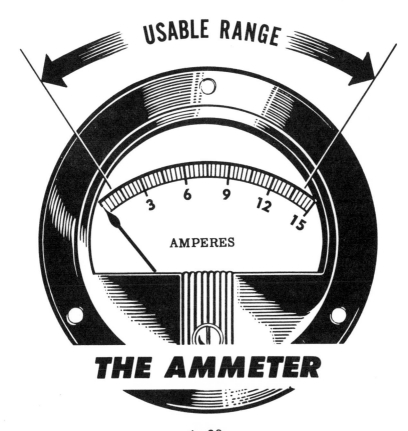

THE AMMETER

Demonstration—Ammeter Ranges

To show the importance of selecting the proper meter range for current measurement, the instructor first connects two dry cells in series to form a battery. Then the positive terminal of the 0-10 amp range ammeter is connected with a length of pushback wire to the positive terminal of the battery. Next, a lamp socket is connected between the negative terminal of the ammeter and the negative terminal of the battery.

The lamp bulb is used as a switch to control current flow. The lamp lights when it is inserted in the socket, and the meter pointer moves slightly—indicating a current flow. The meter reading indicates that the current flow is very low for the meter range used. The pointer is near the low end of the meter scale and the current cannot be read accurately.

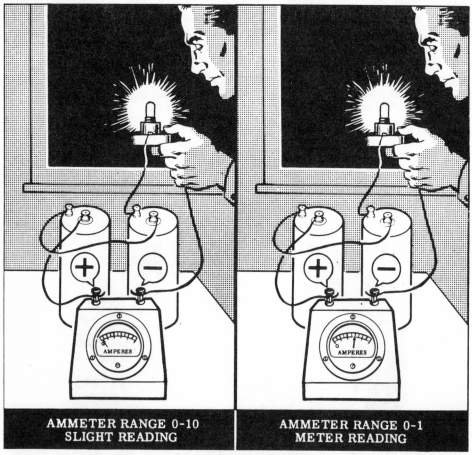

AMMETER RANGE 0-10
SLIGHT READING

AMMETER RANGE 0-1
METER READING

Next, the 0-1 amp range is used instead of the 0-10 amp range. Observe that when the lamp is inserted, its light indicates the current flow is the same as before. However, the meter reading now is near the midscale position of the meter scale, indicating a current flow of slightly more than one-half ampere. Since the reading is near midscale, this is the correct meter range for measuring the current.

1-70

Demonstration--Ammeter Ranges (continued)

To show the effect of using a meter having too low a range, the instructor next uses the 0-500 ma. range instead of the 0-1 amp range. Because the current flow is greater than the maximum range of the meter, the pointer deflects beyond the range of the scale and you are unable to read the amount of current flow. If this excess current flows through the meter for any length of time, it will cause serious damage to the meter. For that reason it is more important that the meter range be high enough, than that it be low enough, to obtain a good reading.

FINDING THE CORRECT METER RANGE

METER NO. 1
RANGE TOO HIGH

METER NO. 2
CORRECT RANGE

METER NO. 3
RANGE TOO LOW

MILLIAMMETER RANGE 0-500
READING TOO HIGH

To find the correct meter range where the current expected is not known, you should always start with a meter having a high maximum range and replace it with meters having lower ranges until a meter reading is obtained near mid-scale.

Demonstration—Reading Meter Scales

You have observed that the correct ammeter range to use in measuring the current flow through the lamp is the 0-1 amp range. To show the effects of parallax on meter readings, the instructor uses a 0-1 amp range instead of the 0-500 ma. range. Now, with the lamp inserted, the meter indicates a current flow somewhat greater than one-half ampere. The instructor will ask several trainees to read the meter simultaneously from different positions and record their readings. Notice that the readings taken at wide angles differ considerably from those obtained directly in front of the meter.

Now the entire class reads the meter and interpolates the reading by estimating between scale divisions. Since the meter scale permits reading to two places directly, the interpolation is the third figure of the reading. For example, the scale divisions between .6 and .7 are .62, .64, .66 and .68. If the meter pointer is between the .62 and .64 scale divisions and is halfway between these divisions, the meter reading is .630 ampere. A reading one-fourth of the way past the .62 division is .625 ampere, three-fourths of the way past the .62 division is .635 ampere, etc. Observe that the estimated or interpolated value obtained by everyone is more accurate than the nearest scale division, but there is disagreement among the interpolated readings.

INTERPOLATION OF METER READING

Review of How Current Is Measured

To review what you have found out about how current is measured, consider some of the important facts you have studied and seen demonstrated.

1. <u>AMPERE</u> — Unit of rate of flow of electrons, equal to 1 coulomb per second.

2. <u>MILLIAMPERE</u> — A unit of current equal to one-thousandth ampere.

$$1\,ma. = \frac{1}{1000}\ amp$$

3. <u>MICROAMPERE</u> — A unit of current equal to one-millionth ampere.

$$1\,\mu a = \frac{1}{1{,}000{,}000}\ amp$$

4. <u>AMMETER</u> — A meter used to measure currents of one ampere and greater.

5. <u>MILLIAMMETER</u> — A meter used to measure currents between one-thousandth ampere and one ampere.

6. <u>MICROAMMETER</u> — A meter used to measure currents between one-millionth ampere and one-thousandth ampere.

7. <u>PARALLAX</u> — Meter reading error due to taking a reading from an angle.

8. <u>INTERPOLATION</u> — Estimating the meter reading between two scale divisions.

The Basic Meter Movement

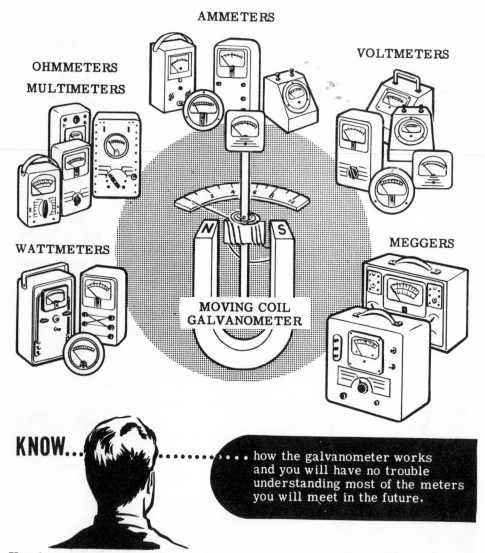

AMMETERS

VOLTMETERS

OHMMETERS
MULTIMETERS

MEGGERS

WATTMETERS

MOVING COIL
GALVANOMETER

KNOW... .... how the galvanometer works
and you will have no trouble
understanding most of the meters
you will meet in the future.

You have used meters for sometime now to show you whether or not an electric current was flowing and how much current was flowing. As you proceed further with your work in electricity, you will find yourself using meters more and more often. Meters are the right hand of anyone working in electricity or electronics, so now is the time for you to find out how they operate. All the meters you have used and nearly all the meters you will ever use are made with the same type of meter "works" or movement. This meter movement is based on the principles of an electric current-measuring device called the "moving coil galvanometer." Nearly all modern meters use the moving coil galvanometer as a basic meter movement, so once you know how it works you will have no trouble understanding all the meters you will be using in the future.

The Basic Meter Movement (continued)

The galvanometer works on the principle of magnetic attraction and re-pulsion. According to this principle, which you have already learned, like poles repel each other and unlike poles attract each other. This means that two magnetic North poles will repel each other as will two magnetic South poles, while a North pole and South pole will attract one another. You can see this very well if you suspend a bar magnet on a rigidly mounted shaft, between the poles of a horseshoe magnet.

If the bar magnet is allowed to turn freely, you will find that it turns until its North pole is as close as possible to the South pole of the horseshoe magnet and its South pole is as close as possible to the North pole of the horseshoe magnet. If you turn the bar magnet to a different position, you will feel it trying to turn back to the position where the opposite poles are as near as possible to each other. The further you try to turn the bar magnet away from this position, the greater force you will feel. The greatest force will be felt when you turn the bar magnet to the position in which the like poles of each magnet are as close as possible to each other.

HOW MAGNET POLES EXERT A FORCE

BAR MAGNET
turns to
bring opposite poles
as close together
as possible

BAR MAGNET
resists the turning
motion of hand
since like poles
repel each other

The Basic Meter Movement (continued)

The forces of attraction and repulsion between magnetic poles become greater when stronger magnets are used. You can see this if you attach a spring to the bar magnet in such a way that the spring will have no tension when the North poles of the two magnets are as close as possible to each other. With the magnets in this position the bar magnet would normally turn freely to a position which would bring its North pole as close as possible to the South pole of the horseshoe magnet. With the spring attached it will turn only part way, to a position where its turning force is balanced by the force of the spring. If you were to replace the bar magnet with a stronger magnet, the force of repulsion between the like poles would be greater and the bar magnet would turn further against the force of the spring.

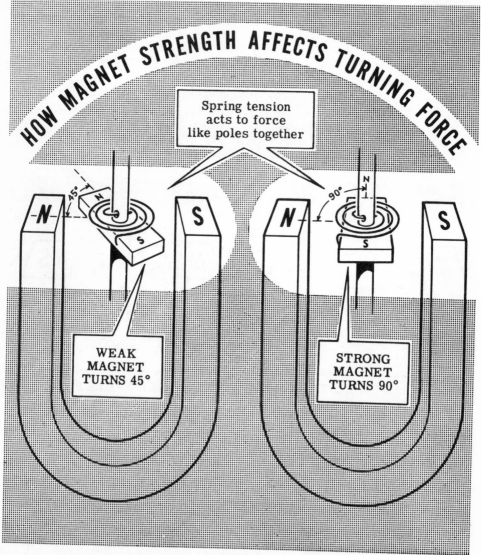

The Basic Meter Movement (continued)

If you remove the bar magnet and replace it with a coil of wire, you have a galvanometer. Whenever an electric current flows through this coil of wire, it acts like a magnet. The strength of this wire coil magnet depends on the size, shape and number of turns in the coil <u>and</u> the amount of electric current flowing through the coil. If the coil itself is not changed in any way, the magnetic strength of the coil will depend on the amount of current flowing through the coil. The greater the current flow in the coil, the stronger the magnetic strength of the wire coil magnet.

If there is no current flow in the coil, it will have no magnetic strength and the coil will turn to a position where there will be no tension on the spring. If you cause a small electric current to flow through the coil, the coil becomes a magnet and the magnetic forces—between the wire coil magnet and the horseshoe magnet—cause the coil to turn until the magnetic turning force is balanced by the force due to tension in the spring. When a larger current is made to flow through the coil, the magnet strength of the coil is increased and the wire coil turns further against the spring tension.

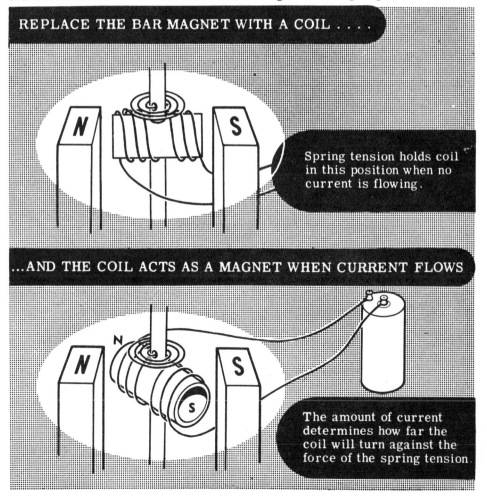

REPLACE THE BAR MAGNET WITH A COIL . . . .

Spring tension holds coil in this position when no current is flowing.

...AND THE COIL ACTS AS A MAGNET WHEN CURRENT FLOWS

The amount of current determines how far the coil will turn against the force of the spring tension.

The Basic Meter Movement (continued)

When you want to find out how much current is flowing in a circuit, all you need to do is to connect the coil into the circuit and measure the angle through which the coil turns away from its position at rest. To measure this angle, and to calculate the amount of electric current which causes the coil to turn through this angle, is very difficult. However, by connecting a pointer to the coil and adding a scale for the pointer to travel across, you can read the amount of current directly from the scale.

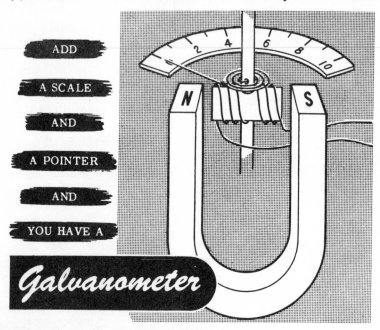

ADD

A SCALE

AND

A POINTER

AND

YOU HAVE A

Galvanometer

Now that you have added a scale and a pointer, you have a basic DC meter, known as the D'Arsonval-type movement, which depends upon the operation of magnets and their magnetic fields. Actually, there are two magnets in this type of meter; one a stationary permanent horseshoe magnet, the other an electromagnet. The electromagnet consists of turns of wire wound on a frame, and the frame is mounted on a shaft fitted between two permanently-mounted jewel bearings. A lightweight pointer is attached to the coil, and turns with it to indicate the amount of current flow. Current passing through the coil causes it to act as a magnet with poles being attracted and repelled by those of the horseshoe magnet. The strength of the magnetic field about the coil depends upon the amount of current flow. A greater current produces a stronger field, resulting in greater forces of attraction and repulsion between the coil sides and the magnet's poles.

The magnetic forces of attraction and repulsion cause the coil to turn so that the unlike poles of the coil and magnet will be brought together. As the coil current increases, the coil becomes a stronger magnet and turns further because of the greater magnetic forces between the coil and magnet poles. Since the amount by which the coil turns depends upon the amount of coil current, the meter indicates the current flow directly.

Meter Movement Considerations

While galvanometers are useful in laboratory measurements of extremely small currents, they are not portable, compact or rugged enough for use in military equipment. A modern meter movement uses the principles of the galvanometer but is portable, compact, rugged and easy to read. The coil is mounted on a shaft fitted between two permanently-mounted jewel bearings. To indicate the amount of current flow a lightweight pointer is attached to the coil and turns with the coil.

Balance springs on each end of the shaft exert opposite turning forces on the coil and, by adjusting the tension of one spring, the meter pointer may be adjusted to read zero on the meter scale. Since temperature change affects both coil springs equally, the turning effect of the springs on the meter coil is canceled out. As the meter coil turns, one spring tightens to provide a retarding force, while the other spring releases its tension. In addition to providing tension, the springs are used to carry current from the meter terminals through the moving coil.

In order that the turning force will increase uniformly as the current increases, the horseshoe magnet poles are shaped to form semi-circles. This brings the coil as near as possible to the north and south poles of the permanent magnet. The amount of current required to turn the meter pointer to full-scale deflection depends upon the magnet strength and the number of turns of wire in the moving coil.

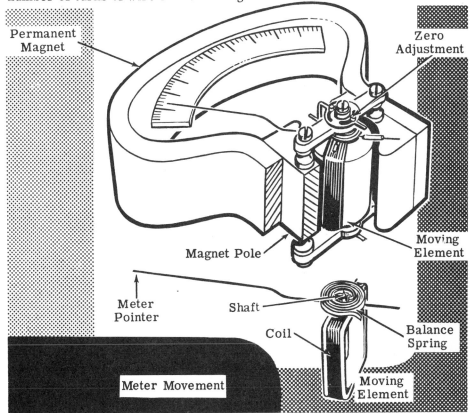

How Meter Ranges Are Changed

Meter ranges could be changed by using magnets of different strength or by changing the number of turns in the coil, since either of these changes would alter the amount of current needed for full-scale deflection. However, the wire used in the coil must always be large enough to carry the maximum current of the range the meter is intended for, and therefore changing the wire size would only be practical in the small current ranges, since large wire cannot be used as a moving coil. To keep the wire size and the coil small, basic meter movements are normally limited to a range of 1 milliampere or less. Also, for using a meter for more than one range, it is impractical to change the magnet or the coil each time the range is changed.

For measuring large currents a low range meter is used with a shunt, which is a heavy wire connected across the meter terminals to carry most of the current. This shunt allows only a small part of the current to actually flow through the meter coil. Usually a 0-1 milliampere meter is used, with the proper-sized shunt connected across its terminals to achieve the desired range. The 0-1 milliammeter is a basic meter movement which you will find in various types of meters you will use.

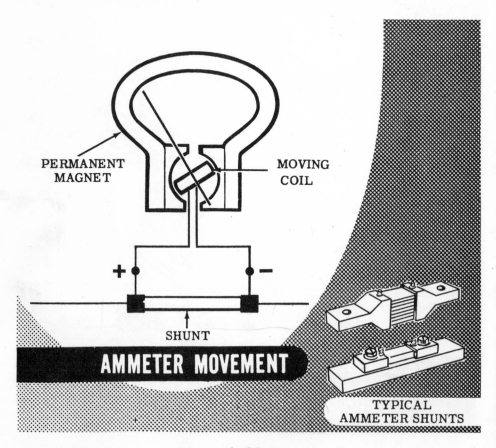

PERMANENT
MAGNET

MOVING
COIL

+   −

SHUNT

AMMETER MOVEMENT

TYPICAL
AMMETER SHUNTS

Multi-Range Ammeters

You have seen that you can change the range of an ammeter by the use of shunts. The range will vary according to the resistive value of the shunt. Some ammeters are built with a number of internal shunts, and a switching arrangement which is used to parallel different shunts across the meter movement to measure different currents. Thus a single meter movement can be used as a multi-range ammeter. A scale for each range is painted on the meter face. The diagram below shows a multi-range ammeter with a 0-3, 0-30, 0-300 ampere range. Note the three scales on the meter face.

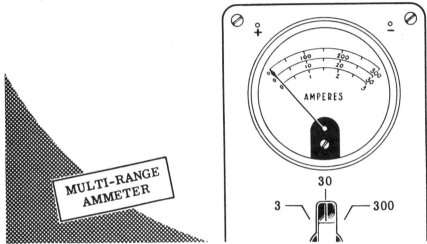

When a multi-range ammeter is used to measure an unknown current, the highest range is always used first, then the next highest range, and so on until the needle is positioned about midscale. In this way you can be assured that the current is not excessive for the meter range, and you will never have the unfortunate experience of burning out a meter movement, or of wrapping the needle around the stop-peg.

Some multimeters use external shunts, and do away with internal shunts and the switching arrangement. Changing range for such a meter involves shunting it with the appropriate shunt. In the diagram the ammeter is calibrated to read 30 amperes full-scale by shunting it with the 30-ampere shunt.

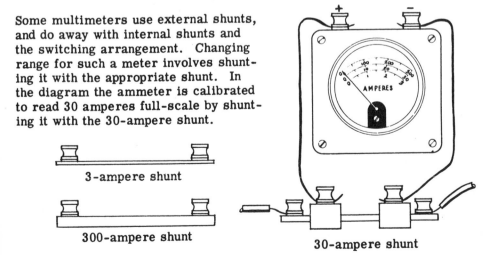

3-ampere shunt

300-ampere shunt

30-ampere shunt

Review of Meter Movement

It is very possible that you may never need to repair a meter but, in order to properly use and care for meters, you need to know how a meter works. Suppose you review what you have studied.

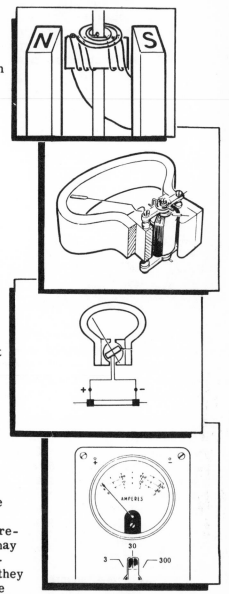

METER COIL — Moving coil which acts as a magnet when current flows in the coil.

METER MOVEMENT — Current-measuring instrument consisting of a moving coil suspended between the poles of a horseshoe magnet. Current in the coil causes the coil to turn.

BASIC AMMETER MOVEMENT — 0-1 ma. milliammeter movement with shunt wire across the meter terminals to increase the meter scale range.

MULTI-RANGE AMMETER — A single meter movement used for measuring different current ranges. Each range requires a different shunt. The shunts may be inside the meter movement and controlled by a switching arrangement or they may be external, in which case they are connected in parallel with the meter binding posts.

What EMF Is

Current flow takes place whenever most of the electron movement in a material is in one direction. You have found out that this movement is from a (-) charge to a (+) charge and occurs only as long as a difference in charge exists.

To create a charge, electrons must be moved, either to cause an excess or a lack of electrons at the point where the charge is to exist. A charge may be created by any of the six sources of electricity which you have studied about previously. These sources furnish the energy required to do the work of moving electrons to form a charge. Regardless of the kind of energy used to create a charge, it is changed to electrical energy once the charge is created; and the amount of electrical energy existing in the charge is exactly equal to the amount of the source energy required to create this charge.

When the current flows, the electrical energy of the charges is utilized to move electrons from less positive to more positive charges. This electrical energy is called electromotive force (emf) and is the moving force which causes current flow. Electrons may be moved to cause a charge by using energy from any of the six sources of electricity; but, when electrons move from one charge to another as current flow, the moving force is emf.

THE FORCE OF STEAM MAKES A STEAM LOCOMOTIVE MOVE

EMF IS THE FORCE THAT MAKES ELECTRONS MOVE

What EMF Is (continued)

An electric charge, whether positive or negative, represents a reserve of energy. This reserve energy is potential energy as long as it is not being used. The potential energy of a charge is equal to the amount of work done to create the charge, and the unit used to measure this work is the <u>volt</u>. The electromotive force of a charge is equal to the potential of the charge and is expressed in volts.

When two unequal charges exist, the electromotive force between the charges is equal to the difference in potential of the two charges. Since the potential of each charge is expressed in volts the difference in potential is also expressed in volts. The difference in potential between two charges is the electromotive force acting between the charges—commonly called voltage.

Voltage or a difference in potential exists between any two charges which are not exactly equal. Even an uncharged body has a potential difference with respect to a charged body; it is positive with respect to a negative charge and negative with respect to a positive charge. Voltage exists, for example, between two unequal positive charges or between two unequal negative charges. Thus voltage is purely relative and is not used to express the actual amount of charge, but rather to compare one charge to another and indicate the electromotive force between the two charges being compared.

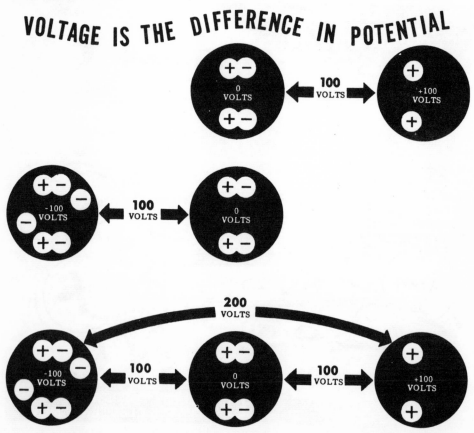

VOLTAGE IS THE DIFFERENCE IN POTENTIAL

How EMF Is Maintained

Of the six sources of electricity, you will usually use only magnetism and chemical action. Electric charges obtained from friction, pressure, heat and light are only used in special applications and are never used as a source of electric power.

In order to cause continuous current flow, electric charges must be maintained so that the difference of potential remains the same at all times. At the terminals of a battery, opposite charges exist caused by the chemical action within the battery, and as current flows from the (-) terminal to the (+) terminal the chemical action maintains the charges at their original value. A generator acts in the same manner, with the action of a wire moving through a magnetic field maintaining a constant charge on each of the generator terminals. The voltage between the generator or battery terminals remains constant and the charges on the terminals never become equal to each other as long as the chemical action continues in the battery and as long as the generator wire continues to move through the magnetic field.

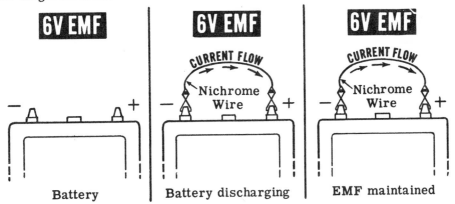

| Battery | Battery discharging | EMF maintained |

If the charges were not maintained at the terminals, as in the case of two charged bars shown below, current flow from the (-) terminal to the (+) terminal would cause the two charges to become equal as the excess electrons of the (-) charge moved to the (+) charge. The voltage between the terminals then would fall to zero volts and current flow would no longer take place.

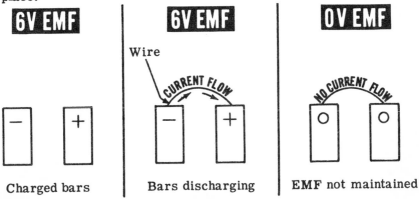

| Charged bars | Bars discharging | EMF not maintained |

1-85

Voltage and Current Flow

Whenever two points of unequal charge are connected, a current flows from the more negative to the more positive charge. The greater the emf or voltage between the charges, the greater the amount of current flow. Electrical equipment is designed to operate with a certain amount of current flow, and when this amount is exceeded the equipment may be damaged. You have seen all kinds of equipment such as electric lamps, motors, radios, etc. with the voltage rating indicated. The voltage will differ on certain types of equipment, but it is usually 110 volts. This rating on a lamp, for example, means that 110 volts will cause the correct current flow. Using a higher voltage will result in a greater current flow and "burn out" the lamp, while a lower voltage will not cause enough current flow.

If a motor is designed to operate on 110 volts and you connect it to a 220-volt electric power line, the motor will be "burned out" due to excessive current flow; but the same motor placed across a 50-volt line will not operate properly because not enough current will flow. While current flow makes equipment work, it takes emf or voltage to cause the current to flow, and the value of the voltage determines how much current will flow.

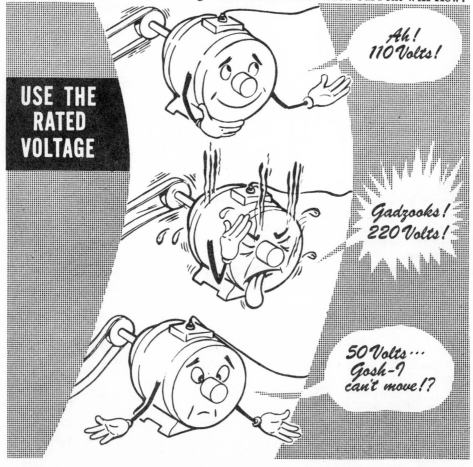

Voltage and Current Flow (continued)

Electromotive force—voltage—is used like any other type of force. To drive a nail you might use any number of different size hammers but only one size would furnish exactly the right amount of force for a particular nail. You would not use a sledge hammer to drive a tack nor a tack hammer to drive a large spike. Choosing the correct size hammer to drive a nail is just as important as finding the correct size nail to use for a given job.

Similarly, electrical devices and equipment operate best when the correct current flows, but for a given device or equipment you must choose the correct amount of voltage to cause just the right amount of current flow. Too large a voltage will cause too much current flow, while too small a voltage will not cause enough current flow.

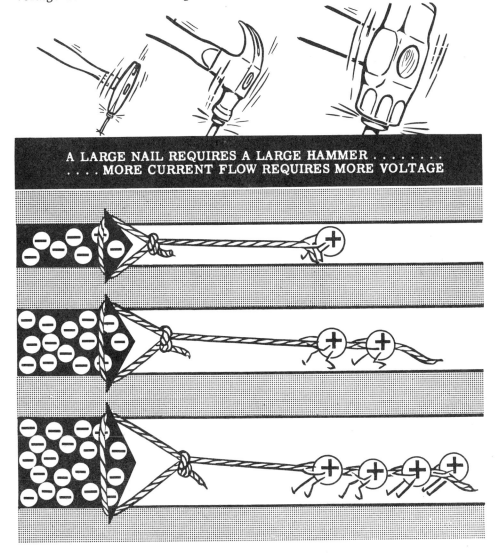

A LARGE NAIL REQUIRES A LARGE HAMMER . . . .
. . . . MORE CURRENT FLOW REQUIRES MORE VOLTAGE

HOW VOLTAGE IS MEASURED

Units of Voltage

The electromotive force between two unequal charges is usually expressed in volts but, when the difference in potential is only a fraction of a volt or is more than a thousand volts, other units are used. For voltages of less than one volt, millivolts and microvolts are used, just as milliamperes and microamperes are used to express currents less than one ampere. While current seldom exceeds one thousand amperes, voltage often exceeds one thousand volts, so that the kilovolt—equal to one thousand volts—is used as the unit of measurement. When the potential difference between two charges is between one-thousandth of a volt and one volt, the unit of measure is the millivolt; when it is between one-millionth volt and one-thousandth volt, the unit is the microvolt.

Meters for measuring voltage have scale ranges in microvolts, millivolts, volts and kilovolts, depending on the units of voltage to be measured. Ordinarily you will work with voltages between 1 and 500 volts and use the volt as a unit. Voltages of less than 1 volt and more than 500 volts are not used except in special applications of electrical equipment.

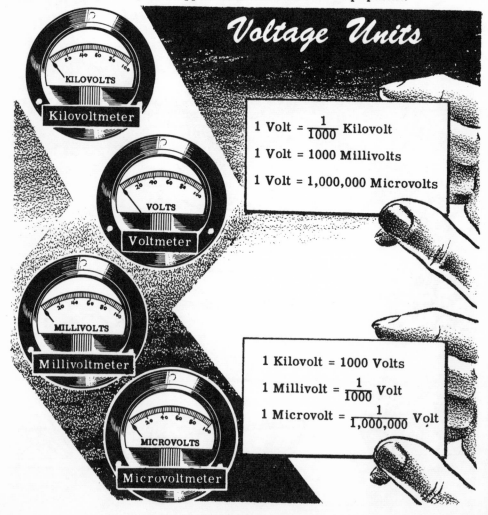

Voltage Units

Kilovoltmeter

Voltmeter

Millivoltmeter

Microvoltmeter

$1 \text{ Volt} = \frac{1}{1000} \text{ Kilovolt}$

$1 \text{ Volt} = 1000 \text{ Millivolts}$

$1 \text{ Volt} = 1{,}000{,}000 \text{ Microvolts}$

$1 \text{ Kilovolt} = 1000 \text{ Volts}$

$1 \text{ Millivolt} = \frac{1}{1000} \text{ Volt}$

$1 \text{ Microvolt} = \frac{1}{1{,}000{,}000} \text{ Volt}$

HOW VOLTAGE IS MEASURED

Changing Units of Voltage

Units of voltage measurement are changed in the same way that units of current are changed. In order to change millivolts to volts, the decimal point is moved three places to the left, and to change volts to millivolts the decimal point is moved three places to the right. Similarly, in changing microvolts to volts, the decimal point is moved six places to the left, and in changing volts to microvolts the decimal point is moved six places to the right. These examples show that, in changing units, the same rules of moving the decimal point apply to both voltage and current.

Kilo (meaning one thousand) is not used to express current, but since it is used to express voltage, you need to know how to change kilovolts to volts and the reverse. To change kilovolts to volts the decimal point is moved three places to the right, and to change volts to kilovolts it is moved three places to the left. For example, 5 kilovolts equals 5,000 volts, since the decimal point is after the 5. Three zeros are added to provide the necessary places. Also, 450 volts equals 0.45 kilovolt as the decimal point is moved three places to the left.

CHANGING VOLTAGE UNITS

VOLTS TO KILOVOLTS

Move the decimal point 3 places to the left.

450 volts = .45 kilovolt

KILOVOLTS TO VOLTS

Move the decimal point 3 places to the right.

5 kilovolts = 5000 volts

VOLTS TO MILLIVOLTS

Move the decimal point 3 places to the right.

15 volts = 15000 millivolts

MILLIVOLTS TO VOLTS

Move the decimal point 3 places to the left.

500 millivolts = .5 volt

VOLTS TO MICROVOLTS

Move the decimal point 6 places to the right.

15 volts = 15,000,000 microvolts

MICROVOLTS TO VOLTS

Move the decimal point 6 places to the left.

3505 microvolts = .003505 volt

How a Voltmeter Works

An ammeter measures the rate at which charges are moving through a material. Since the rate of current flow varies with the voltage difference between charges, a greater current flow through a given material indicates a greater voltage across the given material. Voltage is measured by a voltmeter, which measures the current flow through a given material, called a multiplier resistor, connected in series with it. A little later you will find out more about resistors and resistance. For a given multiplier, the meter will indicate a large current if the voltage is high, or a small current if the voltage is low. The meter scale can then be marked in volts.

The multiplier resistor determines the scale range of a voltmeter. Since the multiplier is built into most of the voltmeters you will use, you can measure voltage by making very simple connections. Whenever the (+) meter terminal is connected to the (+) terminal of the voltage source and the (-) meter terminal to the (-) terminal of the voltage source, with nothing else connected in series, the meter reads voltage directly. When using a voltmeter it is important to observe the correct meter polarity and to use a meter with a maximum scale range greater than the maximum voltage you expect to read.

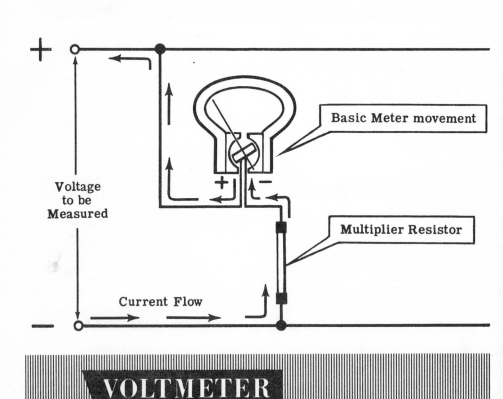

VOLTMETER

How a Voltmeter is Used

A voltmeter is used to measure electrical pressure anywhere in a circuit. If it is to measure a source of voltage such as a battery, the negative side of the voltmeter is always connected to the negative side of the battery, and the positive side of the voltmeter is always connected to the positive side of the battery. If these connections are reversed, the meter needle will move to the left of the zero mark, and a reading cannot be obtained.

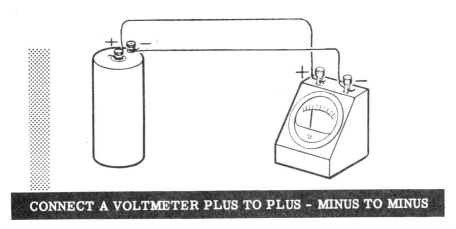

CONNECT A VOLTMETER PLUS TO PLUS - MINUS TO MINUS

When the voltmeter is to measure the voltage drop across a load, the negative lead is connected to the side of load into which the electrons enter (the - side), and the positive lead is connected to the side of the load from which the electrons emerge (the + side).

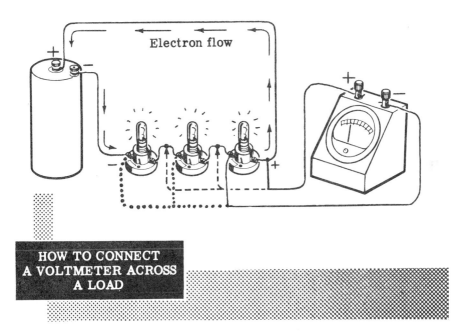

HOW TO CONNECT A VOLTMETER ACROSS A LOAD

Demonstration—Voltage and Current Flow

In order to show the effect of voltage on current flow, the instructor connects six dry cells in series to form a 9-volt battery, connecting (+) to (-) between the cells. Using an 0-10 volt voltmeter, he connects the (-) meter terminal to the (-) battery terminal. He then touches the (+) meter terminal to each cell (+) terminal in turn. Observe that the cell voltages add and that, using the battery (-) terminal and the various cell (+) terminals, voltages of 1.5, 3, 4.5, 6, 7.5 and 9 volts are obtainable.

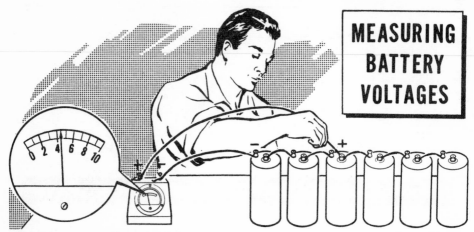

Next, two pushback wire leads are connected to the terminals of a lamp socket and the voltmeter is connected across the socket terminals. The socket lead from the (-) meter terminal is connected to the (-) battery terminal, and a 6-volt lamp is inserted in the socket. As the instructor touches the socket lead which connects to the (+) meter terminal to each of the battery (+) terminals in turn, notice that as the voltage indicated by the voltmeter reading rises the lamp light is brighter—indicating that more current is flowing. You see that the lamp, which is rated for 6 volts, lights with excessive brightness on 7.5 and 9 volts, indicating that the voltage is beyond the lamp rating. You also see that for voltages of less than 6 volts the lamp is dim—indicating that the voltage is too low for proper operation.

Demonstration—Voltage and Current Flow (continued)

Two cells are now removed from the battery to form a 6-volt battery. The instructor connects the voltmeter across this battery, making certain to observe the correct meter polarity, and you see that it reads 6 volts. Now three lamp sockets are connected in parallel; this parallel combination is connected across the 6-volt battery, and lamps are inserted into the sockets. As each lamp is inserted notice that each lamp lights with the same brilliance as that of the first lamp, which indicates an increase in current flow between the battery terminals, but that the voltmeter indicates very little change in the charges at the battery terminals.

VOLTAGE ACROSS PARALLEL LAMPS

DC VOLTS

The instructor stresses the importance of correct connection of the voltmeter. A voltmeter should always be connected so that its positive lead goes to the plus side and its negative lead goes to the minus side of the voltage points under measurement. If the leads are incorrectly placed the needle will read down scale so that an accurate reading cannot be obtained, and it will also be impossible to determine whether or not the voltmeter range you are using is high enough to include the voltages under measurement. The meter may be damaged, too, even during the comparatively short time it takes to reverse the meter leads.

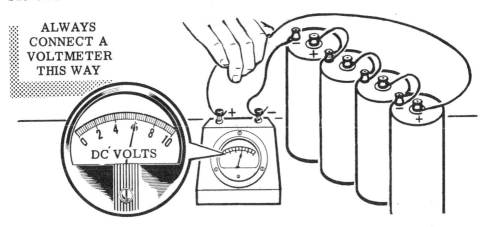

ALWAYS CONNECT A VOLTMETER THIS WAY

DC VOLTS

HOW VOLTAGE IS MEASURED

Multi-range Voltmeters

The range of any voltmeter can be increased by the addition of a multiplier to the voltmeter circuit, in series with the basic meter movement. The multiplier causes reduction of the deflection of the pointer on the meter, and by using multipliers of known values, the deflection can be reduced as much as desired.

Multi-range voltmeters, like multi-range ammeters, are instruments which you will use frequently. They are physically very similar to ammeters, and their multipliers are usually located inside the meter, with suitable switches or sets of terminals on the outside for selecting range. Proper range is selected by starting with the highest range and working downward, until the needle reads about midscale.

Because they are lightweight, portable, and can be set up for different voltage ranges by the flick of a switch, multi-range voltmeters are extremely useful.

The simplified drawing below shows a three-range, multi-range voltmeter.

TYPICAL 3-RANGE MULTI-RANGE VOLTMETER

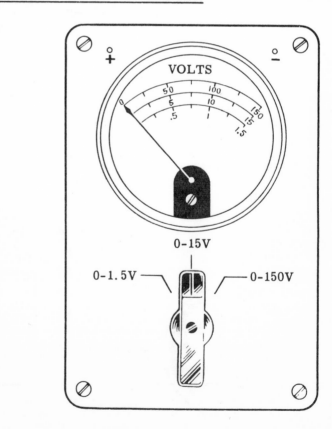

Demonstration—Voltmeter Ranges

To demonstrate the proper method to use in selecting the correct voltmeter range to measure a DC voltage, the instructor connects separate wire leads to the (-) battery terminal and to the (+) 22.5-volt battery terminal. Across these leads, he connects each of the voltmeters in turn. As you see, the deflection on the 0-300 volt range is too small to read properly, and the deflection on the 0-10 volt range is beyond the maximum range of the meter, while on the 0-100 volt range the deflection is in the usable range of the meter, being slightly more than 1/5 of full-scale deflection.

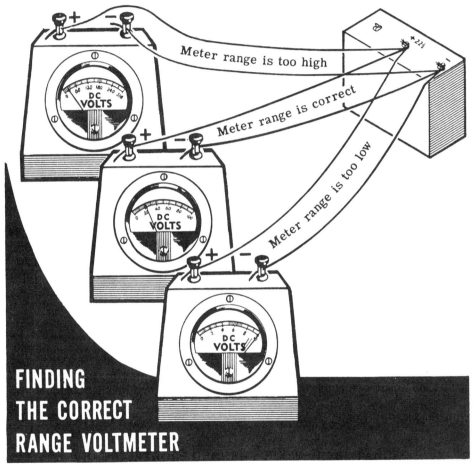

FINDING THE CORRECT RANGE VOLTMETER

To further illustrate the importance of choosing the correct meter range, the procedure is repeated for various voltages obtained by connecting dry cell batteries in series. Notice that, whether the voltage used is 3 volts or 135 volts, the instructor always uses the highest meter range first and reduces the range until the proper range is selected.

Next, a high range voltmeter is used on a low voltage to check the polarity of the voltage. You see that the instructor does not use a low range meter for this check, nor does he maintain the meter connection any longer than is necessary to determine whether the pointer turns in the right direction.

HOW VOLTAGE IS MEASURED

Demonstration—Range Selection and Correct Voltmeter Connection

To show how to select the correct range on a multirange voltmeter, the instructor constructs a six-volt dry-cell battery by connecting four dry cells in series and connecting a lamp socket across the battery terminals. He inserts a lamp and, using the multirange voltmeter 0-1.5, 15, 150 with the selector on the meter set on the 0-150 scale, measures the voltage across the lamp socket terminals and then across the battery terminals. Then he sets the selector on the meter on the 0-15 scale and repeats the performance. He finds that the 0-15 is the correct scale and that the lamp voltage equals the battery voltage.

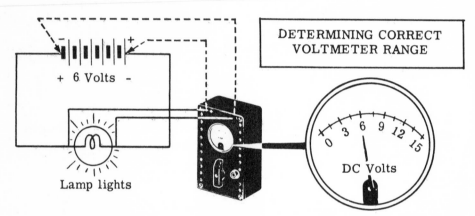

Using the same circuit, he connects the voltmeter (its selector is set on the 0-15 scale) in series with the circuit by breaking one of the connections to the lamp; the voltmeter reads the full battery voltage. Next he removes the lamp from its socket and the voltmeter reading drops to zero. He notes that a voltmeter connected as an ammeter reads voltage but does not allow enough current to flow to light the lamp, because only a very small current can flow through the large resistance of the multiplier built into the 0-15 voltmeter range.

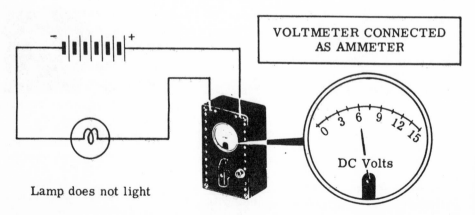

HOW VOLTAGE IS MEASURED

Review of Voltage Units and Measurement

Now suppose you look again at what you have studied and seen concerning the units of voltage and how voltage is measured.

VOLTAGE UNITS

1 kilovolt = 1000 volts

1 millivolt = $\frac{1}{1000}$ volt

1 microvolt = $\frac{1}{1,000,000}$ volt

1 volt = $\frac{1}{1000}$ kilovolt

1 volt = 1000 millivolts

1 volt = 1,000,000 microvolts

CHANGING VOLTAGE UNITS

To Change	Move the Decimal Point
Kilovolts to Volts	Three places to the RIGHT
Volts to Kilovolts	Three places to the LEFT
Volts to Millivolts	Three places to the RIGHT
Millivolts to Volts	Three places to the LEFT
Volts to Microvolts	Six places to the RIGHT
Microvolts to Volts	Six places to the LEFT
Millivolts to Microvolts	Three places to the RIGHT
Microvolts to Millivolts	Three places to the LEFT

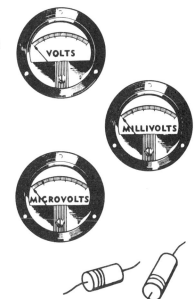

VOLTMETER — Basic meter movement with a series-connected multiplier, calibrated to measure voltage.

MILLIVOLTMETER — Voltmeter calibrated to measure voltages of more than 1 millivolt and less than 1 volt.

MICROVOLTMETER — Voltmeter calibrated to measure voltages of more than 1 microvolt and less than 1 millivolt.

MULTIPLIERS — Materials used in series with a basic meter movement to determine the voltage range of a voltmeter.

WHAT CONTROLS CURRENT FLOW—RESISTANCE

What Resistance Is

The opposition to current flow is not the same for all materials. Current flow itself is the movement of "free" electrons through a material, and the number of "free" electrons in a material determines its opposition to current flow. Atoms of some materials give up their outer electrons easily and such materials offer little opposition to current flow, while other materials hold onto their outer electrons and such materials offer considerable opposition to current flow. Every material has some opposition to current flow, whether large or small, and this opposition is called resistance.

Materials having little resistance give up many Free electrons.

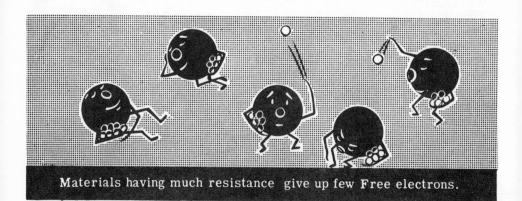

Materials having much resistance give up few Free electrons.

What Resistance Is (continued)

In order to picture resistance in a situation involving more familiar components, picture again the drain pipe that you read about earlier in this section. As you remember, the drain pipe contained a large number of golf
balls firmly held in place by wires and each of these represented an atom
with its bound electrons. The space in between the golf balls was filled
with small metal balls the size of air rifle shot. Each of these metal balls
represented a free electron. When the metal balls were removed from one
end and rammed into the other end, a flow of these balls was begun in the
pipe.

To get the concept of resistance, imagine that each golf ball is covered with
a special type of glue. This glue will not come off the golf ball but it will
cause the steel balls to stick to it. The strength of the glue varies with the
type of material being represented. If the material is copper the glue is
very weak and the free electrons will not be held strongly. However, if the
material is glass, the glue is very strong and will hold onto the free electrons and not let them go. A push (voltage) that would cause billions of
metal balls to come out of the open end each second when a weak glue is
used, would cause only two or three of the metal balls to come out when a
powerful glue is used.

The resistance of a material may be compared to the strength of the glue
just described. When the push (voltage) is kept the same, there will be a
smaller and smaller flow of metal balls (or electrons) as the strength of
the glue (or resistance) is increased.

An atom does not have any glue on it, but the electric fields of the positive
charges in the nucleus hold the electric fields of the outer electrons in very
much the same manner. This force of attraction may be large or small
depending upon the structure of the atom (type of material).

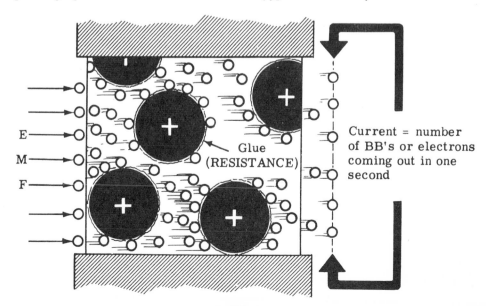

Glue
(RESISTANCE)

Current = number
of BB's or electrons
coming out in one
second

What Resistance Is (continued)

You know that an electric current is the movement of "free" electrons in a material and that an electric current does not begin flowing all by itself, because it needs a source of electrical force to move the "free electrons" through the material. You have also found out that an electric current will not continue to flow if the source of electrical energy is removed. You can see from all this that there is something in a material that resists the flow of electric current—something that holds on to the "free" electrons and will not release them until sufficient force is applied. This opposition to electrical current flow is called resistance. This resistance corresponds to the strength of the "glue" described on the previous sheet.

With a constant amount of electrical force (voltage), the more opposition you have to current flow (resistance), the smaller will be the number of electrons flowing through the material (current). Using the same source of voltage, the lower the resistance, the greater the current.

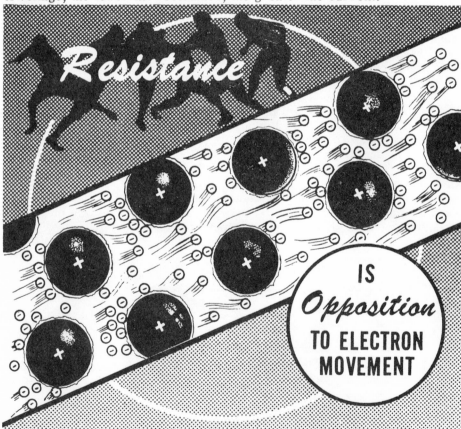

Thus if you have a fixed source of voltage, you can increase the current by decreasing the resistance, and you can decrease the current by increasing the resistance. By increasing or decreasing the amount of resistance—opposition to electron movement—in a circuit, you can adjust the amount of current flow to meet the operating needs of a piece of electrical equipment.

Conductors and Insulators

You may have heard it said that a conductor is a poor insulator and that an insulator is a poor conductor. While this statement does not tell exactly what a conductor or an insulator is, it is nevertheless a true statement. Conductors are materials which offer very little opposition to the flow of current and therefore are used to carry or conduct electricity. Insulators are materials which offer much opposition to the flow of current and therefore are used to block or insulate against the flow of current. Both conductors and insulators conduct current but in vastly different amounts, the current flow in an insulator being so small it is usually considered to equal zero.

Materials which are good conductors have a plentiful supply of free electrons while insulating materials do not, since they will not easily give up the electrons in the outer orbits of their atoms. Metals are the best conductors, with copper, aluminum and iron wire being used commonly to conduct current. Carbon and ordinary water are non-metallic materials sometimes used as conductors, while such materials as glass, paper, rubber, ceramics and certain plastics are commonly used as insulators.

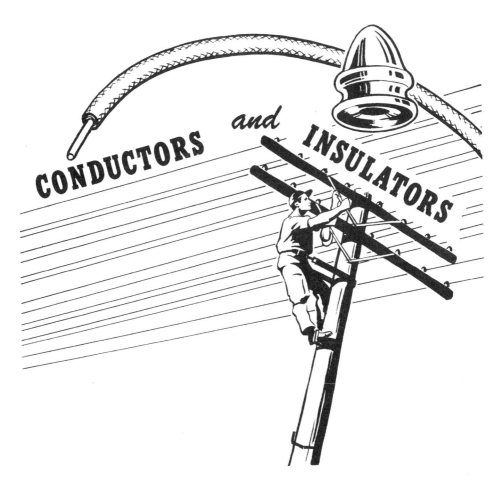

Factors Controlling Resistance—Material

Even the very best conductors have some resistance which limits the flow of electric current through them. The resistance of any object, such as a wire conductor for example, depends upon four factors—the material of which it is made, its length, its cross-sectional area and its temperature. Suppose you examine each of these factors controlling resistance and see how each one affects the total resistance of an object.

You already know that the material of which an object is made affects its resistance. The ease with which different materials give up their outer electrons is a very important factor in determining the resistance of an object. If you had four wires identical in length and cross-sectional area but made of different materials—silver, copper, aluminum and iron—you would find that each had a different resistance. A dry cell connected across each of them would cause a different current to flow. Silver is the best conductor of electricity—with copper, aluminum and iron having more resistance in that order. All materials conduct an electric current to some extent, and all materials can be assigned a value of "resistivity" which indicates just how well that material will conduct an electric current.

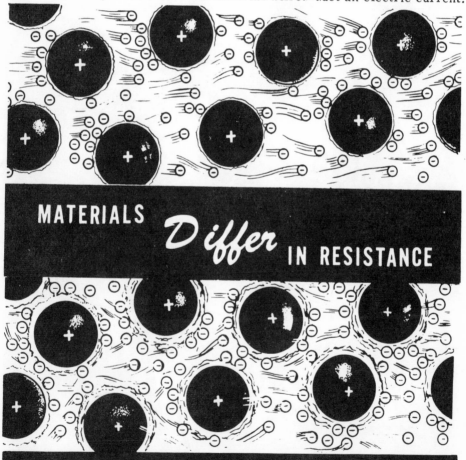

MATERIALS *Differ* IN RESISTANCE

Factors Controlling Resistance—Length

The next factor greatly affecting the resistance of a conductor is its length. The longer the length, the greater the resistance; and the shorter the length, the lower the resistance. You know that a material such as iron resists the flow of electric current, simply because of the manner in which each atom holds on to its outer electrons. It is easy to see that the more iron you put in the path of an electric current, the less will be the current flow.

Suppose you were to connect an iron wire four inches long and 1/100 inch thick in series with an ammeter. As soon as you connect this across a dry cell, a certain amount of current will flow. The amount of current that flows depends upon the voltage of the dry cell and the number of times the electron gets "stuck" or "attracted" by the atoms in its path between the terminals of the voltage source. If you were to double the length of the iron wire, making it eight inches long, there would be twice as much iron in the path of the electric current and the electron would be held by twice as many atoms in its path between the terminals of the voltage source. By doubling the length of the electric current path between the terminals of the dry cell, you have put twice as many attractions in the way, and you have doubled the resistance.

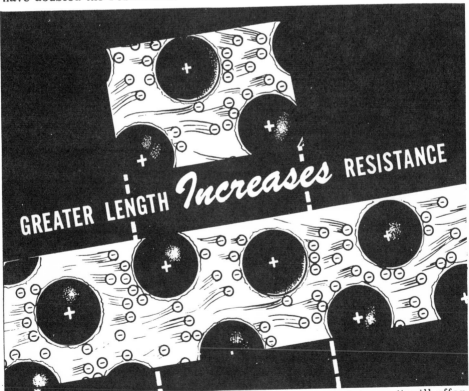

GREATER LENGTH *Increases* RESISTANCE

The longer the length of a conductor, the greater resistance it will offer to electric current flow. The shorter the length of a given type of conductor, the less resistance it will offer to the flow of an electric current.

Factors Controlling Resistance—Cross-Sectional Area

Another factor affecting the resistance of a conductor is its cross-sectional area. To understand what cross-sectional area means, suppose you imagine a wire cleanly cut across any part of its length. The area of the cut face of the wire is the cross-sectional area. The greater this area, the lower is the resistance of the wire; and the smaller this area, the higher is the resistance of the wire.

To see how this works suppose that you were to connect an iron wire four inches long and 1/100 inch thick in series with an ammeter. As soon as you connect this across a dry cell, a certain amount of current will flow. The amount of current that flows depends upon the voltage of the dry cell and the path of iron wire put in the way of the current flow between the terminals of the voltage source. You can see that the electric current has a pretty narrow wire (1/100 inch thick) to travel through. If you were to remove the iron wire and replace it with another wire which has the same length but twice the cross-sectional area, the current flow would double. This happens because you now have a "wider path" for the electric current to flow through—twice as many free electrons are available to make up the current which has the same length of path to flow through.

The larger the cross-sectional area of a conductor, the lower the resistance; and the smaller the cross-sectional area, the higher the resistance.

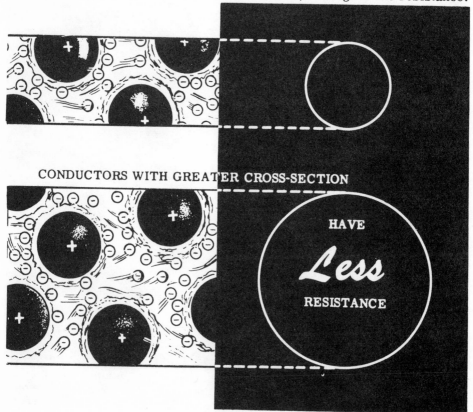

CONDUCTORS WITH GREATER CROSS-SECTION HAVE *Less* RESISTANCE

WHAT CONTROLS CURRENT FLOW—RESISTANCE

Factors Controlling Resistance—Temperature

The final factor affecting the resistance of a conductor is its temperature. For most materials the hotter the material, the more resistance it offers to the flow of an electric current; and the colder the material, the less resistance it offers to the flow of an electric current. This effect comes about because a change in the temperature of a material changes the ease with which that material releases its outer electrons.

You can see this effect by connecting a length of resistance wire, a switch and a dry cell in series. When you close the switch a certain amount of electric current will flow through the wire. In a short time the wire will begin to heat up. As the wire begins to heat up, its atoms hold less tightly onto the outer electrons. As the wire gets hotter and hotter, more and more electrons are freed. Furthermore, the heat causes the free electrons to vibrate greatly, which results in many collisions between them. Because the free electrons are constantly colliding with one another, they cannot flow through the wire as easily as they could before the wire became hot. The heat, then, has caused the resistance of the wire to increase. You can see the resistance go up by watching the meter; as the wire gets hotter and hotter, the resistance to the electric current rises and the meter reading will fall lower and lower. When the wire has reached its maximum heat, its resistance will stop increasing and the meter reading will remain at a steady value.

Some materials such as carbon and electrolytic solutions lower their resistance to an electric current as the temperature increases, and the electric current increases as the temperature increases. The effect of temperature upon resistance varies with the type of material — in materials such as copper and aluminum, it is very slight. The effect of temperature on resistance is the least important of the four factors controlling resistance — material, length, cross-sectional area and temperature.

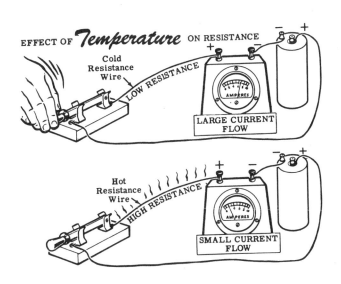

EFFECT OF *Temperature* ON RESISTANCE

Cold Resistance Wire
LOW RESISTANCE
AMPERES
LARGE CURRENT FLOW

Hot Resistance Wire
HIGH RESISTANCE
AMPERES
SMALL CURRENT FLOW

Units of Resistance

When one volt causes one ampere of current flow,
the resistance is one ohm.

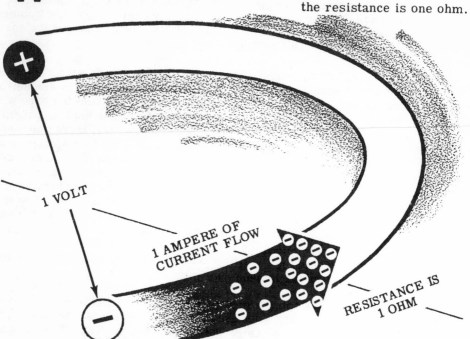

1 VOLT

1 AMPERE OF CURRENT FLOW

RESISTANCE IS 1 OHM

To measure current the ampere is used as a unit of measure and to measure voltage the volt is used. These units are necessary in order to compare different currents and different voltages. In the same manner, a unit of measure is needed to compare the resistance of different conductors. The basic unit of resistance is the ohm, equal to that resistance which will allow exactly one ampere of current to flow when one volt of emf is applied across the resistance.

Suppose you connect a copper wire across a voltage source of 1 volt and adjust the length of the wire until the current flow through the wire is exactly one ampere. The resistance of the length of copper wire then is exactly 1 ohm. If you were to use wire of any other materials—iron, silver, etc.—you would find that the wire length and size would not be the same as that for copper. However, in each case you could find a length of the wire which would allow exactly 1 ampere of current to flow when connected across a 1-volt voltage source, and each of these lengths would have a resistance of 1 ohm. The resistances of other lengths and sizes of wire are compared to these 1-ohm lengths, and their resistances are expressed in ohms.

Like other parts of a circuit, a symbol is used to indicate resistance.

RESISTANCE

Units of Resistance (continued)

Most of the time you will use resistance values which can be expressed in ohms but for certain special applications you may use small values of less than one ohm or values greater than one million ohms. Fractional values of resistance are expressed in microhms and very large values are expressed in megohms. One microhm equals one-millionth ohm, while one megohm is equal to a million ohms.

Units of resistance are changed in the same manner as units of current or voltage. To change microhms to ohms the decimal point is moved six places to the left, and to change ohms to microhms the decimal point is moved six places to the right. To change megohms to ohms the decimal point is moved six places to the right, and to change ohms to megohms it is moved six places to the left.

For resistances between one thousand and one million ohms the unit used is the kilohm (K) which is always abbreviated in use. Ten kilohms is written 10K and equals 10,000 ohms. To change kilohms to ohms the decimal point is moved three places to the right, and to change ohms to kilohms the decimal point is moved three places to the left.

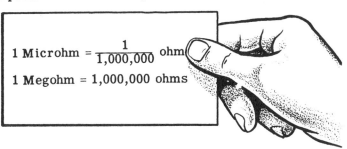

$$1 \text{ Microhm} = \frac{1}{1,000,000} \text{ ohm}$$

$$1 \text{ Megohm} = 1,000,000 \text{ ohms}$$

CHANGING RESISTANCE UNITS

MICROHMS TO OHMS
Move the decimal point 6 places to the left

35000 microhms = .035 ohm

OHMS TO MICROHMS
Move the decimal point 6 places to the right

3.6 ohms = 3,600,000 microhms

KILOHMS TO OHMS
Move the decimal point 3 places to the right

6 kilohms = 6000 ohms

OHMS TO KILOHMS
Move the decimal point 3 places to the left

6530 ohms = 6.530 kilohms

MEGOHMS TO OHMS
Move the decimal point 6 places to the right

2.7 megohms = 2,700,000 ohms

OHMS TO MEGOHMS
Move the decimal point 6 places to the left

650,000 ohms = .65 megohm

How Resistance Is Measured

Voltmeters and ammeters are meters you are familiar with and have used to measure voltage and current. Meters used to measure resistance are called ohmmeters. These meters differ from ammeters and voltmeters particularly in that the scale divisions are not equally spaced, and the meter requires a built-in battery for proper operation. When using the ohmmeter, no voltage should be present across the resistance being measured except that of the ohmmeter battery; otherwise, the ohmmeter will be damaged.

Ohmmeter ranges usually vary from 0-1000 ohms to 0-10 megohms. The accuracy of the meter readings decreases at the maximum end of each scale, particularly for the megohm ranges, because the scale divisions become so closely spaced that an accurate reading cannot be obtained. Unlike other meters, the zero end of the ohmmeter scale is at full-scale deflection of the meter pointer.

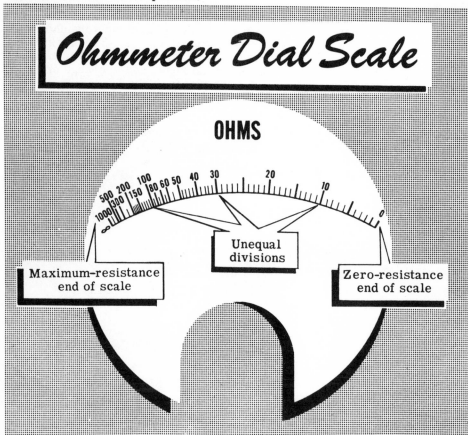

Special ohmmeters called "meggers" are required to measure values of resistance over 10 megohms, since the built-in voltage required is very high for ranges above 10 megohms. Some meggers use high voltage batteries and others use a special type of hand generator to obtain the necessary voltage. While ohmmeters are used to measure the resistance of conductors, the most important use of meggers is to measure and test insulation resistance.

Resistors—Construction and Properties

There is a certain amount of resistance in all of the electrical equipment which you use. However, sometimes this resistance is not enough to control the flow of current to the extent desired. When additional control is required—for example, when starting a motor—resistance is purposely added to that of the equipment. Devices which are used to introduce additional resistance are called resistors.

You will use a wide variety of resistors, some of which have a fixed value and others which are variable. All resistors are made either of special resistance wire, of graphite (carbon) composition, or of metal film. Wire-wound resistors are usually used to control large currents while carbon resistors control currents which are relatively small.

Vitreous enameled wire-wound resistors are constructed by winding resistance wire on a porcelain base, attaching the wire ends to metal terminals, and coating the wire and base with powdered glass and baked enamel to protect the wire and conduct heat away from it.

Fixed wire-wound resistors are also used which have coating other than vitreous enamel.

Fixed Wire-wound Resistors

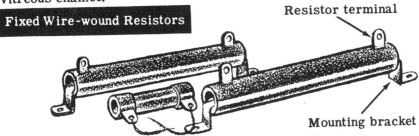

Resistor terminal

Mounting bracket

Wire-wound resistors may have fixed taps which can be used to change the resistance value in steps, or sliders which can be adjusted to change the resistance to any fraction of the total resistance.

Adjustable Wire-wound Resistors

Wire-wound Resistor With Fixed Taps

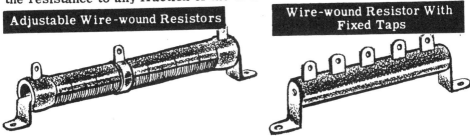

Precision wound resistors of Manganin wire are used where the resistance value must be very accurate such as in test instruments.

Precision Wire-wound Resistors

Resistors—Construction and Properties (continued)

Carbon resistors are constructed of a rod of compressed graphite and binding material, with wire leads attached to each end of the rod. The rod is then either painted or covered by an insulating coating of ceramic. Leads used for this type of resistor are called pigtail leads.

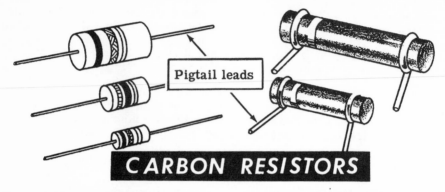

Pigtail leads

CARBON RESISTORS

Some carbon resistors are made by coating a porcelain tube with a carbon film, and in some cases the film is coated in a spiral similar to winding a wire around the tube. The carbon coating is covered with baked enamel, for protection and to conduct heat away from the carbon film so that it does not overheat and burn out.

LARGE CARBON RESISTORS

Metal film resistors are constructed in the same manner as spiral-coated carbon resistors except that the film is metallic instead of carbon.

METAL FILM RESISTORS

Resistors—Construction and Properties (continued)

You will not always use resistors of fixed value, since very often you will need to change resistance while the equipment is in operation. To do this you will use both carbon and wire-wound variable resistors, depending on the amount of current to be controlled—wire-wound for large currents and carbon for small currents.

Wire-wound variable resistors are constructed by winding resistance wire on a porcelain or bakelite circular form, with a contact arm which can be adjusted to any position on the circular form by means of a rotating shaft. A lead connected to this movable contact can then be used, with one or both of the end leads, to vary the resistance used.

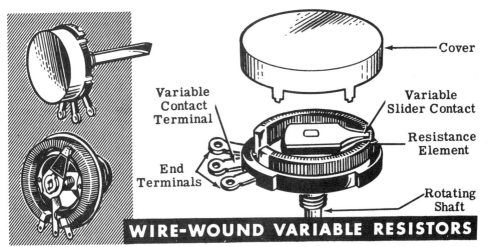

WIRE-WOUND VARIABLE RESISTORS

For controlling small currents, carbon variable resistors are constructed by depositing a carbon compound on a fiber disk. A contact on a movable arm acts to vary the resistance as the arm shaft is turned.

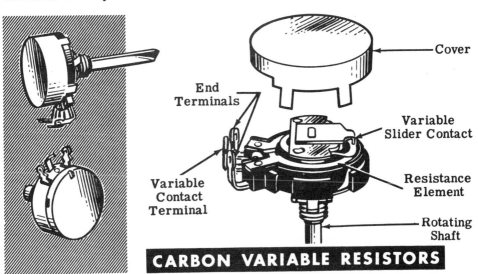

CARBON VARIABLE RESISTORS

Resistors—Construction and Properties (continued)

Variable resistors of either type—wire-wound or carbon—may usually be used in two ways, as a rheostat or as a potentiometer. Some variable resistors have only two terminals and these can only be used as rheostats. A three-terminal variable resistor connected as a rheostat has only two leads connected to the electrical circuit and is used to vary the resistance between these two leads. If the variable contact terminal and one end terminal are connected together directly and act as only one lead in the circuit, the variable resistor acts as a rheostat.

**TWO-TERMINAL
VARIABLE RESISTORS**

**THREE-TERMINAL
VARIABLE RESISTORS**

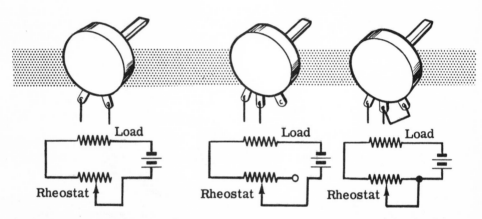

If the three terminals of a variable resistor each connect to different parts of the circuit, it is connected as a potentiometer. With this kind of connection the resistance between the end terminals is always the same, and the variable arm provides a contact which can be moved to any position between the end terminals. A potentiometer does not vary the total resistance between the end terminals but, instead, varies the amount of resistance between each end and the center contact with both resistances changing as the variable contact is moved—one increasing as the other decreases.

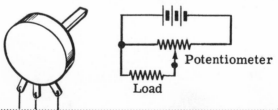

Resistor Color Code

You can find the resistance value of any resistor by using an ohmmeter, but in some cases it is easier to find the value of a resistor by its marking. Most wire-wound resistors have the resistance value printed in ohms on the body of the resistor. If they are not marked in this manner, you must use an ohmmeter. Many carbon resistors also have their values printed on them, but carbon resistors are often mounted so that you cannot read the printed marking. Also, heat often discolors the resistor body, making it impossible to read a printed marking, and in addition, some carbon resistors are so small that a printed marking could not be read. To make the value of carbon resistors easy to read, a color code marking is used.

Carbon resistors are of two types, radial and axial, which differ only in the way in which the wire leads are connected to the body of the resistor. Both types use the same color code, but the colors are painted in a different manner on each type.

Radial lead resistors are constructed with the wire leads wound around the ends of the carbon rod which makes up the body of the resistor. The leads come off at right angles and the entire resistor body—including the leads wound around the body—is painted but not insulated, since the paint is not a good insulator. Because of this poor insulation, this type of resistor must be mounted where it will not come into contact with other parts of a circuit. Radial lead resistors are rarely found in modern equipment although they were widely used in the past.

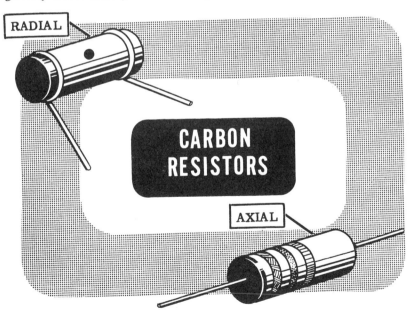

RADIAL

CARBON RESISTORS

AXIAL

Axial lead resistors are made with the leads molded into the ends of the carbon rod of the resistor body. The leads extend straight out from the ends and in line with the body of the resistor. The carbon rod is completely coated with a ceramic material which is a good insulator.

Resistor Color Code (continued)

As mentioned on the previous sheet, the radial lead type and the axial lead type resistors both use the same color code, but the colors are painted on in a different manner for each of the two types. Radial resistors are coded with the body-end-dot system—as are a few axial type resistors. Most axial resistors are coded by the end-to-center band system of marking.

In each color code system of marking, three colors are used to indicate the resistance value in ohms, and a fourth color is sometimes used to indicate the tolerance of the resistor. By reading the colors in the correct order and by substituting numbers from the color code, you can immediately tell all you need to know about a resistor. As you practice using the color code shown on the next sheet, you will soon get to know the numerical value of each color and you will be able to tell the value of a resistor at a glance.

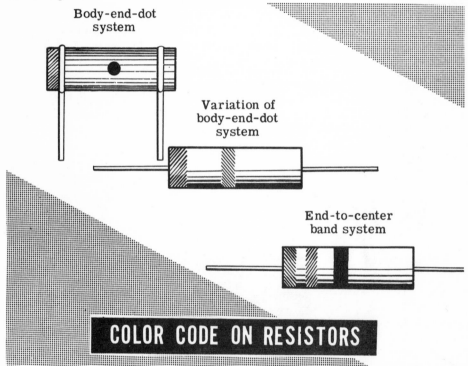

Body-end-dot
system

Variation of
body-end-dot
system

End-to-center
band system

COLOR CODE ON RESISTORS

Before you go on to the color code, you should find out something about resistor tolerance. It is very difficult to manufacture a resistor to the exact value required. For many uses the <u>actual</u> resistance in ohms can be 20 percent higher or lower than the value <u>marked</u> on the resistor without causing any difficulty. Many times the <u>actual</u> resistance required need be no closer than 10 percent higher or lower than the <u>marked</u> value. This percentage variation between the marked value and the <u>actual</u> value of a resistor is known as the "tolerance" of a resistor. A resistor coded for a 5-percent tolerance will be <u>no more than</u> 5 percent higher or lower than the value indicated by the color code.

Resistor Color Code (continued)

This is how you use the color code—

Color	Number	Tolerance	Color	Number	Tolerance
Black	0	-	Violet	7	-
Brown	1	-	Gray	8	-
Red	2	-	White	9	-
Orange	3	-	Gold	-	5%
Yellow	4	-	Silver	-	10%
Green	5	-	No Color	-	20%
Blue	6	-			

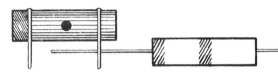

Body-End-Dot Marking

Resistors using this system of marking are coded by having the body of the resistor a solid color, one end of another color and a dot of a third color near the middle of the resistor. For example, you may have a resistor with a green body, red end and orange dot. The body color indicates the first digit, the end color the second digit and the dot the number of zeros to be added to the digits. The value of the resistor then is 52,000 ohms, obtained as follows—

Body	End	Dot
1st digit	2nd digit	Number of zeros
Green	Red	Orange
5 ————————	2 ————————	000

52,000 ohms

End-to-Center Band Marking

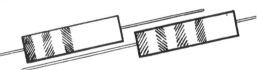

Axial resistors are usually marked with bands of color at one end of the resistor. The body color is not used to indicate the resistor value and may be any color that is not identical to any of the color bands. For example, you may have a resistor with a brown body, having three bands of color (red, green and yellow) at one end. The color bands are read from the end toward the center and the resistor value is 250,000 ohms, obtained as follows—

1st Band	2nd Band	3rd Band
1st digit	2nd digit	Number of zeros
Red	Green	Yellow
2 ————————	5 ————————	0000

250,000 ohms

Resistor Color Code (continued)

Whenever the center dot or the third band are black the resistor value is less than 100 ohms, since black means that no zeros are to be added to the digits. Suppose you have two resistors—one with a brown body, green end and black dot, the other with a red band, an orange band and a black band.

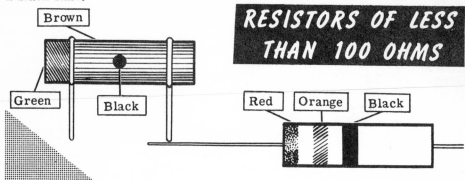

You read these resistor values and find that they are 15 ohms and 23 ohms, obtained as follows—

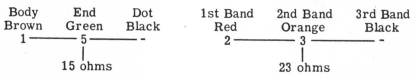

Body	End	Dot		1st Band	2nd Band	3rd Band
Brown	Green	Black		Red	Orange	Black
1 ——	5 ——	-		2 ——	3 ——	-
	15 ohms				23 ohms	

If the same color is used more than once, the body, end and dot may all be the same color or any two may be the same; but the color code is used in exactly the same way as before. For example, a 33,000-ohm resistor will be entirely orange if the body-end-dot marking is used, or will have three orange bands if the end-to-center marking is used.

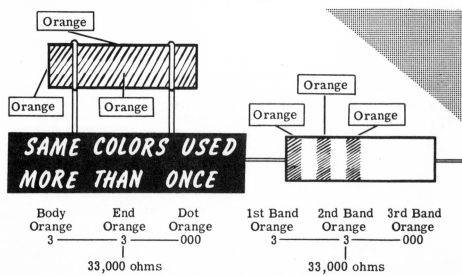

Body	End	Dot		1st Band	2nd Band	3rd Band
Orange	Orange	Orange		Orange	Orange	Orange
3 ——	3 ——	000		3 ——	3 ——	000
	33,000 ohms				33,000 ohms	

Resistor Color Code (continued)

If only three colors are used, the tolerance (accuracy) of the coded value is 20 percent; but, if a fourth color is used, it indicates that the tolerance is less than 20 percent as indicated by the color code. A silver dot any place on the resistor indicates a tolerance of 10 percent while a gold dot indicates a tolerance of 5 percent. A fourth band on axial resistors is used to indicate tolerance and, if it is a color other than silver or gold, the tolerance in percentage corresponds to the number assigned that color in the color code.

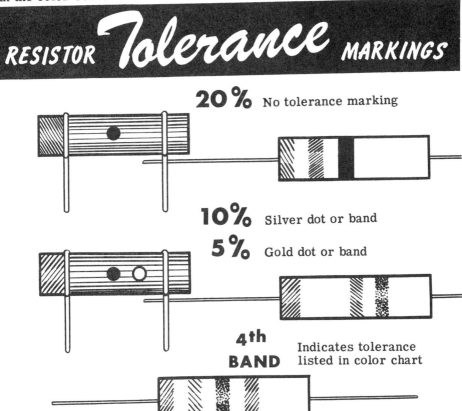

RESISTOR *Tolerance* MARKINGS

20% No tolerance marking

10% Silver dot or band

5% Gold dot or band

4th BAND Indicates tolerance listed in color chart

Carbon resistors are made in values which have only two significant figures followed by zeros. Resistors are available between 1 and 99 ohms differing in value by only 1 ohm—for example, 55 and 56 ohms; but between 100 and 1,000 ohms the difference is 10 ohms—for example, 550 and 560 ohms. Similarly between 1,000 and 10,000 the nearest values differ by 100 ohms, and between 100,000 and 1,000,000 the nearest values differ by 10,000 ohms. If you need a value which is not obtainable—for example, 5,650 ohms—two resistors in series are used. To obtain 5,650 ohms you can use several combinations: 5,600 and 50 ohms, 5,000 and 650 ohms, 5,200 and 450 ohms, etc. However, for most of your work in electricity the closest value obtainable is used since accuracy beyond two digits is not normally required.

Demonstration—the Ohmmeter

To demonstrate the correct use of the ohmmeter for measuring resistance the instructor next shows how to operate and use the multirange ohmmeter for measuring resistance. During this demonstration you see that the instructor uses only the ohmmeter ranges—R, R x 10, R x 100 and R x 1000—turning the RANGE SELECTOR SWITCH to one of these ranges before inserting the test leads.

With the test leads inserted in the meter jacks marked RES OHMS, the instructor touches the test prods together to find out if the meter deflects to approximately full scale. The range selector switch is set at the desired range and the OHMMETER ADJUSTER control is adjusted to obtain exactly full-scale deflection—zero ohms on the meter scale. To measure a resistor, the instructor "zeros" the meter after selecting the correct range and then touches the test prods to the two leads of the resistor. The meter will then indicate a resistance reading. If the range used is R the resistance is read directly on the top scale of the meter, but should one of the other ranges be used the scale reading is multiplied by the multiplier for that range. For example, if the meter is set to the range R x 100 and the meter scale reading is 50, the resistance is 5,000 ohms.

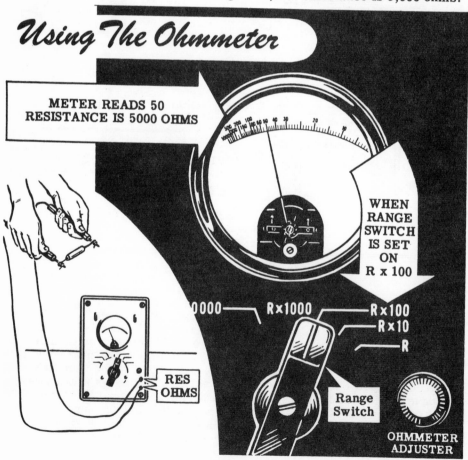

Using The Ohmmeter

METER READS 50
RESISTANCE IS 5000 OHMS

WHEN RANGE SWITCH IS SET ON R x 100

0000 — R x 1000 — R x 100
— R x 10
— R

RES OHMS

Range Switch

OHMMETER ADJUSTER

Demonstration—the Ohmmeter (continued)

As several resistors are measured, observe that each time the meter range is changed it must be "zeroed" again, as the zero adjustment is slightly different for each range. While the instructor measures those resistors which you have previously checked with the color code, compare the measured values to those you obtained at that time. Allowing for the tolerance rating of the resistors, the values should be about the same, but in most cases the meter reading is more accurate.

While the instructor measures the various resistors, you can see the importance of choosing the correct meter range. Low values of resistance read 0 ohms on the higher ohmmeter ranges, and high values of resistance read the maximum scale reading on the lower ohmmeter ranges. For example, a 100-ohm resistor measured on the R x 10,000 scale reads 0 ohms, and a 10,000-ohm resistor measured on the R scale reads infinite ohms. In order to find the correct ohmmeter range to use, the best procedure, as illustrated by the instructor, is to place the test prods on the resistor leads and turn the ohmmeter range switch through all the ranges until a range is found which gives a reading near mid-scale. Remember though, before an accurate reading can be made, the ohmmeter must be "zeroed" on the range being used.

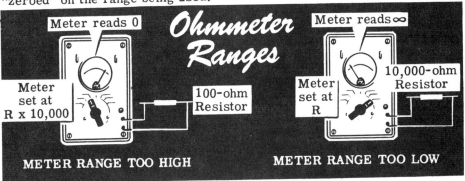

Next the instructor connects one meter test prod to the center terminal of a variable resistor and the other test prod to one of the outside terminals of the variable resistor. To show how resistance can be varied he turns the shaft, and you see that the resistance between these terminals changes as the shaft turns. With the meter leads connected across the outside terminals of the variable resistor, the shaft is again turned and you see that the resistance between these terminals is not varied.

MEASUREMENT OF VARIABLE RESISTANCES

WHAT CONTROLS CURRENT FLOW—RESISTANCE

Demonstration—Resistance Factors

You have seen the different resistors measured, and perhaps you have wondered how resistors of identical size and shape can have such a range of resistance values. In carbon resistors the carbon rod is made of finely ground graphite (carbon) mixed with a filler material, and by varying the amount of carbon used in the mixture the resistance is varied over a wide range. For wire resistors the resistance is changed by using a different size or length of wire and by using wires of different materials, but using the same size porcelain or bakelite forms.

To show the effect of the type material on the resistance of a conductor the instructor takes two equal lengths of wire—one of copper pushback wire and the other of nichrome—and measures their resistance. Notice that the copper wire has less than 1 ohm of resistance while the nichrome wire has more than 1 ohm of resistance.

Using nichrome wire, the instructor next demonstrates the effect of length and cross-section on resistance. To show the effect of conductor length on resistance, two lengths of wire are used, one being twice as long as the other. Using the ohmmeter, the resistance of each wire is measured, and you see that the longer wire has twice the resistance of the other.

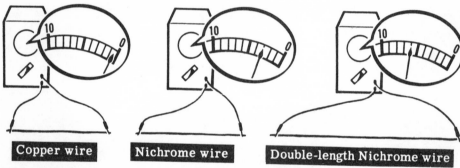

Copper wire · Nichrome wire · Double-length Nichrome wire

The longer wire is then bent double and twisted to form one length equal to the length of the short wire, but having twice the cross-section. Now when the resistances are measured you see that the length of doubled wire has the lower resistance because of its greater cross-section. Wires having greater cross-section not only have lower resistance but also can carry more current, since more paths are available for current flow. You will find out more about the effects of increased cross-section later, when you work with parallel circuits.

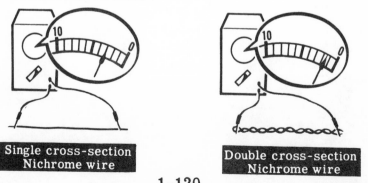

Single cross-section Nichrome wire · Double cross-section Nichrome wire

WHAT CONTROLS CURRENT FLOW—RESISTANCE

Review of Resistance

Before going on, briefly review what you have read and seen concerning resistance and how it is measured.

CONDUCTOR — A material which gives up "free" electrons easily and offers little opposition to current flow.

INSULATOR — A material which does not give up "free" electrons easily and offers great opposition to current flow.

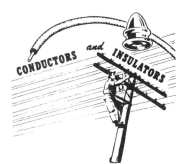

RESISTANCE — Opposition offered by a material to the flow of current.

OHM — Basic unit of resistance measure equal to that resistance which allows 1 ampere of current to flow when an emf of 1 volt is applied across the resistance.

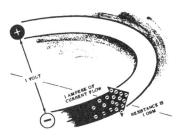

MEGOHM — One megohm equals one million ohms.

$$1\,\text{Meg}\,\Omega = 1,000,000\ \Omega$$

MICROHM — One microhm equals one-millionth ohm.

$$1\,\mu\,\Omega = \frac{1}{1,000,000}\ \Omega$$

OHMMETER — Meter used to measure resistance directly.

RESISTOR — Device having resistance used to control current flow.

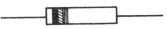

Review of Current, Voltage and Resistance

As a conclusion to your study of electricity in action you should consider again what you have found out about current, voltage and resistance.

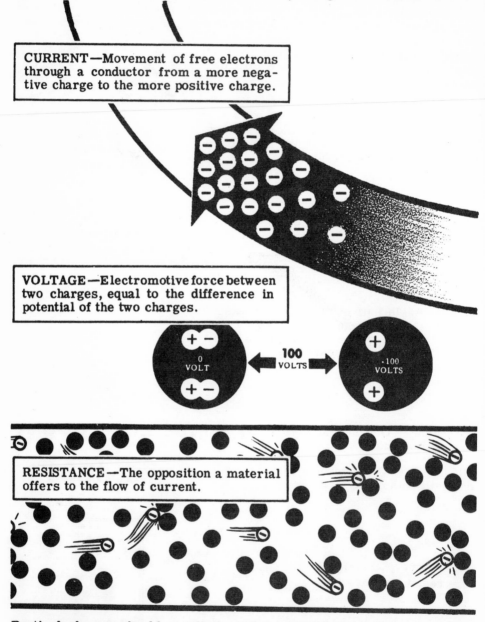

CURRENT—Movement of free electrons through a conductor from a more negative charge to the more positive charge.

VOLTAGE—Electromotive force between two charges, equal to the difference in potential of the two charges.

0 VOLT

100 VOLTS

·100 VOLTS

RESISTANCE—The opposition a material offers to the flow of current.

Particularly you should recall the relationships between current, voltage and resistance. Current flow is caused by the voltage between two points and is limited by the resistance between the points. In continuing your study you will next find out about electric circuits and how they use current, voltage and resistance.

INTRODUCING OHM'S LAW

The Relationship Between Voltage, Current and Resistance

Voltage, as you know, is the amount of electromotive force (emf) that is applied across a load (resistance) in order to make an electron current flow through the resistance. It should be easy for you to see that the greater the voltage you apply across a resistance the greater will be the number of electrons that flow through in a second. Similarly, the lower the voltage you apply, the smaller will be the electron current.

Resistance, as you know, is the effect that impedes the flow of electrons. If you increase the resistance of the load across which a constant voltage is applied, less electron current will flow. Similarly, the lower you make the resistance, the greater will be the electron flow.

This relationship between voltage, resistance and current as described in the two previous paragraphs was studied by the German mathematician George Simon Ohm. His description, now known as Ohm's law, says that current varies directly with the voltage and inversely with the resistance. The mathematical analysis of this law is of no concern to you at present, but you will learn about it when you get into Volume 2

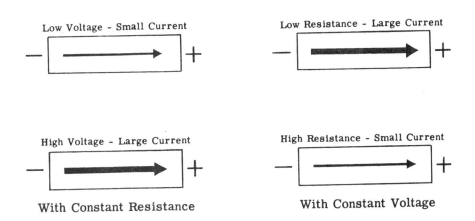

INTRODUCING OHM'S LAW

Electron Current Flow

Low Voltage - Small Current

Low Resistance - Large Current

High Voltage - Large Current

High Resistance - Small Current

With Constant Resistance

With Constant Voltage

INDEX TO VOL. 1

(Note: A cumulative index covering all five volumes in this series will be found at the end of Volume 5.)

basic
electricity

by VAN VALKENBURGH,
NOOGER & NEVILLE, INC.

VOL. 2

HAYDEN BOOK COMPANY, INC.
Rochelle Park, New Jersey

PREFACE

The texts of the entire Basic Electricity and Basic Electronics courses, as currently taught at Navy specialty schools, have now been released by the Navy for civilian use. This educational program has been an unqualified success. Since April, 1953, when it was first installed, over 25,000 Navy trainees have benefited by this instruction and the results have been outstanding.

The unique simplification of an ordinarily complex subject, the exceptional clarity of illustrations and text, and the plan of presenting one basic concept at a time, without involving complicated mathematics, all combine in making this course a better and quicker way to teach and learn basic electricity and electronics. The Basic Electronics portion of this course will be available as a separate series of volumes.

In releasing this material to the general public, the Navy hopes to provide the means for creating a nation-wide pool of pre-trained technicians, upon whom the Armed Forces could call in time of national emergency, without the need for precious weeks and months of schooling.

Perhaps of greater importance is the Navy's hope that through the release of this course, a direct contribution will be made toward increasing the technical knowledge of men and women throughout the country, as a step in making and keeping America strong.

Van Valkenburgh, Nooger and Neville, Inc.

New York, N. Y.
October, 1954

TABLE OF CONTENTS

VOL. 2 — BASIC ELECTRICITY

BASIC ELECTRICITY

Vol. 2

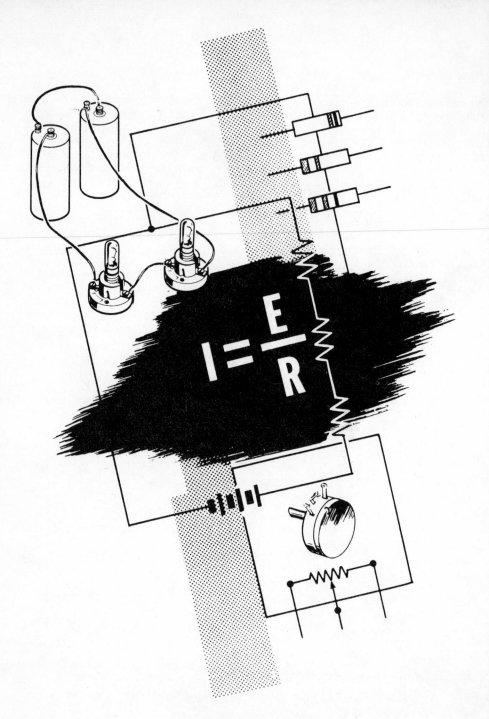

$$I = \frac{E}{R}$$

Direct current circuits

Electric Circuits

Wherever two charges are connected by a conductor, a pathway for current flow exists; and if the charges are unequal, current flows from the negative to the positive charge. The amount of current flow depends on the voltage difference of the charges and the resistance of the conductor. If two charged bars are connected by a copper wire, for example, current will flow from the more negative to the more positive bar, but only long enough to cause each bar to have an equal charge. Although current flows briefly, this kind of connection is not an electrical circuit.

An electric circuit is a completed electrical pathway, consisting not only of the conductor in which the current flows from the negative to the positive charge, but also of a path through a voltage source from the positive charge back to the negative charge. As an example, a lamp connected across a dry cell forms a simple electric circuit. Current flows from the (-) terminal of the battery through the lamp to the (+) battery terminal, and continues by going through the battery from the (+) to the (-) terminal. As long as this pathway is unbroken, it is a closed circuit and current flows; but, if the path is broken at any point, it is an open circuit and no current flows.

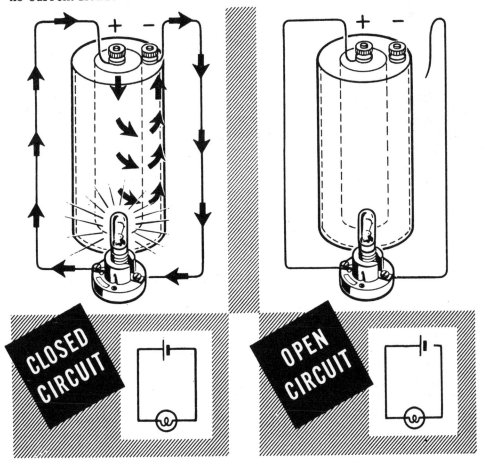

Electric Circuits (continued)

A closed loop of wire is not always a circuit. Only if a source of emf is part of the loop do you have an electric circuit. In any electric circuit where electrons move around a closed loop, current, voltage and resistance are present. The pathway for current flow is actually the circuit, and its resistance controls the amount of current flow around the circuit.

Direct current circuits consist of a source of DC voltage, such as batteries, plus the combined resistance of the electrical equipment connected across this voltage. While working with DC circuits, you will find out how the total resistance of a circuit is changed by using various combinations of resistances, how these combinations control the circuit current and affect the voltage.

As you will see shortly, there are two basic types of circuits; series circuits and parallel circuits. No matter how complex a circuit you may work with, it can always be broken down into either a series circuit connection or a parallel circuit connection.

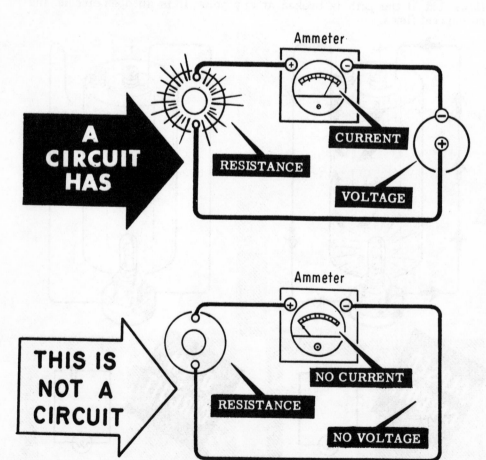

Simple Circuit Connections

Only the resistances in the external circuit, between the terminals of the voltage source, are used to determine the type of circuit. When you have a circuit consisting of only one device having resistance, a voltage source and the connecting wires, it is called a SIMPLE circuit. For example, a lamp connected directly across the terminals of a dry cell forms a simple circuit. Similarly, if you connect a resistor directly across the terminals of a dry cell, you have a simple circuit since only one device having resistance is being used.

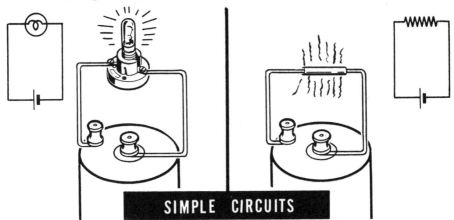

SIMPLE CIRCUITS

Simple circuits may have other devices connected in series with a lamp but the nature of the circuit does not change unless more than one resistance is used. A switch and a meter inserted in series with the lamp do not change the type of circuit since they have negligible resistance.

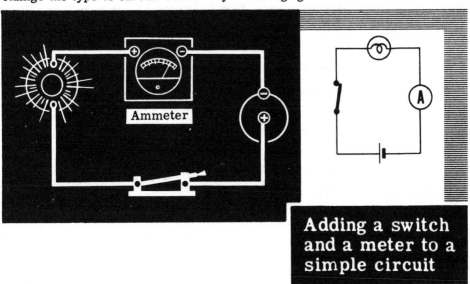

Ammeter

Adding a switch and a meter to a simple circuit

Whenever you use more than one device having resistance in the same circuit, they will be connected to form either a SERIES or PARALLEL circuit, or a combination SERIES-PARALLEL circuit.

Switches

You already know that, in order for current to flow through a circuit, a closed path must be provided between the + and - terminals of the voltage source. Any break in the closed path opens the circuit and stops the flow of current.

CURRENT FLOW REQUIRES A CLOSED PATH

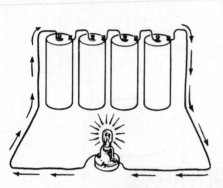

Current flow through
a closed path

No closed path—
no current flow

Until now we have stopped current flow by removing a battery lead. Since this is not a suitable method for opening a practical circuit, switches are actually used.

A CIRCUIT MAY BE OPENED BY:

Removing a battery lead or . . . . opening a switch

Switches (continued)

A switch is a device used to open and close a circuit or part of a circuit when desired. You have been using switches all your life—in lamps, flashlights, radio, car ignition, etc. You will meet many other kinds of switches while working with equipment.

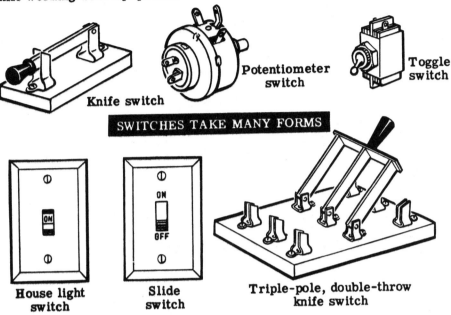

Knife switch

Potentiometer switch

Toggle switch

SWITCHES TAKE MANY FORMS

House light switch

Slide switch

Triple-pole, double-throw knife switch

In the demonstrations and experiments to follow, a switch will be inserted in one of the battery leads. You will use a "single-pole, single-throw knife switch," which looks like this:

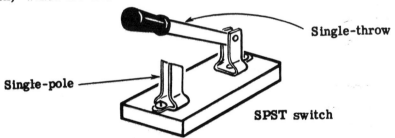

Single-throw

Single-pole

SPST switch

and is represented symbolically like this:

Closed

Open

Circuit Symbols

Electrical circuit connections are usually shown in symbol form in the same manner as the dry cell and battery symbols which you have used previously. You will find that symbols are not only used to represent various types of equipment and show circuit connections, but are also used to express current, voltage and resistance.

To express the amounts of current, voltage, resistance and power, the following symbols are commonly used:

$E =$ voltage $I =$ current $R =$ resistance $P =$ power

$V =$ volts $A =$ amperes $\Omega =$ ohms $W =$ watts

For example, in a simple circuit consisting of a lamp connected across a dry cell the voltage, current and resistance would be expressed as shown:

$E = 1.5\,V$ (volts) $I = 0.3\,A$ (ampere) $R = 5\,\Omega$ (ohms) $P = 0.45\,W$ (watt)

Circuit Symbols for Resistors

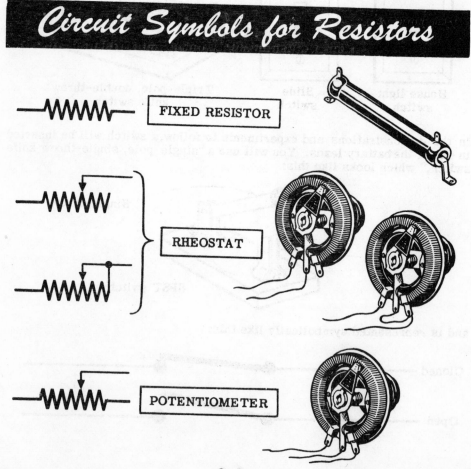

FIXED RESISTOR

RHEOSTAT

POTENTIOMETER

Series Circuit Connections

Whenever you connect resistances end to end, they are said to be series-connected. If all the resistances around a circuit are connected end to end so that there is only one path for current flow, they form a series circuit. You have already found out how to connect cells in series to form a battery. An important difference between cells and resistances connected in series is that cells must be connected with the proper polarity but resistances are not polarized.

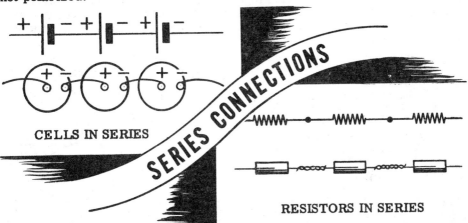

CELLS IN SERIES

SERIES CONNECTIONS

RESISTORS IN SERIES

Suppose you should connect a terminal of one lamp socket to a terminal on another socket, leaving one terminal on each socket unconnected. Lamps placed in these sockets would be series-connected, but you would not have a series circuit. To complete your series circuit, you would have to connect the lamps across a voltage source, such as a battery, using the unconnected terminals to complete the circuit. Any number of lamps, resistors or other devices having resistance can be used to form a series circuit, provided they are connected end to end across the terminals of a voltage source with only one path for current flow between these terminals.

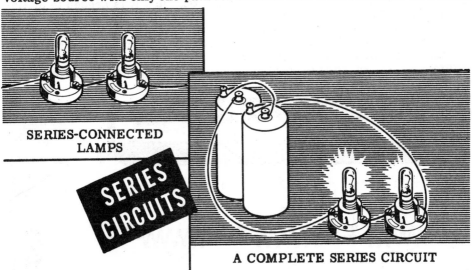

SERIES-CONNECTED LAMPS

SERIES CIRCUITS

A COMPLETE SERIES CIRCUIT

Resistances in Series

One of the factors of resistance is length, with the resistance of a conductor increasing as the conductor length increases.

If you add one length of wire to another, the resistance of the entire length of wire is equal to the sum of the resistances of the original lengths. For example, if two lengths of wire—one having a resistance of 4 ohms and the other of 5 ohms—are connected together, the total resistance between the unconnected ends is 9 ohms. Similarly, when other types of resistances are connected in series, the total resistance equals the sum of the individual resistances.

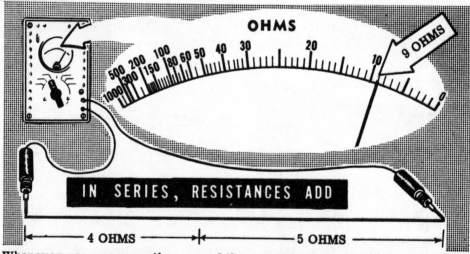

Whenever you use more than one of the same device or quantity in an electrical circuit, some method of identifying each individual device or quantity is necessary. For example, if three resistors of different values are used in a series circuit, something other than just R is needed to distinguish each resistor. A system of identification called "subscripts" is used and consists of following the symbol of the device or quantity by a very small identification number. R_1, R_2 and R_3 are all symbols for resistors but each identifies a particular resistor. Similarly E_1, E_2 and E_3 are all different values of voltage used in the same circuit, with the small subscript number identifying the particular voltage.

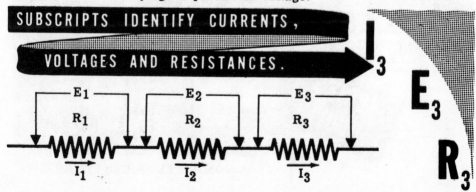

Resistances in Series (continued)

While numbers are used to identify individual electrical devices or quantities, a small letter "t" following the symbol indicates the total amount. You have found that when resistances are connected in series the total resistance equals the sum of the individual resistances. This might be expressed as $R_t = R_1 + R_2 + R_3$ where R_1, R_2 and R_3 represent resistors. The symbol R is also used to represent the resistance of other electrical devices.

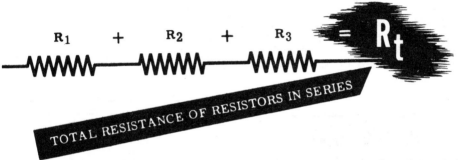

TOTAL RESISTANCE OF RESISTORS IN SERIES

You will find that, although subscripts are one method of identifying individual devices or quantities, other methods are also used. Some of these other methods are shown below and compared to the subscript method of marking. Regardless of the method used, the marking serves only one purpose—identification of individual devices or quantities—and does not indicate a value.

OTHER MARKINGS USED
FOR IDENTIFICATION

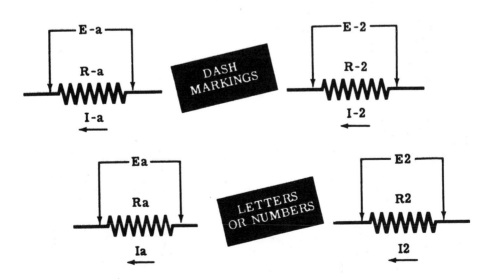

Current Flow in Series Circuits

In a series circuit there is only one path for current flow. This means that all the current must flow through each resistance in the circuit. All parts of the circuit then must be able to pass the maximum current which flows, and the total resistance of the circuit must be large enough to reduce the amount of current to a value which can be safely passed by all the circuit resistances.

Ammeters placed at each end of all the resistances of a series circuit would read the same amount of current flow through each resistance. In a circuit containing devices such as lamps in series, each lamp for proper operation should be rated with the same amount of current. Lamps rated to operate at higher currents than the circuit current will light only dimly, while lamps rated for less than the circuit current will light very brightly, and perhaps even burn out due to the excess current. The same effect would be noticed if the circuit contained other types of resistances.

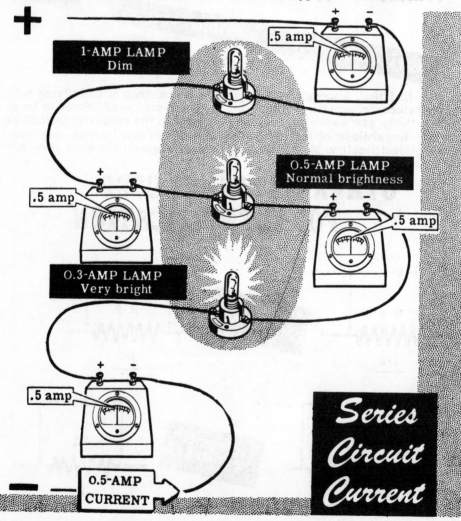

1-AMP LAMP
Dim

.5 amp

0.5-AMP LAMP
Normal brightness

.5 amp

.5 amp

0.3-AMP LAMP
Very bright

.5 amp

0.5-AMP
CURRENT

Series Circuit Current

Voltage in Series Circuits

Whenever a force is exerted to move something against some form of opposition, the force is expended. For example, a hammer striking a nail exerts a force which moves the nail against the opposition offered by the wood, and as the nail moves, the force exerted is expended. Similarly, as emf moves electrons through a resistor, the force is expended, resulting in a loss of emf called "voltage drop."

Starting at one end of a series circuit consisting of three resistors of equal value connected across a six-volt battery, the potential drops will be two volts across resistor R_1, four volts across R_1 and R_2, and six volts across R_1, R_2, and R_3, the entire circuit. The voltage across each resistor is two volts, and adding the voltages across the three resistors results in the original total voltage of six volts.

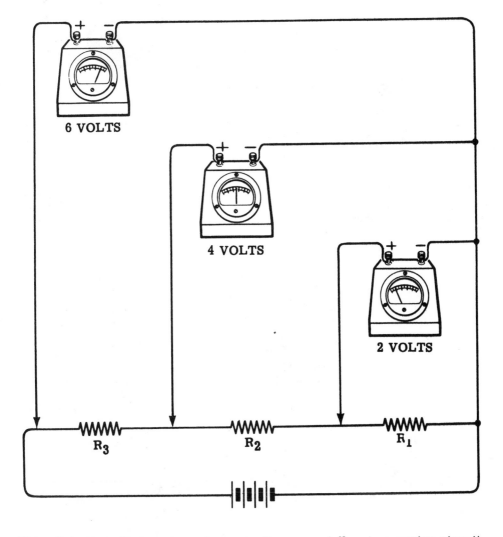

This drop in voltage occurs because the current flow in a series circuit is always the same throughout the circuit.

Demonstration—Series Circuit Resistance

To demonstrate the effect of connecting resistances in series, the instructor will measure the resistance of three lamps individually and then measure their resistance in series.

First the instructor connects three lamp sockets in series and inserts 6-volt lamps in the sockets. He then uses the ohmmeter to measure the resistance of each lamp, and you see that each lamp measures about one ohm.

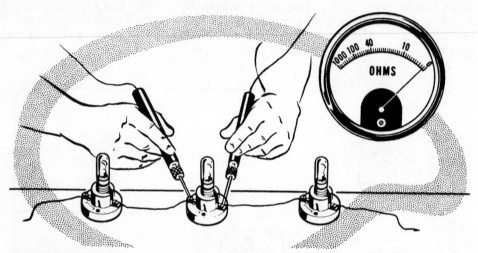

Then the instructor measures the resistance of the three lamps in series, and you see that the total resistance is about 3 ohms. Thus the total resistance of series-connected resistances is seen to be equal to the sum of all the individual resistances.

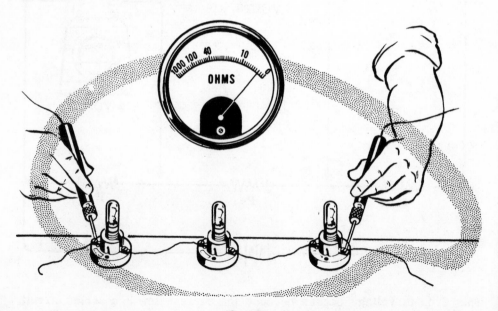

Demonstration—Series Circuit Resistance (continued)

Using four dry cells connected in series to form a six-volt battery as a voltage source, the instructor demonstrates the effect of adding resistance in series. The voltmeter is connected across the battery and reads six volts, while the ammeter is connected in series with the negative lead of the battery to show the amount of current flow from the battery. With the ammeter in series, a single lamp socket is connected across the battery and a 6-volt lamp is inserted in the socket. You see that the lamp lights to normal brilliancy and that the ammeter reading is about 0.5 ampere. As the instructor moves the voltmeter to connect it directly across the lamp, you see that the voltage across the lamp is 6 volts.

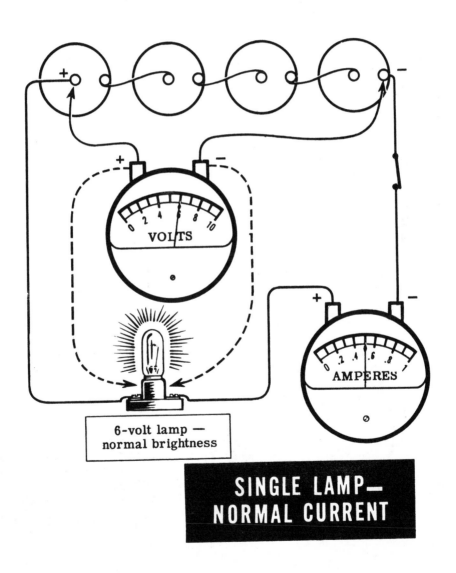

6-volt lamp —
normal brightness

SINGLE LAMP—
NORMAL CURRENT

Demonstration—Series Circuit Resistance (continued)

Next, the single lamp socket is replaced by three sockets in series and 6-volt lamps are inserted in the sockets. The lamps now light at well below normal brilliance and the ammeter reading is about one-third its previous value. A voltmeter reading taken across the total circuit reads 6 volts and across each lamp the voltage is 2 volts. Since the voltage from the battery is not changed but the current decreased, the resistance must be greater. Adding the voltage across each lamp shows that the sum of the voltages across the individual resistances equals the total voltage.

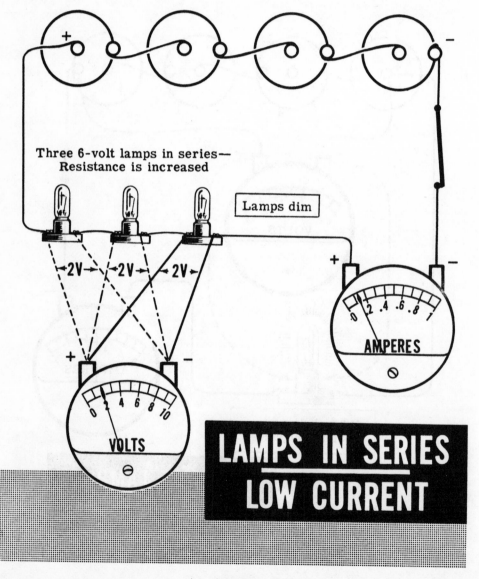

Three 6-volt lamps in series—
Resistance is increased

Lamps dim

2V   2V   2V

AMPERES

VOLTS

LAMPS IN SERIES
LOW CURRENT

Demonstration—Series Circuit Current

To show the effect of changing resistances on the amount of current flow and how different equipment requires different amounts of current for proper operation, one of the 6-volt lamps is replaced by a 2.5-volt lamp of less resistance. You see that the two 6-volt lamps increase to almost half of normal brilliancy while the 2.5-volt lamp is dim. The ammeter reading shows that the current increases, indicating that decreasing the resistance of one part of the circuit decreases the total opposition to current flow. Replacing another of the 6-volt lamps with a 2.5-volt lamp further decreases the total resistance and increases the total circuit current.

The brilliance of the lamps increases as the current flow increases, and with the last 6-volt lamp replaced by a lower resistance 2.5-volt lamp, you see that the circuit current for the three 2.5-volt lamps is approximately the same as that of a single 6-volt lamp. Also, the three lamps light at about normal brilliancy because the current is only slightly less than the rated value of these lamps, as is the voltage measured across each lamp.

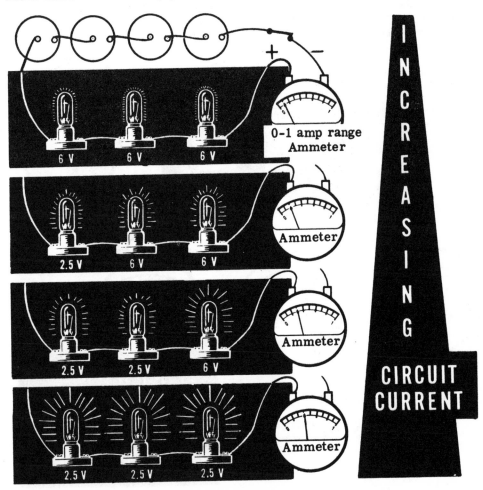

Demonstration—Series Circuit Voltage

The rated voltage of three 2.5-volt lamps in series is 7.5 volts so that the 6-volt battery does not cause the rated current to flow. By adding one more dry cell, the instructor shows how increasing the circuit voltage without changing the resistance will cause a greater current flow as you can see by the increased brilliancy of the lamps and the increased current reading. Voltage readings taken across the lamps show that the voltage across each lamp is the rated voltage of 2.5 volts. Removing one cell of the battery at a time and taking voltage readings across the lamps, the instructor shows that the voltages across the lamps equal each other and always add to equal the total battery voltage.

Now using five cells to form a 7.5-volt battery, the instructor replaces one of the 2.5-volt lamps with a 6-volt lamp having greater resistance. Voltmeter readings across the lamps still total 7.5 volts when added, but are not all equal. The voltages across the lower resistance 2.5-volt lamps are equal but less than 2.5 volts, while the voltage across the higher resistance 6-volt lamp is greater than 2.5 volts. You can see that for resistors in series the voltage divides in proportion across the various resistances connected in series, with more voltage drop across the larger resistance and less voltage drop across the smaller resistance.

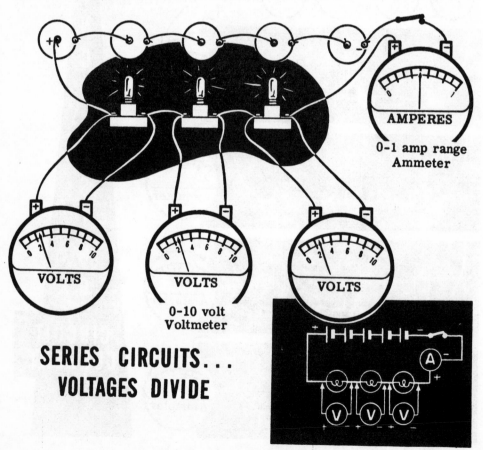

AMPERES

0-1 amp range
Ammeter

VOLTS

VOLTS

VOLTS

0-10 volt
Voltmeter

SERIES CIRCUITS...
VOLTAGES DIVIDE

Demonstration—Open Circuits

You already know that in order for a current to pass through a circuit a closed path is required. Any break in the closed path causes an "open" circuit, and stops current flow. Each time you open a switch, you are causing an open circuit.

Anything which causes an "open" other than actually opening a switch interferes with the proper operation of the circuit, and must be corrected. An open circuit may be caused by a loose connection, a burned-out resistor or lamp filament, poor joints or loose contacts, or broken wire.

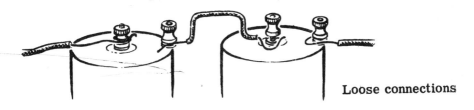

OPEN CIRCUITS can be caused by . . . . .

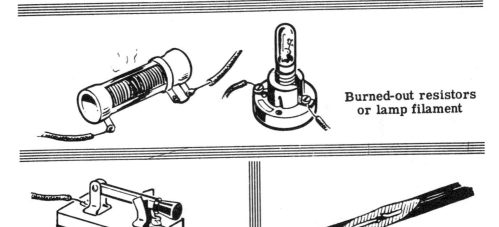

Loose connections

Burned-out resistors or lamp filament

Loose contacts

Broken wire

These faults can often be detected visually, and you may find that, in performing the experiments to follow, you will encounter one or more of these "opens."

In some cases it is not possible to visually detect the cause of an open circuit. The instructor will demonstrate how to use the ohmmeter or a test lamp to find the cause of trouble.

Demonstration—Open Circuits (continued)

The instructor connects five dry cells, a knife switch and three lamp sockets in series. He then inserts 2.5-volt lamps in the sockets. When he closes the switch the lamps light with normal brilliancy. He then loosens one of the lamps and they all go out, indicating an open circuit. (A loosened lamp simulates a burned-out filament or other open.)

Creating an "OPEN"

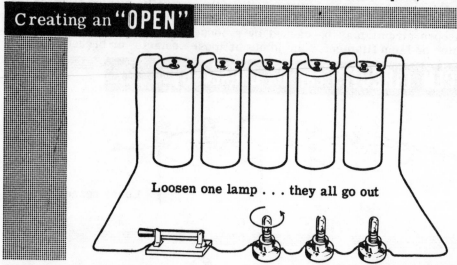

Loosen one lamp . . . they all go out

To locate the open with the ohmmeter the instructor first opens the knife switch to remove the voltage source, since an ohmmeter must never be used on a circuit with the power connected. He then touches the ohmmeter test leads across each unit in the circuit—the three lamps in this case. You see that for two of the lamps the ohmmeter indicates a resistance under 10 ohms, but for the loosened lamp the ohmmeter indicates infinity. Since an open does not allow any current to flow, its resistance must be infinite. The ohmmeter check for an open, then, is to find the series-connected element in the circuit which measures infinite resistance on the ohmmeter.

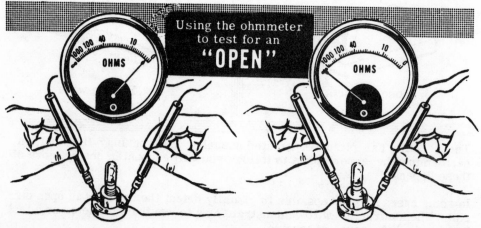

Using the ohmmeter to test for an "OPEN"

Good bulb — resistance less than 10 Ω   "Open"— infinite resistance

Demonstration—Open Circuits (continued)

The second method used to locate an open is to test the circuit by means of a test lamp. The instructor 'attaches leads to the terminals of a lamp socket and inserts a 2.5-volt lamp. He closes the circuit switch and touches the test lamp leads across each lamp in the circuit. The lamp does not light until he touches the terminals of the loosened lamp. The test lamp then lights, indicating he has found the open.

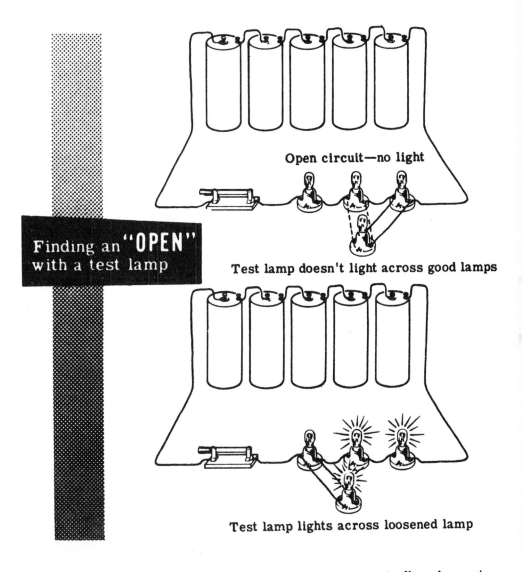

Open circuit—no light

Finding an "OPEN" with a test lamp

Test lamp doesn't light across good lamps

Test lamp lights across loosened lamp

The test lamp completes the circuit and allows current to flow, bypassing the open. You will use this method often to detect opens which cannot be seen.

Demonstration—Short Circuits

You have seen how an open prevents current flow by breaking the closed path between terminals of the voltage source. Now you will see how a "short" produces just the opposite effect, creating a "short circuit" path of low resistance through which a larger than normal current flows.

A short occurs whenever the resistance of a circuit or part of a circuit drops from its normal value to essentially zero resistance. This happens if the two terminals of a resistance in a circuit are directly connected; the voltage source leads contact each other, two current-carrying uninsulated wires touch, or the circuit is improperly wired.

A "Short" OCCURS WHEN...

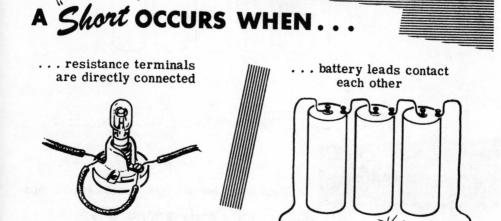

. . . resistance terminals
are directly connected

. . . battery leads contact
each other

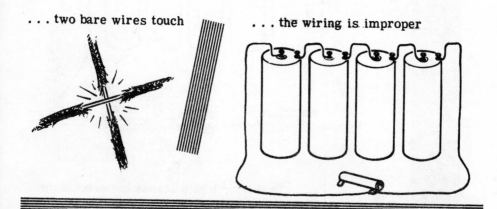

. . . two bare wires touch

. . . the wiring is improper

These shorts are called "external shorts" and can usually be detected by visual inspection.

Demonstration—Short Circuits (continued)

When a short occurs in a simple circuit, the resistance of the circuit becomes so very small—essentially zero—that a very large current flows.

The effect of a **"SHORT"** on current flow

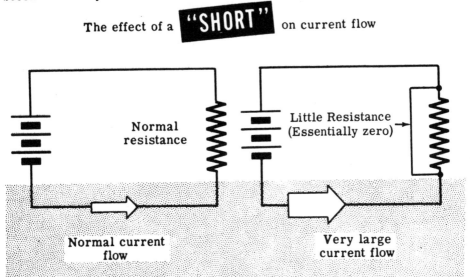

In a series circuit, a short across one or more parts of the circuit results in reduction of the total resistance of the circuit and corresponding increased current, which may damage the other equipment in the circuit.

A *Shorted Circuit* RESULTS IN GREATER THAN NORMAL CURRENT

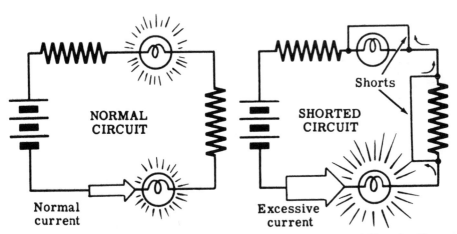

Circuits are usually protected against excessive current flow by the use of fuses, which you will learn about later. But it is important that you understand the reasons for and results of shorts so that you can avoid accidentally shorting your circuits and causing damage to meters or other equipment.

Demonstration—Short Circuits (continued)

The instructor connects three dry cells in series with a 0-1 amp range ammeter and three lamp sockets. He inserts 2.5-volt lamps in the sockets and closes the switch. You see that the lamps light equally but are dim, and the ammeter indicates a current flow of about 0.5 amp.

A NORMAL SERIES CIRCUIT

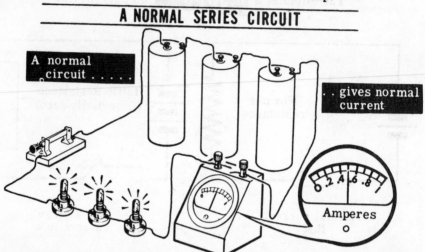

A normal circuit . . . . .

. . gives normal current

Amperes

The instructor then touches the ends of an insulated lead to the terminals of one of the lamps, "short-circuiting" the current around that lamp. You see that the lamp goes out, the other two lamps become brighter, and the ammeter shows that the current has increased to about 0.6 amp. When he moves the lead to short out two of the lamps, you see that they both go out, the third lamp becomes very bright, and the current increases to about 0.9 amp. Since the lamp is rated at only 0.5 amp, this excessive current would soon burn out the lamp filament.

SEEING THE EFFECT OF A SHORT IN A SERIES CIRCUIT

High current results in an overloaded lamp

Short circuit →

Amperes

If the instructor were to short out all three lamps, the lack of resistance of the circuit would cause a very great current to flow which would damage the ammeter.

Review of Series Circuit Connections

Consider now what you have found out so far about electric circuits and particularly series circuits. While a complete electric circuit always consists of a complete path for current flow through the voltage source and across the terminals of the voltage source, you have discovered that—for all practical purposes—the path through the voltage source is disregarded in considering a circuit. Only the connections and effect of the resistances connected across the terminals of the voltage source are considered.

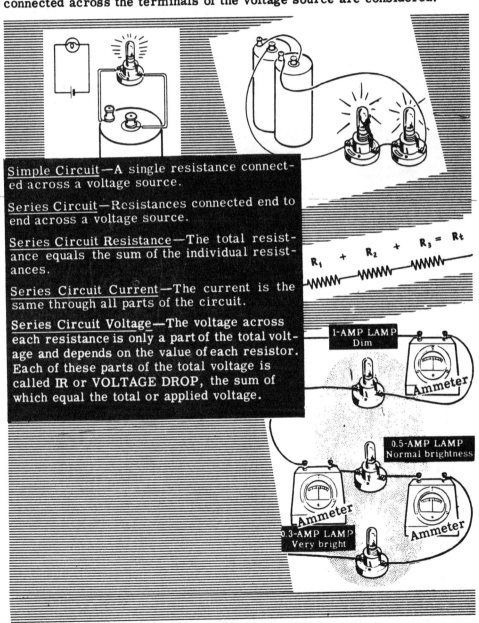

Simple Circuit—A single resistance connected across a voltage source.

Series Circuit—Resistances connected end to end across a voltage source.

Series Circuit Resistance—The total resistance equals the sum of the individual resistances.

Series Circuit Current—The current is the same through all parts of the circuit.

Series Circuit Voltage—The voltage across each resistance is only a part of the total voltage and depends on the value of each resistor. Each of these parts of the total voltage is called **IR** or **VOLTAGE DROP**, the sum of which equal the total or applied voltage.

$$R_1 + R_2 + R_3 = R_t$$

1-AMP LAMP
Dim

Ammeter

0.5-AMP LAMP
Normal brightness

Ammeter

0.3-AMP LAMP
Very bright

Ammeter

Ohm's Law in Simple Circuits

You have found out that voltage and resistance affect the current flow in a circuit, and that voltage drops across a resistance. The basic relationships of current, voltage and resistance are as follows:

1. Current in a circuit increases when the voltage is increased for the same resistance.

2. Current in a circuit decreases when the resistance is increased for the same voltage.

These two relationships combined are Ohm's Law, the most basic law of electric circuits, usually stated as follows:

THE CURRENT FLOWING IN A CIRCUIT CHANGES IN THE SAME DIRECTION THAT THE VOLTAGE CHANGES, AND IN THE OPPOSITE DIRECTION THAT THE RESISTANCE CHANGES.

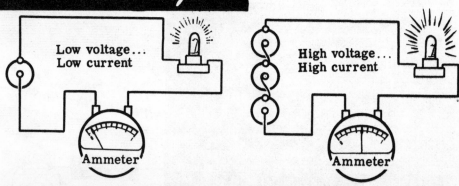

...IN THE SAME DIRECTION THAT THE VOLTAGE CHANGES...

. . IN THE OPPOSITE DIRECTION THAT THE RESISTANCE CHANGES

Ohm's Law in Simple Circuits (continued)

You have seen that if a certain current of electricity flows in a circuit, it flows because a certain electromotive force, or voltage, forces it to flow, and that the amount of current is limited by the resistance of the circuit. In fact, the amount of current depends upon the amount of electrical pressure, or voltage, and the amount of resistance. This fact was discovered by a man named George S. Ohm and is expressed by the now famous Ohm's Law which is the fundamental equation of all electrical science. Since it was first stated in 1827, this law has been of outstanding importance in electrical calculation. One of the most common ways of expressing Ohm's Law is that THE CURRENT FLOWING IN A CIRCUIT IS DIRECTLY PROPORTIONAL TO THE APPLIED VOLTAGE, AND INVERSELY PROPORTIONAL TO THE RESISTANCE. When you put this word statement into a mathematical relationship you get

$$\text{CURRENT} = \frac{\text{ELECTROMOTIVE FORCE (or VOLTAGE)}}{\text{RESISTANCE}}$$

or

$$\text{AMPERES} = \frac{\text{VOLTS}}{\text{OHMS}}$$

$$I = \frac{E}{R}$$

Ohm's Law can also be written in two other forms.

$$E = I \times R$$

$$\text{VOLTAGE} = \text{CURRENT} \times \text{RESISTANCE}$$

or

$$\text{VOLTS} = \text{AMPERES} \times \text{OHMS}$$

This enables you to find the voltage when you know the current and resistance.

If you know the voltage and the current, you can find the resistance then by simply applying the following form of Ohm's Law.

$$\text{RESISTANCE} = \frac{\text{VOLTAGE}}{\text{CURRENT}} \qquad R = \frac{E}{I}$$

or

$$\text{OHMS} = \frac{\text{VOLTS}}{\text{AMPERES}}$$

Ohm's Law in Simple Circuits (continued)

Ohm's law is used in electric circuits and parts of circuits to find the un-known quantity of current, voltage or resistance when any two of these quantities are known. In its basic form Ohm's law is used to find the cur-rent in a circuit if the voltage and resistance are known. To find the cur-rent through a resistance, the voltage across the resistance is divided by the resistance.

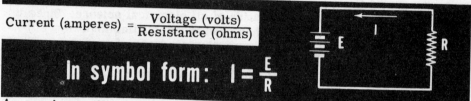

$$\text{Current (amperes)} = \frac{\text{Voltage (volts)}}{\text{Resistance (ohms)}}$$

In symbol form: $I = \dfrac{E}{R}$

As you know, the current in a circuit increases if the voltage increases and the resistance remains the same. By giving values to E and R, you can see how this works. Suppose that R is 10 ohms and E is 20 volts. Since the current equals 20 divided by 10, the current is 2 amperes as shown:

$$\text{Current} = \frac{\text{voltage}}{\text{resistance}}$$

$$I = \frac{E}{R}$$

$$I = \frac{20}{10} = 2 \text{ amperes}$$

Now if E is increased to 40 volts without changing the resistance, the cur-rent increases to 4 amperes.

$$I = \frac{E}{R}$$

$$I = \frac{40}{10} = 4 \text{ amperes}$$

Similarly, if the voltage remains the same and the resistance is increased, the current decreases. Using the original values where E is 20 volts and R is 10 ohms, you found that the current is 2 amperes. If R is increased to 20 ohms without changing the voltage, the current decreases to 1 ampere.

$$I = \frac{E}{R}$$

$$I = \frac{20}{20} = 1 \text{ ampere}$$

Ohm's Law in Simple Circuits (continued)

While $I = \frac{E}{R}$ is the basic form of Ohm's law and is used to find current, by expressing the law in other forms, it may be used to obtain either E or R.

To use Ohm's law to find the resistance when voltage and current are known, the voltage is divided by the current.

Resistance = $\frac{\text{Voltage}}{\text{Current}}$

In symbol form: $R = \frac{E}{I}$

As an example, if the current through a lamp connected across a 6-volt battery is 2 amperes, the resistance of the lamp is 3 ohms.

$R = \frac{E}{I}$

$R = \frac{6}{2} = 3 \text{ ohms}$

A third use for Ohm's law is to find the voltage when the current and resistance are known. To find the voltage across a resistance, the current is multiplied by the resistance.

Voltage = Current x Resistance

$E = I \times R$

In writing electrical laws as formulas, the multiplication sign is not normally used, so that Ohm's law for voltage is expressed as: $E = IR$

To find the voltage across a 5-ohm resistor when 3 amperes of current are flowing, you must multiply I times R, so that the voltage equals 15 volts.

$E = IR$

$E = 3 \times 5 = 15 \text{ volts}$

In using Ohm's law, the quantities must always be expressed in the basic units of current, voltage and resistance. If a quantity is given in larger or smaller units, it must first be changed so that it is expressed in amperes, volts or ohms.

Establishing Total Resistance in Series Circuits

In the previous topic you learned that the total resistance in a series circuit is equal to the sum of the individual resistances in that circuit. Total resistance in a series circuit, called R_T, may be established by using Ohm's Law if the amount of current in the circuit and the impressed voltage are known.

Consider the schematic diagram below. Note that the total impressed voltage, E_T, is 100 volts, and that the total current in the circuit, I_T, is two amperes. Note also, that there are three resistors in series. This fact will not cause any difficulty in solving the problem if you remember that the total current flowing in a circuit is the result when the total voltage is applied across the total resistance in the circuit. Using Ohm's Law, then, the total resistance is equal to the total voltage divided by the total current.

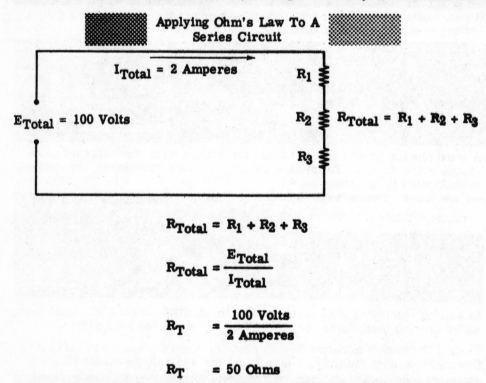

Applying Ohm's Law To A Series Circuit

I_{Total} = 2 Amperes

R_1

E_{Total} = 100 Volts

R_2 $R_{Total} = R_1 + R_2 + R_3$

R_3

$$R_{Total} = R_1 + R_2 + R_3$$

$$R_{Total} = \frac{E_{Total}}{I_{Total}}$$

$$R_T = \frac{100 \text{ Volts}}{2 \text{ Amperes}}$$

$$R_T = 50 \text{ Ohms}$$

In the previous topic you also learned that when the voltage drops in a series circuit are added together, the total value is equal to the total impressed voltage, or

$$E_{Total} = E_1 + E_2 + E_3$$

You learned, too, that the current flowing in a series circuit is everywhere the same, or

$$I_{Total} = I_1 = I_2 = I_3$$

This is true even though the various resistors in the series circuit may all be of different values.

OHM'S LAW

Ohm's Law in Series Circuits

You can use Ohm's law in working with series circuits, either as applied to the entire circuit or to only a part of the circuit. It can only be used to find an unknown quantity for a certain part of the circuit when two factors are known. Consider a circuit consisting of three resistors connected in series across 100 volts, with a circuit current flow of 2 amperes. If two of the resistor values, R_1 and R_2, are known to be 5 ohms and 10 ohms respectively, but the third resistor value R_3 is not known, the value of R_3 and the current and voltage for each resistor may be determined by applying Ohm's law to each part of the circuit.

To find the unknown values, you should first make a simple sketch, see the diagram below, for recording the information which you already have and that which you will obtain as you use Ohm's Law for various parts of the circuit. This sketch will enable you to visualize the various components of the circuit and their relationships with one another.

Next you should record all of the known factors concerning each resistor. You know that R_1 equals 5 ohms and R_2 equals 10 ohms and also that the circuit current is 2 amperes. Since there is only one path for current in a series circuit, the current is the same in every part of the circuit and is equal to 2 amperes.

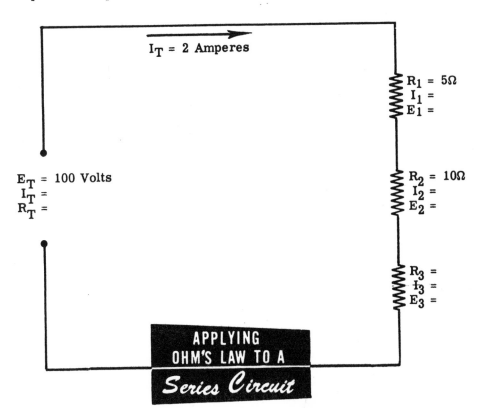

$I_T = 2$ Amperes

$R_1 = 5\Omega$
$I_1 =$
$E_1 =$

$E_T = 100$ Volts
$I_T =$
$R_T =$

$R_2 = 10\Omega$
$I_2 =$
$E_2 =$

$R_3 =$
$I_3 =$
$E_3 =$

APPLYING
OHM'S LAW TO A
Series Circuit

Ohm's Law in Series Circuits (continued)

For R_1 and R_2 you have two known quantities—resistances and currents—and can therefore find the voltages. Using Ohm's law to find the voltage across R_1, for example, the current—2 amperes—is multiplied by the resistance—5 ohms—resulting in a voltage of 10 volts across R_1. Similarly the voltage across R_2 is found by multiplying the current by the resistance —2 amperes times 10 ohms—resulting in a voltage of 20 volts across R_2.

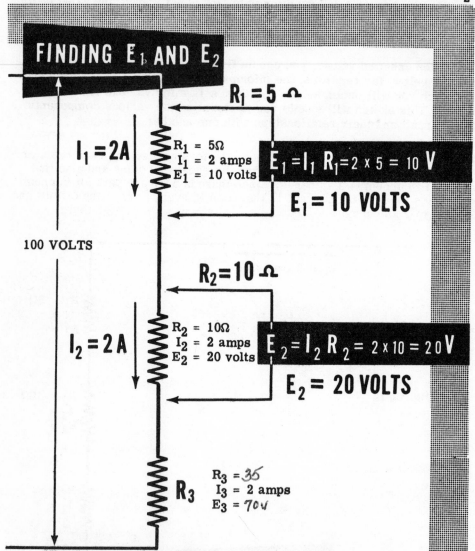

FINDING E_1 AND E_2

$R_1 = 5\ \Omega$

$I_1 = 2A$

$R_1 = 5\Omega$
$I_1 = 2$ amps
$E_1 = 10$ volts

$E_1 = I_1 R_1 = 2 \times 5 = 10\ V$

$E_1 = 10$ VOLTS

100 VOLTS

$R_2 = 10\ \Omega$

$I_2 = 2A$

$R_2 = 10\Omega$
$I_2 = 2$ amps
$E_2 = 20$ volts

$E_2 = I_2 R_2 = 2 \times 10 = 20\ V$

$E_2 = 20$ VOLTS

R_3

$R_3 = 35$
$I_3 = 2$ amps
$E_3 = 70\ v$

Your sketch now is complete except for the resistance value and voltage across R_3. If you can obtain the correct value of either the resistance or the voltage for R_3, the other quantity can easily be found by applying Ohm's law to R_3.

Ohm's Law in Series Circuits (continued)

Since the three resistors are connected across 100 volts, the voltages across the three resistors must equal 100 volts when added together. If the voltages across R_1 and R_2 are equal to 10 volts and 20 volts respectively, the total voltage across the two equals 30 volts. Then the voltage across R_3 must equal the difference between the total 100 volts and the 30-volt total across R_1 and R_2, or 70 volts. Ohm's law can be used to find the resistance of R_3 by dividing the voltage—70 volts—by the current —2 amperes—so that R_3 equals 35 ohms.

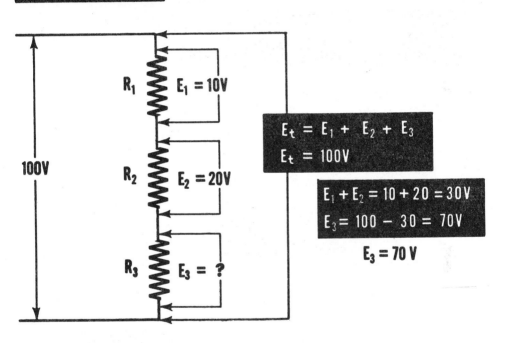

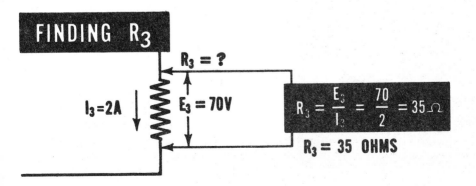

Ohm's Law in Series Circuits (continued)

You can also use another method of finding the unknown quantities for R_3. Since the total circuit voltage and current is known, the total circuit resistance can be found by dividing the voltage—100 volts—by the current—2 amperes. The total resistance then is 50 ohms and, since this total must equal the sum of R_1, R_2 and R_3, the value of R_3 is equal to the difference between 50 ohms and R_1 plus R_2. The sum of R_1 and R_2 equals 15 ohms, leaving a difference of 35 ohms as the resistance value of R_3. With the resistance value and current for R_3 known, the voltage is found by multiplying the two known quantities. Multiplying the resistance—35 ohms—by the current—2 amperes—results in a voltage of 70 volts across R_3. The results are the same as those previously obtained.

ANOTHER WAY TO FIND R_3 AND E_3

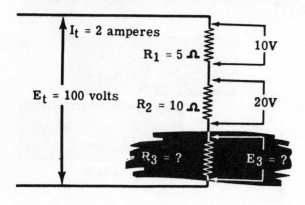

$I_t = 2$ amperes

$R_1 = 5\,\Omega$ 10V

$E_t = 100$ volts $R_2 = 10\,\Omega$ 20V

$R_3 = ?$ $E_3 = ?$

$R_t = \dfrac{E_t}{I_t} = \dfrac{100}{2} = 50\,\Omega$

$R_t = 50\,\Omega$

Also

$R_t = R_1 + R_2 + R_3$

To find R_3

$R_1 + R_2 = 5 + 10 = 15\,\Omega$

$R_3 = 50 - 15 = 35\,\Omega$

$R_3 = 35$ OHMS

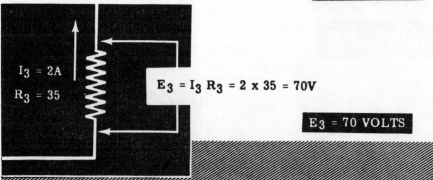

$I_3 = 2A$

$R_3 = 35$

$E_3 = I_3 R_3 = 2 \times 35 = 70V$

$E_3 = 70$ VOLTS

Ohm's Law in Series Circuits (continued)

With the values of R_3 and E_3 known, your table is now complete, giving all the values of resistance, voltage and current for each of the three resistors in the circuit. From the completed table of values you can find the total circuit resistance, voltage and current. Since the circuit is series-connected, the current for the total circuit is the same as that for any part of the circuit, while the total voltage and the total resistance are found by adding the individual voltages and resistances.

Completed Table of Values

Part of Circuit	Resistance	Voltage	Current
R_1	5 Ohms	10 Volts	2 Amperes
R_2	10 Ohms	20 Volts	2 Amperes
R_3	35 Ohms	70 Volts	2 Amperes

The total resistance (R_t) is equal to 50 ohms, the total current (I_t) is 2 amperes, and the total voltage (E_t) is 100 volts. Now you know all of the circuit values.

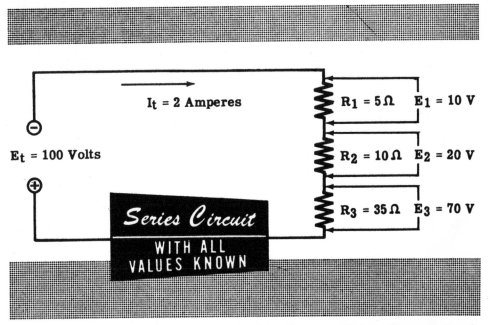

To find unknown circuit quantities always solve completely those parts of the circuit for which you know two quantities, by applying Ohm's law to that part of the circuit. Apply the rules for current, voltage and resistance in series circuits to find other unknown quantities which cannot be found by means of Ohm's law.

Demonstration of Ohm's Law

To show how Ohm's law may be used to find the resistance needed, the instructor connects four dry cells to form a 6-volt battery. Then choosing desired values of current such as .3, .6 and 1 amperes, he determines the resistances which will give these currents when connected across the 6-volt battery. Using Ohm's law, the voltage—6 volts—is divided by the desired currents—.3, .6 and 1 amperes—giving required resistances of 20, 10 and 6 ohms. To check these values, he connects two 3-ohm resistors in series to form a 6-ohm resistance and connects it in series with an ammeter across the 6-volt battery. You can see that the resulting current is approximately 1 ampere. By adding more resistors in series to form 10- and 20-ohm resistances, the instructor shows that these resistance values also result in the desired currents.

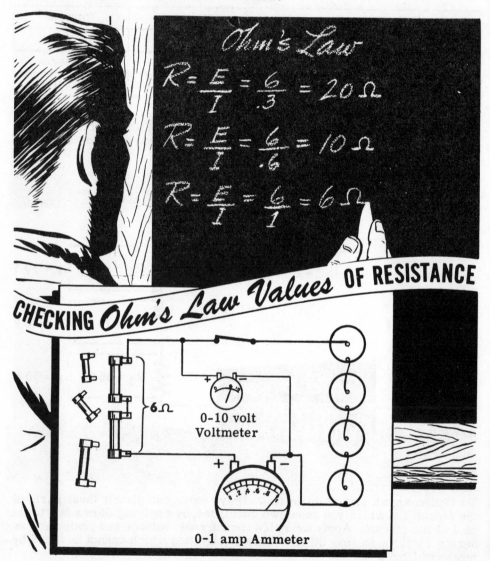

Demonstration of Ohm's Law (continued)

Current and voltage may also be used to find the value of a resistance in a circuit when the resistance is unknown. To demonstrate this use of Ohm's law, the instructor connects two resistors, having no resistance marking, to form a series circuit across a six-volt battery with an ammeter connected to measure the current flow. The voltage across each resistor is read and you see that these two voltages, added, equal the battery voltage. By dividing the voltages across the resistors by the circuit current, the instructor obtains the resistance value of the resistors. To show that the answers are correct, the resistances are measured with an ohmmeter and you see that the values obtained by Ohm's law equal those indicated on the ohmmeter. As several such problems are worked, you see that rated current and voltage can be used to find the value of resistance needed in a circuit, and the measured values of current and voltage can be used to find the value of an unknown resistance in a circuit.

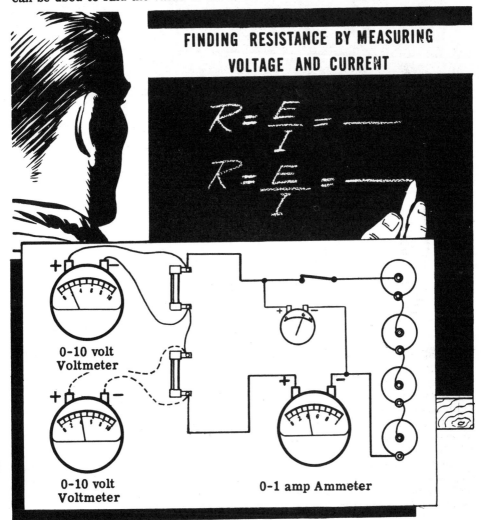

FINDING RESISTANCE BY MEASURING VOLTAGE AND CURRENT

$$R = \frac{E}{I} = \underline{\qquad}$$

$$R = \frac{E}{I} = \underline{\qquad}$$

0-10 volt Voltmeter

0-10 volt Voltmeter

0-1 amp Ammeter

Demonstration of Ohm's Law (continued)

How to use Ohm's law to find the voltage required to give the correct current flow through a known resistance will now be demonstrated. Using a 10-ohm resistance consisting of two 2-ohm resistors and two 3-ohm resistors in series, the instructor determines the voltages needed to obtain .3, .6 and .9 ampere of current flow by multiplying 10 ohms by each current in turn. The voltage values obtained are 3, 6 and 9 volts respectively. To check these values the 10-ohm resistance in series with an ammeter is connected across cells connected to give these voltages. With the 3-volt battery of cells, you see that the current is .3 amperes, for the 6-volt battery it is .6 amperes, and for the 9-volt battery it is .9 amperes, showing that the Ohm's law values are correct.

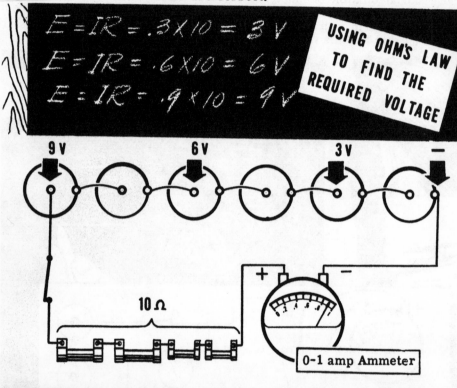

$$E = IR = .3 \times 10 = 3 \, V$$
$$E = IR = .6 \times 10 = 6 \, V$$
$$E = IR = .9 \times 10 = 9 \, V$$

USING OHM'S LAW TO FIND THE REQUIRED VOLTAGE

9 V 6 V 3 V −

10 Ω + −

0-1 amp Ammeter

Next the instructor shows how Ohm's law may be used to measure current in a series circuit. Using a 9-volt battery of dry cells connected across six 3-ohm resistors in series, the instructor determines the total circuit resistance to be 18 ohms by adding the resistance values. By dividing the 9 volts by 18 ohms he determines that the circuit current is .5 amperes. Measuring the voltage across each individual resistor and dividing by the resistor value also results in a current value of .5 amperes for the circuit. The instructor then connects an ammeter to check the current and you see that the current value checks. Several similar demonstrations all show that, when two values are known for any part of a circuit, the unknown value can be determined directly by using Ohm's law.

Review of Ohm's Law

Ohm's law is a tool used in electricity in place of a meter to find an unknown factor concerning a circuit or part of a circuit when two of the factors are known. You can use it in place of an ohmmeter, voltmeter or ammeter to find resistance, voltage or current provided that you know two of the quantities and desire to find the third. Like any tool, Ohm's law becomes easier to use with practice, and the more often you use it, the more skilled you will become in its use. You have read about it, discussed it and seen it demonstrated; now suppose you review its use in finding unknown circuit quantities. Remember that all quantities must be expressed in basic units—volts, amperes and ohms.

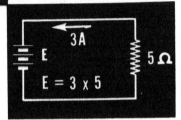

Voltage equals current multiplied by resistance

VOLTS = AMPERES x OHMS

$$E = IR$$

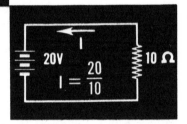

Current equals voltage divided by resistance

AMPERES = VOLTS ÷ OHMS

$$I = \frac{E}{R}$$

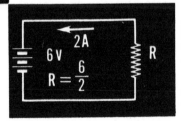

Resistance equals voltage divided by current

OHMS = VOLTS ÷ AMPERES

$$R = \frac{E}{I}$$

While it is not necessary to memorize many of the formulas you will use in electricity, Ohm's law should be memorized since you will use it more frequently than any other.

Extending the Range of Voltmeters

The following is a practical application of Ohm's Law in series circuits.

In the diagram below, note that the meter is in series with the multiplier resistor and that both these components are placed across the voltage source which is being measured. The equivalent circuit shows the basic meter movement as a resistance which is placed in series with the multiplier resistor. The current through both the multiplier resistor and the meter movement is the same since the components are in series with each other. For any given type of meter movement a high resistance series multiplier will limit the current to a very small value (by Ohm's Law). For the same meter movement a low resistance series multiplier will permit a comparatively large amount of current to flow through the circuit. The resistance value of series multipliers is always chosen, however, so as to limit the current enough to prevent damage to the meter but at the same time provide the required indications.

As you learned in Volume I of this course, a voltmeter is simply an ammeter which measures the current flow through a given material called a series multiplier resistor. The "voltmeter" movement with which you will come in contact most frequently is the very familiar 0-1 ma. milliammeter. You can see why the series multiplier is such a necessary factor in measuring voltages. If no multiplier were incorporated in the unit, the low resistance of the one-milliamp meter movement would act like a short circuit, causing high currents to flow for all but the smallest voltages being measured. The series multiplier then, limits the current through the meter to a maximum of 1 milliamp and provides a standard by which the voltmeter range can be determined. For a given multiplier, the meter will indicate a large current if the voltage being measured is high, or a small current if the voltage being measured is low. The meter may be equipped with scales of different ranges or a multiplication factor may be used to establish accurate readings.

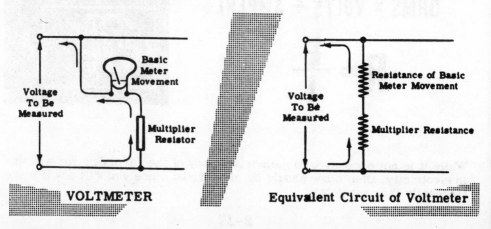

VOLTMETER   **Equivalent Circuit of Voltmeter**

Extending the Range of Voltmeters (continued)

Certain factors regarding the use of series multipliers in extending the ranges of voltmeters were described on the previous sheet. You will now learn how to use the familiar Ohm's Law in calculating the resistance value of series multipliers.

Suppose that you wish to use a 0-1 ma. milliammeter as a 0-10 volt volt-meter. Assume, for this problem, that the meter movement resistance is 50 ohms.

Calculate the resistance value of the multiplier which will permit measurements of ten volts (or less) without damage to the meter. See the diagram below.

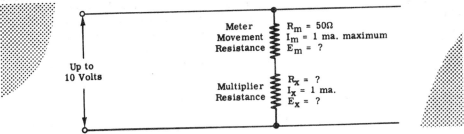

Recall that the total voltage in a series circuit is equal to the sum of the individual voltage drops in the circuit or, as in this case

$$E_{Total} = E_m + E_x$$

You know that the total voltage to be measured will be ten volts. You also know that the total allowable current through the meter movement I_m, must not exceed a maximum of one milliampere. Since the current (I_m) and resistance (R_m) of the meter movement are known, you can find the IR drop across the meter. Using Ohm's Law, then,

or, by substituting,
$$E_m = I_m R_m$$
$$E_m = .001 \times 50$$
$$E_m = .05 \text{ volts}$$

In order to find the multiplier resistance R_x, you must first find E_x, the voltage across the multiplier. Recall the formula given above for total voltage in a series circuit.

$$E_{total} = E_m + E_x$$
Solving for E_x you find that $E_{total} - E_m = E_x$
$$E_x = 10 - .05$$
$$E_x = 9.95 \text{ volts}$$

Using Ohm's Law, it is a simple matter to find R_x since I_x is known to be one milliampere ($I_m = I_x$).

$$R_x = \frac{E_x}{I_x} = \frac{9.95}{.001}$$

$$R_x = 9,950 \text{ ohms}$$

Extending the Range of Voltmeters (continued)

You have just learned how to calculate the resistance value of a multiplier which permits measurement of voltages not higher than ten volts. This example was used for the purposes of illustration only, because you will probably be provided with a 0-10 volt voltmeter. The examples which follow however, are concerned with much higher voltages, and are similar to problems involving series multipliers which you may have to solve in the future.

Suppose that you wish to extend the range of your meter so that it will measure voltages up to 100 volts, DC. Assume that the meter movement is the very familiar 0-1 milliamp, 50-ohm Weston movement. What value of resistance must be used as a series multiplier to limit the current through the meter to a maximum of one milliampere even when the voltage being measured is as high as 100 volts? See the diagram below.

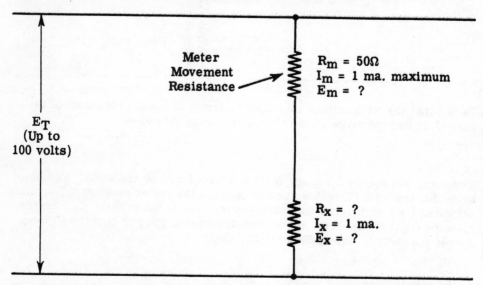

Recall that $I_m = I_x$, since the multiplier and meter form a series circuit across the line. Recall also, that the sum of E_m and E_x must equal the total voltage E_T. Solving for E_m

$$E_m = I_m \times R_m = .001 \times 50 = .05 \text{ volts}$$

Since you now have the value for E_m find the value of E_x by substituting in the formula

$$E_T = E_m + E_x$$
$$E_x = E_T - E_m = 100 - .05$$
$$E_x = 99.95 \text{ volts}$$

Using Ohm's Law, solve for R_x

$$R_x = \frac{E_x}{I_x} = \frac{99.95}{.001} = 99,950 \text{ ohms}$$

Extending the Range of Voltmeters (continued)

In another problem, find the value of multiplier necessary to extend the range of the meter movement (same as above) to 300 volts.

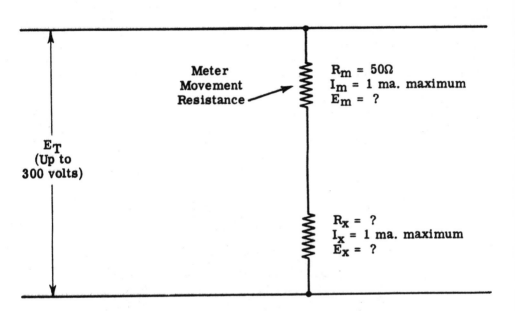

As before, solve for E_m

$$E_m = I_m R_m = .001 \times 50$$
$$E_m = .05 \text{ volts}$$

Substitute in formula, below, to find E_x

$$E_T = E_m + E_x$$
$$E_x = E_T - E_m$$
$$E_x = 300 - .05$$
$$E_x = 299.95 \text{ volts}$$

Using Ohm's Law, solve for R_x

$$R_x = \frac{E_x}{I_x} = \frac{299.95}{.001}$$

$$R_x = 299,950 \text{ ohms}$$

What Power Is

Power—whether electrical or mechanical—means the rate of doing work. Work is done whenever a force causes motion. If a mechanical force is used to lift or move a weight, work is done. However, force exerted without causing motion—such as the force of a spring under tension between two objects which do not move—is not work.

Previously you found that electrical force is voltage and that voltage causes current flow—movement of electrons. Voltage existing between two points without causing current flow is similar to the spring under tension without moving, and is not doing work. Whenever voltage causes electron movement, work is done in moving electrons from one point to another. The rate at which this work is done is called electric power.

The same total amount of work may be done in different amounts of time. For example, a given number of electrons may be moved from one point to another in one second or in one hour, depending on the rate at which they are moved; and the total work done will be the same in each case. If all the work is done in one second, more electrical energy will be changed to heat or light per second than if the total amount of work is done in an hour.

No work being done   Work being done

LOW POWER —
fewer electrons per minute

HIGH POWER —
more electrons per minute

Units of Electric Power

The basic unit of power is the watt, which equals the voltage multiplied by the current—electrical force times coulombs of electrons moved past a point per second. This represents the rate at which work is being done in moving electrons through a material. The symbol P indicates electrical power. To find the power used in a resistance—

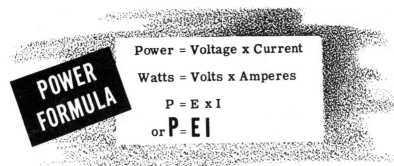

POWER FORMULA

Power = Voltage x Current

Watts = Volts x Amperes

P = E x I

or $P = EI$

In a circuit consisting of a 15-ohm resistor across a voltage source of 45 volts, 3 amperes of current flow through the resistor. The power used can be found by multiplying the voltage and current.

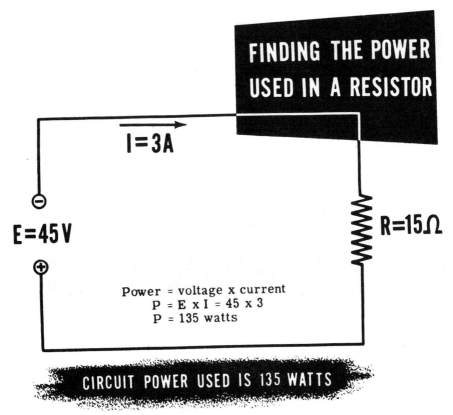

FINDING THE POWER USED IN A RESISTOR

I = 3A

E = 45V

R = 15Ω

Power = voltage x current
P = E x I = 45 x 3
P = 135 watts

CIRCUIT POWER USED IS 135 WATTS

Units of Electric Power (continued)

By substituting Ohm's law expressions in the formula for watts, the formula may be expressed in terms of current and resistance or voltage and resistance. According to Ohm's law, E = IR. By replacing E in the power formula with its equal value (IR), power can be determined without knowing the voltage.

VARIATION OF THE POWER FORMULA

$$P = EI$$

SUBSTITUTING (IR) FOR E: $P = (IR)I$ OR $I \times R \times I$

SINCE I x I IS I^2: $P = I^2 R$

Similarly, $I = \dfrac{E}{R}$ and, if $\dfrac{E}{R}$ is substituted for I in the power formula, power can be found with only the voltage and current known.

ANOTHER VARIATION

$$P = EI$$

SUBSTITUTING $\dfrac{E}{R}$ FOR I: $P = E\left(\dfrac{E}{R}\right)$ OR $\dfrac{E \times E}{R}$

SINCE E x E IS E^2: $P = \dfrac{E^2}{R}$

For quantities of power beyond 1,000 watts the unit used is the kilowatt, while quantities smaller than a watt are expressed in milliwatts.

LARGE AND SMALL UNITS OF POWER

1 kilowatt = 1000 watts
1 kw = 1000 w

1 milliwatt = $\dfrac{1}{1000}$ watt

1 mw = $\dfrac{1}{1000}$ w

Power Rating of Equipment

From your own experience you have probably found that most electrical equipment is rated for both voltage and power—volts and watts. Electric lamps rated at 117 volts for use on a 117-volt power line are also rated in watts, and are usually identified by wattage rather than volts.

Perhaps you have wondered what this rating in watts means and indicates. The wattage rating of an electric lamp or other electrical equipment indicates the rate at which electrical energy is changed into another form of energy, such as heat or light. The faster a lamp changes electrical energy to light, the brighter the lamp will be; thus, a 100-watt lamp furnishes more light than a 75-watt lamp. Electric soldering irons are made in various wattage ratings with the higher wattage irons changing electrical energy to heat faster than those of a low wattage rating. Similarly the wattage rating of motors, resistors and other electrical devices indicates the rate at which they are designed to change electrical energy into some other form of energy. If the normal wattage rating is exceeded, the equipment or device will overheat and perhaps be damaged.

Power Rating of Equipment (continued)

When more power is used in a resistance, the rate at which electrical energy is changed to heat increases and the temperature of the resistance rises. If the temperature rises too high the material of the resistance may change its composition, expand, contract or burn due to the heat. For that reason all types of electrical equipment are rated for a maximum wattage. This rating may be in terms of watts or often in terms of maximum voltage and current, which effectively give the rating in watts.

Resistors are rated in watts in addition to ohms of resistance. Resistors of the same resistance value are available in different wattage values. Carbon resistors, for example, are commonly made in wattage ratings of 1/4, 1/2, 1 and 2 watts. The larger the size of carbon resistor the higher its wattage rating, since a larger amount of material will absorb and give up heat more easily.

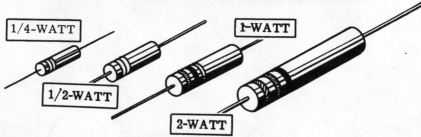

COMPARATIVE SIZE OF CARBON RESISTORS OF DIFFERENT WATTAGE RATINGS

1/4-WATT

1-WATT

1/2-WATT

2-WATT

When resistors of wattage ratings greater than 2 watts are needed, wire-wound resistors are used. Such resistors are made in ranges between 5 and 200 watts, with special types being used for power in excess of 200 watts.

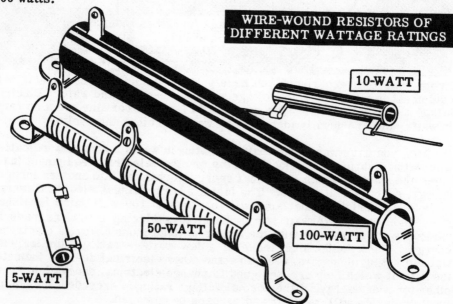

WIRE-WOUND RESISTORS OF DIFFERENT WATTAGE RATINGS

10-WATT

50-WATT

100-WATT

5-WATT

Fuses

When current passes through a resistor, electric energy is transformed into heat, which raises the temperature of the resistor. If the temperature rises too high, the resistor may be damaged. The metal wire in a wound resistor may melt, opening the circuit and interrupting current flow. This effect is used to advantage in fuses.

Fuses are metal resistors with very low resistance values, which are designed to "blow out" and thus open the circuit when the current exceeds the fuse's rated value. When the power consumed by the fuse raises the temperature of the metal too high, the metal melts and the fuse "blows." Blown fuses can be identified by a broken filament and darkened glass.

You have already learned that excessive current may seriously damage electrical equipment—motors, instruments, radio receivers, etc. The purpose of the fuse is to protect such equipment from excessive current. It is connected in series with the equipment, so that the fuse will open the circuit before the excessive current does damage to the equipment. Fuses are cheap, other equipment much more expensive.

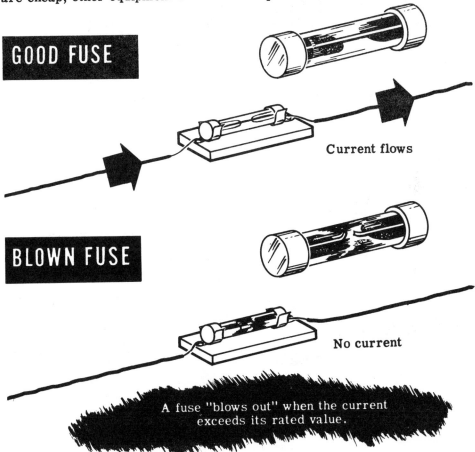

GOOD FUSE

Current flows

BLOWN FUSE

No current

A fuse "blows out" when the current exceeds its rated value.

Fuses (continued)

Although it is the power used by a fuse which causes it to blow, fuses are rated by the current which they will conduct without burning out, since it is high current which damages equipment. Since various types of equipment use different currents, fuses are made in many sizes, shapes and current ratings.

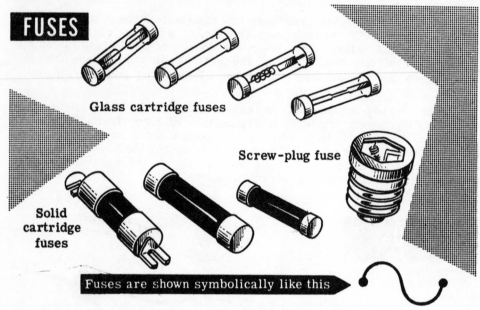

FUSES

Glass cartridge fuses

Screw-plug fuse

Solid cartridge fuses

Fuses are shown symbolically like this

It is important that you always use fuses with the proper current rating—slightly higher than the greatest current you expect in the circuit. Too low a rating will result in unnecessary blow-outs, while too high a rating may allow dangerously high currents to pass. In the demonstrations to follow, the circuits will be "fused" to protect the ammeter. Since the range of the ammeter is 0 to 1 ampere, a 1.5-amp fuse will be used.

The fuse is inserted in the circuit by connecting the fuse holder in series and snapping the fuse into the holder.

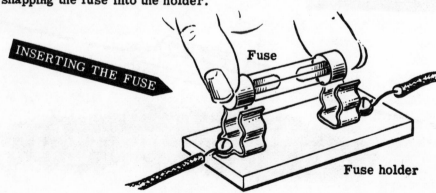

INSERTING THE FUSE

Fuse

Fuse holder

Demonstration of Power in Series Circuits

To show that power can be determined when any two of the circuit variables —current, voltage and resistance—are known, the instructor connects three 15-ohm, 10-watt resistors in series across a 9-volt dry cell battery.

After measuring the voltage across each resistor, he applies the power formula $P = \dfrac{E^2}{R}$ to find the power for each resistor. You see that the power used by each resistor is about 0.6 watt and that the total power is about 1.8 watts.

FINDING POWER WHEN VOLTAGE AND RESISTANCE ARE KNOWN

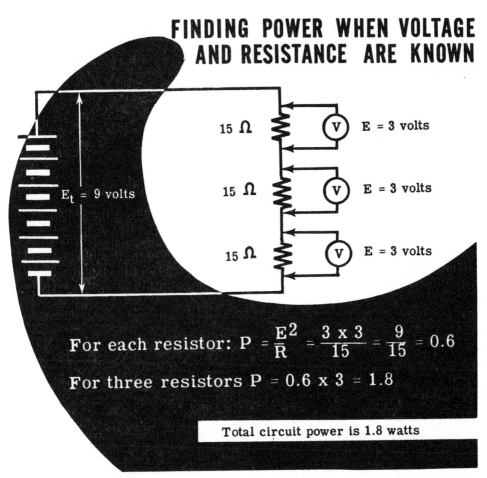

For each resistor: $P = \dfrac{E^2}{R} = \dfrac{3 \times 3}{15} = \dfrac{9}{15} = 0.6$

For three resistors $P = 0.6 \times 3 = 1.8$

Total circuit power is 1.8 watts

To show that the same results are obtained using current and resistance or current and voltage, the instructor connects an ammeter in the circuit to measure current. The power used by each resistor is then found by using the power formula in two ways: $P = I^2R$ and $P = EI$. Notice that the power in watts is very nearly the same for each variation of the power formula used, with the negligible difference being due to meter inaccuracies and slight errors in meter readings.

ELECTRIC POWER

Demonstration of Power in Series Circuits (continued)

To show the effect of the power rating of a resistor on its operation in a circuit, the instructor connects two 15-ohm resistors—one 10-watt and one 1-watt resistor—in a series circuit as shown below. The ammeter reads the circuit current and, using the power formula $P = I^2R$, you find that the power used in each resistor is approximately 1.35 watts. As this is slightly more than the power rating of the 1-watt resistor you see that it heats rapidly, while the 10-watt resistor remains relatively cool. To check the power used in each resistor, the voltages across them are measured with a voltmeter and multiplied by the current. Notice that the power is the same as that previously obtained, and that the power used by each resistor is exactly equal.

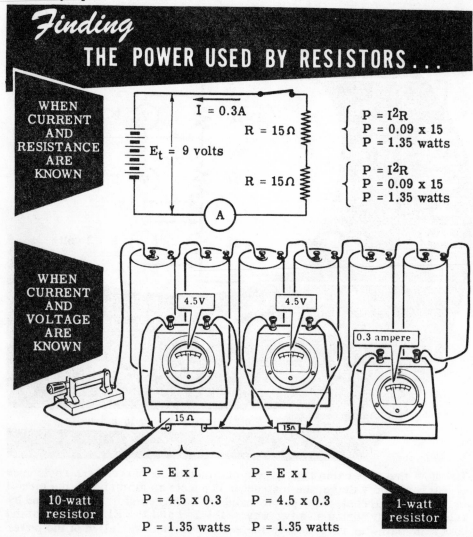

Finding **THE POWER USED BY RESISTORS...**

WHEN CURRENT AND RESISTANCE ARE KNOWN

$I = 0.3A$
$R = 15\,\Omega$
$E_t = 9$ volts
$R = 15\,\Omega$
A

$P = I^2R$
$P = 0.09 \times 15$
$P = 1.35$ watts

$P = I^2R$
$P = 0.09 \times 15$
$P = 1.35$ watts

WHEN CURRENT AND VOLTAGE ARE KNOWN

4.5V   4.5V   0.3 ampere

15 Ω   15 Ω

10-watt resistor

$P = E \times I$
$P = 4.5 \times 0.3$
$P = 1.35$ watts

$P = E \times I$
$P = 4.5 \times 0.3$
$P = 1.35$ watts

1-watt resistor

Demonstration of Power in Series Circuits (continued)

Next, the 1-watt resistor is replaced by one rated at 1/2 watt. Observe that it heats more rapidly than the 1-watt resistor and becomes very hot, indicating that the power rating has been exceeded. As the power for each resistor is found (using current and resistance, then voltage and current as a check), you see that each resistor is using the same amount of power. This shows that the power rating of a resistor does not determine the amount of power used in a resistor. Instead the power rating only indicates the maximum amount of power that may be without damaging the resistor.

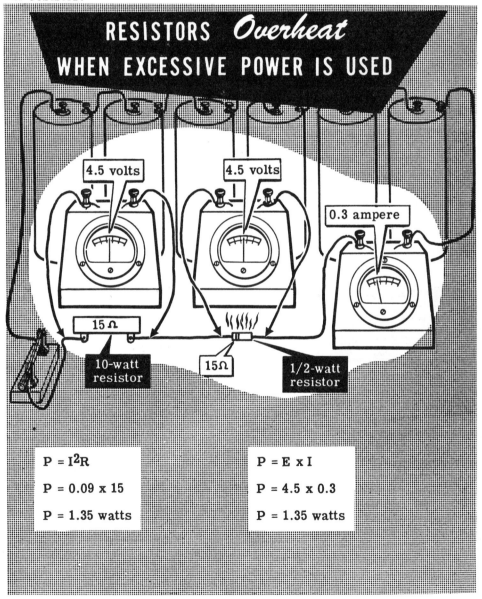

$$P = I^2R$$

$$P = 0.09 \times 15$$

$$P = 1.35 \text{ watts}$$

$$P = E \times I$$

$$P = 4.5 \times 0.3$$

$$P = 1.35 \text{ watts}$$

Demonstration on the Use of Fuses

You have seen how a resistor overheats when it uses more power than its power rating. Now you will see how this effect is put to use to protect electrical equipment from damage due to excessive currents.

The instructor connects four dry cells in series to form a 6-volt battery. He then connects a 15-ohm 10-watt resistor, a knife switch, a fuse holder and the ammeter in series across the battery, and inserts a 1/8-amp fuse in the fuse holder. When he closes the switch, you see that the fuse "blows." This opens the circuit so that no current can flow, as you see by the zero reading of the ammeter.

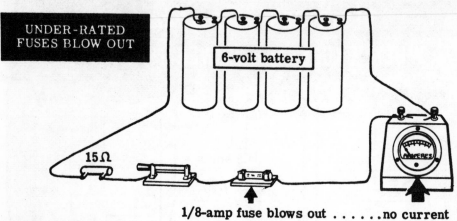

UNDER-RATED FUSES BLOW OUT

6-volt battery

15 Ω

1/8-amp fuse blows out . . . . . . no current

However, when the instructor inserts a 1/2-amp fuse in the fuse holder, you see that it does not blow, and the ammeter shows a current flow.

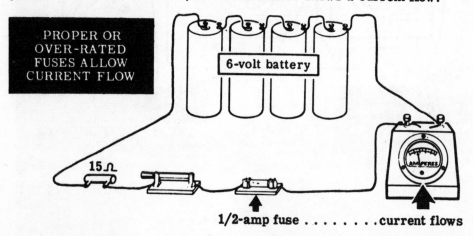

PROPER OR OVER-RATED FUSES ALLOW CURRENT FLOW

6-volt battery

15 Ω

1/2-amp fuse . . . . current flows

Since the resistance of the circuit is 15 ohms and the voltage is 6 volts, the current flow by Ohm's law is about 0.4 amp ($\frac{6 \text{ volts}}{15 \text{ ohms}}$). Since the 1/8 amp (0.125 amp) fuse "blows out" when the current exceeds its rating, it will not carry 0.4 amp. However, the 1/2 amp (0.5 amp) fuse carries the current without blowing, since its rating exceeds the actual current flow.

Demonstration of How Fuses Protect Equipment

Using the circuit as shown, immediately below, note that a 15-ohm resistor limits the current through the circuit sufficiently to keep a half-ampere fuse from burning out. The circuit operates without damage to the ammeter.

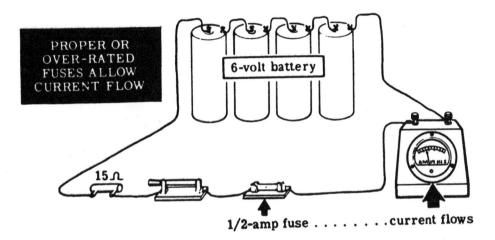

PROPER OR OVER-RATED FUSES ALLOW CURRENT FLOW

6-volt battery

15 Ω

1/2-amp fuse . . . . current flows

If you were to short-circuit the resistor, as in the diagram below, the fuse would burn out and open the circuit without damage to the ammeter or line wire. Because the fuse serves as the predetermined weakest link in this circuit, it is an electrical safety device. In choosing fuses be sure not to choose one whose rating is too high for the expected current flow. If trouble occurs, the highly over-rated fuse may not burn out before the meter does so that all protection is lost for the meter.

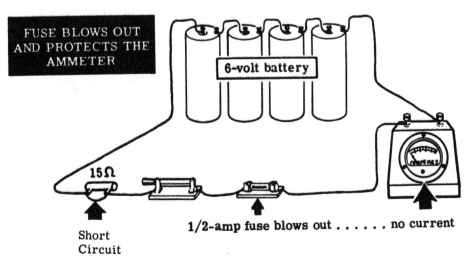

FUSE BLOWS OUT AND PROTECTS THE AMMETER

6-volt battery

15 Ω

Short Circuit

1/2-amp fuse blows out . . . . . . no current

Review of Electric Power

Whenever an electric current flows, work is done in moving electrons through the conductor. The work may be done slowly or rapidly. All of the electrons to be moved may be moved in either a short or long period of time, and the rate at which the work is done is called electric power. Now let's review electric power, the power formula and power rating of equipment.

ELECTRIC POWER — The rate of doing work in moving electrons through a material. The basic unit of power is the watt represented by the letter P.

POWER FORMULA — Electric power used in a resistance equals the voltage across the resistance terminals times the current flow through the resistance. It is also equal to the current squared times the resistance or, the voltage squared divided by the resistance.

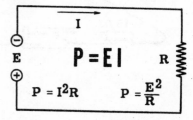

$$P = EI$$
$$P = I^2R \qquad P = \frac{E^2}{R}$$

POWER RATING — Electrical equipment is rated according to the rate at which it uses electric power The power used is converted from electrical energy into heat or light.

75 Watts

150 Watts

RESISTOR POWER RATINGS — Resistors are rated both in ohms of resistance and the maximum power which can safely be used in the resistor. High wattage resistors are constructed larger than low wattage resistors to provide a greater surface for dissipating heat.

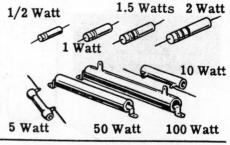

1/2 Watt   1.5 Watts   2 Watt

1 Watt

10 Watt

5 Watt   50 Watt   100 Watt

FUSES — Fuses are metal resistors of low resistance values designed to open an electric circuit if the current through the resistor exceeds the fuse's rated value.

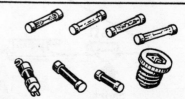

Parallel Circuit Connections

When you connect resistances side by side with the ends connected, they are parallel-connected. For such a connection there is more than one path for current flow and, if the resistances in a circuit are so connected, the circuit is a parallel circuit. Similarly, cells connected in parallel to form a battery provide more than one current path through the battery, with each cell furnishing only a part of the total battery current.

If two lamp sockets are placed side by side, with adjacent terminals of the sockets connected together, the lamps are parallel-connected but do not form a parallel circuit. If the two points at which the sockets are connected together are used as terminals and placed across a voltage source, they form a complete parallel circuit.

Most electric power lines form parallel circuits, with each lamp, motor or other type of resistance being connected in parallel across the power line. Each of these devices provides a different path for current flow between the terminals of the line voltage source.

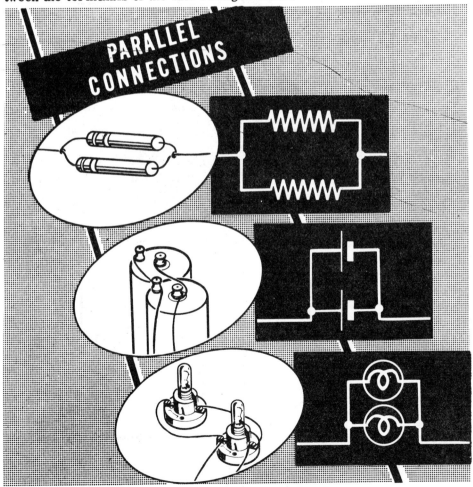

PARALLEL CONNECTIONS

Voltage in Parallel Circuits

Parallel resistances connected across a voltage source have the same voltage applied to each resistance, although the currents may differ depending on the values of resistance. All resistances which are to be connected in parallel must have the same voltage rating for proper operation, though each may pass a different amount of current.

You have used lamps and electric appliances on electric power lines, and have found that they are rated for normal operation on a 117-volt power line. In use, they are connected in parallel across the power line which is the voltage source.

The voltage across each is the same since they are all connected across the same voltage source.

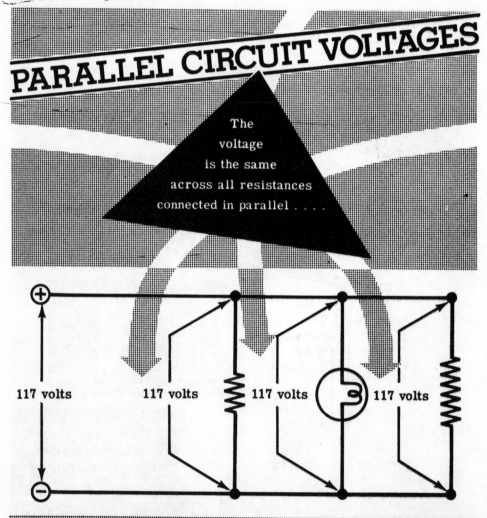

PARALLEL CIRCUIT VOLTAGES

The voltage is the same across all resistances connected in parallel . . . .

117 volts   117 volts   117 volts   117 volts

Current Flow in Parallel Circuits

Current divides among the various branches of a parallel circuit in a manner depending on the resistance of each branch. If an electric lamp, an iron, a radio and a vacuum cleaner are connected in parallel, the current through each branch will vary since each piece of equipment offers different resistance to current flow.

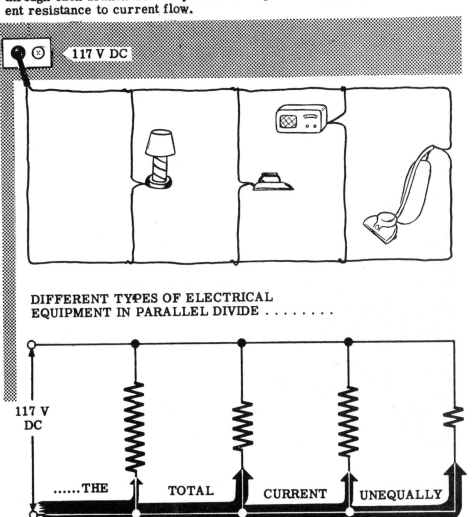

117 V DC

DIFFERENT TYPES OF ELECTRICAL
EQUIPMENT IN PARALLEL DIVIDE . . . .

117 V
DC

. . . . . . THE   TOTAL   CURRENT   UNEQUALLY

In the following demonstration and experiment on parallel circuits, resistors and lamps will be used to show division of current. Resistors of various values will be used to represent different types of electrical equipment. Regardless of the form the resistance may take, the rule is the same: Branches in a parallel circuit with low resistance draw more current than branches with high resistance.

Current Flow in Parallel Circuits (continued)

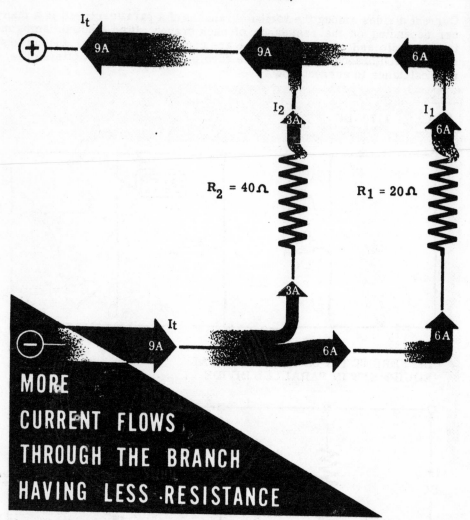

$R_2 = 40\,\Omega$

$R_1 = 20\,\Omega$

MORE
CURRENT FLOWS
THROUGH THE BRANCH
HAVING LESS RESISTANCE

When unequal resistances are connected in parallel, the opposition to current flow is not the same for each branch of the circuit. A small value of resistance offers less opposition, and thus the smaller resistances in parallel circuits pass more current than the larger resistances. If two resistances—R_1 and R_2—are connected in parallel and R_1 has only half the resistance of R_2, the current through R_1 will be twice that of R_2. Also, if R_1 has one-third the resistance of R_2, the current through R_1 will be three times as great as that through R_2, etc.

Current is always greatest through the path of least opposition. As an example, suppose your parallel circuit consists of two resistors, R_1 and R_2, where R_1 equals 20 ohms and R_2 equals 40 ohms. Through this circuit the total current - regardless of its value - will divide, with twice as much current flowing through R_1 as flows through R_2.

Current Flow in Parallel Circuits

Resistances connected side by side—parallel connection—provide alternate paths for current flow between the terminals of the voltage source. The total circuit current divides, with part of the total current flowing through each possible path. Each resistance is rated to pass a certain maximum current, but the total circuit current can be greater than this individual rated value, if the current divides and flows through more than one path.

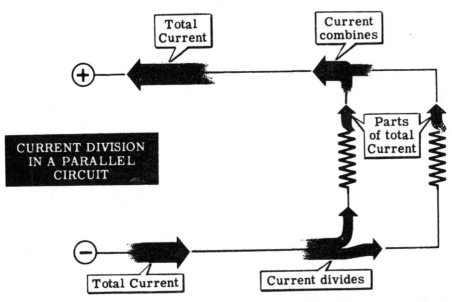

For parallel circuits consisting of equal resistances in parallel the currents through each resistor will be equal, since each path offers an equal amount of opposition to current flow. In such a circuit the current through each resistance is equal to the total current divided by the number of resistances connected in parallel.

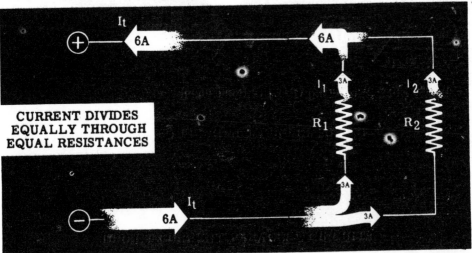

Resistances in Parallel

Resistances in parallel are like water pipes in parallel. In each case, the total cross-section is increased and the opposition to current flow—resistance—is decreased. Two water pipes of the same size placed side by side carry twice as much water as a single pipe; and equal resistances connected side by side—parallel connection—pass twice as much current as a single resistance. This greater current flow indicates that the total resistance of the parallel-connected resistances is less than that of a single resistance.

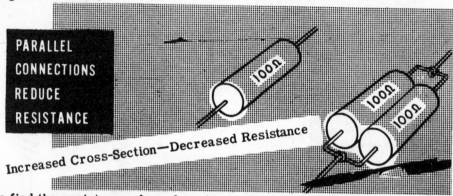

PARALLEL CONNECTIONS REDUCE RESISTANCE

Increased Cross-Section—Decreased Resistance

To find the resistance of <u>equal</u> resistances connected in parallel, you need only to divide the value of one resistance by the number of resistances. Suppose that your circuit consists of four 200-ohm resistances in parallel. The total resistance of the parallel connection is one-fourth that of a single 200-ohm resistance or equal to 50 ohms. This parallel connection will act in the circuit as though it were a single 50-ohm resistance.

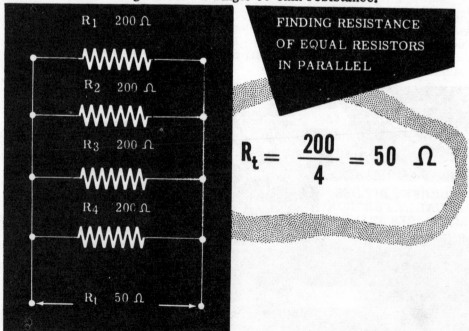

R_1 200 Ω

R_2 200 Ω

R_3 200 Ω

R_4 200 Ω

R_t 50 Ω

FINDING RESISTANCE OF EQUAL RESISTORS IN PARALLEL

$$R_t = \frac{200}{4} = 50 \ \Omega$$

Resistances in Parallel (continued)

If the circuit you are working with consists of unequal resistances in parallel, you cannot find the total resistance quite as easily as if they were of equal value. Two water pipes—one large and one small—will carry more water than either pipe alone, and two resistors of unequal value will pass more current than either resistor alone. Although the total opposition to current flow offered by the parallel resistances is less than that of either resistance alone, it cannot be found by dividing either of the known values by two.

For a parallel circuit consisting of two resistors, R_1 and R_2, where R_1 equals 60 ohms and R_2 equals 40 ohms, the total resistance is less than 40 ohms but does not equal 20 ohms. You could find the total resistance by using an ohmmeter and would find that the measured total resistance is 24 ohms. However, it may not always be possible to use an ohmmeter, and instead you will need to use another method to find the total resistance.

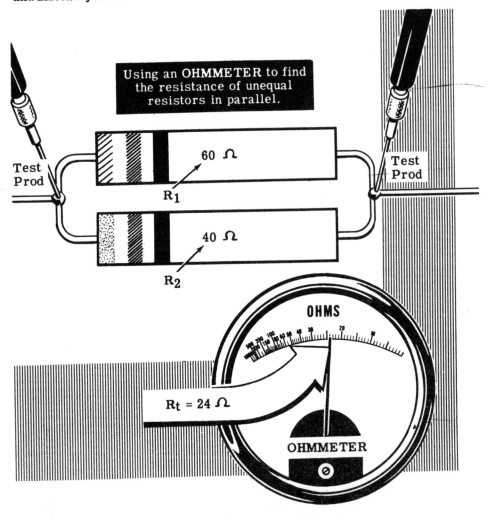

Using an **OHMMETER** to find the resistance of unequal resistors in parallel.

Test Prod

60 Ω

R_1

Test Prod

40 Ω

R_2

OHMS

$R_t = 24\ \Omega$

OHMMETER

Resistances in Parallel—Two Unequal Resistors

When resistors are connected in parallel, the effect on the circuit is the same as having one resistor with a resistance value that is less than that of the smaller of the two parallel components. You may refer to this "one" resistor as a single or equivalent resistor. You will now see what happens to the total resistance of two resistors of unequal value, when the components are connected in parallel.

On the previous sheet you were told that it is often impossible to use an ohmmeter for measuring values of resistance. In such cases another tool must be used to ascertain total resistance. The tool referred to is derived from the very familiar Ohm's Law. You have already learned that in parallel circuits

$$E_t = E_1 = E_2$$

and that

$$I_t = I_1 + I_2$$

The resistance is found by first substituting the Ohm's Law formula for current in each part of the I_t equation, above. As you know

and since

❶ $I_t = \dfrac{E}{R_t}$

then (by substitution)

❷ $I_t = I_1 + I_2$

❸ $\dfrac{E}{R_t} = \dfrac{E}{R_1} + \dfrac{E}{R_2}$

Now, recall that the voltage is the same in each part of the circuit, as illustrated in formula number three. By dividing both sides of equation number three by the voltage "E," we find that

$$\frac{1}{R_t} = \frac{1}{R_1} + \frac{1}{R_2}$$

and in simplifying find the following:

$$\frac{1}{R_T} = \frac{R_2 + R_1}{R_1 R_2}$$

$$R_1 R_2 = R_T (R_2 + R_1)$$

$$R_T = \frac{R_1 R_2}{R_1 + R_2}$$

The formula states, in effect, that total resistance in a parallel circuit composed of two resistors of unequal value, is found by multiplying the value of one resistor by the value of the second, adding the value of one resistor to the value of the second, and then dividing the first figure by the second figure.

Resistances in Parallel (continued)

If the values of two resistances connected in parallel are known, you can find the total resistance of the parallel combination by using a formula and solving for the total resistance. The solution involves three steps— multiplication, addition and division. For example, to find the total resistance of the 60-ohm and 40-ohm resistors in parallel, you use the following steps.

1. Multiply the two resistance values.
   60 x 40 = 2400

2. Add the two resistance values.
   60 + 40 = 100

3. Divide the product by the sum.
   2400 ÷ 100 = 24

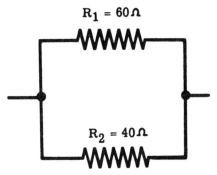

$R_1 = 60\,\Omega$

$R_2 = 40\,\Omega$

The total resistance of the parallel combination of the 60-ohm and 40-ohm resistor then is 24 ohms, and the combination will act as though it were a single resistance of that value.

This formula is expressed as follows:

$$R_t = \frac{R_1 \times R_2}{R_1 + R_2}$$

The formula shows that R_t equals the product of R_1 and R_2 divided by their sum. To find R_t the numerical values of R_1 and R_2 are used and the three steps to the solution are performed.

$$R_t = \frac{60 \times 40}{60 + 40}$$

1. Multiply — $R_t = \dfrac{60 \times 40}{60 + 40} = \dfrac{2400}{60 + 40}$

2. Add — $R_t = \dfrac{2400}{60 + 40} = \dfrac{2400}{100}$

3. Divide — $R_t = \dfrac{2400}{100} = 24$ ohms

$R_1 = 60\,\Omega$

$R_t = 24\,\Omega$

$R_2 = 40\,\Omega$

Resistances in Parallel—Three or More Unequal Resistors

Combinations of three or more unequal resistances in parallel are sometimes used. To find the resistance of such combinations, you first find the
total resistance of any two of the resistances. Combine this total in the
same way with another of the resistance values and you have the total for
three resistances. Continue to combine the total with additional resistances until all of the resistances have been combined to give the total resistance of all the parallel resistances.

For example, if three resistors—R_1, R_2 and R_3—are connected in parallel,
you would first find the total resistance of R_1 and R_2 in parallel. Next you
combine this value with R_3 and obtain the total resistance of R_1, R_2 and
R_3. This total is the total resistance of the three resistors in parallel.

If R_1 equals 300 ohms, R_2 equals 200 ohms and R_3 equals 60 ohms, the
total resistance is found by combining 300 ohms and 200 ohms and then
combining this result with 60 ohms.

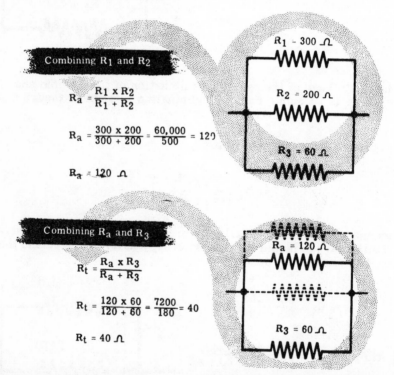

Combining R_1 and R_2

$$R_a = \frac{R_1 \times R_2}{R_1 + R_2}$$

$$R_a = \frac{300 \times 200}{300 + 200} = \frac{60,000}{500} = 120$$

$$R_a = 120 \ \Omega$$

$R_1 = 300 \ \Omega$

$R_2 = 200 \ \Omega$

$R_3 = 60 \ \Omega$

Combining R_a and R_3

$$R_t = \frac{R_a \times R_3}{R_a + R_3}$$

$$R_t = \frac{120 \times 60}{120 + 60} = \frac{7200}{180} = 40$$

$$R_t = 40 \ \Omega$$

$R_a = 120 \ \Omega$

$R_3 = 60 \ \Omega$

The total resistance of the three resistors connected in parallel is 40 ohms,
and the combination will act as a single 40-ohm resistor in the circuit.
You can easily see that this method for finding total resistance becomes
very cumbersome as the number of resistors in parallel increases. On the
next sheet you will use another, fairly simple method for finding the total
resistance of three resistors in parallel. This new method, however, may
be applied to finding the total resistance of any number of resistors in
parallel, with comparative ease.

DIRECT CURRENT PARALLEL CIRCUITS

Resistance in Parallel—Three or More Unequal Resistors (continued)

Finding the total resistance in parallel circuits which are composed of three or more resistors may be accomplished by using the "reciprocal" method. Refer to the development of the formula for finding total resistance of two resistors in parallel.

You already know that in parallel circuits

$$E_t = E_1 = E_2 = E_3 = \text{etc.}$$

and that

$$I_t = I_1 + I_2 + I_3 + \text{etc.}$$

The resistance of the parallel circuit is found by first substituting the Ohm's Law formula for current in each part of the equation for I_t, above. As you know

❶ $I_t = \dfrac{E}{R_t}$

and since

❷ $I_t = I_1 + I_2 + I_3 + \text{etc.}$

you find (by substitution) that

❸ $\dfrac{E}{R_t} = \dfrac{E}{R_1} + \dfrac{E}{R_2} + \dfrac{E}{R_3} + \text{etc.}$

Now, recall that the voltage is the same across each parallel component. By dividing both sides of equation number three by the voltage "E," you find that the reciprocal equation is

$$\frac{1}{R_t} = \frac{1}{R_1} + \frac{1}{R_2} + \frac{1}{R_3} + \text{etc.}$$

Consider the parallel circuit on the previous sheet. This time you will find the total resistance by using the reciprocal formula just derived. Note that $R_1 = 300$ ohms, $R_2 = 200$ ohms, and $R_3 = 60$ ohms.

By substituting these resistance values in the reciprocal equation you find that

$$\frac{1}{R_t} = \frac{1}{60} + \frac{1}{200} + \frac{1}{300}$$

In order to add these resistances you must find the least common denominator; in this case 600. Then

$$\frac{1}{R_t} = \frac{10}{600} + \frac{3}{600} + \frac{2}{600}$$

Resistance in Parallel—Three or More Unequal Resistors (continued)

$$\frac{1}{R_t} = \frac{15}{600} = .025$$

$$\frac{1}{R_t} = \frac{.025}{1}$$

$$R_t = \frac{1}{.025} = 40 \text{ ohms}$$

You can see that if the parallel circuit under analysis is composed of six or eight resistors of unequal value, it will be a simple matter to find the total resistance by using the reciprocal formula. However, suppose the resistance values are such that no suitable least common denominator can be found. How would you solve the problem then?

The answer is simple. Recall the equation, above,

$$\frac{1}{R_t} = \frac{1}{60} + \frac{1}{200} + \frac{1}{300}$$

and take the reciprocal of both sides. You then have

$$R_t = \frac{1}{\dfrac{1}{60} + \dfrac{1}{200} + \dfrac{1}{300}}$$

In simplifying, you see that

$$R_t = \frac{1}{.0167 + .005 + .0033} = \frac{1}{.0250}$$

$$R_t = 40 \text{ ohms}$$

If the parallel circuit is composed of a number of resistors (2, 3, 4, 5, etc.) of equal value the total current flowing in the circuit will divide equally for all of the parallel branches. The combined resistance of all the branches is considered to be equal to the value of a single resistor divided by the number of resistors in the circuit. For example, if six resistors of 36 ohms resistance each are connected in parallel, the combined resistance of the circuit is 36 divided by 6, or 6 ohms, since six paths are being presented to the flow of current instead of just one.

Demonstration—Parallel Circuit Voltages

1. While the current through the various branches of a parallel circuit is not always the same, the voltage across each branch resistance is equal to that across the others. The instructor connects three lamp sockets in parallel and inserts 250-ma. lamps in each of the three parallel-connected sockets. You see that each lamp lights with the same brilliance as when only a single lamp is used, and that for three lamps the circuit current is 750 ma. Also you can see that the voltmeter reading across the battery terminals is the same whether one, two or three lamps are used.

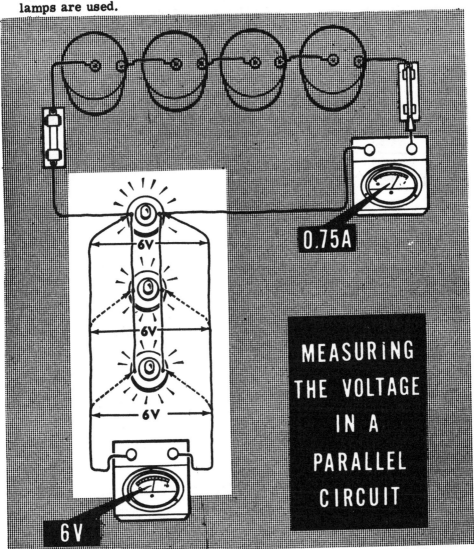

Removing the voltmeter leads from the battery terminals, the instructor connects the voltmeter across the terminals of each lamp socket in turn. You see that the voltage is the same across each of the lamps and is equal to that of the voltage source—the battery.

Demonstration—Parallel Circuit Current

2. To demonstrate the division of current the instructor places a 250-ma. lamp with a 150-ma. lamp as shown. The ammeter now shows that the total circuit current is 400 ma. The instructor connects the ammeter first in series with one lamp, then in series with the other and you see that the 400-ma. total current divides, with 250 ma. flowing through one lamp and 150 ma. through the other. The ammeter is then connected to read the total circuit current at that end of the parallel combination opposite the end at which it was originally connected. You can see that the total circuit current is the same at each end of the parallel circuit, the current dividing to flow through the parallel branches of the circuit and combining again after passing through these branches.

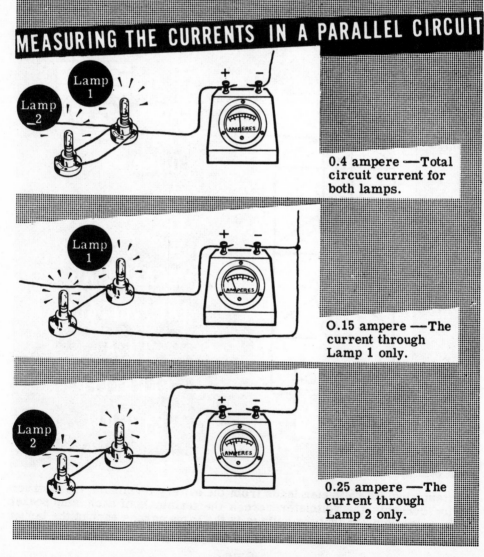

MEASURING THE CURRENTS IN A PARALLEL CIRCUIT

0.4 ampere —Total circuit current for both lamps.

0.15 ampere —The current through Lamp 1 only.

0.25 ampere —The current through Lamp 2 only.

Demonstration—Parallel Circuit Resistance

3. When the total current flow in a circuit increases with no change in the voltage, a decrease in total resistance is indicated. To show this effect, the instructor connects two lamp sockets in parallel. This parallel combination is connected across the terminals of a 6-volt battery of dry cells with an ammeter inserted in one battery lead to measure the total circuit current. As a voltmeter is connected across the battery terminals you see that the voltage is 6 volts. When only one lamp is inserted, the ammeter indicates a current flow of approximately 250 ma. and the voltmeter reads 6 volts. With both lamps inserted, the current reading increases but the voltage remains at 6 volts—indicating that the parallel circuit offers less resistance than a single lamp.

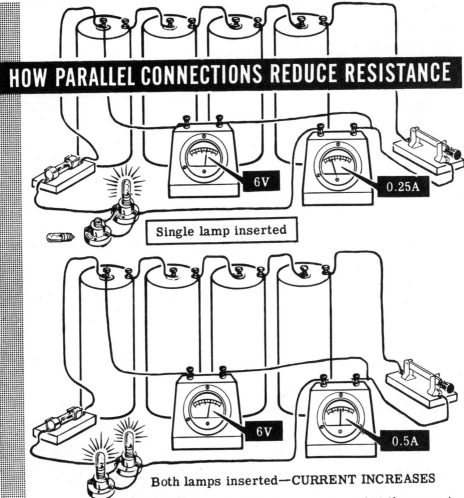

HOW PARALLEL CONNECTIONS REDUCE RESISTANCE

6V

0.25A

Single lamp inserted

6V

0.5A

Both lamps inserted—CURRENT INCREASES

4. As each of the lamps is inserted in turn, you see that the ammeter reading for each lamp alone is 250 ma., but with both lamps inserted the total current indicated is 500 ma. This shows that the circuit current of 500 ma. divides into two 250-ma. currents, with each flowing through a separate lamp.

Demonstration—Parallel Resistances

To show how parallel connection of resistances decreases the total resistance, the instructor measures the resistance of three 300-ohm resistors individually with the ohmmeter. When two of the 300-ohm resistors are paralleled, the total resistance should be 150 ohms; this is shown by so connecting them and measuring the parallel resistance with the ohmmeter. As another 300-ohm resistor is connected in parallel, you see that the resistance is lowered to a value of 100 ohms. This shows that connecting <u>equal</u> resistances in parallel not only reduces the total resistance, but also shows that the total resistance can be found by dividing the value of a single resistance by the number of resistances used.

Measuring the resistance
of parallel-connected resistors of equal resistance

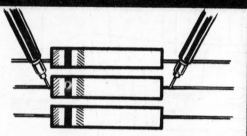

Resistance of individual resistors

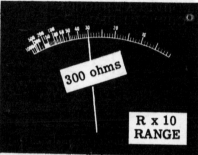

300 ohms

R x 10 RANGE

Resistance of two 300-ohm resistors in parallel

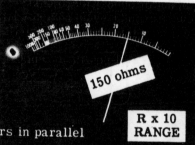

150 ohms

R x 10 RANGE

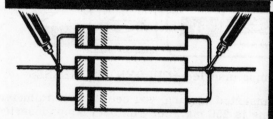

Resistance of three 300-ohm resistors in parallel

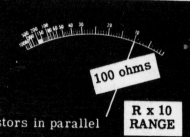

100 ohms

R x 10 RANGE

Demonstration—Parallel Resistances (continued)

Next, a 200-ohm resistor is connected in parallel with a 300-ohm resistor. Solving the formula for parallel resistance shows that the total resistance should be 120 ohms. An ohmmeter reading shows that this value is correct.

Measuring the resistance of parallel-connected resistors

# of unequal resistance

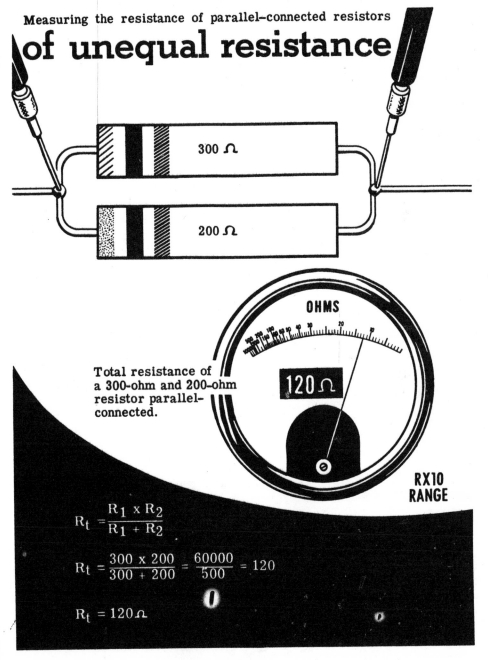

300 Ω

200 Ω

OHMS

120 Ω

Total resistance of a 300-ohm and 200-ohm resistor parallel-connected.

RX10 RANGE

$$R_t = \frac{R_1 \times R_2}{R_1 + R_2}$$

$$R_t = \frac{300 \times 200}{300 + 200} = \frac{60000}{500} = 120$$

$$R_t = 120\,\Omega$$

Review of Parallel Circuits

Now review what you have found out and seen concerning parallel circuits and their effect on resistance, voltage and current, before you work with these circuits yourself. Observe that parallel circuits are the opposite of series circuits—with voltages being equal and currents dividing in parallel circuits, while currents are equal and voltage divides for a series circuit.

<u>PARALLEL CIRCUIT</u> — Resistances connected side by side across a voltage source.

<u>PARALLEL CIRCUIT RESISTANCE</u> — The total resistance is less than that of the smallest individual resistance.

<u>PARALLEL CIRCUIT CURRENT</u> — The current divides to flow through the parallel branches of the circuit.

<u>PARALLEL CIRCUIT VOLTAGE</u> — The voltage across each resistance is the same and equals that of the voltage source.

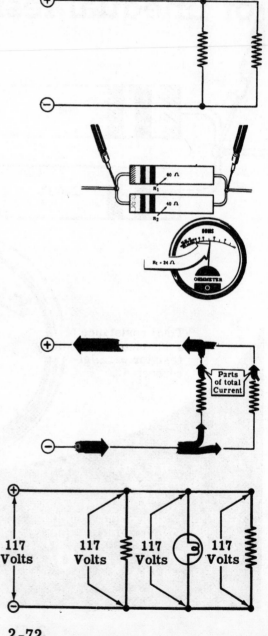

Applying Ohm's Law to Parallel Circuits

Unknown quantities of resistance, current and voltage in parallel circuits may be found by using Ohm's law. Suppose you want to use an ohmmeter to measure the resistance of a resistor connected in parallel with one or more other resistances. You must disconnect the resistor to be measured from the circuit; otherwise the ohmmeter will read the total resistance of the parallel combination of resistors. In such cases, you will find that it is usually easier to use Ohm's law than the ohmmeter.

To measure the current flow through one particular resistance of a combination of parallel resistances, you will have to disconnect the circuit and insert an ammeter to read only the current flow through that particular resistance. Again you will save time and effort by using Ohm's law.

Without disconnecting the circuit you can read the voltage across each resistance of a parallel circuit by connecting a voltmeter across the entire circuit, since the voltage across each resistance equals that across the parallel combination. The voltage across a resistor can be divided by the resistance to obtain the current. If you have no voltmeter, but can obtain the circuit current and resistance, you can use Ohm's law to find the voltage.

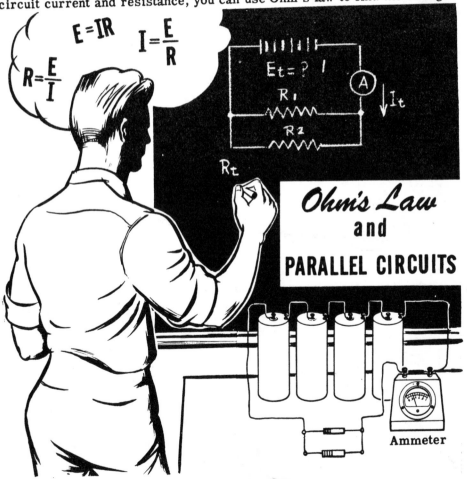

Finding Resistances in Parallel Circuits

This is how you use Ohm's law to find resistances in parallel circuits —

Suppose a parallel circuit consists of three resistors — R_1, R_2 and R_3 — of unknown values connected across 45 volts. The total circuit current is 6 amperes and the current flowing through R_1 is 1.5 amperes; the current flowing through R_2 is 3 amperes, and the current flowing through R_3 is unknown.

To find the unknown resistance values, first sketch the circuit and fill in all of the known values of resistance, voltage and current; then make up a table of these values and the unknown values for each resistance. For those circuit branches where any two quantities are known you solve for the unknown quantity, using either Ohm's law or the rules regarding total resistance, current and voltage in a parallel circuit.

1. Sketch the circuit and the known values.

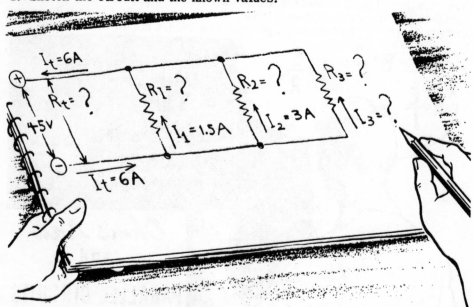

2. Tabulate all the known quantities.

	R_1	R_2	R_3	R_t
Resistance				
Current	1.5	3		6
Voltage	45	45	45	45

Finding Resistances in Parallel Circuits (continued)

Since both the current and voltage are known for R_1 and R_2, you can find their resistance values.

3. Find R_1 and R_2, using Ohm's law.

$$R_1 = \frac{45}{1.5} = 30 \text{ ohms} \qquad\qquad R_2 = \frac{45}{3} = 15 \text{ ohms}$$

To find the value of R_3, you must first determine the current through it. The total circuit current is 6 amperes and equals the sum of the three branch currents. The sum of the currents through R_1 and R_2 is 4.5 amperes, with the remainder of the total circuit current flowing through R_3.

4. Find the current through R_3 by subtraction.

$$I_3 = 6 - 4.5 = 1.5 \text{ amperes}$$

With the voltage and current for R_3 both known, its resistance value may be obtained.

5. Find R_3, using Ohm's law.

$$R_3 = \frac{45}{1.5} = 30 \text{ ohms}$$

	R_1	R_2	R_3	R_t
Resistance	30	15	30	
Current	1.5	3	1.5	6
Voltage	45	45	45	45

Finding Resistances in Parallel Circuits (continued)

The total circuit resistance (R_t) can be obtained either by using the formula for the total resistance of parallel resistances or applying Ohm's law to the total circuit current and voltage.

6. Find R_t, using Ohm's law: $R_t = \dfrac{45}{6} = 7.5$ ohms

7. Find R_t, using the formula for parallel resistances.

$$R_a = \frac{R_1 \times R_2}{R_1 + R_2} = \frac{30 \times 15}{30 + 15} = \frac{450}{45} = 10 \text{ ohms}$$

$$R_t = \frac{R_a \times R_3}{R_a + R_3} = \frac{10 \times 30}{10 + 30} = \frac{300}{40} = 7.5 \text{ ohms}$$

The two results obtained are equal and are used as a check on the accuracy of the solution.

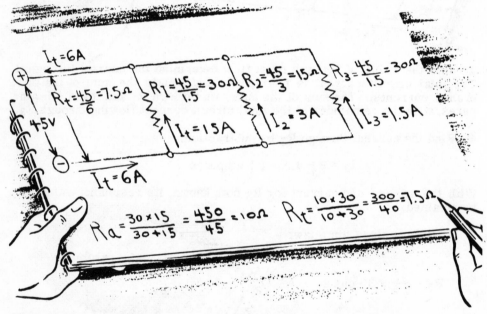

Your table is now complete with all circuit values known—

	R_1	R_2	R_3	R_t
Resistance	30	15	30	7.5
Current	1.5	3	1.5	6
Voltage	45	45	45	45

Finding Currents in Parallel Circuits

This is how you use Ohm's law to find currents in parallel circuits—

To solve for currents in parallel circuits you use the same procedure as that used in solving for resistances, except that the unknown quantities are currents. For example, a parallel circuit consists of four resistors—R_1, R_2, R_3 and R_4—connected across 120 volts. If the resistance of R_1 is 80 ohms, R_2 is 48 ohms, R_3 is 30 ohms, and R_4 is 60 ohms, the individual resistor currents can be obtained by applying Ohm's law; and the total circuit current will equal the sum of these currents. Knowing the circuit voltage and total current, you can find the total circuit resistance.

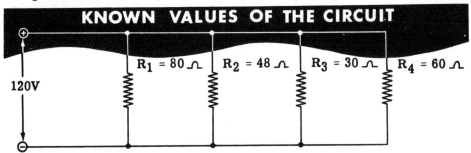

KNOWN VALUES OF THE CIRCUIT

$R_1 = 80\,\Omega$ | $R_2 = 48\,\Omega$ | $R_3 = 30\,\Omega$ | $R_4 = 60\,\Omega$

120V

TABLE OF KNOWN VALUES

	R_1	R_2	R_3	R_4	R_t
Resistance	80	48	30	60	-
Current	-	-	-	-	-
Voltage	120	120	120	120	120

1. Find the resistor currents, using Ohm's law.

$$I_1 = \frac{120}{80} = 1.5 \text{ amperes} \qquad I_3 = \frac{120}{30} = 4 \text{ amperes}$$

$$I_2 = \frac{120}{48} = 2.5 \text{ amperes} \qquad I_4 = \frac{120}{60} = 2 \text{ amperes}$$

OHM'S LAW VALUES OF CURRENT

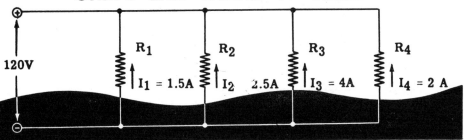

120V

R_1 R_2 R_3 R_4

$I_1 = 1.5A$ I_2 2.5A $I_3 = 4A$ $I_4 = 2\,A$

2. The total circuit current equals the sum of the branch currents.

$$I_t = I_1 + I_2 + I_3 + I_4 = 1.5 + 2.5 + 4 + 2 = 10 \text{ amperes}$$

Finding Currents in Parallel Circuits (continued)

3. Find the total resistance, using Ohm's law: $R_t = \frac{E_t}{I_t} = \frac{120}{10} = 12$ ohms

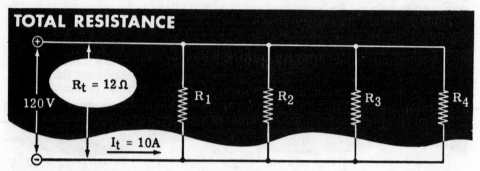

4. Check the total resistance, using the parallel resistance formula.

1 $R_a = \frac{R_1 \times R_2}{R_1 + R_2} = \frac{80 \times 48}{80 + 48} = \frac{3840}{128} = 30$ ohms

2 $R_b = \frac{R_a \times R_3}{R_a + R_3} = \frac{30 \times 30}{30 + 30} = \frac{900}{60} = 15$ ohms

3 $R_t = \frac{R_b \times R_4}{R_b + R_4} = \frac{15 \times 60}{15 + 60} = \frac{900}{75} = 12$ ohms

CHECKING TOTAL RESISTANCE

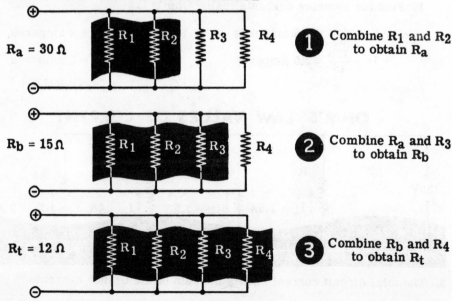

Finding Currents in Parallel Circuits (continued)

5. With all of the voltage, current and resistance values known, your table of values can be completed.

COMPLETE TABLE OF VALUES

	R_1	R_2	R_3	R_4	R_t
Resistance	80	48	30	60	12
Current	1.5	2.5	4	2	10
Voltage	120	120	120	120	120

Parallel circuit voltage may also be found by using Ohm's law. Since the voltage across each resistor is equal in a parallel circuit, the circuit voltage can be found if the values of resistance and current are both known for any of the circuit resistors. For example, from the above table of values, if the voltages are assumed to be unknown, the circuit voltage can be obtained by multiplying together the known resistance and current values for any of the circuit resistances. Using the values for each resistor in turn, you find that the circuit voltage is 120 volts in each case.

$$E_1 = I_1R_1 = 1.5 \times 80 = 120 \text{ volts}$$

$$E_2 = I_2R_2 = 2.5 \times 48 = 120 \text{ volts}$$

$$E_3 = I_3R_3 = 4 \times 30 = 120 \text{ volts}$$

$$E_4 = I_4R_4 = 2 \times 60 = 120 \text{ volts}$$

$$E_t = I_tR_t = 12 \times 10 = 120 \text{ volts}$$

CHECKING PARALLEL CIRCUIT VOLTAGES

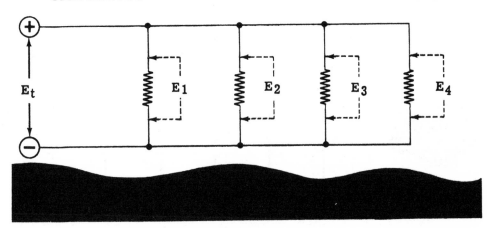

Power in Parallel Circuits

You have seen that the power used by a resistor is equal to the current through the resistor multiplied by the voltage across the resistor (P = EI), and you have also seen how the total power in a series circuit is equal to the sum of the powers used by each resistance in the circuit. This is also true in parallel circuits; that is, the total power used by a parallel circuit is equal to the sum of the power used by all resistances in the circuit, and can be found by multiplying the total voltage across the circuit by the total circuit current.

TOTAL POWER IN A PARALLEL CIRCUIT . . .

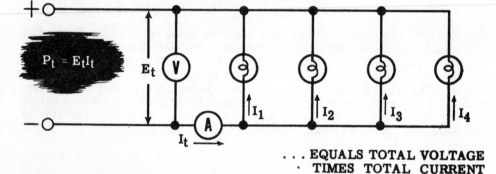

. . . EQUALS TOTAL VOLTAGE
· TIMES TOTAL CURRENT

The circuit power can also be found by using the rules for parallel circuits to find the total resistance of the circuit if the resistance of all the parts is known. Then total power can be determined by measuring either circuit current or voltage and using the alternate power formulas.

FINDING TOTAL POWER USING . . .

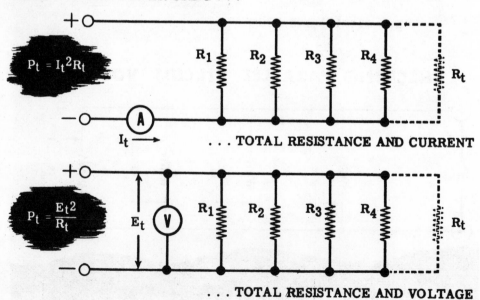

. . . TOTAL RESISTANCE AND CURRENT

. . . TOTAL RESISTANCE AND VOLTAGE

Demonstration—Ohm's Law and Parallel Resistances

To .show how an ammeter and voltmeter may be used as a substitute for an ohmmeter to find the values of the individual and total resistances in a parallel combination, the instructor connects four dry cells in series, to be used as a voltage source. He connects the voltmeter across the dry cell battery to make certain the voltage remains constant at 6 volts. Then the ammeter is connected in series with the (-) terminal of the battery to read the current. He then connects a fuse, a resistor and a switch in series between the (+) terminals of the ammeter and battery. You see that the voltage remains at 6 volts and the current indicated is 0.2 amperes. From Ohm's law the resistance value then is 30 ohms; a check of the color code shows that this is the correct value.

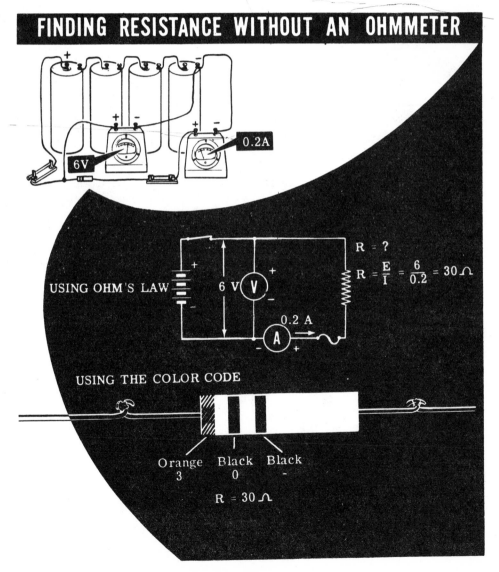

FINDING RESISTANCE WITHOUT AN OHMMETER

6V 0.2A

USING OHM'S LAW

6 V

0.2 A

$R = ?$

$R = \dfrac{E}{I} = \dfrac{6}{0.2} = 30\,\Omega$

USING THE COLOR CODE

Orange   Black   Black
3   0   -

$R = 30\,\Omega$

Demonstration—Ohm's Law and Parallel Resistances (continued)

As another resistor is added in parallel, you see that the current reading
is 0.6 ampere with no change in voltage. Since the first resistor passes
0.2 ampere, the current through the second resistor is 0.4 ampere. The
Ohm's law value of the second resistor then is 6 volts divided by 0.4 ampere or 15 ohms. The total resistance of the parallel combination is equal
to 6 volts divided by the total current, 0.6 ampere or 10 ohms.

ADDING A RESISTOR IN PARALLEL REDUCES THE TOTAL RESISTANCE

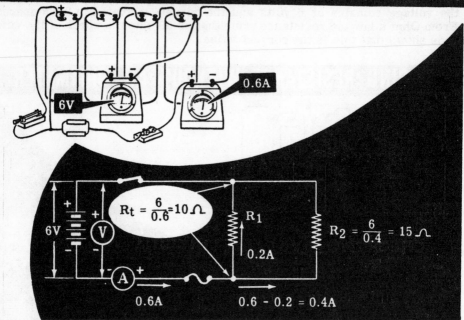

With another resistor added in parallel, you see a further increase in current of 0.2 ampere—showing that the Ohm's law value of the added resistor is 30 ohms. The total current is now 0.8 ampere, resulting in a
total resistance value of 7.5 ohms for the parallel combination.

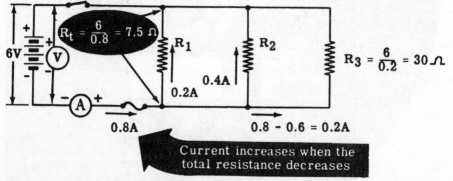

When the instructor disconnects the battery and the various resistors, he
checks the total and individual resistances and you see that the Ohm's law
and color code values are correct.

Demonstration—Ohm's Law and Parallel Circuit Current

Using only three series-connected cells as a voltage source, the instructor connects the voltmeter across the battery. He then connects four resistors—two 15-ohm and two 30-ohm resistors—across the battery. From Ohm's law the current through the 15-ohm resistors will be 0.3 ampere each and through each 30-ohm resistor 0.15 ampere. The total current will be the sum of the currents through the individual resistances or 0.9 ampere.

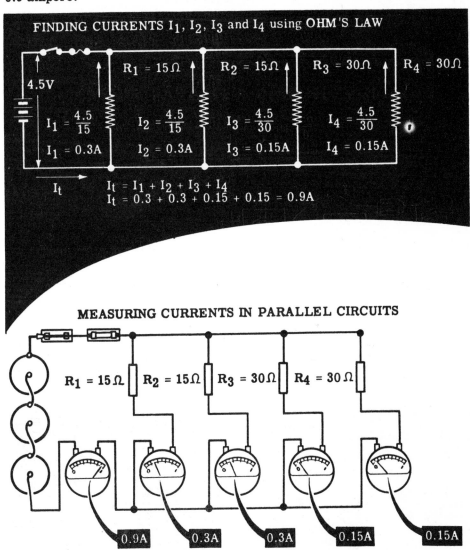

FINDING CURRENTS I_1, I_2, I_3 and I_4 using OHM'S LAW

$R_1 = 15\,\Omega$ $R_2 = 15\,\Omega$ $R_3 = 30\,\Omega$ $R_4 = 30\,\Omega$

4.5V

$I_1 = \dfrac{4.5}{15}$ $I_2 = \dfrac{4.5}{15}$ $I_3 = \dfrac{4.5}{30}$ $I_4 = \dfrac{4.5}{30}$

$I_1 = 0.3A$ $I_2 = 0.3A$ $I_3 = 0.15A$ $I_4 = 0.15A$

I_t

$I_t = I_1 + I_2 + I_3 + I_4$
$I_t = 0.3 + 0.3 + 0.15 + 0.15 = 0.9A$

MEASURING CURRENTS IN PARALLEL CIRCUITS

$R_1 = 15\,\Omega$ $R_2 = 15\,\Omega$ $R_3 = 30\,\Omega$ $R_4 = 30\,\Omega$

0.9A 0.3A 0.3A 0.15A 0.15A

As the instructor inserts an ammeter in the circuit—first to read the total circuit current, then that of the individual resistances—you see that the actual currents are the same as those found by applying Ohm's law.

Demonstration—Power in Parallel Circuits

To demonstrate that the power used by a parallel circuit is equal to the power used by all of the parts of the circuit, the instructor connects three lamp sockets in parallel across a six-volt battery, with a 0-1 amp range ammeter in series with the battery lead, and a 0-10 volt voltmeter across the battery terminals. He then inserts 6-volt, 250-ma. lamps in the lamp sockets, but does not tighten them. When he closes the switch you see that the voltmeter indicates battery voltage, but the ammeter shows no current flow, so that no power is being used by the circuit.

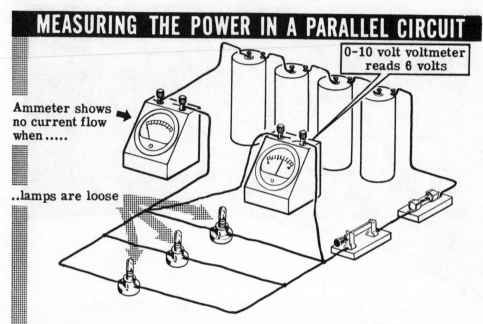

MEASURING THE POWER IN A PARALLEL CIRCUIT

0-10 volt voltmeter reads 6 volts

Ammeter shows no current flow when .....

..lamps are loose

As the instructor tightens one of the lamps, you see that it lights and the ammeter shows a current flow of about 0.25 amp. The power used by this one lamp, then, is about 6 volts x 0.25 amp., or 1.5 watts.

POWER USED BY ONE LAMP IN A PARALLEL CIRCUIT

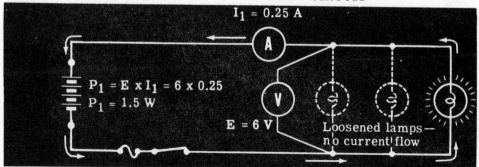

$I_1 = 0.25$ A

$P_1 = E \times I_1 = 6 \times 0.25$
$P_1 = 1.5$ W

$E = 6$ V

Loosened lamps— no current flow

You already know that the voltage across any part of a parallel circuit is equal to the source voltage, so that the voltage across the lamp is equal to the battery voltage.

Demonstration—Power in Parallel Circuits (continued)

As the instructor loosens the first lamp and tightens each of the other lamps in turn, you see that the current—and hence the power used by each lamp—is about the same. The current measured each time is the current through the one tightened lamp only.

MEASURING POWER IN INDIVIDUAL LAMPS

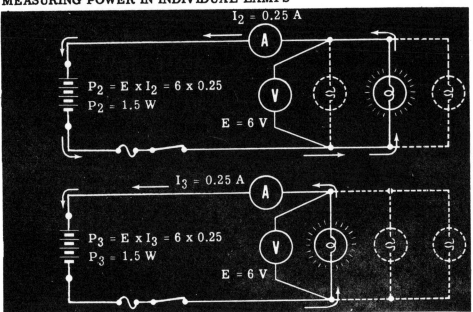

Next the instructor tightens all three lamps in their sockets. You see that they all light and that the ammeter shows the circuit current to be about 0.75 amp. The voltage is still about 6 volts, so that the circuit power (P_t) equals 0.75 x 6, or about 4.5 watts.

MEASURING TOTAL CIRCUIT POWER

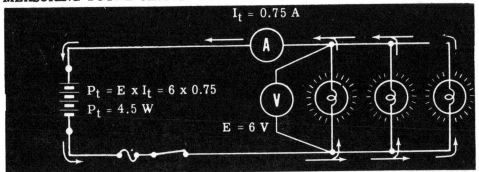

The total circuit power is found to be about 4.5 watts. If you add the power used individually by each of the lamps, the sum is equal to 4.5 watts (1.5 + 1.5 + 1.5 = 4.5). Therefore, you see that the total power used by a parallel circuit is equal to the sum of the power used by each part of the circuit.

Demonstration—Power in Parallel Circuits (continued)

The instructor now replaces the three lamp sockets with 30-ohm resistors. He then removes the voltmeter leads from the battery and closes the switch, and you notice that the ammeter shows a current flow of about 0.6 amp.

The total resistance found by applying the rules for parallel circuits is 10 ohms, so that the circuit power is equal to $(0.6)^2 \times 10 = 3.6$ watts $(P = I^2 R)$.

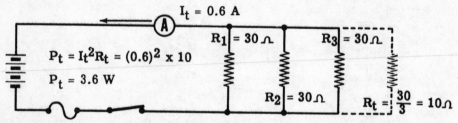

USING TOTAL CURRENT AND RESISTANCE TO MEASURE CIRCUIT POWER

The instructor then removes the ammeter and connects the voltmeter to the battery leads. When the switch is closed the voltage is seen to be about 6 volts, so that the circuit power is equal to $\frac{(6)^2}{10} = 3.6$ watts $(P = \frac{E^2}{R})$.

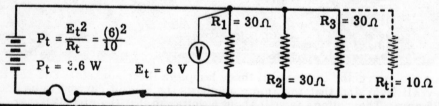

USING TOTAL VOLTAGE AND RESISTANCE TO MEASURE CIRCUIT POWER

Finally the instructor replaces the ammeter in the circuit and, when power is applied, you see that the current is about 0.6 amp and the voltage is about 6 volts, so that the total circuit power is equal to $6 \times 0.6 = 3.6$ watts $(P = EI)$.

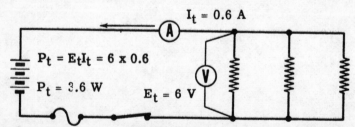

USING TOTAL VOLTAGE AND CURRENT TO MEASURE CIRCUIT POWER

Thus you see that the total power in a parallel circuit may be determined, as in a series circuit, whenever any <u>two</u> of the factors—current, voltage and resistance—are known.

OHM'S LAW IN PARALLEL CIRCUITS

Extending the Range of Ammeters

Here is a practical application of Ohm's Law in parallel circuits. You will now learn how the value, or the amount of resistance in a shunt is calculated.

In an earlier topic you learned that the Weston movement for meters, with the 0-1 milliampere range, is practically a basic type and is one with which you will become most familiar. This movement burns out very quickly if more than one milliampere of current is allowed to pass through it. You also learned, however, that this movement can be used without damaging effects, in circuits carrying comparatively high currents, if a shunt resistor of proper value is placed in parallel with the movement. The purpose of the shunt is to bypass a sufficient amount of current around the meter, leaving only enough in the one milliampere movement to give an accurate indication without overheating. Readings are then taken from the appropriate scale on the meter face, or, if the meter scales are not provided, a multiplication factor is applied to the meter reading to determine the exact value.

The resistance value for shunt resistors can be found by using Ohm's Law. In this example, the meter should be deflected full scale by two milliamps. Assume that the resistance of the meter movement is 50 ohms. (Your instructor will provide you with the resistance value of the meter movement with which you are working.) Assume also, that one milliampere of current through the meter causes full-scale deflection. See the diagram below. Using Ohm's Law you find that the voltage drop across the movement is

$$E_m = I_m R_m$$
$$E_m = .001 \times 50$$
$$E_m = .05 \text{ volts}$$

Since the meter movement parallels the shunt resistor R_s, the voltage across the meter and the shunt is the same. The resistance R_s may now be found by using Ohm's Law, because the voltage across the shunt E_s is equal to E_m, and the current through the shunt I_s must be one milliampere since one milliamp is causing full-scale meter deflection.

$$R_s = \frac{E_s}{I_s} = \frac{.05}{.001} = 50 \text{ ohms}$$

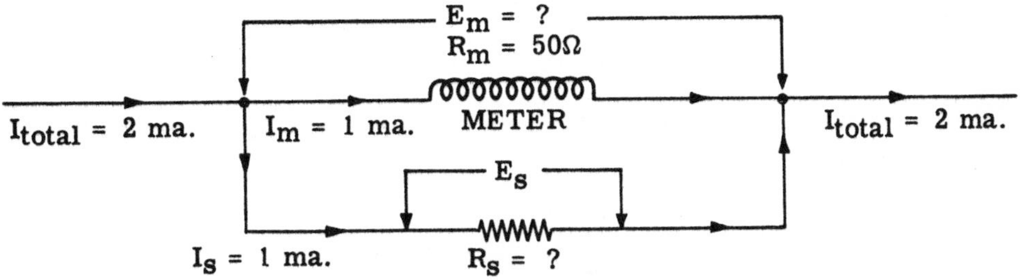

$$E_m = ?$$
$$R_m = 50\Omega$$

$I_{total} = 2$ ma. $I_m = 1$ ma.   METER $I_{total} = 2$ ma.

$$E_s$$

$I_s = 1$ ma. $R_s = ?$

Extending the Range of Ammeters (continued)

You have learned how to calculate the resistance value of a milliammeter shunt. The value of practically every shunt you will use may be found in the same way. Now you will see some other examples of calculations which you may well have to make in the near future.

Using the same 0-1 ma. milliammeter movement, find the resistance of the shunt which permits safe, full-scale deflection of a three-milliamp current. Note that if the meter movement is in full-scale deflection, one milliamp is flowing in the meter branch of the parallel circuit, and the remaining two milliamps must be flowing through the shunt resistor. The resistance of the meter movement is the same as before; namely, 50 ohms. The voltage drop across the meter is found first.

$$E_m = I_m R_m = .001 \times 50 = .05 \text{ volts}$$

The voltage across the shunt resistor is the same as that across the meter movement. It is a simple matter then, to solve for R_S since both the current and the voltage are known.

$$R_S = \frac{E_S}{I_S} = \frac{.05}{.002} = 25 \text{ ohms}$$

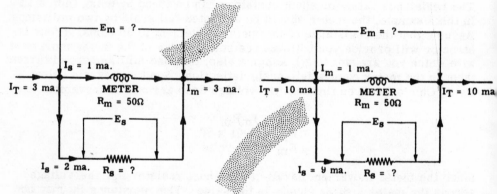

In another example, assume that you wish to extend the range of a 0-1 ma. milliammeter (whose meter movement resistance is 50 ohms) to ten milliamperes. Calculate the resistance value of the appropriate shunt.

Note that if the total current is ten milliamperes, one milliamp will flow through the meter (for full-scale deflection) and nine milliamperes must flow through the shunt resistor. Find the voltage drop across the meter.

$$E_m = I_m R_m = .001 \times 50 = .05 \text{ volts}$$

As you know, E_m is equal to E_S since the meter and R_S are in parallel. Find the resistance of R_S.

$$R_S = \frac{E_S}{I_S} = \frac{.05}{.009} = 5.55 \text{ ohms}$$

OHM'S LAW AND PARALLEL CIRCUITS

Review of Ohm's Law and Parallel Circuits

If a circuit consists of two resistors—R_1 and R_2—in parallel, the following rules for using Ohm's law apply—

R_t, I_t and E_t are used together.

R_1, I_1 and E_1 are used together.

R_2, I_2 and E_2 are used together.

Only quantities having the same subscript can be used together to find an unknown by means of Ohm's law.

Unknown quantities may also be found by applying the following rules for parallel circuits:

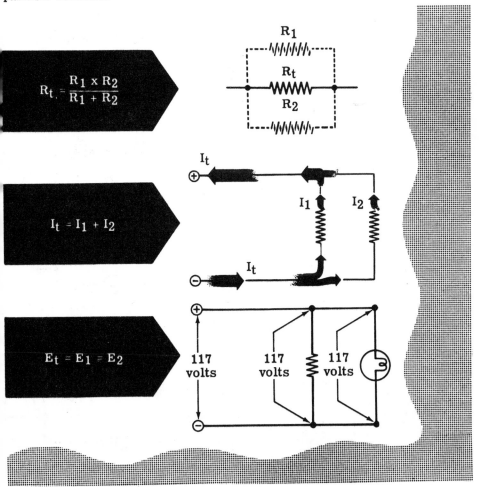

$$R_t = \frac{R_1 \times R_2}{R_1 + R_2}$$

$$I_t = I_1 + I_2$$

$$E_t = E_1 = E_2$$

DIRECT CURRENT SERIES-PARALLEL CIRCUITS

Series-Parallel Circuit Connections

Circuits consisting of three or more resistors may be connected in a com plex circuit, partially series and partially parallel. There are two basic types of series-parallel circuits: One in which a resistance is connected in series with a parallel combination, and the other in which one or more branches of a parallel circuit consist of resistances in series.

If you were to connect two lamps in parallel (side-by-side connection) and connect one terminal of a third lamp to one terminal of the parallel combination, the three lamps would be connected in series-parallel. Resistances other than lamps may also be connected in the same manner to form series-parallel circuits.

You can connect the three lamps to form another type of series-parallel circuit by first connecting two lamps in series, then connecting the two terminals of the third lamp across the series lamps. This forms a parallel combination with one branch of the parallel circuit consisting of two lamps in series.

Such combinations of resistance are frequently used in electrical circuits, particularly electric motor circuits and control circuits for electrical equipment.

TWO WAYS OF CONNECTING LAMPS IN SERIES-PARALLEL

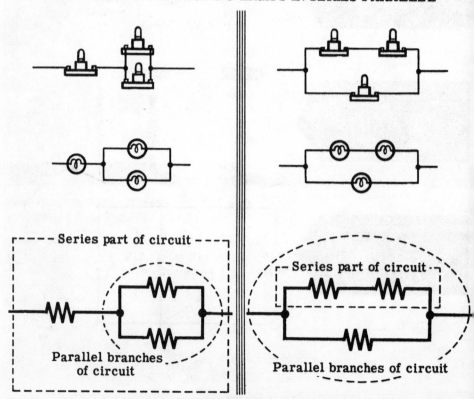

Resistances in Series-Parallel

No new formulas are needed to find the total resistance of resistances connected in series-parallel. Instead you break the complete circuit into parts consisting of simple series and parallel circuits, then solve each part separately and combine the parts. Before using the rules for series and parallel resistances, you must decide what steps to use in simplifying the circuit.

For example, suppose you want to find the total resistance of three resistances—R_1, R_2 and R_3—connected in series-parallel, with R_1 and R_2 connected in parallel, and R_3 connected in series with the parallel combination. To simplify the circuit you would use two steps, with the circuit broken down into two parts—the parallel circuit of R_1 and R_2, and the series resistance R_3. First you find the parallel resistance of R_1 and R_2, using the formula for parallel resistances. This value is then added to the series resistance R_3 to find the total resistance of the series-parallel circuit.

If the series-parallel circuit consists of R_1 and R_2 in series, with R_3 connected across the   the steps are reversed. The circuit is broken down into two parts—the series circuit of R_1 and R_2, and the parallel resistance R_3. First you find the series resistance of R_1 and R_2 by adding; then combine this value with R_3, using the formula for parallel resistance.

Combine R_1 and R_2 to find total resistance (R_a) of parallel combination

Add R_a and R_3 to find total circuit resistance (R_t)

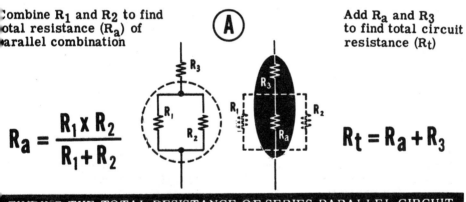

$$R_a = \frac{R_1 \times R_2}{R_1 + R_2}$$

$$R_t = R_a + R_3$$

FINDING THE TOTAL RESISTANCE OF SERIES-PARALLEL CIRCUIT

Add R_1 and R_2 to find total resistance (R_a) of series-connected branch

Combine the parallel combination of R_a and R_3 to find the total circuit resistance (R_t)

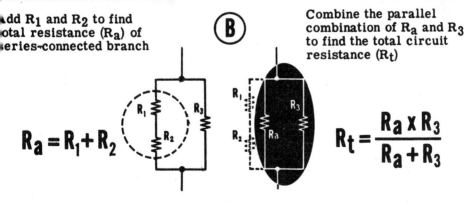

$$R_a = R_1 + R_2$$

$$R_t = \frac{R_a \times R_3}{R_a + R_3}$$

Resistances in Series-Parallel (continued)

Complex circuits may be simplified and their breakdown made easier by redrawing the circuits before applying the steps to combine resistances.

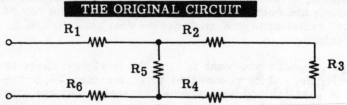

1. Start at one end of the circuit and draw all series resistances in a straight line until you reach a point where the circuit has more than one path to follow. At that point draw a line across the end of the series resistance.

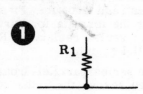

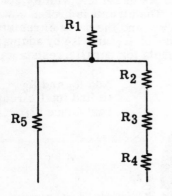

2. Draw the parallel paths from this line in the same direction as the series resistances.

4. The circuit is continued from the center of the parallel connecting line, adding the series resistance to complete the redrawn circuit.

3. Where the parallel paths combine, a line is drawn across the ends to join the paths.

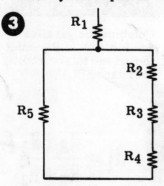

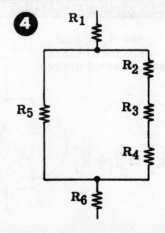

DIRECT CURRENT SERIES-PARALLEL CIRCUITS

Resistances in Series-Parallel (continued)

The basic steps in finding the total resistance of a complex series-parallel circuit are as follows—

1. Redraw the circuit if necessary.

2. If any of the parallel combinations have branches consisting of two or more resistors in series, find the total value of these resistors by adding them.

3. Using the formula for parallel resistances, find the total resistance of the parallel parts of the circuit.

4. Add the combined parallel resistances to any resistances which are in series with them.

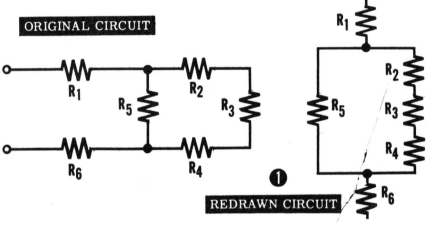

ORIGINAL CIRCUIT

REDRAWN CIRCUIT

❶

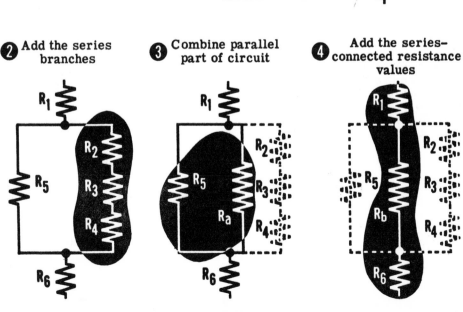

❷ Add the series branches

❸ Combine parallel part of circuit

❹ Add the series-connected resistance values

Resistances in Series-Parallel (continued)

This is how you break down complex circuits to find the total resistances—

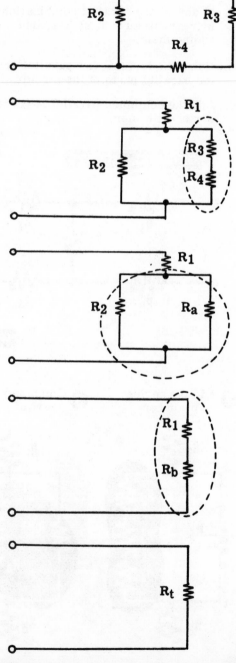

Suppose your circuit consists of four resistors—R_1, R_2, R_3 and R_4—connected as shown, and you want to find the total resistance of the circuit.

First, the circuit is redrawn and the series branch resistors R_3 and R_4 are combined by addition as an equivalent resistance R_a.

$$R_a = R_3 + R_4$$

Next, the parallel combination of R_2 and R_a is combined (using the parallel resistance formula) as an equivalent resistance, R_b.

$$R_b = \frac{R_2 \times R_a}{R_2 + R_a}$$

The series resistor R_1 is added to the equivalent resistance—R_b—of the parallel combination to find the total circuit resistance, R_t.

$$R_t = R_1 + R_b$$

R_t = total resistance of series-parallel circuit.

$$R_t = \text{Total Resistance}$$

2-94

Resistances in Series-Parallel (continued)

More complicated circuits only require more steps, not any additional formulas. For example, the total resistance of a circuit consisting of nine resistors may be found as shown—

1. Redraw the circuit.

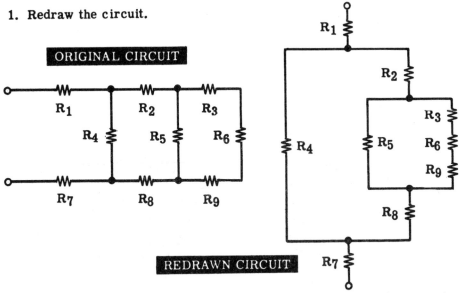

ORIGINAL CIRCUIT

REDRAWN CIRCUIT

2. Combine the series branch resistors R_3, R_6 and R_9.

$$R_a = R_3 + R_6 + R_9$$

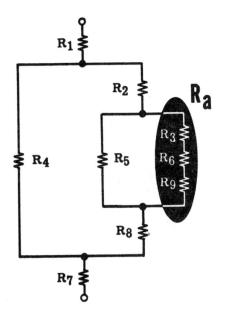

3. Combine the parallel resistances R_5 and R_a.

$$R_b = \frac{R_5 \times R_a}{R_5 + R_a}$$

Resistances in Series-Parallel (continued)

4. Combine the series resistances R_2, R_b and R_8.

$$R_c = R_2 + R_b + R_8$$

5. Combine the parallel resistances R_4 and R_c.

$$R_d = \frac{R_4 \times R_c}{R_4 + R_c}$$

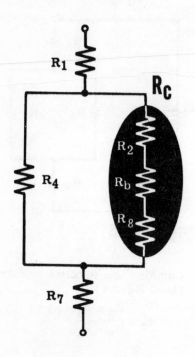

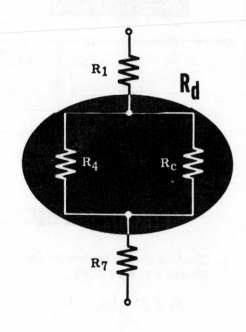

6. Combine the series resistances R_1, R_d and R_7.

$$R_t = R_1 + R_d + R_7$$

7. R_t is the total resistance of the circuit, and the circuit will act as a single resistor of this value when connected across a source of emf.

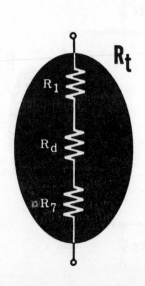

Current in Series-Parallel Circuits

The total circuit current for a series-parallel circuit depends upon the total resistance offered by the circuit when connected across a voltage source. Current flow in the circuit will divide to flow through all parallel paths and come together again to flow through series parts of the circuit. It will divide to flow through a branch circuit and then repeat this division if the branch circuit subdivides into secondary branches.

As in parallel circuits, the current through any branch resistance is inversely proportional to the amounts of resistance—the greater current flows through the least resistance. However, all of the branch currents always add to equal the total circuit current.

The total circuit current is the same at each end of a series-parallel circuit and equals the current flow through the voltage source.

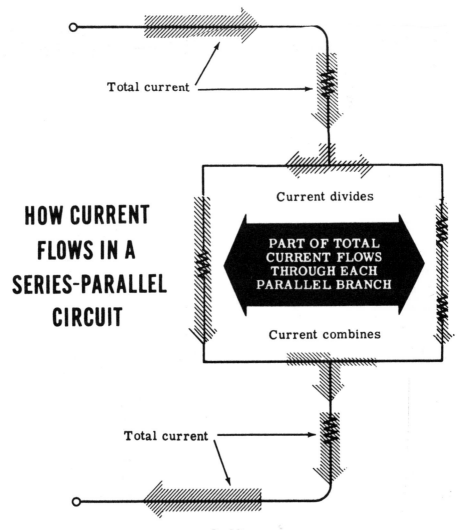

HOW CURRENT FLOWS IN A SERIES-PARALLEL CIRCUIT

Total current

Current divides

PART OF TOTAL CURRENT FLOWS THROUGH EACH PARALLEL BRANCH

Current combines

Total current

Voltage in Series-Parallel Circuits

Voltage drops across a series-parallel circuit occur in the same way as in series and parallel circuits. Across series parts of the circuit the voltage drops are equal only for equal resistances, while across parallel parts of the circuit the voltage across each branch is the same.

Series resistances forming a branch of a parallel circuit will divide the voltage across the parallel circuit. In a parallel circuit consisting of a branch with a single resistance and a branch with two series resistances, the voltage across the single resistor equals the sum of the voltages across the two series resistances. The voltage across the entire parallel circuit is exactly the same as that across either of the branches.

The voltage drops across the various paths between the two ends of the series-parallel circuit always add up to the total voltage applied to the circuit.

HOW THE VOLTAGE DIVIDES IN A SERIES - PARALLEL CIRCUIT

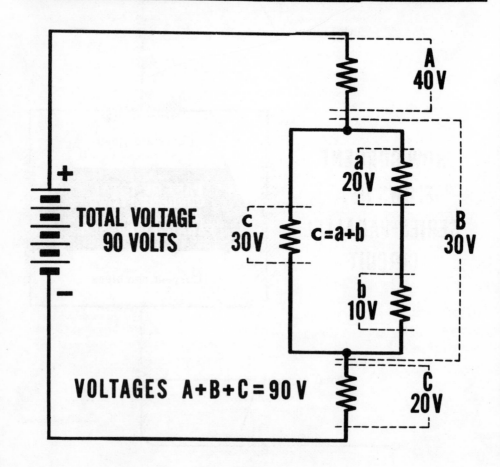

A
40V

a
20V

TOTAL VOLTAGE
90 VOLTS

c
30V

c=a+b

B
30V

b
10V

VOLTAGES A+B+C=90V

C
20V

Demonstration—Series-Parallel Connections

Simple series-parallel circuit connections using three resistors are shown first. You see that three resistors having color code values of 30 ohms each are connected together, with one resistor in series with a parallel combination of the other two. This forms a series-parallel circuit and the total resistance is found by combining the parallel 30-ohm resistors to obtain their equivalent resistance, which is 15 ohms, and adding this value to the series 30-ohm resistor—making a total resistance of 45 ohms. You see that, with the resistors so connected, the ohmmeter reads 45 ohms across the entire circuit.

Next, two resistors are connected in series and the third resistor is connected in parallel across the series combination. The total resistance is found by adding the two resistors in the series branch, to obtain the equivalent value of 60 ohms. This value is in parallel with the third 30-ohm resistor, and combining them results in a value of 20 ohms for the total resistance. This value is checked with an ohmmeter and you see that the meter reading is 20 ohms.

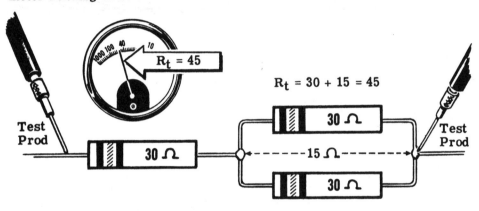

$R_t = 45$

$R_t = 30 + 15 = 45$

Test Prod

30 Ω

15 Ω

30 Ω

30 Ω

Test Prod

HOW DIFFERENT SERIES-PARALLEL CONNECTIONS
.... AFFECT RESISTANCE

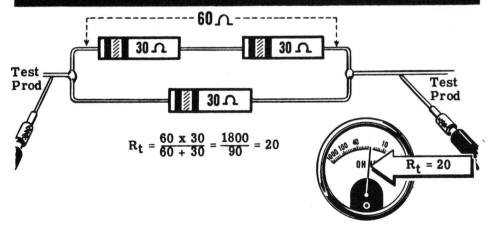

60 Ω

Test Prod

30 Ω

30 Ω

30 Ω

Test Prod

$$R_t = \frac{60 \times 30}{60 + 30} = \frac{1800}{90} = 20$$

$R_t = 20$

Demonstration—Current in Series-Parallel Circuits

Next the instructor connects a series-parallel circuit—consisting of two 30-ohm resistors connected in parallel and a 15-ohm resistor in series with one end of the parallel resistors—across a six-volt dry cell battery. To show the path of current flow through the circuit, the instructor connects an ammeter in series with each resistor in turn—showing the current flow through each. You see that the current for the 15-ohm series resistor is 0.2 amperes as is the current at each battery terminal, while the current through the 30-ohm resistors is 0.1 amperes each.

The circuit connections are changed with the 15-ohm and one 30-ohm resistor forming a series-connected branch in parallel with the other 30-ohm resistor. As the instructor connects the ammeter to read the various currents, you see that the battery current is 0.33 ampere, the 30-ohm resistor current is 0.2 ampere and the current through the series branch is 0.13 ampere.

SEEING HOW THE CURRENT FLOWS THROUGH SERIES-PARALLEL CIRCUITS

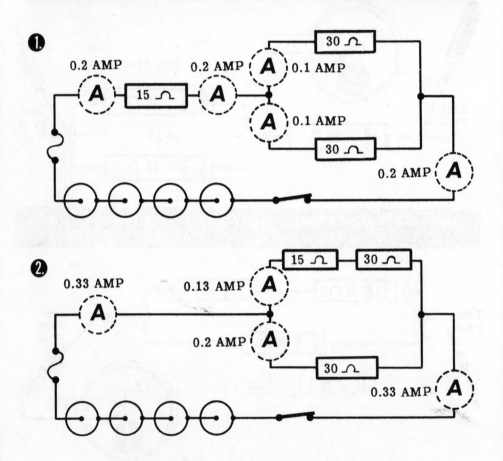

DIRECT CURRENT SERIES-PARALLEL CIRCUITS

Demonstration—Voltage in Series-Parallel Circuits

To demonstrate the division of voltage across series-parallel circuits, the instructor connects several resistors to form a complex circuit having more than one complete path between the battery terminals. As the instructor traces several possible paths across the circuit and measures the voltage across each resistance, you see that—regardless of the path chosen—the sum of the voltages for any one path always equals the battery voltage. Also, you see that the voltage drop across resistors of equal value differs, depending on whether they are in a series or parallel part of the circuit and on the total resistance of the path in which they are located.

SEEING HOW VOLTAGE DIVIDES IN A SERIES-PARALLEL CIRCUIT

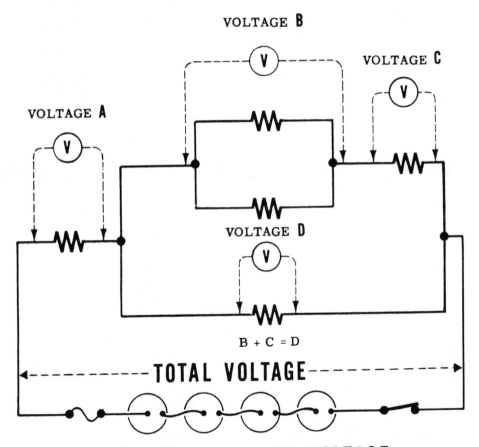

VOLTAGE **B**

VOLTAGE **C**

VOLTAGE **A**

VOLTAGE **D**

B + C = D

TOTAL VOLTAGE

VOLTAGES A + D = TOTAL VOLTAGE
VOLTAGES A + B + C = TOTAL VOLTAGE

DIRECT CURRENT SERIES-PARALLEL CIRCUITS

Review of Series-Parallel Circuits

Complex circuits—series-parallel circuits—can be broken down into series and parallel parts so that you may find resistances, currents and voltages. Now you will review the method of breaking down a complex circuit into its basic series and parallel parts.

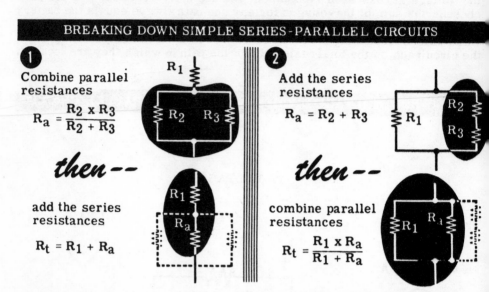

BREAKING DOWN SIMPLE SERIES-PARALLEL CIRCUITS

1 Combine parallel resistances

$$R_a = \frac{R_2 \times R_3}{R_2 + R_3}$$

then --

add the series resistances

$$R_t = R_1 + R_a$$

2 Add the series resistances

$$R_a = R_2 + R_3$$

then --

combine parallel resistances

$$R_t = \frac{R_1 \times R_a}{R_1 + R_a}$$

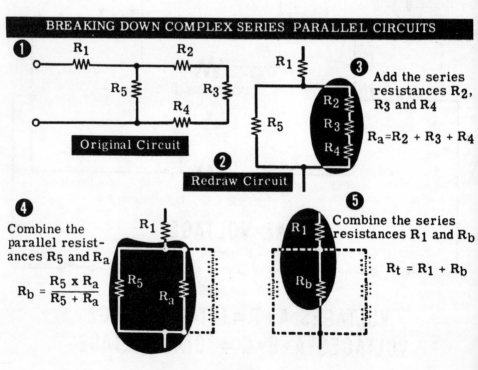

BREAKING DOWN COMPLEX SERIES PARALLEL CIRCUITS

1 R_1 R_2 R_5 R_3 R_4

Original Circuit

2 *Redraw Circuit*

3 Add the series resistances R_2, R_3 and R_4

$$R_a = R_2 + R_3 + R_4$$

4 Combine the parallel resistances R_5 and R_a

$$R_b = \frac{R_5 \times R_a}{R_5 + R_a}$$

5 Combine the series resistances R_1 and R_b

$$R_t = R_1 + R_b$$

Why Kirchhoff's Laws Are Important

KNOW... .... •••• KIRCHHOFF'S LAWS
and you can simplify
complex circuits

The total circuit resistance, current and voltage of a complex circuit are
easily obtained by breaking down the circuit, if all values for each part of
the circuit are known. However, you may find that certain resistances are
not known, or that you are only concerned with one part of a circuit. To
make the solution of any part of a complex circuit easy, two general rules
are used—one concerning current and the other concerning voltage. These
rules are Kirchhoff's laws—the first law for currents and the second law
for voltages. You have been using both of these rules or laws, referring
to them as rules for current flow and voltage drops in the various types of
circuits. Now you are ready to find out more about Kirchhoff's laws and
how they are used to find unknown quantities in any part of a circuit. While
the laws relate only to current and voltage, if they are used to find the
current and voltage relating to an unknown resistance, the resistance can
then be determined by using Ohm's law.

Kirchhoff's First Law

You have found out about current flow in the three types of circuits—series, parallel and series-parallel. You found that the entire circuit current flows through each resistance of a series circuit. In parallel circuits the current divides to flow through more than one path and comes together again after passing through these paths. Series-parallel circuits provide more than one path in some parts of the circuit and only one path in other parts.

Regardless of the circuit connections, you found that the current entering a circuit was exactly the same as that leaving the circuit. This is a direct application of Kirchhoff's First Law, which states that <u>the current entering a junction is equal to the current leaving the junction.</u> The law applies not only to the circuit as a whole but also to every junction within the circuit.

Thus at a junction of three resistances, where two currents—I_1 and I_2—in two of the resistances flow toward the junction and one current—I_3—in the third resistance flows away from the junction, I_3 must equal $I_1 + I_2$.

HOW KIRCHHOFF'S FIRST LAW WORKS

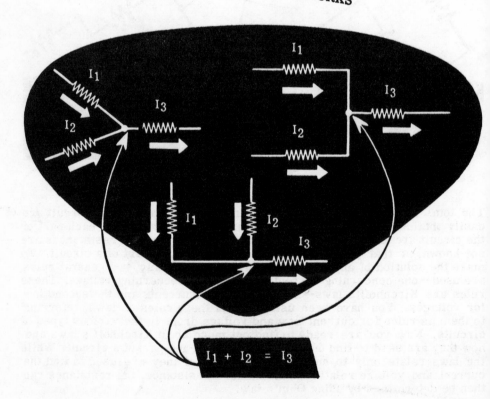

Kirchhoff's First Law (continued)

In a complete circuit, the current through each resistance will flow toward a junction at one end of the resistance but away from the junction at the other end of the resistance. To use Kirchhoff's first law you should first indicate the current paths through each resistance of the circuit. Then determine which currents flow toward and which flow away from each junction in the circuit. If certain currents are not known, their value and direction both may be determined by applying Kirchhoff's first law.

The direction of the unknown current is first determined by comparison of the known currents flowing toward and away from the junction. By adding all the known currents flowing toward the junction and those flowing away from the junction, you can determine the direction of the unknown current. At a junction where two currents—I_1 and I_2—enter the junction and two currents—I_3 and I_4—leave the junction, if I_1 is unknown it may be found by subtracting I_2 from the sum of I_3 and I_4. Suppose that I_2 is 4 amperes, I_3 is 6 amperes and I_4 is 3 amperes, then I_1 is equal to 9 amp $(I_3 + I_4)$ minus 4 amp (I_2) or 5 amp.

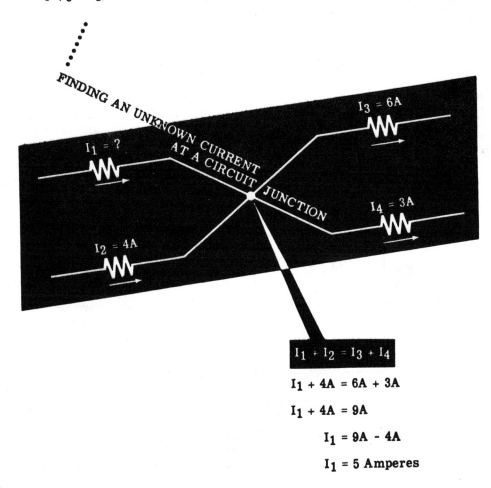

FINDING AN UNKNOWN CURRENT AT A CIRCUIT JUNCTION

$I_1 = ?$

$I_3 = 6A$

$I_2 = 4A$

$I_4 = 3A$

$$I_1 + I_2 = I_3 + I_4$$

$$I_1 + 4A = 6A + 3A$$

$$I_1 + 4A = 9A$$

$$I_1 = 9A - 4A$$

$$I_1 = 5 \text{ Amperes}$$

Kirchhoff's First Law (continued)

This is how you use Kirchhoff's first law to find the unknown currents in a circuit—

Suppose your circuit consists of seven resistors—R_1, R_2, R_3, R_4, R_5, R_6 and R_7—connected as shown. If the currents through R_1, R_4, R_6 and R_7 are not known, but the currents and their direction through R_2, R_3 and R_5 are known, the unknown currents may be found by applying Kirchhoff's first law to the circuit.

THIS IS HOW YOUR CIRCUIT LOOKS

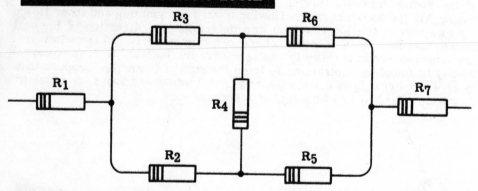

In this circuit the current I_2 is 7 amperes flowing toward R_5, the current I_3 is 3 amperes flowing toward R_6, and the current I_5 is 5 amperes flowing toward R_7. Draw the circuit in symbol form designating all currents, with values and direction if known. Identify each junction of two or more resistances with a letter.

THE CIRCUIT IN SYMBOL FORM

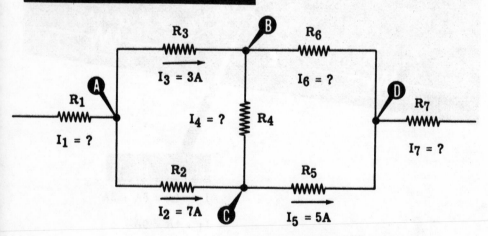

Circuit Junctions—A, B, C and D
Known Currents—I_2, I_3, and I_5
Unknown Currents—I_1, I_4, I_6 and I_7

Kirchhoff's First Law (continued)

Find the unknown currents at all junctions where only one current is unknown, later using these new values to find unknown values at other junctions. From the circuit you can see that junctions A and C have only one unknown. Suppose you start by finding the unknown current at junction A—

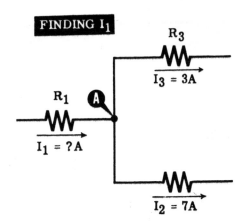

Of the three currents at junction A—I_1, I_2 and I_3—both I_2 and I_3 are known and flow away from the junction. Then I_1 must flow toward the junction, and its value must equal the sum of I_2 and I_3.

$$I_1 = I_2 + I_3$$
$$I_1 = 7 \text{ amp} + 3 \text{ amp}$$
Then $I_1 = 10$ amp

Next find the unknown current at junction C—

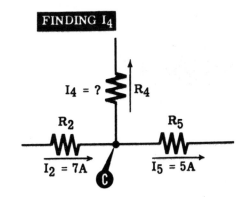

At C two currents—I_2 and I_5—are known and only I_4 is unknown. Since I_2 flowing toward C is greater than I_5 flowing away from C, the third current I_4 must flow away from C. Also, if the current flowing toward C equals that flowing away, I_2 equals I_4 plus I_5.

$$I_2 = I_4 + I_5$$
$$7 \text{ amp} = I_4 + 5 \text{ amp}$$
Then $I_4 = 2$ amp

Kirchhoff's First Law (continued)

Now that the value and direction of I_4 are known, only I_6 is unknown for junction <u>B</u>. You can find the amount and direction of I_6 by applying the law for current at <u>B</u>.

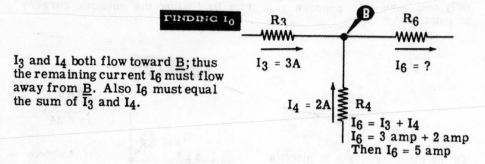

I_3 and I_4 both flow toward <u>B</u>; thus the remaining current I_6 must flow away from <u>B</u>. Also I_6 must equal the sum of I_3 and I_4.

$I_6 = I_3 + I_4$
$I_6 = 3$ amp $+ 2$ amp
Then $I_6 = 5$ amp

With I_6 known, only I_7 remains unknown at junction <u>D</u>.

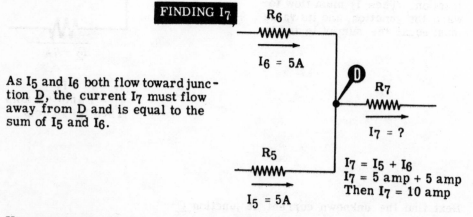

As I_5 and I_6 both flow toward junction <u>D</u>, the current I_7 must flow away from <u>D</u> and is equal to the sum of I_5 and I_6.

$I_7 = I_5 + I_6$
$I_7 = 5$ amp $+ 5$ amp
Then $I_7 = 10$ amp

You now know all of the circuit currents and their directions through the various resistances.

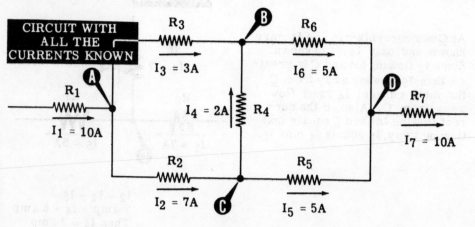

CIRCUIT WITH ALL THE CURRENTS KNOWN

Kirchhoff's Second Law

While working with the various types of circuits, you found that for any path between the terminals of a voltage source, the sum of the voltage drops across the resistances in each path equaled the voltage of the source. This is one way of using Kirchhoff's Second Law, which states that the sum of the voltage drops around a circuit equals the voltage applied across the circuit. In the circuit shown, the voltage drops across each resistance differ, but the sum of those in any one path across the terminals add to equal the battery voltage.

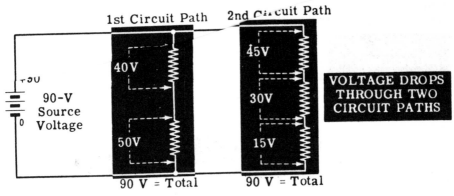

If more than one voltage source is included in the circuit, the actual voltage applied to the circuit is the combined voltage of all voltage sources and the voltage drops will be equal to this combined voltage. The combined voltage will depend on whether the voltages combine to add or subtract. For example, if two batteries are used in the same circuit, they may be connected to either aid or oppose each other. In either case, the total voltage drops across the circuit resistances will equal the sum or difference of the batteries.

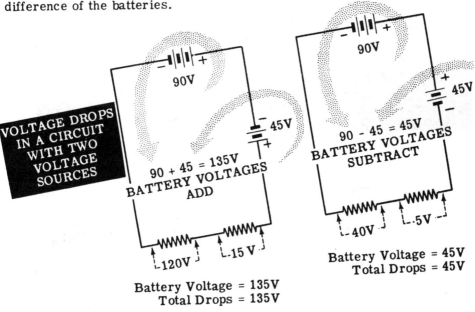

Kirchhoff's Second Law (continued)

Whenever all but one of the voltage drops are known in a path between two junctions, the unknown voltage can be determined by applying Kirchhoff's second law if the voltage between the junctions is known. The junctions may be the terminals of a voltage source or they may be two junctions within the circuit itself.

If three resistors—R_1, R_2 and R_3—are connected in series across a known voltage of 45 volts, and the voltage drops of R_1 and R_3 are 6 and 19 volts respectively, the voltage drop across R_2 is found by applying the law for circuit voltages, Kirchhoff's second law.

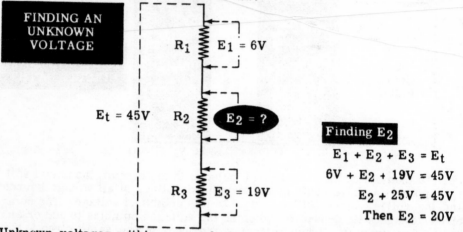

FINDING AN UNKNOWN VOLTAGE

R_1 $E_1 = 6V$

$E_t = 45V$ R_2 $E_2 = ?$

R_3 $E_3 = 19V$

Finding E_2

$E_1 + E_2 + E_3 = E_t$

$6V + E_2 + 19V = 45V$

$E_2 + 25V = 45V$

Then $E_2 = 20V$

Unknown voltages within a complex circuit are found by first finding the voltage across each branch of the circuit, and then, by applying the law, finding the voltage drops across each resistance in the various branches. For series-parallel circuits the voltage across parallel parts of the circuit is used as the total voltage across the various resistances within that part of the circuit. To find the unknown voltages in the series-parallel circuit shown, the law for voltages is applied to each path across the current independently.

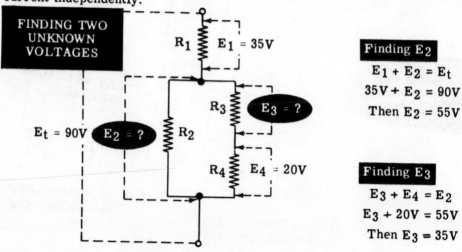

FINDING TWO UNKNOWN VOLTAGES

R_1 $E_1 = 35V$

R_3 $E_3 = ?$

$E_t = 90V$ $E_2 = ?$ R_2

R_4 $E_4 = 20V$

Finding E_2

$E_1 + E_2 = E_t$

$35V + E_2 = 90V$

Then $E_2 = 55V$

Finding E_3

$E_3 + E_4 = E_2$

$E_3 + 20V = 55V$

Then $E_3 = 35V$

Demonstration—Kirchhoff's First Law

To demonstrate the law of circuit currents, the instructor connects a 15-ohm resistor in series with a parallel combination of three 15-ohm resistors and then connects the entire circuit across a 9-volt dry cell battery with a switch and fuse in series. This circuit is shown in the illustration.

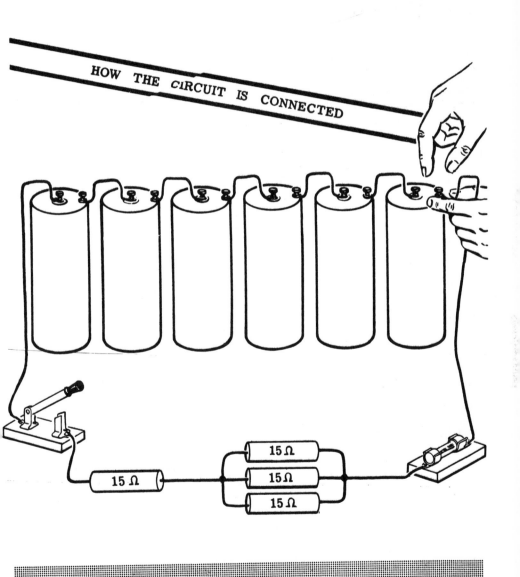

HOW THE CIRCUIT IS CONNECTED

Demonstration—Kirchhoff's First Law (continued)

The total resistance of the circuit is 20 ohms, resulting in a total circuit current of 0.45 ampere by Ohm's law. This total current must flow through the circuit from the (-) to (+) battery terminals. At junction (a), the circuit current—0.45 ampere—divides to flow through the parallel resistors toward junction (b). Since the parallel resistors are equal, the current divides equally, with 0.15 ampere flowing through each resistor. At junction (b), the three parallel currents combine to flow away from the junction through the series resistor.

As the instructor connects the ammeter to read the current in each lead at the junction, you see that the sum of the three currents flowing toward the junction equals the current flowing away from the junction.

CHECK THE CURRENT FLOW AT A CIRCUIT JUNCTION

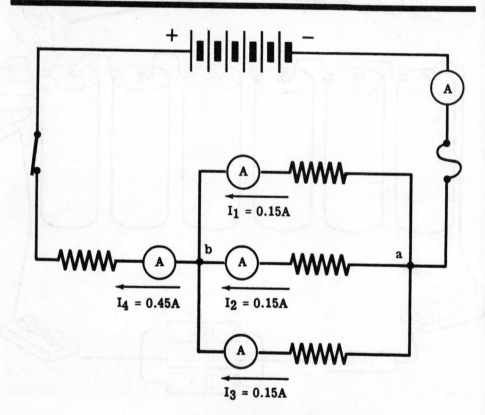

$$\text{Current flowing toward the junction} = \text{Current flowing away from the junction}$$

$$I_1 + I_2 + I_3 = I_4$$
$$0.15 + 0.15 + 0.15 = 0.45A$$

Demonstration—Kirchhoff's Second Law

Using the same circuit, the instructor measures the voltage across each resistance in the circuit and also the battery voltage. For each path between the terminals of the battery, you see that the sum of the voltage drops equals the battery voltage.

CHECKING THE VOLTAGE DROPS IN EACH PATH THROUGH A CIRCUIT

$$\left.\begin{array}{c}\text{Circuit}\\\text{Voltage Drops}\end{array}\right\} = \left\{\begin{array}{c}\text{Source}\\\text{Voltage (Battery)}\end{array}\right.$$

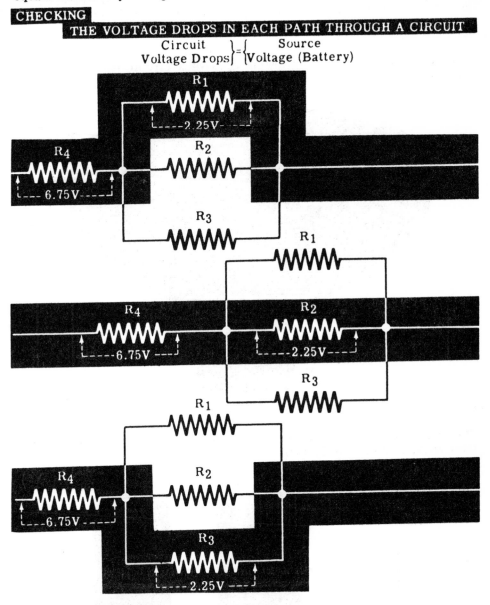

Next, the instructor connects the resistors in a more complex circuit. Again the voltages of the individual resistors are measured, and you see that the sum of the voltages in any complete path across the circuit equals the battery voltage.

Review of Kirchhoff's Laws

When working with complex circuits, you need to be able to simplify them by redrawing the circuit, combining resistances, using Ohm's law and applying Kirchhoff's laws: Most unknown values in a complex circuit can be found by applying Kirchhoff's laws to either part or all of the circuit. Now let's review these basic laws of circuit currents and voltages.

Kirchhoff's First Law

The total current entering (flowing toward) a circuit junction equals the total current leaving (flowing away from) the junction.

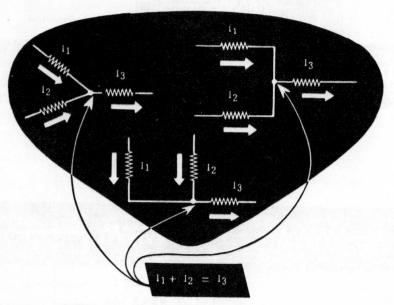

$$I_1 + I_2 = I_3$$

Kirchhoff's Second Law

The total voltage drops across the resistances of a closed circuit equal the total voltage applied to the circuit.

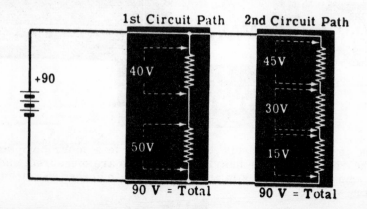

Review of Direct Current Circuits

Now, as a review, suppose you compare the types of circuits you have found out about and seen in operation. Also review the basic formulas which apply to direct current circuits.

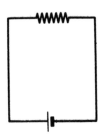

SIMPLE CIRCUIT — A single resistance connected across a voltage source.

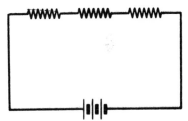

SERIES CIRCUIT — Resistances connected end to end across a voltage source.

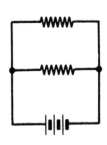

PARALLEL CIRCUIT — Resistances connected side by side across a common voltage source.

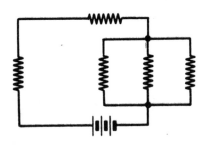

SERIES-PARALLEL CIRCUIT — Resistances connected partly in series and partly in parallel.

Review of Direct Current Circuits (continued)

OHM'S LAW — The current flowing in a circuit changes in the same direction that voltage changes, and the opposite direction that resistance changes.

$$\text{Current} = \frac{\text{Voltage}}{\text{Resistance}}$$

$$I = \frac{E}{R}$$

OHM'S LAW VARIATIONS —

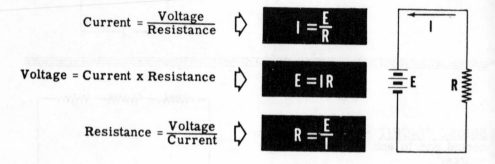

$$\text{Current} = \frac{\text{Voltage}}{\text{Resistance}} \qquad I = \frac{E}{R}$$

$$\text{Voltage} = \text{Current} \times \text{Resistance} \qquad E = IR$$

$$\text{Resistance} = \frac{\text{Voltage}}{\text{Current}} \qquad R = \frac{E}{I}$$

ELECTRIC POWER -- The rate of doing work in moving electrons through a conductor.

KIRCHHOFF'S FIRST LAW -- The total current entering (flowing toward) a circuit junction equals the total current leaving (flowing away from) the junction.

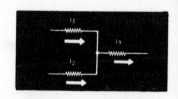

KIRCHHOFF'S SECOND LAW -- The total voltage drops across the resistances of a closed circuit equal the total voltage applied to the circuit.

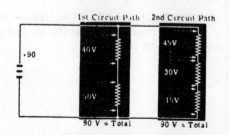

1st Circuit Path   2nd Circuit Path

90

40V   45V

30V

50V   15V

90 V = Total   90 V = Total

INDEX

INDEX TO VOL. 2

(Note: A cumulative index covering all five volumes in this series will be found at the end of Volume 5.)

basic
electricity

by VAN VALKENBURGH,
NOOGER & NEVILLE, INC.

VOL. 3

HAYDEN BOOK COMPANY, INC.
Rochelle Park, New Jersey

PREFACE

The texts of the entire Basic Electricity and Basic Electronics courses, as currently taught at Navy specialty schools, have now been released by the Navy for civilian use. This educational program has been an unqualified success. Since April, 1953, when it was first installed, over 25,000 Navy trainees have benefited by this instruction and the results have been outstanding.

The unique simplification of an ordinarily complex subject, the exceptional clarity of illustrations and text, and the plan of presenting one basic concept at a time, without involving complicated mathematics, all combine in making this course a better and quicker way to teach and learn basic electricity and electronics. The Basic Electronics portion of this course will be available as a separate series of volumes.

In releasing this material to the general public, the Navy hopes to provide the means for creating a nation-wide pool of pre-trained technicians, upon whom the Armed Forces could call in time of national emergency, without the need for precious weeks and months of schooling.

Perhaps of greater importance is the Navy's hope that through the release of this course, a direct contribution will be made toward increasing the technical knowledge of men and women throughout the country, as a step in making and keeping America strong.

Van Valkenburgh, Nooger and Neville, Inc.

New York, N. Y.
October, 1954

TABLE OF CONTENTS

Vol. 3 — Basic Electricity

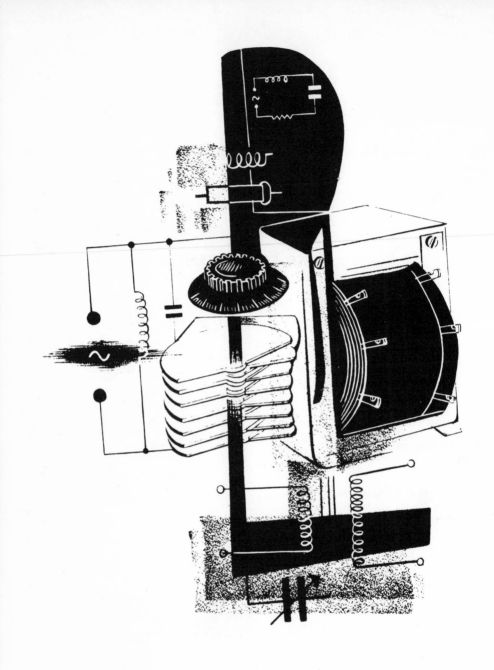

Alternating current circuits

Alternating Current Power Transmission

As you probably know, most electric power lines carry alternating current. Very little direct current is used for electric lighting and power.

There are many good reasons for this choice of AC over DC for electric power transmission. Alternating current voltage can be increased or decreased easily and without appreciable power loss, through the use of a transformer, while direct current voltages cannot be changed without a considerable power loss. This is a very important factor in the transmission of electric power, since large amounts of power must be transmitted at very high voltages. At the power station the voltage is "stepped up" by transformers to very high voltages and sent over the transmission line; then at the other end of the line, other transformers "step down" the voltage to values which can be used for lighting and power.

Various kinds of electrical equipment require different voltages for proper operation, and these voltages can easily be obtained by using a transformer and an AC power line. To obtain such voltages from a DC power line requires both a complicated and inefficient circuit.

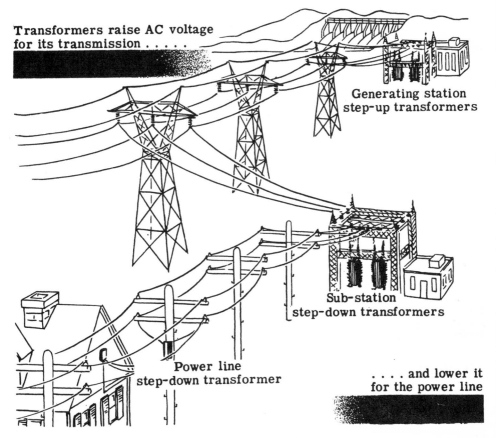

Transformers raise AC voltage for its transmission . . . . .

Generating station step-up transformers

Sub-station step-down transformers

Power line step-down transformer

. . . . and lower it for the power line

Alternating Current Power Transmission (continued)

Since the power transmitted equals the voltage multiplied by the current (P = EI), and the size of the wire limits the maximum current which can be used, the voltage must be increased if more power is to be transmitted over the same size wires. Also, excessive current flow causes over-heating of the wires, resulting in large power loss, so that the maximum current is kept as low as possible. The voltage, however, is limited only by the insulation of the transmission line. Since the insulation can be easily strengthened, the voltage can be increased considerably, permitting the transfer of large amounts of power with smaller wires and much less **power loss.**

IN POWER TRANSMISSION THE CURRENT IS LIMITED BY *Wire Size*

When current flows through a wire to reach the electrical device using power-er, there is a power loss in the wire proportional to the square of the current (P = I²R). Any reduction in the amount of current flow required to transmit power results in a reduction in the amount of power lost in the transmission line. By using high voltage, lower current is required to transmit a given amount of power. Transformers are needed to raise the voltage for power transmission and lower it for use on electric power lines and, since transformers can only be used with AC, nearly all electric power lines are AC rather than DC.

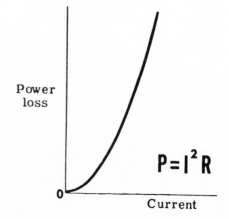

POWER LOSS

IN TRANSMISSION IS PROPORTIONAL
TO THE SQUARE OF THE CURRENT

Power loss

$P = I^2 R$

0   Current

DC and AC Current Flow

Alternating current—AC—flows back and forth in a wire at regular inter-vals, going first in one direction and then the other. You know that direct current flows only in one direction, and that current is measured by count-ing the number of electrons flowing past a point in a circuit in one second.

Suppose a coulomb of electrons moves past a point in a wire in one second with all of the electrons moving in the same direction; the current flow then is one ampere DC. If a half coulomb of electrons moves in one di-rection past a point in a half second, then reverses direction and moves past the same point in the opposite direction during the next half second, a total of one coulomb of electrons passes the point in one second—and the current flow is one ampere AC.

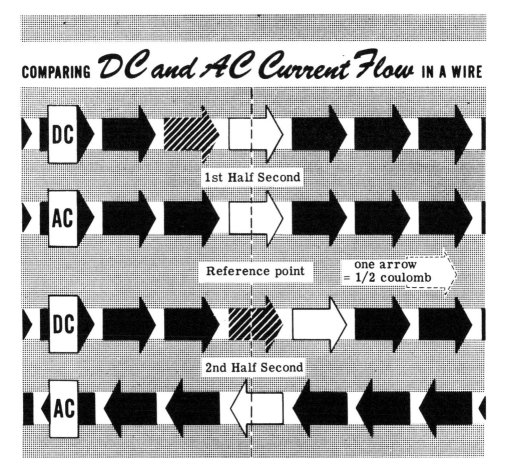

COMPARING *DC and AC Current Flow* IN A WIRE

1st Half Second

Reference point one arrow = 1/2 coulomb

2nd Half Second

Waveforms

Waveforms are graphical pictures showing how voltages and currents
vary over a period of time. The waveforms for direct current are
straight lines, since neither the voltage nor current vary for a given circuit. If you connect a resistor across a battery and take measurements
of voltage across, and current through, the resistor at regular intervals
of time, you find no change in their values. Plotting the values of E and I,
each against time, you obtain straight lines—the waveforms of the circuit
voltage and current.

WAVEFORMS ARE PICTURES OF VOLTAGE OR CURRENT VARIATIONS

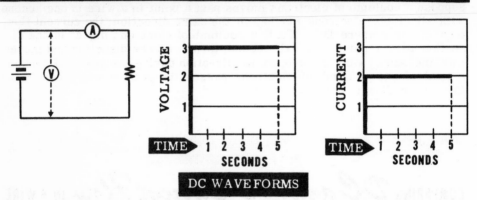

DC WAVEFORMS

Imagine that you have a zero-center voltmeter and ammeter, and can take
readings above and below zero when the polarity of the measured voltage
and current is reversed. If you reverse the battery leads while taking the
measurements, you find that the waveforms consist of two straight lines—
one above and one below zero. By connecting the ends of these lines to
form a continuous line, you can obtain the waveforms of voltage and current. These waveforms show that the current and voltage are AC rather
than DC, since they indicate the changing direction of the current flow and
the reversal in polarity of the voltage.

AC WAVEFORMS

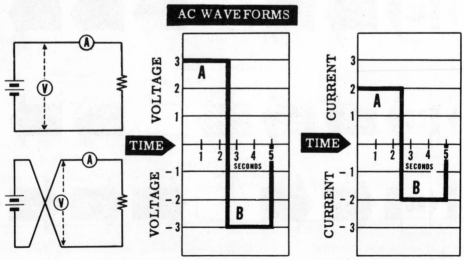

Waveforms (continued)

Another type of waveform is pulsating direct current, which represents variations in voltage and current flow without a change in the direction of current flow. This waveform is common to the DC generator, since the generator output contains a ripple or variation due to commutator action. Battery waveforms do not vary unless the circuit itself changes, such as reversing the battery terminals to obtain an AC waveform.

If, in a circuit consisting of a resistor and a switch connected across a battery, you open and close the switch, causing the current to stop and start but not to reverse direction, the circuit current is pulsating direct current. The waveforms for this pulsating current resemble AC waveforms, but do not go below zero since the current does not change its direction.

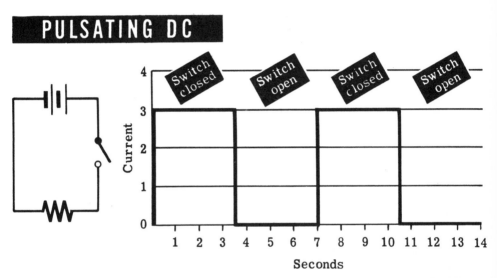

Waveforms of voltage and current are not always made of straight lines connecting points. In most cases waveforms are curved, representing gradual changes in voltage and current. This is particularly true of pulsating DC waveforms.

Also, pulsating direct current does not always vary between zero and a maximum value, but may vary over any range between these values. The waveform of a DC generator is pulsating DC and does not fall to zero but, instead, varies only slightly below the maximum value.

OTHER WAVEFORMS OF PULSATING DC.....

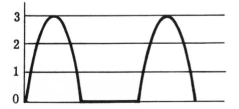
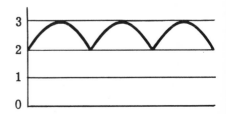

Waveforms (continued)

The waveforms of most alternating currents are curved to represent gradual changes in voltage and current, first increasing then decreasing in
value for each direction of current flow. Most of the alternating current
which you will use has a waveform represented by a sine curve, which you
will find out about a little later. While alternating currents and voltages
do not always have waveforms which are exact sine curves, they are normally assumed to have a sine waveform unless otherwise stated.

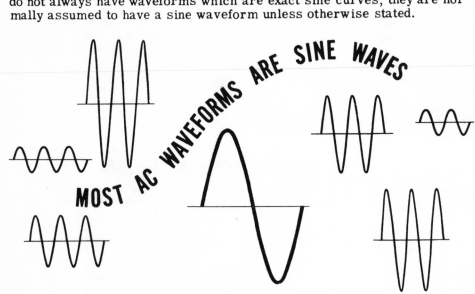

When direct current and alternating current voltages are both present in
the same circuit, the resulting voltage waveform is a combination of the
two voltages. The AC wave is added to the DC wave, with the value of the
DC voltage becoming the axis from which the AC wave moves in each di
rection. Thus the maximum point of DC voltage replaces the zero value
as the AC waveform axis. The resulting waveform is neither DC nor AC
and is called "super-imposed AC," meaning that the AC wave is added to
or placed over the DC wave.

When AC and DC are added together, the AC
axis shifts, resulting in "Superimposed AC"

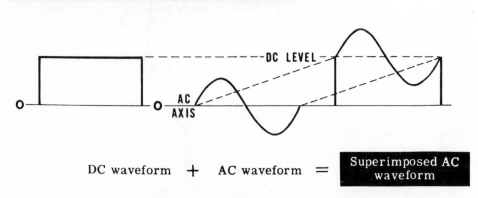

DC waveform + AC waveform = Superimposed AC
waveform

Alternating Current Cycles

When the waveform of an AC voltage or current passes through a complete set of positive and negative values, it completes a cycle. AC current first rises to a maximum and falls to zero in one direction, then rises to maximum and falls to zero in the opposite direction. This completes a cycle of AC current and the cycle repeats as long as the current flows. Similarly, AC voltage first rises to a maximum and falls to zero in one polarity, then rises to maximum and falls to zero in the opposite polarity to complete a cycle. Each complete set of both positive and negative values of either voltage or current is a cycle.

On the next sheet you will see that an AC generator consists of a coil of wire rotating in a magnetic field between two opposite magnetic poles, and that each time a side of the coil passes from one pole to the other the current flow generated in the coil reverses its direction. In passing two opposite poles, the current flows first in one direction and then the other, completing a cycle of current flow.

A CYCLE IS A COMPLETE SET OF POSITIVE AND NEGATIVE VALUES

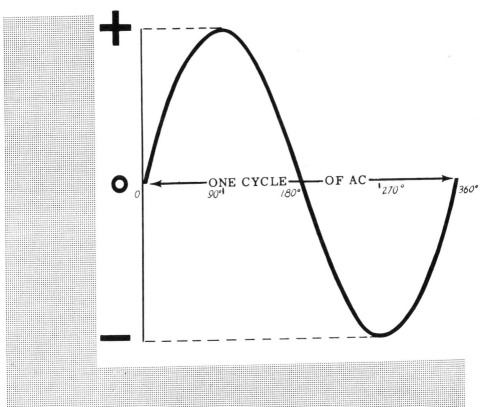

Elementary Generator Construction

An elementary generator consists of a loop of wire placed so that it can be rotated in a stationary magnetic field to cause an induced current in the loop. Sliding contacts are used to connect the loop to an external circuit in order to use the induced current.

The pole pieces are the north and south poles of the magnet which supplies the magnetic field. The loop of wire which rotates through the field is called the "armature." The ends of the armature loop are connected to rings called "slip rings," which rotate with the armature. Brushes ride up against the slip rings to pick up the electricity generated in the armature and carry it to the external circuit.

THE ELEMENTARY GENERATOR

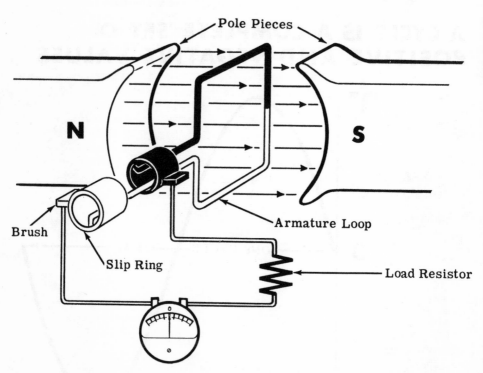

In the description of the generator action as outlined on the following sheets, visualize the loop rotating through the magnetic field. As the sides of the loop cut through the magnetic field, they generate an induced emf which causes a current to flow through the loop, slip rings, brushes, zero-center current meter and load resistor—all connected in series. The induced emf that is generated in the loop, and therefore the current that flows, depends upon the position of the loop in relation to the magnetic field. Now you are going to analyze the action of the loop as it rotates through the field.

Elementary Generator Operation

Here is the way the elementary generator works. Assume that the armature loop is rotating in a clockwise direction, and that its initial position is at A (zero degrees). In position A, the loop is perpendicular to the magnetic field and the black and white conductors of the loop are moving parallel to the magnetic field. If a conductor is moving parallel to a magnetic field, it does not cut through any lines of force and no emf can be generated in the conductor. This applies to the conductors of the loop at the instant they go through position A—no emf is induced in them and, therefore, no current flows through the circuit. The current meter registers zero.

As the loop rotates from position A to position B, the conductors are cutting through more and more lines of force until at 90 degrees (position B) they are cutting through a maximum number of lines of force. In other words, between zero and 90 degrees, the induced emf in the conductors builds up from zero to a maximum value. Observe that from zero to 90 degrees the black conductor cuts down through the field while at the same time the white conductor cuts up through the field. The induced emfs in both conductors are therefore in series-adding, and the resultant voltage across the brushes (the terminal voltage) is the sum of the two induced emfs, or double that of one conductor since the induced voltages are equal to each other. The current through the circuit will vary just as the induced emf varies—being zero at zero degrees and rising up to a maximum at 90 degrees. The current meter deflects increasingly to the right between positions A and B, indicating that the current through the load is flowing in the direction shown. The direction of current flow and polarity of the induced emf depend on the direction of the magnetic field and the direction of rotation of the armature loop. The waveform shows how the terminal voltage of the elementary generator varies from position A to position B. The simple generator drawing on the right is shown shifted in position to illustrate the relationship between the loop position and the generated waveform.

HOW THE ELEMENTARY GENERATOR WORKS

A Position
0°

B Position
90°

Generator
Terminal
Voltage

Elementary Generator Operation (continued)

As the loop continues rotating from position B (90 degrees) to position C (180 degrees), the conductors which are cutting through a maximum number of lines of force at position B cut through fewer lines, until at position C they are moving parallel to the magnetic field and no longer cut through any lines of force. The induced emf therefore will decrease from 90 to 180 degrees in the same manner as it increased from zero to 90 degrees. The current flow will similarly follow the voltage variations. The generator action at positions B and C is illustrated.

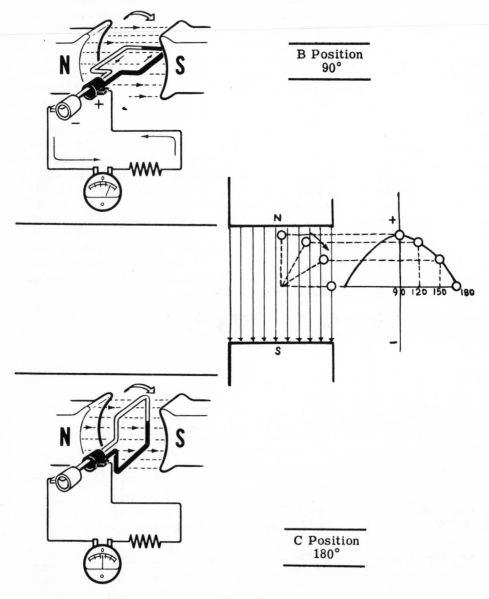

B Position
90°

C Position
180°

Elementary Generator Operation (continued)

From zero to 180 degrees the conductors of the loop have been moving in the same direction through the magnetic field and, therefore, the polarity of the induced emf has remained the same. As the loop starts rotating beyond 180 degrees back to position A, the direction of the cutting action of the conductors through the magnetic field reverses. Now the black conductor cuts up through the field, and the white conductor cuts down through the field. As a result, the polarity of the induced emf and the current flow will reverse. From positions C through D back to position A, the current flow will be in the opposite direction than from positions A through C. The generator terminal voltage will be the same as it was from A to C except for its reversed polarity. The voltage output waveform for the complete revolution of the loop is as shown.

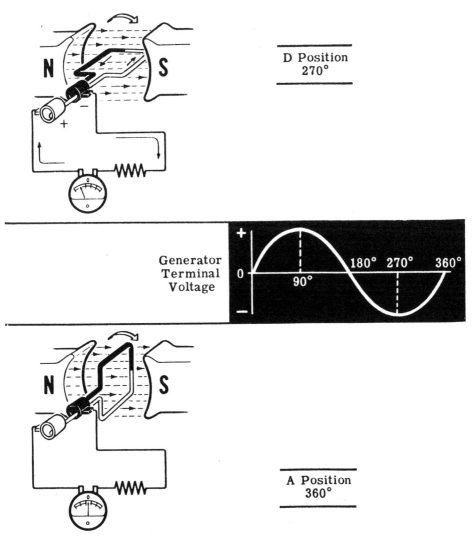

D Position
270°

Generator
Terminal
Voltage

A Position
360°

Elementary Generator Output

Suppose you take a closer look at the output waveform of the elementary generator and study it for a moment. How does it compare to the voltages with which you have been dealing up to this time? The only voltages you have used so far are DC voltages like those obtained from a battery. A DC voltage can be represented as a straight line whose distance above the zero reference line depends upon its value. The diagram shows the DC voltage next to the voltage waveform put out by the elementary AC generator. You see the generated waveform does not remain constant in value and direction, as does the DC curve. In fact, the generated curve varies continuously in value and is as much negative as it is positive.

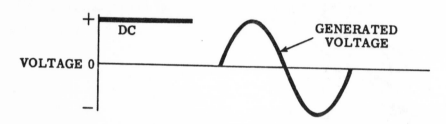

The generated voltage is therefore not DC voltage, since a DC voltage is defined as a voltage which maintains the same polarity output at all times. The generated voltage is called an "alternating voltage," since it alternates periodically from plus to minus. It is commonly referred to as an AC voltage—the same type of voltage that you get from the AC wall socket. The current that flows, since it varies as the voltage varies, must also be alternating. The current is also referred to as AC current. AC current is always associated with AC voltage—an AC voltage will always cause an AC current to flow.

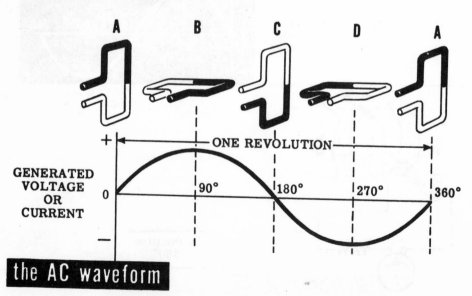

the AC waveform

Alternating Current Frequency

When the armature of an AC generator is rotating, the faster the armature coil turns past the magnetic poles the more often the current reverses each second. Therefore it completes more cycles per second, since each current reversal ends a half cycle of current flow. The number of cycles per second is "frequency."

Alternating current frequency is important to understand, since most AC electrical equipment requires a specific frequency as well as a specific voltage and current for proper operation. The standard commercial frequency used in this country is 60 cycles per second. Lower frequencies cause flicker when used for lighting, since each time the current changes direction it falls to zero—turning an electric lamp off momentarily. With 60 cycles, the lamp turns on and off 120 times each second; however, no flicker is noticeable since the eye cannot react fast enough to see the light turn off.

FREQUENCY IS THE NUMBER OF CYCLES PER SECOND

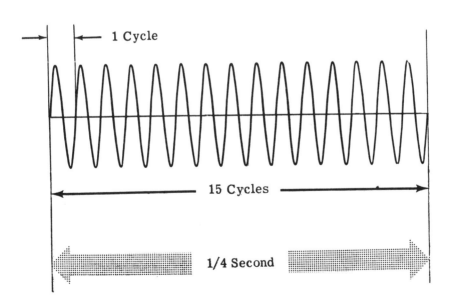

1 Cycle

15 Cycles

1/4 Second

If 15 cycles are completed in 1/4 second, the frequency is 60 cycles per second.

Maximum and Peak-to-Peak Values of a Sine Wave

Suppose you compare a half cycle of an AC sine wave to a DC waveform for the same length of time. If the DC starts and stops at the same moment as the half-cycle sine wave and each rises to the same maximum value, the DC values are greater than the corresponding AC values at all points except the point at which the AC sine wave passes through its maximum value. At this point the DC and AC values are equal. This point on the sine wave is the maximum or peak value.

COMPARISON of DC and AC WAVEFORMS

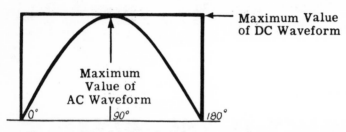

Maximum Value
of DC Waveform

Maximum
Value of
AC Waveform

0°   90°   180°

For each complete cycle of AC there are two maximum or peak values, one for the positive half cycle and the other for the negative half cycle. The difference between the peak positive value and the peak negative value is called the peak-to-peak value of a sine wave. This value is twice the maximum or peak value of the sine wave and is sometimes used for measurement of AC voltages. An oscilloscope and certain types of AC voltmeters measure peak-to-peak values of AC voltages at the input and output of radio amplifiers, phonograph amplifiers, etc.; but usually AC voltages and currents are expressed in effective values (a term you will find out about later), rather than peak-to-peak values.

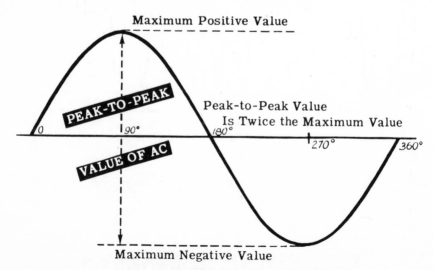

Maximum Positive Value

PEAK-TO-PEAK

Peak-to-Peak Value
Is Twice the Maximum Value

VALUE OF AC

0   90°   180°   270°   360°

Maximum Negative Value

Average Value of a Sine Wave

In comparing a half-cycle AC sine wave to a DC waveform you found that the AC instantaneous values are all less than the DC value except at the peak value of the sine wave. Since all points of the DC waveform are equal to the maximum value, this value is also the average value of the DC wave. The average value of a half cycle of the AC sine wave is less than the peak value, since all but one point on the waveform are lower in value. For all sine waves, the average value of a half cycle is 0.637 of the maximum or peak value. This value is obtained by averaging all the instantaneous values of the sine wave (for a half cycle). Since the shape of the sine wave does not change, even though its maximum value changes, the average value of any sine wave is always 0.637 of the peak value.

AVERAGE VALUES OF WAVEFORMS

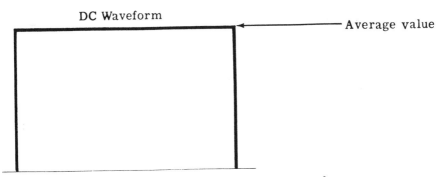

DC Waveform

Average value

DC average value equals maximum value

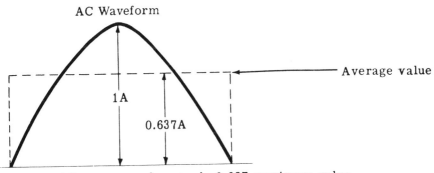

AC Waveform

Average value

1 A

0.637A

AC average value equals 0.637 maximum value

While an AC sine wave with a maximum value of 1 ampere has an average value of 0.637 ampere for each half cycle, the power effect of a 1-ampere AC current is not the same as that of a 0.637-ampere DC current. For this reason, average values of AC current and voltage waves are not often used.

WHAT ALTERNATING CURRENT IS

Effective Value of a Sine Wave

If a direct current flows through a resistance, the resulting energy converted into heat equals I^2R, or E^2/R in watts. An alternating current with
a maximum value of 1 ampere, for instance, is not expected to produce as
much heat as a direct current of 1 ampere, as alternating current does not
maintain a constant value.

The rate at which heat is produced in a resistance forms a convenient basi
for establishing an effective value of alternating current, and is known as
the "heating effect" method.

An alternating current is said to have an effective value of one ampere
when it will produce heat in a given resistance at the same rate as does
one ampere of direct current.

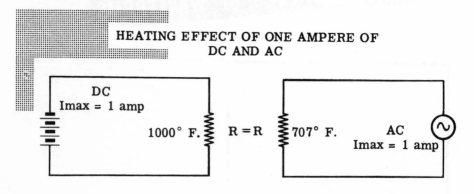

HEATING EFFECT OF ONE AMPERE OF
DC AND AC

DC
Imax = 1 amp
1000° F.   R = R   707° F.   AC
Imax = 1 amp

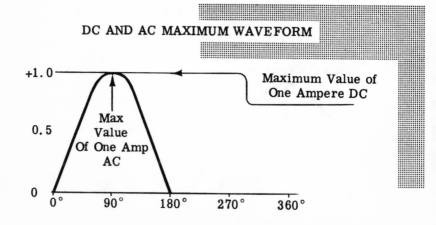

DC AND AC MAXIMUM WAVEFORM

Maximum Value of
One Ampere DC

Max
Value
Of One Amp
AC

$$\text{AC} \quad I_{EFF} = \frac{\text{The Heating Effect Of 1 Maximum AC Ampere}}{\text{The Heating Effect Of 1 Maximum DC Ampere}}$$

$$\text{AC} \quad I_{EFF} = \frac{707° \text{ F}}{1000° \text{ F}} \qquad \text{AC} \quad I_{EFF} = .707$$

Effective Value of a Sine Wave (continued)

The effective value of a sine wave of current may be computed to a fair degree of accuracy by taking equally spaced instantaneous values and extracting the square root of their average, squared values.

For this reason, the effective value is often called the "root-mean-square" (rms) value.

By this method or by means of higher mathematics it may be shown that the effective value (I) of any sine-wave current is always 0.707 times the maximum value (Imax).

Since alternating currents are caused to flow by alternating emf's, the ratio between effective and maximum values of emf's is the same as for currents. The effective, or rms, value (E) of a sine-wave emf is 0.707 times the maximum value (Emax).

When an alternating current or voltage is specified, it is always the effective value that is meant unless there is a definite statement to the contrary. It should be noted that all meters, unless marked to the contrary, read effective values of current and voltage.

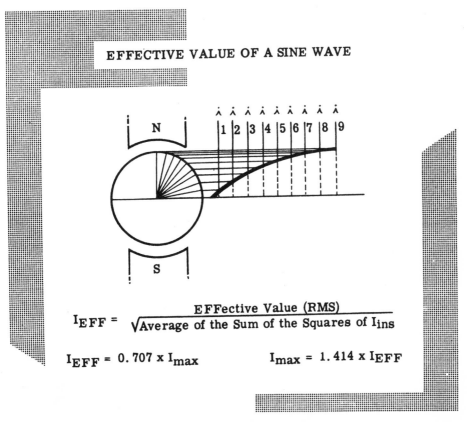

EFFECTIVE VALUE OF A SINE WAVE

$$I_{EFF} = \frac{EFFective\ Value\ (RMS)}{\sqrt{Average\ of\ the\ Sum\ of\ the\ Squares\ of\ I_{ins}}}$$

$$I_{EFF} = 0.707 \times I_{max} \qquad I_{max} = 1.414 \times I_{EFF}$$

Transformers

Electrical energy requires a convenient means for conversion, and for transfer from circuit to circuit. A device called a "transformer" is ideally suited for these purposes. Transformers change voltages from one level to another as needed, and transfer energy from one circuit to another with great efficiency.

Transformers are generally composed of two coils placed close to each other but not connected together. The coil which receives energy from the line voltage source, etc., is called the "primary" and the coil which delivers energy to a load is called the "secondary." Even though the coils are not physically connected together they manage to convert and transfer energy as required. This action is complex and is explained in detail later.

Some transformers take a high input voltage at the primary and deliver a low output voltage at the secondary. These are called "step-down" trans- formers. On the other hand, "step-up" transformers take a low input voltage at the primary and deliver a high output voltage at the secondary. The transformer used in the demonstration on the following sheets is of the step-down variety because it takes 117-volts, AC, at the primary and delivers 6.3-volts, AC, from the secondary as shown below.

One variation in the transformer family is found in a device called the "autotransformer." This device uses only one coil to do all the work. There are two input ("primary") leads and at least two output ("secondary") leads. The primary and secondary leads are attached to, or tapped off, the same coil; the extent to which the input voltage is changed is determined by the points at which the secondary leads are attached. These devices deliver step-up and step-down voltage—just as transformers do.

One type of autotransformer has variable taps or a slider on the windings that allow continuous adjustment of voltage over a large range. These variable autotransformers are often used in laboratories as a source of variable voltage or in industry where a precise voltage must be maintained. You may find that the instructor will use a variable autotransformer for demonstrations rather than a fixed transformer.

MEASURING THE TRANSFORMER'S SECONDARY VOLTAGE

Primary   Secondary

Transformer Symbol

117V AC   6.3V AC

PRIMARY   SECONDARY

Demonstration—AC Voltmeter

Although calibrated to read the effective value of AC voltages, AC voltmeters can also be used to measure the approximate value of a DC voltage. To show how the effective value of an AC voltage compares to a DC voltage, the instructor uses an AC voltmeter to measure both the DC voltage of a 7.5-volt battery and the effective AC voltage output of a 6.3-volt transformer.

Five dry cells are connected to form a 7.5-volt battery, and the 0-25 volt AC voltmeter is used to measure the voltage across the battery terminals. You see that the meter reading is approximately 7.5 volts, but the reading is not as accurate as it would be if a DC voltmeter were used.

MEASURING A BATTERY VOLTAGE WITH AN AC VOLTMETER

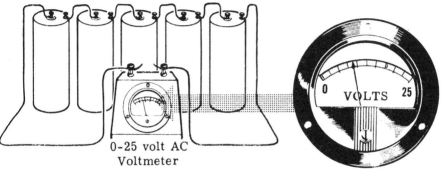

0-25 volt AC
Voltmeter

Next, the instructor connects the 117-volt primary lead of the transformer across the AC power line. The voltage across the secondary leads is then measured with the AC voltmeter, and you see that it is approximately 7.5 volts. Although the transformer is rated at 6.3 volts AC, the secondary voltage will always be higher than its rated value when the transformer is not furnishing power. The size of the load determines the exact value of the secondary voltage. In comparing the measured voltages —7.5 volts DC and 7.5 volts AC—you find that the two meter readings are nearly the same. Some difference in the readings should be expected, as the AC voltage is approximately 7.5 volts effective while the DC voltage is exactly 7.5 volts.

MEASURING THE TRANSFORMER'S SECONDARY VOLTAGE

PRIMARY   SECONDARY

0   VOLTS   25

WHAT ALTERNATING CURRENT IS

Demonstration—Effective Value of AC Voltage

To show that the 7.5 volts effective AC has the same effect as 7.5 volts DC, the 7.5-volt battery and the 6.3-volt transformer are each used to light the same type of lamp. Although the transformer is furnishing power the load is light enough so that for all practical purposes the effective AC voltage can be assumed to be 7.5 volts.

One lamp socket is connected across the battery and another is connected across the secondary leads of the transformer. The instructor then inserts identical lamps in each socket, and you see that the brightness of the two lamps is the same. This shows that the power effect of the two voltages is the same.

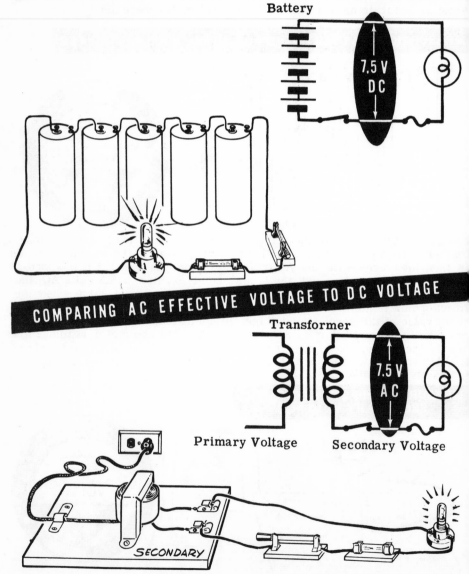

Battery

7.5 V DC

COMPARING AC EFFECTIVE VOLTAGE TO DC VOLTAGE

Transformer

7.5 V AC

Primary Voltage   Secondary Voltage

SECONDARY

WHAT ALTERNATING CURRENT IS

Review of Alternating Current

Alternating current differs from direct current not only in its waveform and electron movement but also in the way it reacts in electrical circuits. Before finding out how it reacts in circuits you should review what you have already found out about AC and the sine wave.

ALTERNATING CURRENT —
Current flow which is constantly changing in amplitude, and reverses its direction at regular intervals.

1st Half Cycle

2nd Half Cycle

WAVEFORM — A graphical picture of voltage or current variations over a period of time.

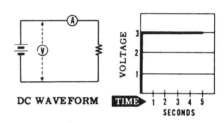

DC WAVEFORM

SINE WAVE — A continuous curve of all the instantaneous values of an AC current or voltage.

CYCLE — A complete set of positive and negative values of an AC current or voltage wave.

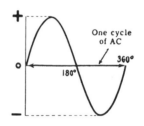

FREQUENCY — The number of cycles per second.

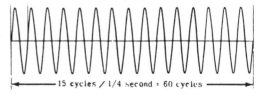

MAXIMUM, EFFECTIVE, AND AVERAGE VALUES of a sine wave.

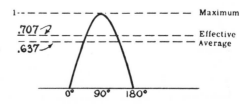

Why DC Meters Cannot Measure AC

There are noticeable differences, particularly in the scales, between DC and AC voltmeters. There is also a basic difference in the meter movements themselves.

DC meters use a basic moving-coil meter movement in which the moving coil is suspended in the magnetic field between the poles of a permanent magnet. Current flow through the coil in the correct direction (polarity) causes the coil to turn, moving the meter pointer up-scale. However, you will recall that a reversal of polarity causes the moving coil to turn in the opposite direction, moving the meter pointer down below zero.

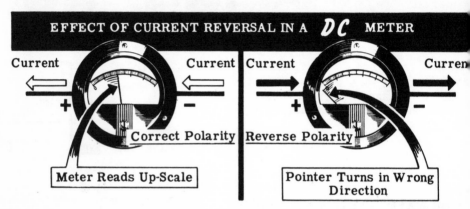

If an AC current were passed through a basic DC meter movement, the moving coil would turn in one direction for a half cycle, then—as the current reversed direction—the moving coil would turn in the opposite direction. For ordinary 60 cycles the pointer would be unable to follow the reversal in current fast enough, and the pointer would vibrate back and forth at zero, the average position of the AC wave. The greater the current flow the further the pointer would attempt to swing back and forth and, in a short time, the excess vibration would break the needle. Even if the pointer could move back and forth fast enough, the speed of movement would be so great that you could not obtain a meter reading.

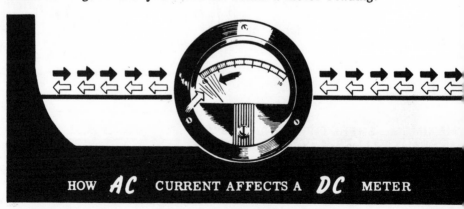

Rectifier Type AC Voltmeters

A basic DC meter movement may be used to measure AC through the use of a rectifier—a device which changes AC to DC. The rectifier permits current flow in only one direction so that, when AC tries to flow through it, current only flows for a half of each complete cycle. The effect of such a rectifier on AC current flow is illustrated below.

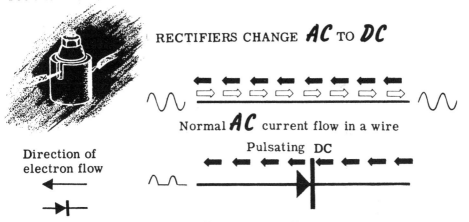

RECTIFIERS CHANGE *AC* TO *DC*

Normal *AC* current flow in a wire

Pulsating DC

Direction of electron flow

Rectifier symbol

Rectifier allows current flow in one direction only

If the rectifier is connected in series with a basic DC meter movement so that it permits current flow only in the direction necessary for correct meter polarity, the meter current flows in pulses. Since these pulses of current are all in the same direction, each causes an up-scale deflection of the meter pointer. The pointer cannot move rapidly enough to return to zero between pulses, so that it continuously indicates the average value of the current pulses.

The meter reads the average of *DC* pulses

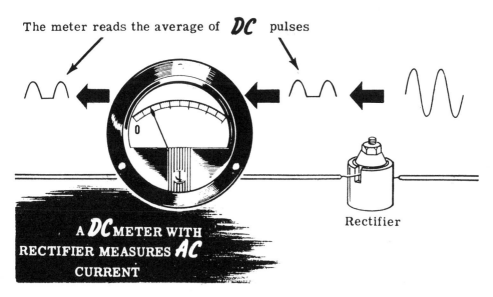

Rectifier

A *DC* METER WITH RECTIFIER MEASURES *AC* CURRENT

Rectifier Type AC Voltmeters (continued)

When certain metallic materials are pressed together to form a junction,
the combination acts as a rectifier having a low resistance to current flow
in one direction and a very high resistance to current flow in the opposite
direction. This action is due to the chemical properties of the combined
materials. The combinations usually used as rectifiers are copper and
copper oxide, or iron and selenium. Dry metal rectifiers are constructed
of disks ranging in size from less than a half inch to more than six inches
in diameter. Copper-oxide rectifiers consist of disks of copper coated on
one side with a layer of copper oxide while selenium rectifiers are constructed of iron disks coated on one side with selenium.

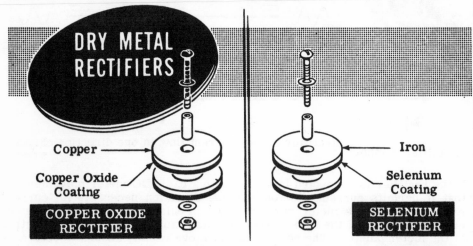

Dry metal rectifier elements (an element is a single disk) are generally
made in the form of washers which are assembled on a mounting bolt, in
any desired series or parallel combination, to form a rectifier unit. The
symbol shown below is used to represent a dry metal rectifier of any type.
Since these rectifiers were made before the electron theory was used to
determine the direction of current flow, the arrow points in the direction
of conventional current flow but in the direction opposite to the electron
flow. Thus the arrow points in opposite direction to that of the current
flow as used in electronics.

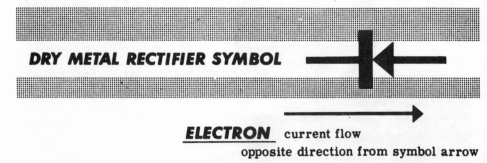

DRY METAL RECTIFIER SYMBOL

ELECTRON current flow
opposite direction from symbol arrow

Rectifier Type AC Voltmeters (continued)

Each dry metal rectifier element will stand only a few volts across its terminals but by stacking several elements in series the voltage rating is increased. Similarly each element can pass only a limited amount of current. When greater current is desired several series stacks are connected in parallel to provide the desired amount of current.

series stacking increases the
VOLTAGE RATING of a dry metal rectifier

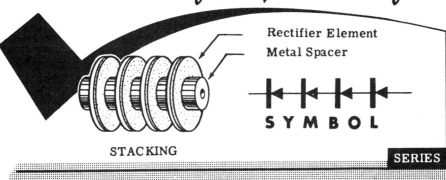

Rectifier Element
Metal Spacer

S Y M B O L

STACKING

SERIES

parallel connection increases the
CURRENT RATING..

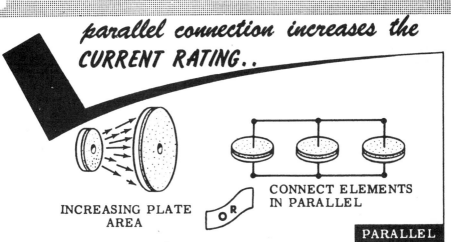

INCREASING PLATE
AREA

OR

CONNECT ELEMENTS
IN PARALLEL

PARALLEL

Dry metal rectifiers are very rugged and have an almost unlimited life if not abused. Because of the low voltage rating of individual units they are normally used for low voltages (130 volts or less) since it becomes impractical to connect too many elements in series. By paralleling stacks or increasing the diameter of the disks, the current rating can be increased to several amperes so that they are often used for low-voltage-high-current applications. Very small units are used to measure AC voltage on a DC voltmeter. Larger units are used in battery chargers and various types of power supplies for electronic equipment.

Rectifiers Type AC Voltmeters (continued)

Rectifier type AC meters are only used as voltmeters and the meter range is determined and changed in the same manner as that of a DC voltmeter. A rectifier type meter cannot be used to measure AC current directly since this would require that the meter be connected in series with the circuit and thus would put the rectifier in series as well. Such would convert all of the current to pulsating DC. However, a rectifier type voltmeter (or millivoltmeter) can be put across an ammeter shunt, thereby providing a means of measuring AC current. These meters are sometimes referred to as rectifier type AC ammeters. Various rectifier type AC meter circuits are shown below:

SIMPLE METER RECTIFIER CIRCUIT ....

1. A simple meter rectifier circuit consists of a multiplier, rectifier and basic meter movement connected in series. For one half cycle, current flows through the meter circuit. During the next half cycle, no current flows, although a voltage exists across the circuit including the rectifier.

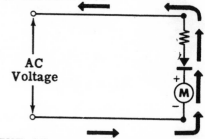

ADDING A RECTIFIER TO THE SIMPLE METER CIRCUIT

2. To provide a return path for the AC current half-cycle pulses not used to operate the meter movement, an additional rectifier is connected across the meter rectifier and meter movement. The unused pulses flow through this branch—not through the meter.

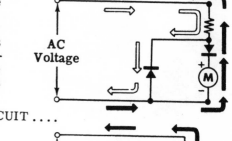

BRIDGE RECTIFIER CIRCUIT ....

3. A bridge circuit using four rectifiers is sometimes used. It is so connected that both halves of the AC current wave must follow paths that lead through the meter in the same direction. Thus, the number of current pulses flowing through the meter movement is doubled.

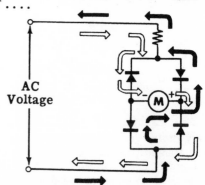

Because the meter reading is the average of the half-cycle current pulses, the scale is not the same as that used for DC. Although the amount of deflection is a result of average current flow through the meter movement, the scale is calibrated to read effective values of voltage.

Moving-Vane Meter Movements

A meter which you can use to measure both AC current and voltage is the moving-vane meter movement. By changing the meter scale calibration, moving-vane meters can be used to measure DC current and voltage. The moving-vane meter operates on the principle of magnetic repulsion between like poles. The current to be measured flows through a field coil producing a magnetic field proportional to the strength of the current. Suspended in this field are two iron vanes — one fixed in position, the other movable and attached to the meter pointer. The magnetic field magnetizes these iron vanes with the same polarity regardless of the direction of current flow in the coil. Since like poles repel, the movable vane pulls away from the fixed vane moving the meter pointer. This motion exerts a turning force against a spring. The distance the vane will move against the force of the spring depends on the strength of the magnetic field, which in turn depends on the coil current.

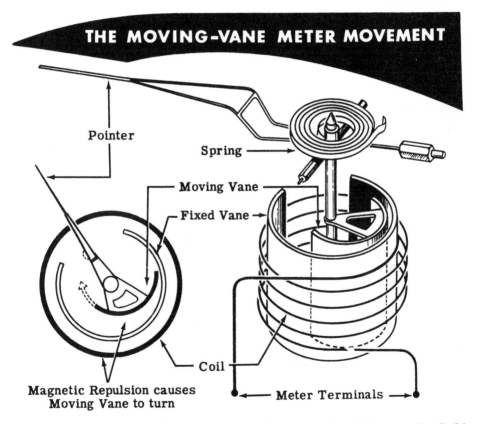

THE MOVING-VANE METER MOVEMENT

Pointer

Spring

Moving Vane

Fixed Vane

Coil

Magnetic Repulsion causes
Moving Vane to turn

Meter Terminals

Moving-vane meters may be used for voltmeters, in which case the field coil consists of many turns of fine wire which generate a strong field with only a small current flow. Ammeters of this type use fewer turns of a heavier wire, and depend on the larger current flow to obtain a strong field. These meters are generally calibrated at 60 cycles AC, but may be used at other AC frequencies.

Hot-Wire and Thermocouple Meters

Hot-wire and thermocouple meters both utilize the heating effect of current flowing through a resistance to cause meter deflection, but each uses this effect in a different manner. Since their operation depends only on the heating effect of current flow, they may be used to measure direct current and alternating current of any frequency.

The hot-wire ammeter deflection depends on the expansion of a high resistance wire caused by the heating effect of the wire itself as current flows through it. A resistance wire is stretched taut between the two meter terminals with a thread attached at a right angle to the center of the wire. A spring connected to the opposite end of the thread exerts a constant tension on the resistance wire. Current flow heats the wire, causing it to expand. This motion is transferred to the meter pointer through the thread and a pivot.

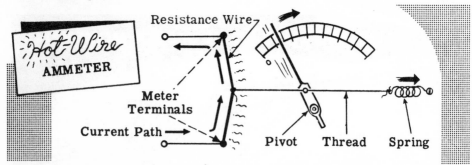

The thermo-couple meter consists of a resistance wire across the meter terminals which heats in proportion to the amount of current flow. Attached to this heating resistor is a small thermo-couple junction of two unlike metal wires which connect across a very sensitive DC meter movement. As the current being measured heats the heating resistor, a small current (which flows only through the thermo-couple wires and the meter movement) is generated by the thermo-couple junction. The current being measured flows only through the resistance wire, not through the meter movement itself. The pointer turns in proportion to the amount of heat generated by the resistance wire.

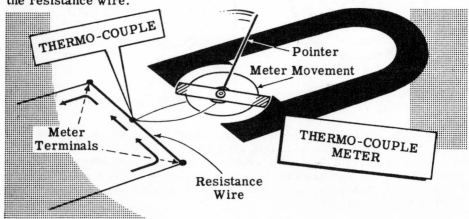

lectrodynamometer Movements

n electrodynamometer movement utilizes the same basic operating prin-
ple as the basic moving-coil DC meter movement, except that the per-
anent magnet is replaced by fixed coils. A moving coil to which the me-
er pointer is attached is suspended between two field coils and connected
i series with these coils. The three coils (two field coils and the moving
oil) are connected in series across the meter terminals so that the same
urrent flows through each.

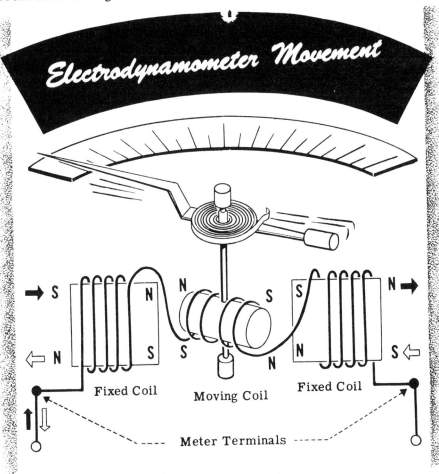

Current flow in either direction through the three coils causes a magnetic
ield to exist between the field coils. The current in the moving coil causes
t to act as a magnet and exert a turning force against a spring. If the current is reversed, the field polarity and the polarity of the moving coil reverse simultaneously, and the turning force continues in the original direc-
ion. Since reversing the current direction does not reverse the turning
force, this type of meter can be used to measure both AC and DC current.
While some voltmeters and ammeters use the dynamometer principle of
operation, its most important application is in the wattmeter about which
you will find out a little later.

Review of AC Meters

To review the principles and construction of AC meters, suppose you compare the various meter movements and their uses. Although there are other types of meters used for AC, you have found out about those which are most commonly used.

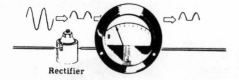

Rectifier

RECTIFIER TYPE AC METER — A basic DC meter movement with a rectifier connected to change AC to DC. Commonly used as an AC voltmeter.

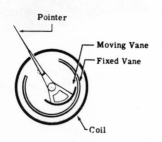

Pointer

Moving Vane

Fixed Vane

Coil

MOVING-VANE METER — Meter which operates on magnetic repulsion principle, using one movable and one fixed vane. Can be used on AC or DC to measure either voltage or current.

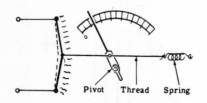

Pivot   Thread   Spring

HOT-WIRE AMMETER — Meter movement based on the expansion of a wire heated by current flow through it. Used only to measure current.

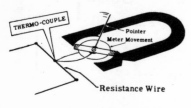

THERMO-COUPLE

Pointer
Meter Movement

Resistance Wire

THERMO-COUPLE AMMETER — Meter movement utilizing the heat of a resistor through which current flows to develop a measurable current in a thermo-couple.

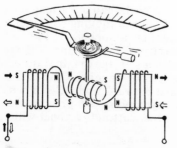

ELECTRODYNAMOMETERS — Commonly used in wattmeters rather than voltmeters and ammeters. Basic principle is identical to that of a D'Arsonval movement except that field coils are used instead of a permanent magnet.

AC Circuits Containing Resistance Only

Many AC circuits consist of pure resistance, and for such circuits the same rules and laws apply as for DC circuits. Pure resistance circuits are made up of electrical devices which contain no inductance or capacitance (you will find out about inductance and capacitance a little later). Devices such as resistors, lamps and heating elements have negligible inductance or capacitance and for practical purposes are considered to be made up of pure resistance. When only such devices are used in an AC circuit, Ohm's Law, Kirchhoff's Laws and the circuit rules for voltage, current and power can be used exactly as in DC circuits.

In using the circuit laws and rules you must use effective values of AC voltage and current. Unless otherwise stated, all AC voltage and current values are given as effective values. Other values such as peak-to-peak voltages measured on the oscilloscope must be changed to effective values before using them for circuit computations.

ALL DC RULES AND LAWS APPLY TO AC CIRCUITS CONTAINING ONLY RESISTANCE

$$E = IR \qquad I_1 + I_2 = I_3$$

$$I = \frac{E}{R} \qquad E_1 + E_2 + E_3 = E_t$$

$$R = \frac{E}{I}$$

PRIMARY   SECONDARY

RESISTANCE IN AC CIRCUITS

Current and Voltage in Resistive Circuits

When an AC voltage is applied across a resistor the voltage increases to a maximum with one polarity, decreases to zero, increases to a maximum with the opposite polarity and again decreases to zero, to complete a cycle of voltage. The current flow follows the voltage exactly: as the voltage increases the current increases; when the voltage decreases the current decreases; and at the moment the voltage changes polarity the current flow reverses its direction. Because of this, the voltage and current waves are said to be "in phase."

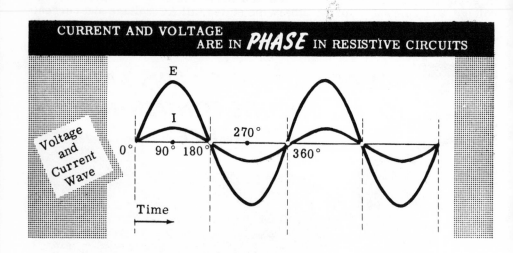

Sine waves of voltages or currents are "in phase" whenever they are of the same frequency and pass through zero simultaneously, both going in the same direction. The amplitude of two voltage waves or two current waves which are "in phase" are not necessarily equal, however. In the case of "in phase" current and voltage waves, they are seldom equal since they are measured in different units. In the circuit shown below the effective voltage is 6.3 volts, resulting in an effective current of 2 amperes, and the voltage and current waves are "in phase."

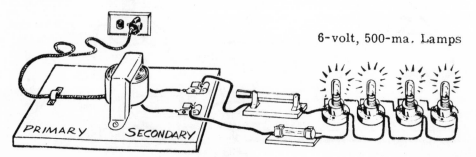

Power in AC Circuits

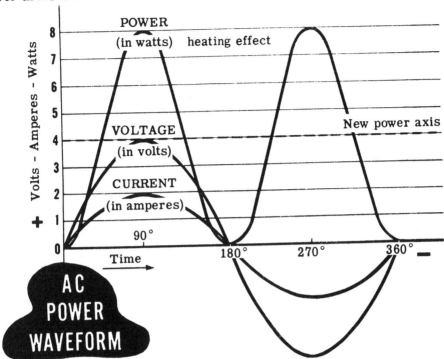

The power used in an AC circuit is the average of all the instantaneous values of power or heating effect for a complete cycle. To find the power, all of the corresponding instantaneous values of voltage and current are multiplied together to find the instantaneous values of power, which are then plotted for the corresponding time to form a power curve. The average of this power curve is the actual power used in the circuit.

For "in phase" voltage and current waves, all of the instantaneous powers are above the zero axis and the entire power curve is above the zero axis. This is due to the fact that whenever two positive values are multiplied together the result is positive, and whenever two negative values are multiplied together the result is also positive. Thus, during the first half cycle of E and I, the power curve increases in a positive direction from zero to a maximum and then decreases to zero just as the E and I waves do. During the second half cycle, the power curve again increases in a positive direction from zero to maximum and then decreases to zero while E and I both increase and decrease in the negative direction. Notice that if a new axis is drawn through the power wave, halfway between its maximum and minimum values, the power wave frequency is twice that of the voltage and current waves.

When two numbers—each being less than 1—are multiplied together, the result is a smaller number than either of the original numbers—for example, 0.5V x 0.5A = 0.25W. For that reason, some or all of the instantaneous values of a power wave may be less than those for the circuit current and voltage waves.

Power in Resistive Circuits

A line drawn through the power wave exactly halfway between its maximum and minimum values is the axis of the power wave. This axis represents the average value of power in a resistive circuit, since the shaded areas above the axis are exactly equal in area to those below the axis. Average power is the actual power used in any AC circuit.

Since all the values of power are positive for AC circuits consisting only of resistance, the power wave axis and the average power for such circuits is equal to exactly one-half the maximum, positive, instantaneous power value. This value can also be found by multiplying the effective values of E and I together. This applies to AC circuits containing resistance only, since AC circuits containing inductance or capacitance may have negative instantaneous power values.

IN AC CIRCUITS WITH RESISTANCE ONLY

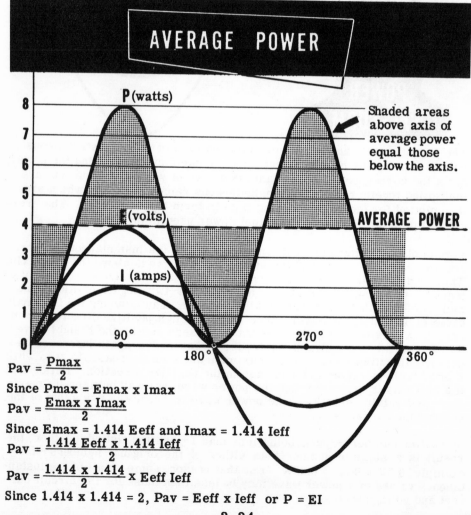

$Pav = \dfrac{Pmax}{2}$

Since Pmax = Emax x Imax

$Pav = \dfrac{Emax \text{ x } Imax}{2}$

Since Emax = 1.414 Eeff and Imax = 1.414 Ieff

$Pav = \dfrac{1.414 \text{ Eeff x } 1.414 \text{ Ieff}}{2}$

$Pav = \dfrac{1.414 \text{ x } 1.414}{2} \text{ x Eeff Ieff}$

Since 1.414 x 1.414 = 2, Pav = Eeff x Ieff or P = EI

Power Factor

When Ieff and Eeff are in phase, the product is power in watts the same as in DC circuits. As you will find out later, the product of Ieff and Eeff is not always power in watts, but is called "volt-amperes." The power in watts in any circuit, AC or DC, no matter what the other circuit elements may be, is always equal to I^2R or E^2/R.

While a source may produce volts and amperes the power in watts may be small or zero. The ratio between the power in watts of a circuit and the volt-amperes of a circuit is called "power factor." In a pure resistive circuit power in watts is equal to Ieff x Eeff so "power factor" in a pure resistive circuit is equal to power in watts divided by volt-amperes which equals 1 (one).

Power factor is expressed in percent or as a decimal.

POWER FACTOR IN RESISTIVE CIRCUITS

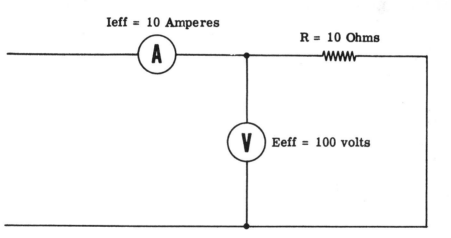

Ieff = 10 Amperes

R = 10 Ohms

Eeff = 100 volts

I^2R or E^2/R = Eeff x Ieff

I^2R or E^2/R = Watts

$$\text{Power Factor} = \frac{I^2R}{\text{Ieff x Eeff}} \text{ or} \frac{E^2/R}{\text{Ieff x Eeff}} = \frac{1000}{1000} = 1. \text{ or } 100\%$$

$$\text{Power Factor} = \frac{\text{Watts}}{\text{Volt-Amperes}}$$

Power Factor = 1.0 or 100% in a pure resistive circuit

Wattmeters

While power may be computed from the measured effective values of E and I in AC circuits containing only resistance, it can be measured directly with a wattmeter. Wattmeters are not used as commonly as the meters with which you are familiar—voltmeters, ammeters and ohmmeters—but in order to find out about AC circuits you will need to use them. Since wattmeters work differently than the meters you have used and are easily damaged if connected incorrectly, you must find out how to operate them properly.

You see the wattmeter looks very much like any other type of meter, except that the scale is calibrated in watts and it has four terminals, instead of the usual two. Two of these terminals are called the "voltage terminals" and the other two are called the "current terminals." The voltage terminals are connected across the circuit exactly as a voltmeter is connected, while the current terminals are connected in series with the circuit current in the same manner as an ammeter is connected.

Two terminals—one voltage terminal and one current terminal—are marked ±. In using the wattmeter, these two terminals must always be connected to the same point in the circuit. This is usually done by connecting them together directly at the meter terminals. For measuring either AC or DC power, the common (±) junction is connected to either side of the power line. The voltage terminal (V) is connected to the opposite side of the power line. The current terminal (A) is connected to the power-consuming load resistance.

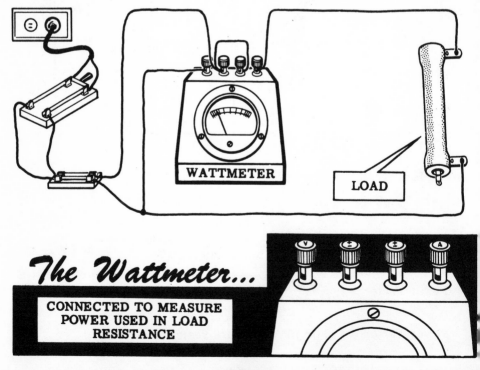

WATTMETER

LOAD

The Wattmeter...

CONNECTED TO MEASURE
POWER USED IN LOAD
RESISTANCE

Wattmeters (continued)

Wattmeters are not constructed with a D'Arsonval or Weston basic meter movement. Instead, they use a dynamometer type movement, which differs from the other types in that it has no permanent magnet to furnish the magnetic field. This field is obtained from the field coils, two coils of wire placed opposite each other just as the poles of the permanent magnets are placed in other types of meters.

These field coils are connected in series across the wattmeter current terminals, so that the circuit current flows through the coils when measurements are being made. A large circuit current makes the field coils act as strong magnets, while a small circuit current makes them act as weak magnets. Since the strength of the meter's magnetic field depends on the value of the circuit current, the wattmeter reading varies as the circuit current varies.

Since the current in the moving coil—the voltage coil—is dependent on the circuit voltage and this turning force is dependent on both the moving coil current and the field coil current, for a fixed current in the moving coil the turning force and meter reading depend only on the circuit current.

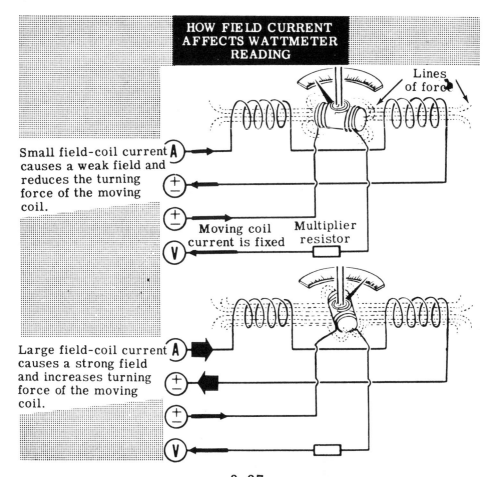

HOW FIELD CURRENT AFFECTS WATTMETER READING

Lines of force

Small field-coil current causes a weak field and reduces the turning force of the moving coil.

Moving coil current is fixed

Multiplier resistor

Large field-coil current causes a strong field and increases turning force of the moving coil.

Wattmeters (continued)

The moving coil of a wattmeter is like those used in the basic meter movement and is connected in series with an internal multiplier resistor to the
voltage terminals of the wattmeter. The voltage terminals are connected
across the circuit voltage in the same manner as a voltmeter, and the
multiplier resistor limits the current flow through the moving coil. Since
the resistance of the multiplier is fixed, the amount of current flow through
it and the moving coil varies with the circuit voltage. A high voltage
causes more current to flow through the multiplier and moving coil than a
low voltage.

For a given magnetic field, determined by the amount of circuit current
(that which flows through the load), the turning force of the moving coil depends on the amount of current flowing through the moving coil. Since this
current depends on the circuit voltage, the meter reading will vary as the
circuit voltage varies. Thus, the meter reading depends on both the circuit
current and the circuit voltage and will vary if either changes. Since power
depends on both voltage and current, the meter measures power.

Wattmeters may be used on DC, or on AC up to 133 cycles, but they must
always be connected properly to prevent damage. When used on AC, the
currents in the field coils and in the moving coil reverse simultaneously,
so the meter turning force is always in the same direction.

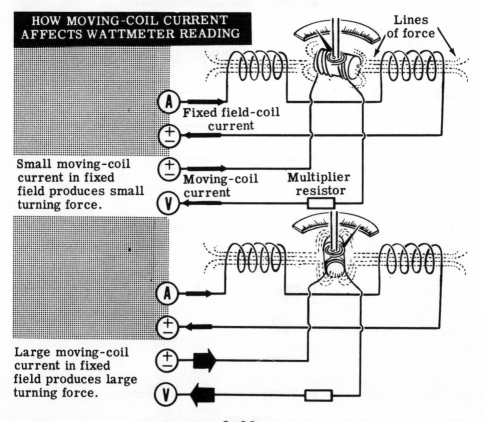

HOW MOVING-COIL CURRENT
AFFECTS WATTMETER READING

Lines of force

Fixed field-coil current

Small moving-coil current in fixed field produces small turning force.

Moving-coil current

Multiplier resistor

Large moving-coil current in fixed field produces large turning force.

Demonstration—Power in Resistive AC Circuits

To show that effective values of AC voltage and current can be used to determine the power used in resistance circuits in the same manner as DC
values, the instructor connects two lamp sockets in parallel across a 7.5-
volt battery—five dry cells in series. Next the 0-10 volt DC voltmeter is
connected across the lamp terminals to measure the circuit voltage.

Six-volt lamps, each rated at 250 ma., are inserted in the sockets and you
see that each lamp lights with equal brilliance. Together they allow 0.5
amperes to flow through the circuit, while the voltage is about 7.5 volts.
Using the power formula (P = EI), the power then is 7.5 x 0.5, or 3.75 watts.

COMPARING POWER USED BY **RESISTIVE** CIRCUITS

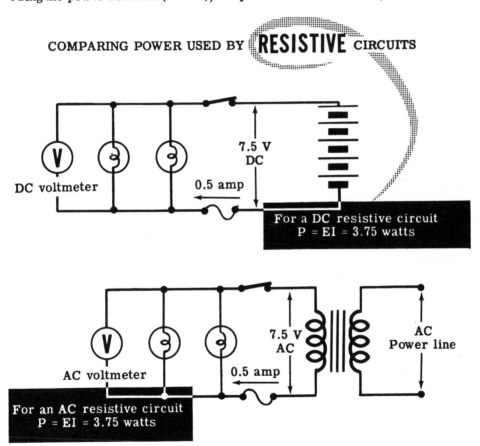

DC voltmeter   7.5 V DC   0.5 amp

For a DC resistive circuit
P = EI = 3.75 watts

AC voltmeter   7.5 V AC   0.5 amp   AC Power line

For an AC resistive circuit
P = EI = 3.75 watts

Next the battery is disconnected and the DC voltmeter is replaced with an
AC meter of the same range. The 6.3-volt transformer is used as an AC
voltage source, and you see that the lamps light as brightly as they did in
the DC circuit. Notice that the voltmeter reading is almost the same as
that obtained using DC, about 7.5 volts.

Applying the power formula, the effective AC power is 7.5 x 0.5, or 3.75
watts, equal to the DC power and causing the same amount of light.

RESISTANCE IN AC CIRCUITS

Demonstration—Power in Resistive AC Circuits (continued)

Wattmeters with a range of less than 75 watts are not generally available and, since it would be difficult to read 3 or 4 watts on a standard 0-75 watt meter scale, a larger amount of power is used to demonstrate power measurement with a wattmeter. To obtain a larger amount of power, the instructor uses the 117-volt AC power line as a power source through a step-down autotransformer, which provides a voltage of about 60 volts AC. He will measure the power used by a resistor, first using a voltmeter and milliammeter and then a wattmeter.

The instructor connects the DPST knife switch and the DP fuse holder in the line cord, as shown below, and inserts 1-amp fuses in the fuse holder. With a 0-500 ma. range AC milliammeter connected in series with one of its leads, the line cord is connected across a 150-ohm, 100-watt resistor. Then a 0-250 volt range AC voltmeter is connected directly across the terminals of the resistor to measure resistor voltage. The line cord plug is inserted in the transformer outlet, and with the switch closed, the line voltage indicated on the voltmeter is about 60 volts, and the 150-ohm resistor allows a current flow of about 0.40 ampere as measured by the milliammeter. The resistor becomes hot due to the power being used, so the switch is opened as soon as the readings have been taken. The current reading may vary slightly as the heated resistor changes in resistance value, so an average current reading is used.

Computing the power used by the resistor you see that it is approximately 24 watts. Assuming that the voltage is 60 volts and the current is exactly 0.40 ampere, the power is then 60 x 0.40, or 24 watts. The actual results may be slightly different, depending on the exact voltage and current readings which are obtained.

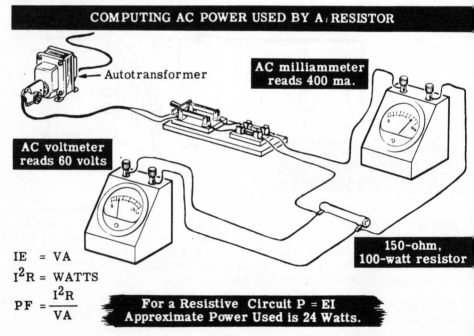

COMPUTING AC POWER USED BY A RESISTOR

Autotransformer

AC milliammeter reads 400 ma.

AC voltmeter reads 60 volts

150-ohm, 100-watt resistor

$IE = VA$

$I^2R = WATTS$

$PF = \dfrac{I^2R}{VA}$

For a Resistive Circuit P = EI
Approximate Power Used is 24 Watts.

Demonstration—Power in Resistive AC Circuits (continued)

Now the milliammeter and voltmeter are removed from the circuit and the wattmeter is connected to measure directly the power used by the resistor. The current and voltage ± terminals are connected together with a short jumper wire to form a common ± terminal. One lead from the fuse block is then connected to this common ± terminal, and the other fuse block lead is connected to the remaining voltage terminal marked **V**. Wires are connected to each end of the resistor and these are in turn connected to the wattmeter—one to the voltage terminal **V** and the other to the current terminal **A**.

When the connections are completed, the autotransformer is connected to the AC power outlet and the switch is closed. You see that the wattmeter indicates that about 24 watts of power is being used. The wattage reading will vary slightly as the resistor heats and changes value, but will become steady when the resistor temperature reaches a maximum. Observe that the measured power is very nearly the same as that obtained using a voltmeter and a milliammeter; and the two results can be considered to be equal for all practical purposes.

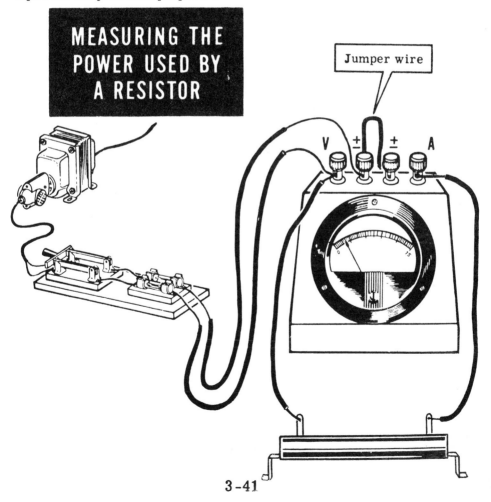

MEASURING THE POWER USED BY A RESISTOR

Jumper wire

Review of Resistance in AC Circuits

Suppose you review some of the facts concerning AC power, power waves and power in resistive circuits. These facts you have already learned will help you to understand other AC circuits, which are not made up of only pure resistance.

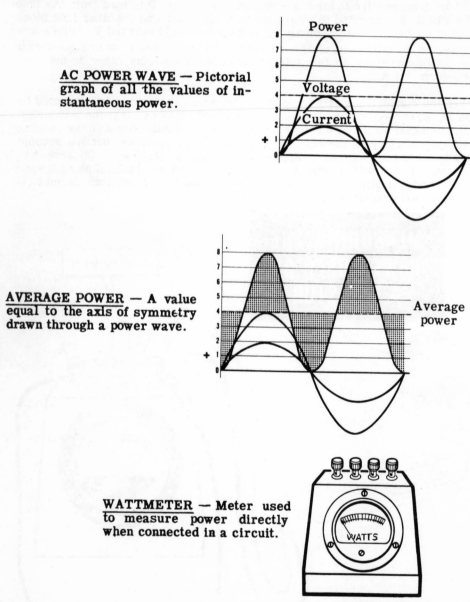

AC POWER WAVE — Pictorial graph of all the values of instantaneous power.

AVERAGE POWER — A value equal to the axis of symmetry drawn through a power wave.

WATTMETER — Meter used to measure power directly when connected in a circuit.

Remember that the power formula (P = EI) can be used to find the power used in a resistive AC circuit, provided effective values of E and I are used.

Emf of Self-Induction

Inductance exists in a circuit because an electric current always produces a magnetic field. The lines of force in this field always encircle the conductor which carries the current, forming concentric circles around the conductor. The strength of the magnetic field depends on the amount of current flow, with a large current producing many lines of force and a small current producing only a few lines of force.

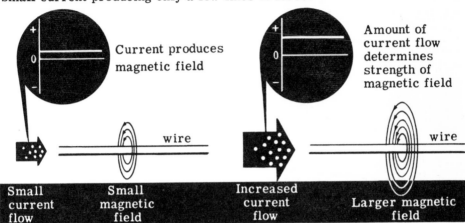

Current produces magnetic field

Amount of current flow determines strength of magnetic field

wire

wire

| Small current flow | Small magnetic field | Increased current flow | Larger magnetic field |

When the circuit current increases or decreases, the magnetic field strength increases and decreases in the same direction. As the field strength increases, the lines of force increase in number and expand outward from the center of the conductor. Similarly, when the field strength decreases, the lines of force contract toward the center of the conductor. It is actually this expansion and contraction of the magnetic field as the current varies which causes an emf of self-induction, and the effect is known as "inductance."

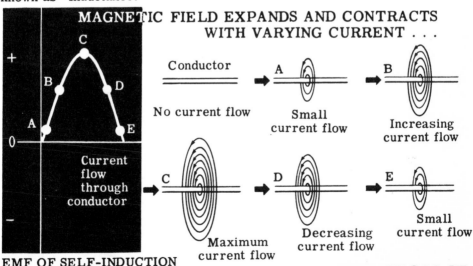

MAGNETIC FIELD EXPANDS AND CONTRACTS WITH VARYING CURRENT . . .

Conductor

No current flow

A Small current flow

B Increasing current flow

Current flow through conductor

C Maximum current flow

D Decreasing current flow

E Small current flow

EMF OF SELF-INDUCTION

CAUSING THE EFFECT KNOWN AS INDUCTANCE

Inductance in a DC Circuit

To see how inductance is caused, suppose your circuit contains a coil like the one shown below. As long as the circuit switch is open, there is no current flow and no field exists around the circuit conductors.

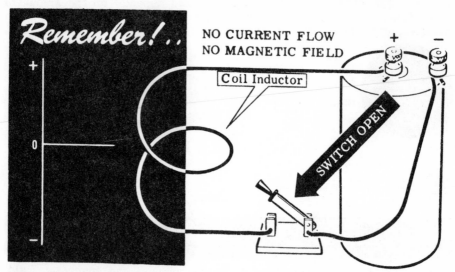

When the switch is closed, current flows through the circuit and lines of force expand outward around the circuit conductors including the turns of the coil. At the instant the switch is closed, the current flow starts rising from zero toward its maximum value. Although this rise in current flow is very rapid, it cannot be instantaneous. Imagine that you actually are able to see the lines of force in the circuit at the instant the current starts to flow. You see that they form a field around the circuit conductors.

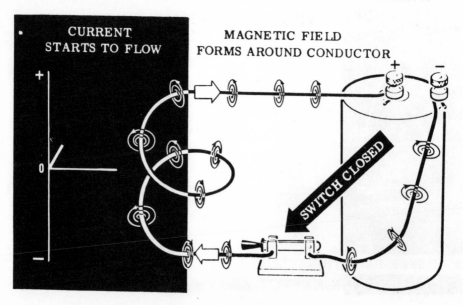

Inductance in a DC Circuit (continued)

As the current continues to increase, the lines of force continue to expand. The fields of adjacent turns of wire interlace.

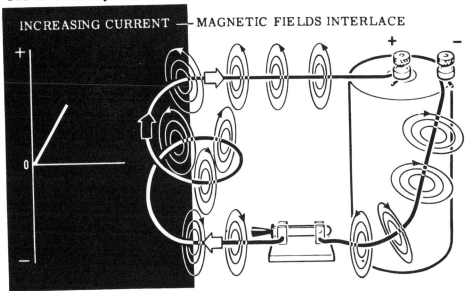

INCREASING CURRENT — MAGNETIC FIELDS INTERLACE

The lines of force around each turn continue their expansion and, in so doing, cut across adjacent turns of the coil. This expansion continues as long as the circuit current is increasing, with more and more lines of force from the coil turns cutting across adjacent turns of the coil.

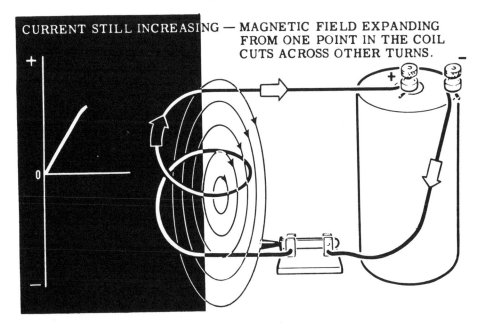

CURRENT STILL INCREASING — MAGNETIC FIELD EXPANDING FROM ONE POINT IN THE COIL CUTS ACROSS OTHER TURNS.

Inductance in a DC Circuit (continued)

Whenever a magnetic field moves across a wire, it induces an emf in the wire. Whenever a current flows through a coil, it induces a magnetic field that cuts adjacent coil turns. Whenever the initial current changes in direction, the induced field changes and the effect of this changing field in cutting the adjacent coil turns is to oppose the change in current. The initial current change is caused by the emf, or voltage, across the coil and this opposing force is an emf of self-induction. Inductance is the measure of the ability of a circuit or coil to generate an emf of self-induction that opposes changes in the current flowing through the coil.

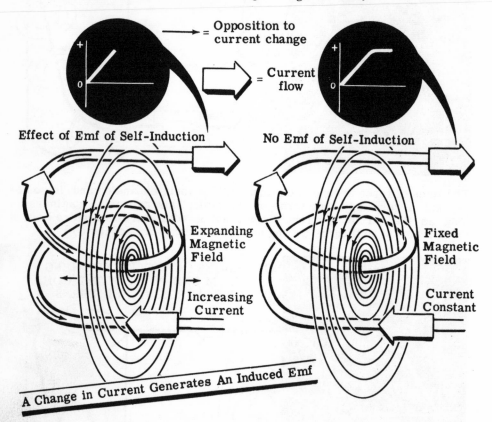

= Opposition to current change

= Current flow

Effect of Emf of Self-Induction

No Emf of Self-Induction

Expanding Magnetic Field

Increasing Current

Fixed Magnetic Field

Current Constant

A Change in Current Generates An Induced Emf

When the circuit current reaches its maximum value, determined by the circuit voltage and resistance, it no longer changes in value and the field no longer expands, so that no emf of self-induction is generated. The field remains stationary but, should the current attempt to rise or fall, the field will either expand or contract and generate an emf of self-induction opposing the change in current flow. For direct current, inductance affects the current flow only when the power is turned on and off, since only at those times does the current change in value.

Inductance in a DC Circuit (continued)

With the current and magnetic field at maximum, no emf of self-induction is generated but if you lowered the source voltage or increased the circuit resistance, the current would decrease. Suppose the source voltage decreases. The current drops toward its new Ohm's law value, determined by E and R. As the current decreases the field also diminishes, with each line of force contracting inward toward the conductor. This contracting or collapsing field cuts across the coil turns in a direction opposite to that caused by the rise in circuit current.

Since the direction of change is reversed, the collapsing field generates an emf of self-induction opposite to that caused by the expanding field, thus having the same polarity as the source voltage. This emf of self-induction then increases the source voltage, trying to prevent the fall in current. However, it cannot keep the current from falling indefinitely since the emf of self-induction ceases to exist whenever the current stops changing. Thus inductance—the effect of emf of self-induction—opposes any change in current flow, whether it be an increase or decrease, slowing down the rate at which the change occurs.

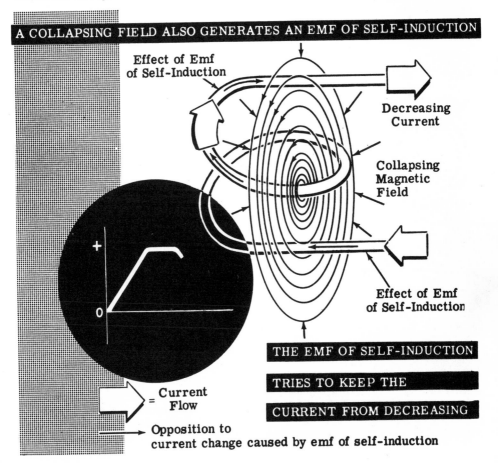

A COLLAPSING FIELD ALSO GENERATES AN EMF OF SELF-INDUCTION

Effect of Emf of Self-Induction

Decreasing Current

Collapsing Magnetic Field

Effect of Emf of Self-Induction

THE EMF OF SELF-INDUCTION

TRIES TO KEEP THE

CURRENT FROM DECREASING

= Current Flow

Opposition to current change caused by emf of self-induction

Inductance in a DC Circuit (continued)

As long as the circuit is closed, the current remains at its Ohm's law value and no induced emf is generated. Now suppose you open the switch to stop the current flow. The current should fall to zero and stop flowing immediately but, instead, there is a slight delay and a spark jumps across the switch contacts.

When the switch is opened, the current drops rapidly toward zero and the field also collapses at a very rapid rate. The rapidly collapsing field generates a very high induced emf, which not only opposes the change in current but also causes an arc across the switch to maintain the current flow. Although only momentary, the induced emf caused by this rapid field collapse is very high, sometimes many times that of the original source voltage. This action is often used to advantage in special types of equipment to obtain very high voltages.

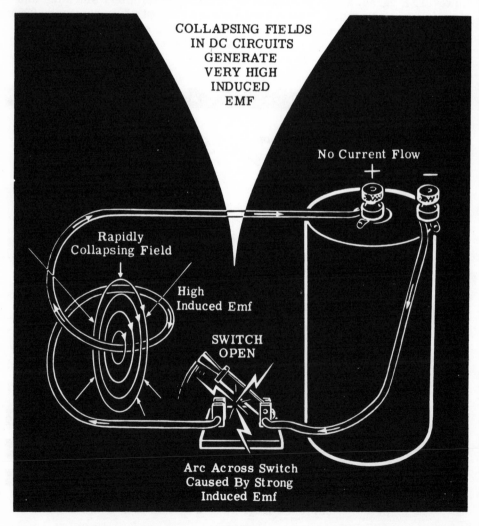

COLLAPSING FIELDS
IN DC CIRCUITS
GENERATE
VERY HIGH
INDUCED
EMF

No Current Flow

Rapidly
Collapsing Field

High
Induced Emf

SWITCH
OPEN

Arc Across Switch
Caused By Strong
Induced Emf

Inductance Symbols

While you cannot see inductance, it is present in every electrical circuit and has an effect on the circuit whenever the circuit current changes. In electrical formulas the letter L is used as a symbol to designate inductance. Because a coil of wire has more inductance than a straight length of the same wire, the coil is called an "inductor." Both the letter and the symbol are illustrated below.

Since direct current is normally constant in value except when the circuit power is turned on and off to start and stop the current flow, inductance affects DC current flow only at these times and usually has very little effect on the operation of the circuit. Alternating current, however, is continuously changing so that the circuit inductance affects AC current flow at all times. Although every circuit has some inductance, the value depends upon the physical construction of the circuit, and the electrical devices used in it. In some circuits the inductance is so small its effect is negligible, even for AC current flow.

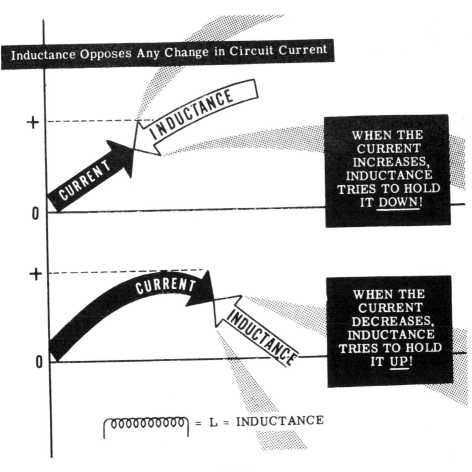

Inductance Opposes Any Change in Circuit Current

WHEN THE CURRENT INCREASES, INDUCTANCE TRIES TO HOLD IT DOWN!

WHEN THE CURRENT DECREASES, INDUCTANCE TRIES TO HOLD IT UP!

= L = INDUCTANCE

Factors Which Affect Inductance

Every complete electric circuit has some inductance since the simplest circuit forms a complete loop or single-turn coil. An induced emf is generated even in a straight piece of wire, by the action of the magnetic field expanding outward from the center of the wire or collapsing inward to the wire center. The greater the number of adjacent turns of wire cut across by the expanding field, the greater the induced emf generated—so that a coil of wire having many turns has a high inductance.

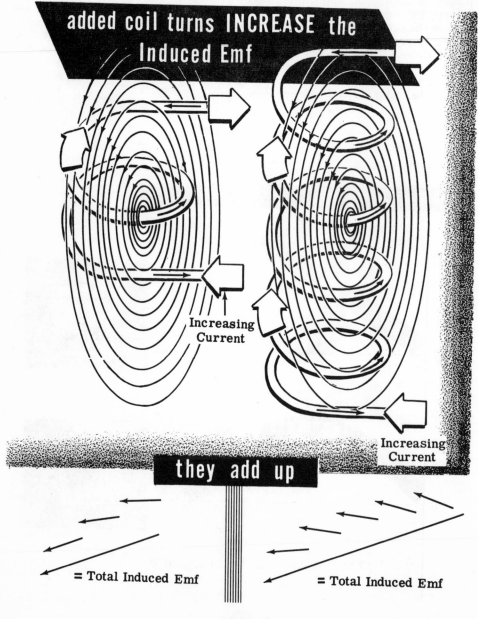

added coil turns INCREASE the Induced Emf

Increasing Current

Increasing Current

they add up

= Total Induced Emf

= Total Induced Emf

Factors Which Affect Inductance (continued)

Any factors which tend to affect the strength of the magnetic field also affect the inductance of a circuit. For example, an iron core inserted in a coil increases the inductance because it provides a better path for magnetic lines of force than air. Therefore, more lines of force are present that can expand and contract when there is a change in current. A copper core piece has exactly the opposite effect. Since copper opposes lines of force more than air, inserting a copper core piece results in less field change when the current changes, thereby reducing the inductance.

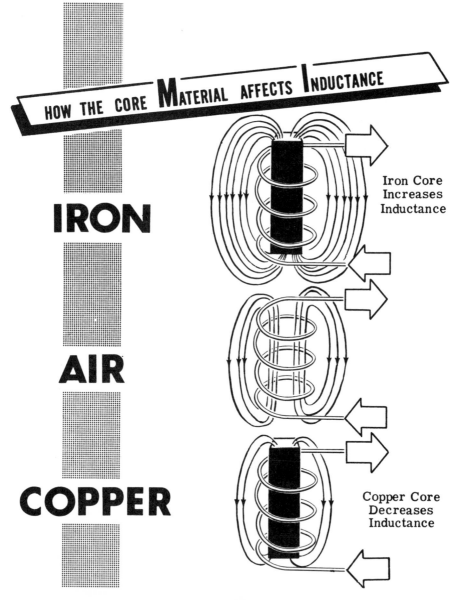

HOW THE CORE **M**ATERIAL AFFECTS **I**NDUCTANCE

IRON

AIR

COPPER

Iron Core
Increases
Inductance

Copper Core
Decreases
Inductance

Units of Inductance

In electrical formulas the letter L is used as a symbol to designate inductance. The basic unit of measure for inductance is the henry. For quantities of inductance smaller than one henry, the millihenry and microhenry are used. A unit larger than the henry is not used since inductance normally is of a value which can be expressed in henries or part of a henry.

Inductance can only be measured with special laboratory instruments and depends entirely on the physical construction of the circuit. Some of the factors most important in determining the amount of inductance of a coil are: the number of turns, the spacing between turns, coil diameter, kind of material around and inside the coil, the wire size, number of layers of wire, type of coil winding and the overall shape of the coil. Wire size does not affect the inductance directly, but it does determine the number of turns that can be wound in a given space. All of these factors are variable, and no single formula can be used to find inductance. Many differently constructed coils could have an inductance of one henry, and each would have the same effect in the circuit.

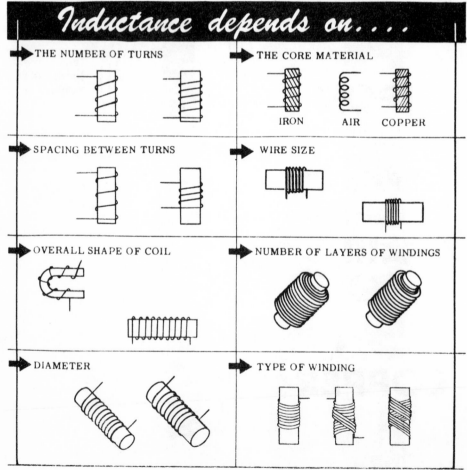

Inductance depends on....

THE NUMBER OF TURNS

THE CORE MATERIAL

IRON   AIR   COPPER

SPACING BETWEEN TURNS

WIRE SIZE

OVERALL SHAPE OF COIL

NUMBER OF LAYERS OF WINDINGS

DIAMETER

TYPE OF WINDING

INDUCTANCE IN AC CIRCUITS

Mutual Induction

The term "mutual induction" refers to the condition in which two circuits are sharing the energy of one of the circuits. It means that energy is being transferred from one circuit to another.

Consider the diagram below. Coil A is the primary circuit which obtains energy from the battery. When the switch is closed, the current starts to flow and a magnetic field expands out of coil A. Coil A then changes electrical energy of the battery into the magnetic energy of a magnetic field. When the field of coil A is expanding, it cuts across coil B, the secondary circuit, inducing an emf in coil B. The indicator (a galvanometer) in the secondary circuit is deflected, and shows that a current, developed by the induced emf, is flowing in the circuit.

The induced emf may be generated by moving coil B through the flux of coil A. However, this voltage is induced without moving coil B. When the switch in the primary circuit is open, coil A has no current and no field. As soon as the switch is closed, current passes through the coil and the magnetic field is generated. This expanding field moves or "cuts" across the wires of coil B, thus inducing an emf without the movement of coil B.

The magnetic field expands to its maximum strength and remains constant as long as full current flows. Flux lines stop their cutting action across the turns of coil B because expansion of the field has ceased. At this point the indicator needle reads zero because no induced emf exists anymore. If the switch is opened, the field collapses back to the wires of coil A. As it does so, the changing flux cuts across the wires of coil B, but in the opposite direction. The current present in the coil causes the indicator needle to deflect, showing this new direction. The indicator, then, shows current flow only when the field is changing, either building up or collapsing. In effect, the changing field produces an induced emf exactly as does a magnetic field moving across a conductor. This principle of inducing voltage by holding the coils steady and forcing the field to change is used in innumerable applications. The transformer, as shown in the diagram below, is particularly suitable for operation by mutual induction.

For purposes of explanation a battery is used in the above example. The transformer is, however, a perfect component for transferring and changing AC voltages as needed.

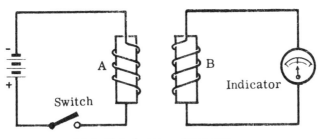

Mutual Induction Circuits

How a Transformer Works

When AC flows through a coil, an alternating magnetic field is generated around the coil. This alternating magnetic field expands outward from the center of the coil and collapses into the coil as the AC through the coil varies from zero to a maximum and back to zero again. Since the alternating magnetic field must cut through the turns of the coil an emf of self induction is induced in the coil which opposes the change in current flow.

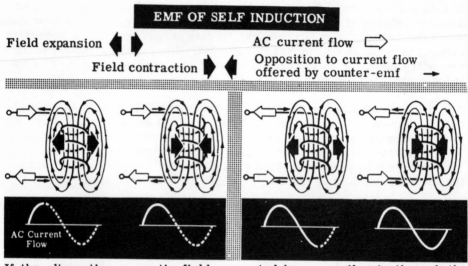

EMF OF SELF INDUCTION

Field expansion ◀ ▶   AC current flow ▭▷

Field contraction ▶ ◀   Opposition to current flow offered by counter-emf →

AC Current Flow

If the alternating magnetic field generated by one coil cuts through the turns of a second coil, an emf will be generated in this second coil just as an emf is induced in a coil which is cut by its own magnetic field. The emf generated in the second coil is called the "emf of mutual induction," and the action of generating this voltage is called "transformer action." In transformer action, electrical energy is transferred from one coil (the primary) to another (the secondary) by means of a varying magnetic field.

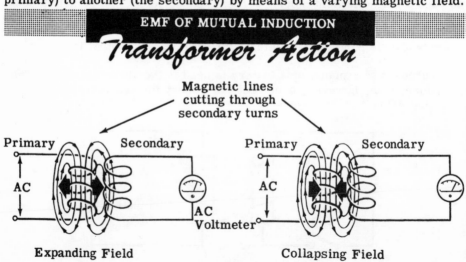

EMF OF MUTUAL INDUCTION

Transformer Action

Magnetic lines cutting through secondary turns

Primary   Secondary   Primary   Secondary

AC   AC Voltmeter   AC

Expanding Field   Collapsing Field

How a Transformer Works (continued)

A simple transformer consists of two coils very close together, electrically insulated from each other. The coil to which the AC is applied is called the "primary." It generates a magnetic field which cuts through the turns of the other coil, called the "secondary," and generates a voltage in it. The coils are not physically connected to each other. They are, however, magnetically coupled to each other. Thus, a transformer transfers electrical power from one coil to another by means of an alternating magnetic field.

Assuming that all the magnetic lines of force from the primary cut through all the turns of the secondary, the voltage induced in the secondary will depend on the ratio of the number of turns in the secondary to the number of turns in the primary. For example, if there are 1000 turns in the secondary and only 100 turns in the primary, the voltage induced in the secondary will be 10 times the voltage applied to the primary ($\frac{1000}{100}$ = 10). Since there are more turns in the secondary than there are in the primary, the transformer is called a "step-up transformer." If, on the other hand, the secondary has 10 turns and the primary has 100 turns, the voltage induced in the secondary will be one-tenth of the voltage applied to the primary ($\frac{10}{100} = \frac{1}{10}$). Since there are less turns in the secondary than there are in the primary, the transformer is called a "step-down transformer." Transformers are rated in KVA because it is independent of power factor.

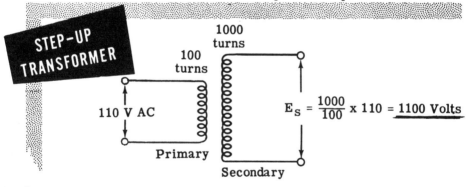

STEP-UP TRANSFORMER

100 turns

1000 turns

110 V AC

$E_S = \frac{1000}{100}$ x 110 = <u>1100 Volts</u>

Primary

Secondary

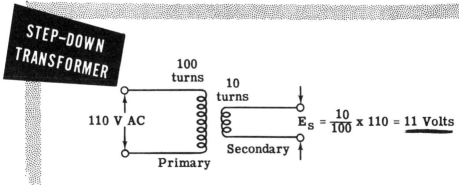

STEP-DOWN TRANSFORMER

100 turns

10 turns

110 V AC

$E_S = \frac{10}{100}$ x 110 = <u>11 Volts</u>

Primary

Secondary

How a Transformer Works (continued)

The current in the primary of a transformer flows in a direction opposite to that which flows in the secondary because of the emf of mutual-induction. An emf of self-induction is also set up in the primary which is in opposition to the applied emf.

When no load is present at the output of the secondary, the primary current is very small because the emf of self-induction is almost as large as the applied emf. If no load is present at the secondary there is no current flow. Thus, the magnetic field of self-induction, which usually bucks the magnetic field of the primary, cannot be developed in the secondary. The magnetic field of the primary may then develop to its maximum strength without opposition from the field which is usually developed by current flow in the secondary. When the primary field is developing to its maximum strength it produces the strongest possible emf of self-induction and this opposes the applied voltage. This is the point, mentioned above, at which the emf of self-induction almost equals the applied emf. Any difference between the emf of self-induction and the applied emf causes a small current to flow in the primary and this is the exciting or magnetizing current.

The current which flows in the secondary is opposite to the current in the primary. As a load is applied to the secondary it causes the momentary collapse of flux lines which produces a demagnetizing effect on the flux linking the primary. The reduction in flux lines reduces the emf of self-induction and permits more current to flow in the primary.

In all cases of electromagnetic induction the direction of the induced emf is such that the magnetic field set up by the resulting current opposes the motion which is producing the emf. This is a statement of Lenz's law which you will learn about in the next section.

In order to find the unknowns in a transformer use the formula $\dfrac{E_p}{E_s} = \dfrac{I_s}{I_p} = \dfrac{T_p}{T_s}$ and cross-multiply to find the required information. Further details about transformers will be included at the end of this section.

2 To 1 Ratio

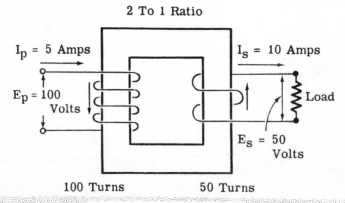

I_p = 5 Amps $\qquad$ I_s = 10 Amps

E_p = 100 Volts $\qquad$ Load

E_s = 50 Volts

100 Turns $\qquad$ 50 Turns

Example of a
Step-Down Transformer

INDUCTANCE IN AC CIRCUITS

Faraday's Law

Michael Faraday was an English scientist who did a great deal of important work in the field of electromagnetism. He is of interest to you at this time because his work in mutual induction eventually led to the development of the transformer.

Faraday is responsible for the law which is used in developing the principles of mutual induction. He found that if the total flux linking a circuit changes with time, an emf is induced in the circuit. Faraday also found that if the rate of flux-change is increased, the magnitude of the induced emf is increased as well. Stated in other terms, Faraday found that the character of an emf induced in a circuit depends upon the amount of flux and also the rate of change of flux which links a circuit.

You have all seen demonstrations of the principle just stated. You have been shown that if a conductor is made to move with respect to a magnetic field an emf is induced in the conductor which is directly proportional to the velocity of the conductor with respect to the field. The other point concerning Faraday's Law which has been demonstrated is the fact that the voltage induced in a coil is proportional to the number of turns of the coil, the magnitude of the inducing flux and the rate of change of this flux.

An example of mutual induction (inducing an emf in a neighboring conductor) is now described. Consider the two coils in the figure below. Electrons are moving as a current in the directions indicated. This current produces a flux of magnetic field and if the current remains constant the number of flux lines produced is fixed. If, however, the current is changed by opening the shorting switch, the number of flux lines in coil A is decreased, and consequently the flux linking coil B is decreased also. This changing flux induces an emf in coil B, as evidenced by the movement of the indicator pointer. Thus, it is seen that energy can be transferred from one circuit to another by the principle of electromagnetic induction.

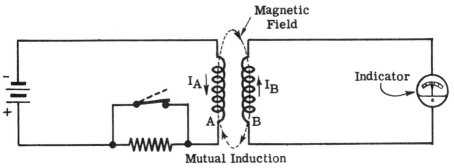

Mutual Induction

A battery is used in the above diagram as a source of emf. The only way current variations can be developed, then, is by the opening or closing of the switch. If an AC voltage source with an extremely low frequency (one cycle per second) is used to replace the battery, the indicator shows continuous variations in current. The indicator needle moves to the left (or right) first, and then reverses its position, to show the reversal in AC flow.

INDUCTANCE IN AC CIRCUITS

Inductive Time Constant in a DC Circuit

In a circuit consisting of a battery, switch and a resistor in series, the current rises to its maximum value at once whenever the switch is closed. Actually it cannot change from zero to its maximum value instantaneously, but the time is so short that it can be considered to be instantaneous.

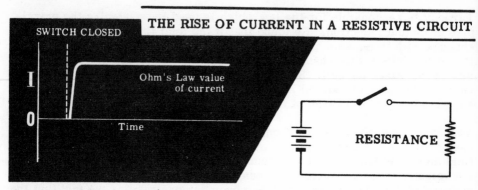

THE RISE OF CURRENT IN A RESISTIVE CIRCUIT

SWITCH CLOSED

Ohm's Law value of current

Time

RESISTANCE

If a coil of wire is used in series with the resistor, the current does not rise instantaneously—it rises rapidly at first, then more slowly as the maximum value is approached. For all inductive circuits the shape of this curve is basically the same, although the total time required to reach the maximum current value varies. The time required for the current to rise to its maximum value is determined by the ratio of the circuit inductance to its resistance in ohms. This ratio L/R—inductance divided by the resistance—is called the "time constant" of the inductive circuit and gives the time in seconds required for the circuit current to rise to 63.2 percent of its maximum value.

This delayed rise in the current of a circuit is caused by "self-inductance," and is used in many practical circuits such as time-delay relay and starting circuits.

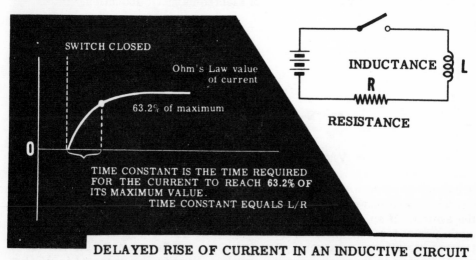

SWITCH CLOSED

Ohm's Law value of current

63.2% of maximum

INDUCTANCE L

R

RESISTANCE

TIME CONSTANT IS THE TIME REQUIRED FOR THE CURRENT TO REACH 63.2% OF ITS MAXIMUM VALUE.
TIME CONSTANT EQUALS L/R

DELAYED RISE OF CURRENT IN AN INDUCTIVE CIRCUIT

Inductive Time Constant in a DC Circuit (continued)

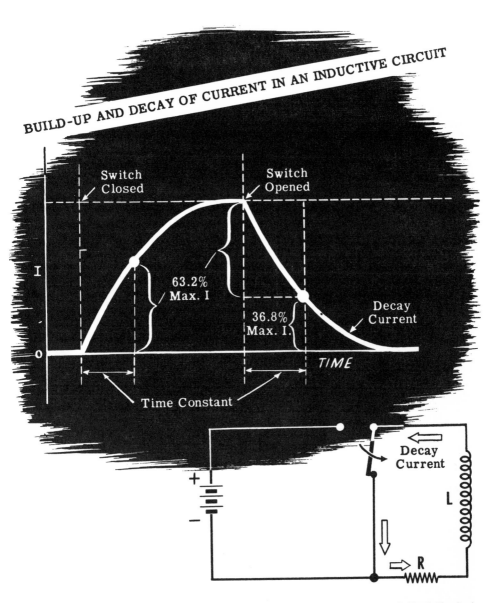

BUILD-UP AND DECAY OF CURRENT IN AN INDUCTIVE CIRCUIT

Switch Closed

Switch Opened

63.2% Max. I

36.8% Max. I

Decay Current

TIME

Time Constant

Decay Current

+

−

L

R

If the coil terminals are shorted together at the same moment that the battery switch is opened, the coil current continues to flow due to the action of the collapsing field. The current falls in the same manner as the original rise in current, except that the curve is in the opposite direction.

Again the "time constant" can be used to determine when the current has decreased by 63.2 percent, or has reached 36.8 percent of its original maximum value. For inductive circuits the lower the circuit resistance, the longer the time constant for the same value of inductance.

INDUCTANCE IN AC CIRCUITS

Inductive Time Constant in a DC Circuit (continued)

The time constant of a given inductive circuit is always the same for both the build-up and decay of the current. If the maximum current value differs, the curve may rise at a different rate but will reach its maximum in the same amount of time; and the general shape of the curve is the same. Thus, if a greater voltage is used, the maximum current will increase but the time required to reach the maximum is unchanged.

Every inductive circuit has resistance, since the wire used in a coil always has resistance. Thus a perfect inductance—an inductor with no resistance—is not possible.

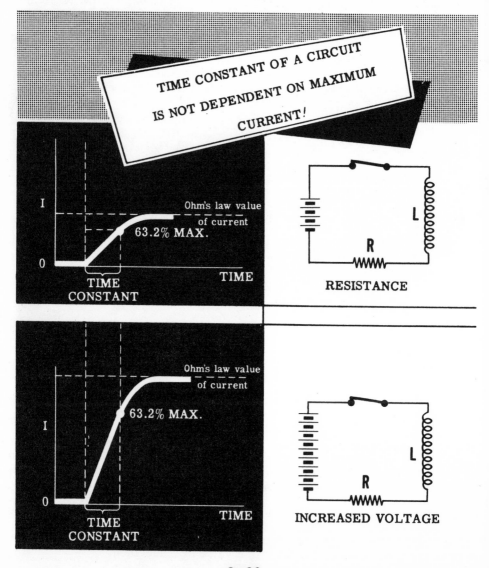

TIME CONSTANT OF A CIRCUIT IS NOT DEPENDENT ON MAXIMUM CURRENT!

Ohm's law value of current

63.2% MAX.

RESISTANCE

Ohm's law value of current

63.2% MAX.

INCREASED VOLTAGE

INDUCTANCE IN AC CIRCUITS

Inductive Reactance

Inductive reactance is the opposition to current flow offered by the inductance of a circuit. As you know, inductance only affects current flow while the current is changing, since the current change generates an induced emf. For direct current the effect of inductance is noticeable only when the current is turned on and off but, since alternating current is continuously changing, a continuous induced emf is generated.

Suppose you consider the effect of a given inductive circuit on DC and AC waveforms. The time constant of the circuit is always the same, determined only by the resistance and inductance of the circuit.

For DC the current waveforms would be as shown below. At the beginning of the current waveform, there is a shaded area between the maximum current value and the actual current flow which shows that inductance is opposing the change in current as the magnetic field builds up. Also, at the end of the current waveform, a similar area exists showing that current flow continues after the voltage drops to zero because of the field collapse. These shaded areas are equal, indicating that the energy used to build up the magnetic field is given back to the circuit when the field collapses.

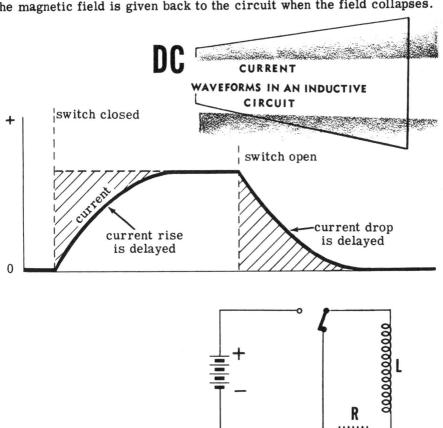

DC CURRENT WAVEFORMS IN AN INDUCTIVE CIRCUIT

switch closed

switch open

current rise is delayed

current drop is delayed

Inductive Reactance (continued)

The same inductive circuit would affect AC voltage and current waveforms as shown below. The current rises as the voltage rises, but the delay due to inductance prevents the current from ever reaching its maximum DC value before the voltage reverses polarity and changes the direction of current flow. Thus, in a circuit containing inductance, the maximum current will be much greater for DC than for AC.

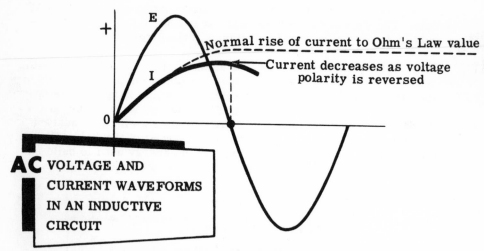

AC VOLTAGE AND CURRENT WAVEFORMS IN AN INDUCTIVE CIRCUIT

If the frequency of the AC wave is low, the current will have time to reach a higher value before the polarity is reversed than if the frequency is high. Thus the higher the frequency, the lower the circuit current through an inductive circuit. Frequency, then, affects the opposition to current flow as does circuit inductance. For that reason, inductive reactance—opposition to current flow offered by an inductance—depends on frequency and inductance. The formula used to obtain inductive reactance is $X_L = 2\pi fL$. In this formula X_L is inductive reactance, f is frequency in cycles per second, L is the inductance in henries, and 2π is a constant number (6.28) representing one complete cycle. Since X_L represents opposition to current flow, it is expressed in ohms.

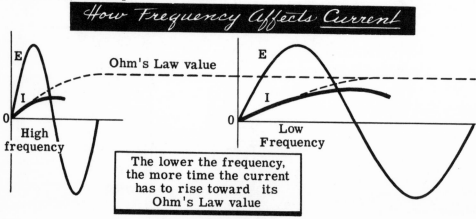

How Frequency Affects Current

The lower the frequency, the more time the current has to rise toward its Ohm's Law value

INDUCTANCE IN AC CIRCUITS

Inductive Reactance (continued)

Actually the circuit current does not begin to rise at the same time the voltage begins to rise. The current is delayed to an extent depending on the amount of inductance in the circuit as compared to the resistance.

If an AC circuit has only pure resistance, the current rises and falls at exactly the same time as the voltage and the two waves are said to be in phase with each other.

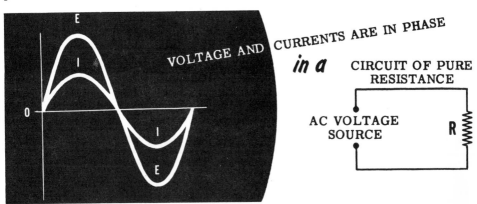

VOLTAGE AND CURRENTS ARE IN PHASE

in a CIRCUIT OF PURE RESISTANCE

With a theoretical circuit of pure inductance and no resistance, the current will not begin to flow until the voltage has reached its maximum value, and the current wave then rises while the voltage falls to zero. At the moment the voltage reaches zero the current starts to drop towards zero, but the collapsing field delays the current drop until the voltage reaches its maximum value in the opposite polarity. This continues as long as voltage is applied to the circuit, with the voltage wave reaching its maximum value a quarter cycle before the current wave on each half cycle. A complete cycle of an AC wave is considered to be 360 degrees, represented by the emf generated in a wire rotated once around in a complete circle between two opposite magnetic poles. A quarter cycle then is 90 degrees; and in a purely inductive circuit the voltage wave leads the current by 90 degrees or, in opposite terms, the current wave lags the voltage by 90 degrees.

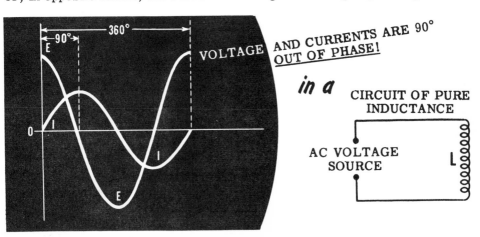

VOLTAGE AND CURRENTS ARE 90° OUT OF PHASE!

in a CIRCUIT OF PURE INDUCTANCE

INDUCTANCE IN AC CIRCUITS

Inductive Reactance (continued)

In a circuit containing both inductive reactance and resistance, the AC current wave will lag the voltage wave by an amount between zero degrees and 90 degrees; or, stated otherwise, it will lag somewhere between "in phase" and "90 degrees out of phase." The exact amount of lag depends on the ratio of circuit resistance to inductance—the greater the resistance compared to the inductance, the nearer the two waves are to being "in phase"; and the lower the resistance compared to the inductance, the nearer the waves are to being a full quarter cycle (90 degrees) "out of phase."

When stated in degrees the current lag is called the "phase angle." If the phase angle between the voltage and the current is 45 degrees lagging, it means that the current wave is lagging the voltage wave by 45 degrees. Since this is halfway between zero degrees—the phase angle for a pure resistive circuit—and 90 degrees—the phase angle for a pure inductive circuit—the resistance and the inductance reactance must be equal, with each having an equal effect on the current flow.

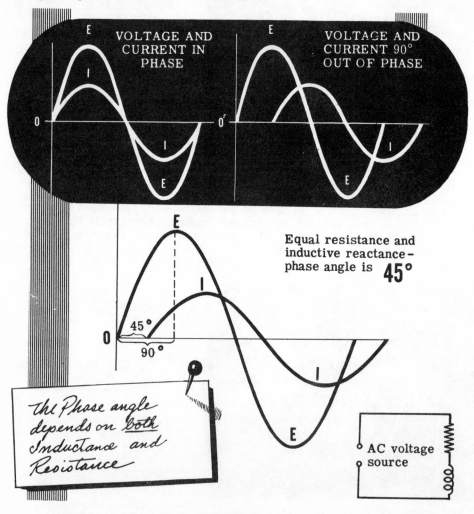

Equal resistance and inductive reactance—phase angle is **45°**

the Phase angle depends on both Inductance and Resistance

AC voltage source

INDUCTANCE IN AC CIRCUITS

Demonstration—Effect of Core Material on Inductance

The instructor wires a series circuit of the flat air-core coil and the 60-watt lamp. When the circuit is energized from the 115-volt AC line, the lamp brilliance is noted.

With the circuit energized, the instructor carefully inserts the iron core into the coil. Note the decrease in lamp brilliance resulting from the increased inductance of the coil. A larger percentage of the 115-volt source voltage is now dropped across the coil.

Next he removes the iron core and inserts a copper core. Note the increase in lamp brilliance resulting from the decreased inductance of the coil. The large eddy current losses in the copper weaken the coil magnetic field, thus decreasing its inductance. A larger percentage of the source voltage is now dropped across the lamp and it, therefore, gets brighter.

He next removes the copper core and inserts the laminated core. Note that the lamp brilliance has dropped greatly. The laminated iron core has increased the coil inductance an even greater amount than the solid iron core because the laminations have greatly reduced the eddy current losses. Most of the source voltage is now dropped across the coil and as a result the lamp barely lights.

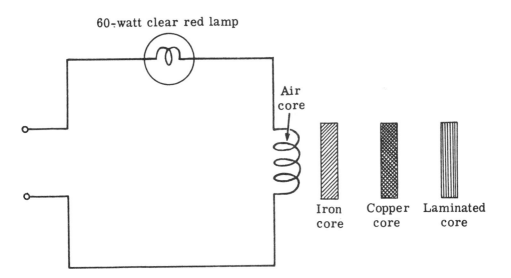

60-watt clear red lamp

Air core

Iron core   Copper core   Laminated core

HOW INDUCTANCE VARIES WITH CORE MATERIAL

INDUCTANCE IN AC CIRCUITS

Demonstration—Generation of Induced EMF

When the current flow in a DC circuit containing inductance is stopped abruptly, by opening a switch, for example, the magnetic field of the inductance tries to collapse instantaneously. The rapid collapse of the field momentarily generates a very high voltage, and this induced emf may cause an arc at the switch. While the field collapse is too rapid to allow measurement of this voltage with a voltmeter, a neon lamp can be used to show that the voltage is much higher than the original battery voltage.

Neon lamps differ from ordinary lamps in that they require a certain voltage before they begin to light. This voltage, called the "starting voltage," varies for different neon lamps. Its value can be determined by increasing the voltage applied across the lamp until it lights. The voltage applied at the time the lamp first lights is the starting voltage.

To find the starting voltage required for the neon lamp, the instructor first connects two 45-volt batteries in series to form a 90-volt battery. Across the 90-volt battery he connects a variable resistor as a potentiometer, with the outside or end terminals of the variable resistor connected to the battery terminals. A lamp socket is connected between the center terminal of the variable resistor and one of the outside terminals, and a 0-100 volt range DC voltmeter is connected across the lamp socket terminals.

With the neon lamp inserted, the instructor varies the voltage applied to the lamp by varying the setting of the variable resistor. The correct starting voltage is found by lowering the voltage to a value which does not light the lamp, and then slowly increasing it until the lamp first lights. You see that the starting voltage required to light the lamp is approximately 70 volts.

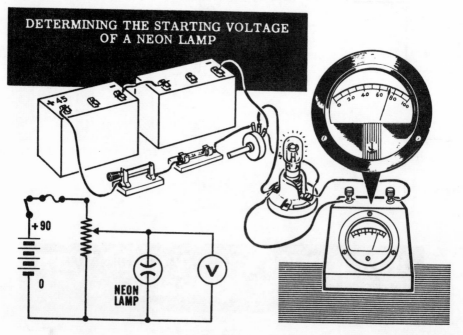

DETERMINING THE STARTING VOLTAGE OF A NEON LAMP

NEON LAMP

INDUCTANCE IN AC CIRCUITS

Demonstration—Generation of Induced Emf (continued)

Next, four dry cells are connected in series to form a 6-volt battery, with the lamp socket connected across its terminals through a fuse and switch. A neon lamp is inserted in the socket, and the choke coil is connected across the lamp terminals.

When the instructor closes the switch, you see that the lamp does not light and the battery voltage measured with an 0-10 volt DC voltmeter is 6 volts. Since six volts is less than the starting voltage of the lamp, some means of obtaining a higher voltage is required in order to cause the lamp to light.

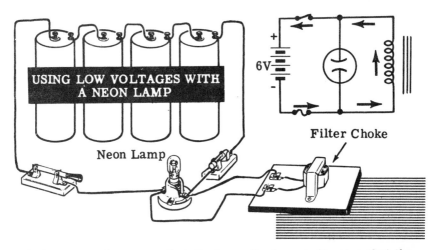

As the switch is opened you see that the lamp flashes, indicating that the voltage across the lamp and coil in parallel is higher than the starting voltage required for the lamp. This voltage is the induced emf generated by the collapsing field of the choke, and is a visible effect of inductance.

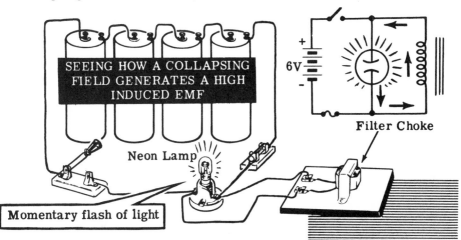

INDUCTANCE IN AC CIRCUITS

Demonstration—Current Flow in Inductive Circuits

To compare the effect of circuit inductance on the amount of current flow in AC and DC circuits, the instructor connects two identical circuits—one using the six-volt battery as a DC voltage source and the other using the 6.3-volt transformer as an AC voltage source, with the correct type of meters (AC or DC) being used in each circuit. At first the two circuits will be compared when 60 ohms of resistance is the only load, with 0-500 ma. range milliammeters, 0-10 volt DC and 0-25 volt AC voltmeters connected to measure the voltage and current. Two 30-ohm resistors in series are used to obtain each resistance. Observe that the current and voltage readings are very nearly the same for the two circuits.

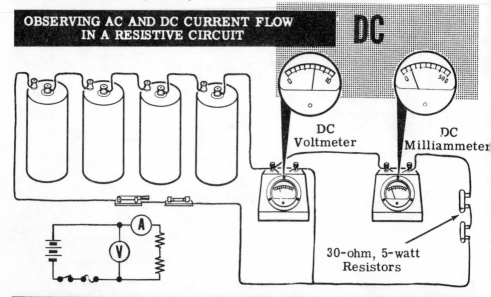

OBSERVING AC AND DC CURRENT FLOW IN A RESISTIVE CIRCUIT

DC

DC
Voltmeter

DC
Milliammeter

30-ohm, 5-watt
Resistors

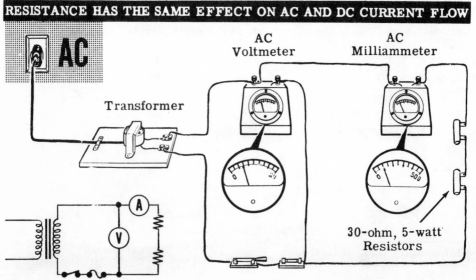

RESISTANCE HAS THE SAME EFFECT ON AC AND DC CURRENT FLOW

AC

AC
Voltmeter

AC
Milliammeter

Transformer

30-ohm, 5-watt
Resistors

Demonstration—Current Flow in Inductive Circuits (continued)

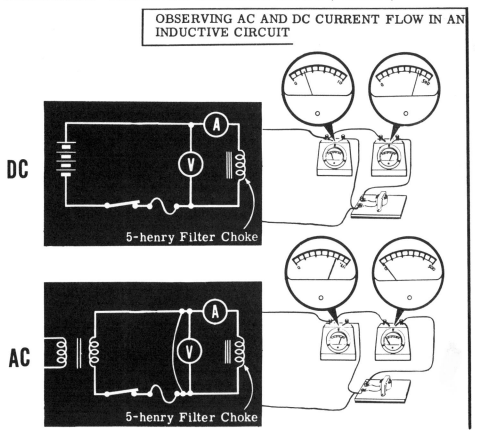

OBSERVING AC AND DC CURRENT FLOW IN AN INDUCTIVE CIRCUIT

DC — 5-henry Filter Choke

AC — 5-henry Filter Choke

Inductance holds back AC current more than DC current

Next, the resistors are removed from the circuits and replaced by 5-henry, 60-ohm filter chokes. With power applied, you see that the current flow in the DC circuit is approximately the same as when the resistors were in the circuit, but the current in the AC circuit is much less and cannot be read on the 0-500 ma. range AC milliammeter, because the deflection is too small to be observed.

Although the filter choke is rated at 2 henries, it only operates at this value when the current is 200 ma. DC. Its inductance is greater for the smaller current values which you commonly use, and its effect can be calculated by assuming an inductance of 5 henries. For DC, the inductance has no effect, and the choke merely acts as a 60-ohm resistor. For AC, since the voltage and current are changing constantly, inductance is an important factor. The effect which inductive reactance has on AC can be calculated by using the formula $X_L = 2\pi fL$ (2π = 6.28, f = 60 cycles which is the power line frequency and L = 5 henries). You can find the inductive reactance, X_L, by substituting these values for the formula symbols and multiplying them together (X_L = 6.28 x 60 x 5 = 1884 Ω). Inductive reactance is expressed in ohms, since it opposes or "resists" AC current flow.

Demonstration—Current Flow in Inductive Circuits (continued)

To further demonstrate that it is the inductive reactance which is reducing the current flow in the AC circuit, the instructor connects a lamp socket in series with the choke in each circuit. With the power applied to each circuit you see that the lamp lights dimly in the DC circuit, but the current in the AC circuit is insufficient to light the lamp.

Using short pieces of wire as jumpers, the instructor shorts across the terminals of the chokes in each circuit. In the DC circuit the lamp brightness increases, showing that the circuit resistance has been reduced. In the AC circuit the lamp lights to a brightness equal to that of the lamp in the DC circuit. Since the lamp brightness is changed from no light to maximum brightness in the AC circuit, you see that the choke or inductance has a great effect on the current in the AC circuit, while in the DC circuit it merely acts as a resistance.

HOW INDUCTIVE REACTANCE AFFECTS THE TOTAL CIRCUIT CURRENT

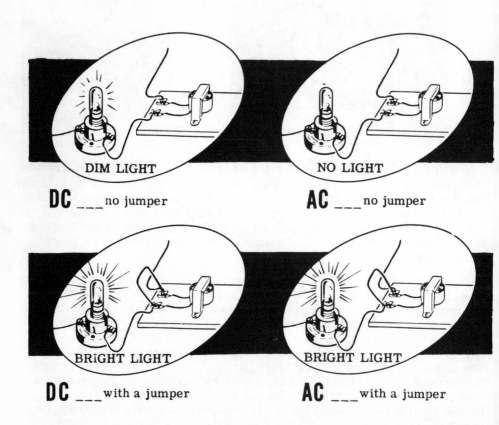

DC ___ no jumper   AC ___ no jumper

DC ___ with a jumper   AC ___ with a jumper

Review of Inductance in AC Circuits

To review inductance, what it is and how it affects current flow, consider facts concerning inductance and inductive reactance.

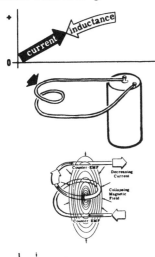

INDUCTANCE — The property of a circuit which opposes any change in the current flow; measured in henries and symbolized by letter L.

INDUCTOR — A coil of wire used to supply inductance in a circuit.

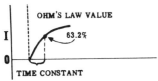

INDUCED EMF — A voltage which is generated within a circuit by the movement of the magnetic field whenever the circuit current changes, and which opposes the current change.

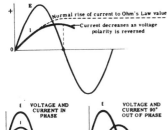

OHM'S LAW VALUE

63.2%

TIME CONSTANT

INDUCTIVE TIME CONSTANT — The ratio of L to R which gives the time in seconds required for the circuit current to rise to 63.2 percent of its maximum value.

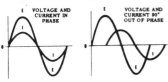

Normal rise of current to Ohm's Law value
Current decreases as voltage polarity is reversed

INDUCTIVE REACTANCE — The action of inductance in opposing the flow of AC current and in causing the current to lag the voltage; measured in ohms and symbolized by letter X_L.

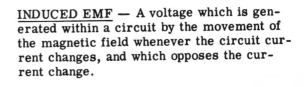

VOLTAGE AND CURRENT IN PHASE

VOLTAGE AND CURRENT 90° OUT OF PHASE

PHASE ANGLE — The amount in degrees by which the current wave lags the voltage wave.

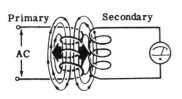

Primary   Secondary

AC

TRANSFORMER ACTION — The method of transferring electrical energy from one coil to another by means of an alternating magnetic field. The coil which generates the magnetic field is called the primary, and the coil in which the voltage is induced is called the secondary. The voltage induced in the secondary depends upon the turns ratio between the secondary and primary.

The Effect of Phase Difference on the Power Wave

In a theoretical circuit containing only pure inductance the current lags the voltage by 90 degrees. To determine the power wave for such a circuit, all of the corresponding instantaneous values of voltage and current are multiplied together to find the instantaneous values of power, which are then plotted to form the power curve.

As you already know the power curve for "in phase" voltages and currents is entirely above the zero axis, since the result is positive when either two positive numbers are multiplied together or two negative numbers are multiplied together. When a negative number is multiplied by a positive number however, the result is a negative number. Thus, in computing instantaneous values of power when the current and voltage are not in phase, some of the values are negative. If the phase difference is 90 degrees, as in the case of a theoretical circuit containing only pure inductance, half the instantaneous values of power are positive and half are negative as shown below. For such a circuit the voltage and current axis is also the power wave axis, and the frequency of the power wave is twice that of the current and voltage waves.

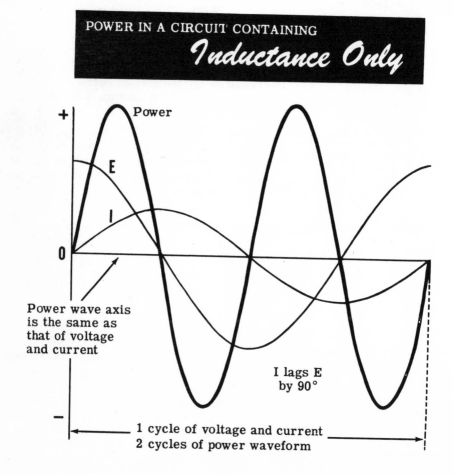

POWER IN A CIRCUIT CONTAINING

Inductance Only

Power

E

I

0

Power wave axis
is the same as
that of voltage
and current

I lags E
by 90°

1 cycle of voltage and current
2 cycles of power waveform

Positive and Negative Power

That portion of a power wave which is above the zero axis is called "positive power" and that which is below the axis is called "negative power." Positive power represents power furnished to the circuit by the power source, while negative power represents power the circuit returns to the power source.

In the case of a pure inductive circuit the positive power furnished to the circuit causes a field to build up. When this field collapses, it returns an equal amount of power to the power source. Since no power is used for heat or light in a circuit containing only pure inductance (if it were possible to have such a circuit), no actual power would be used even though the current flow were large. The actual power used in any circuit is found by subtracting the negative power from the positive power.

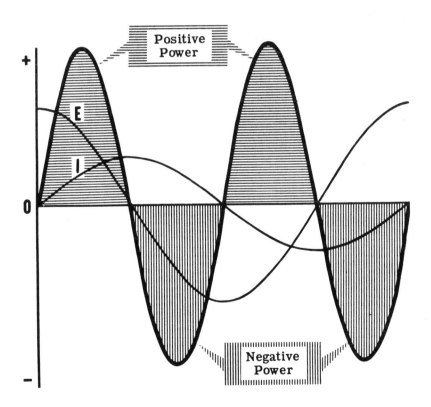

Apparent and True Power

Any practical inductive circuit contains some resistance, and since the phase angle depends on the ratio between the inductive reactance and the resistance, it is always less than 90 degrees. For phase angles of less than 90 degrees the amount of positive power always exceeds the negative power, with the difference between the two representing the actual power used in overcoming the circuit resistance. For example, if your circuit contains equal amounts of inductive reactance and resistance, the phase angle is 45 degrees and the positive power exceeds the negative power, as shown below.

90° Phase Angle (Negative power equals the positive power)

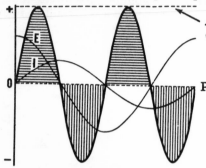

Apparent power E x 1 = V. A.

Power wave axis—True power is zero

$$P. F. = \frac{I^2R \text{ or } \frac{E^2}{R}}{V.A.} = 0\% \text{ at } 90°$$

45° Phase Angle (Positive power exceeds negative power)

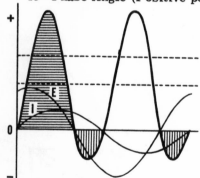

Apparent power Ex1 = V. A.

Power wave axis—True power used (I^2R)

$$P. F. = \frac{I^2R}{V.A.} = 70\% \text{ at } 45°$$

DECREASING THE PHASE ANGLE INCREASES THE TRUE POWER

The average value of actual power, called "true power," is represented by an axis drawn through the power wave halfway between the opposite maximum values of the wave. As the phase angle increases, this axis moves nearer to the axis for voltage and current. In AC circuits the apparent power is found by multiplying the voltage and current just as in DC circuits (Apparent power = Voltage x Current). When apparent power is divided into true power, the resultant decimal is the power factor.

Apparent power and true power for AC circuits are equal only when the circuit consists entirely of pure resistance. The difference between apparent and true power is sometimes called "wattless power" since it does not produce heat or light but does require current flow in a circuit.

Power Factor

You have already learned that in a pure resistive circuit I^2R or E^2/R (power in watts) is equal to Ieff Eeff (apparent power), and that the power factor is equal to 100%. Power factor is the ratio of true power to apparent power.

In an inductive circuit a phase angle exists and power in watts does not equal apparent power, and as a result power factor will be between zero and 100%.

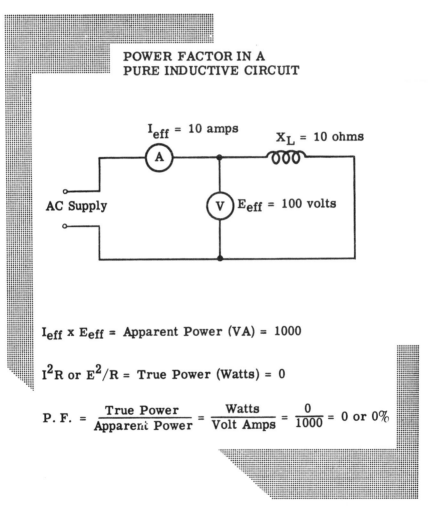

POWER FACTOR IN A
PURE INDUCTIVE CIRCUIT

I_{eff} = 10 amps X_L = 10 ohms

A

AC Supply   V E_{eff} = 100 volts

I_{eff} x E_{eff} = Apparent Power (VA) = 1000

I^2R or E^2/R = True Power (Watts) = 0

$$P.\ F.\ =\ \frac{True\ Power}{Apparent\ Power}\ =\ \frac{Watts}{Volt\ Amps}\ =\ \frac{0}{1000}\ =\ 0\ or\ 0\%$$

Power Factor is a method of determining what percentage of the supplied power is used in watts, and what percentage is returned to the source as wattless power.

Power Factor in a pure inductive circuit is equal to zero percent. The phase angle is 90°.

Measurement of True Power

Since the product of the circuit current and voltage is the apparent power and not the true power, a wattmeter is used to measure the true power used in an AC circuit. Voltmeter and ammeter readings are not affected by the phase difference between circuit current and voltage, since the voltmeter reading is affected only by voltage and the ammeter reading is affected only by current. The wattmeter reading is affected by both the circuit current and voltage and the phase difference between them, as shown below.

When the voltage and current are in phase, the current increases at the same time as the voltage. The circuit current increases the meter field simultaneously with the increase in current through the moving coil which is caused by the voltage. The voltage and current thus act together to increase the turning force on the meter pointer.

**IN-PHASE VOLTAGE AND CURRENT
ACT TOGETHER TO INCREASE
THE WATTMETER READING**

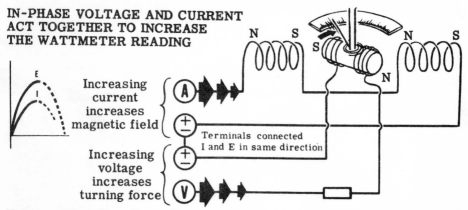

If the current lags the voltage, the meter field does not increase at the same time as the moving coil current. This results in less turning force on the wattmeter pointer. The power indicated then is less than with in-phase voltage and current of the same magnitude.

**OUT-OF-PHASE VOLTAGE AND CURRENT
ACT IN OPPOSITION, DECREASING
THE WATTMETER READING**

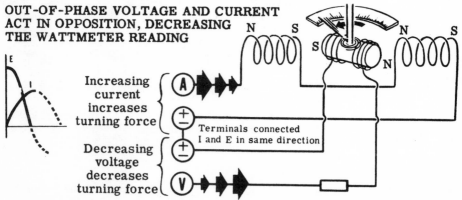

Similarly, if the current leads the voltage, the meter field strength and the moving coil current will not increase at the same time. This results in a lower wattmeter reading, the actual power used by the circuit again being less than the apparent power.

CAPACITANCE IN AC CIRCUITS

Capacitance

When the voltage across an electric circuit changes, the circuit opposes this change. This opposition is called "capacitance." Like inductance, capacitance cannot be seen, but its effect is present in every electrical circuit whenever the circuit voltage changes.

Capacitance Opposes Any Change in Circuit Voltage

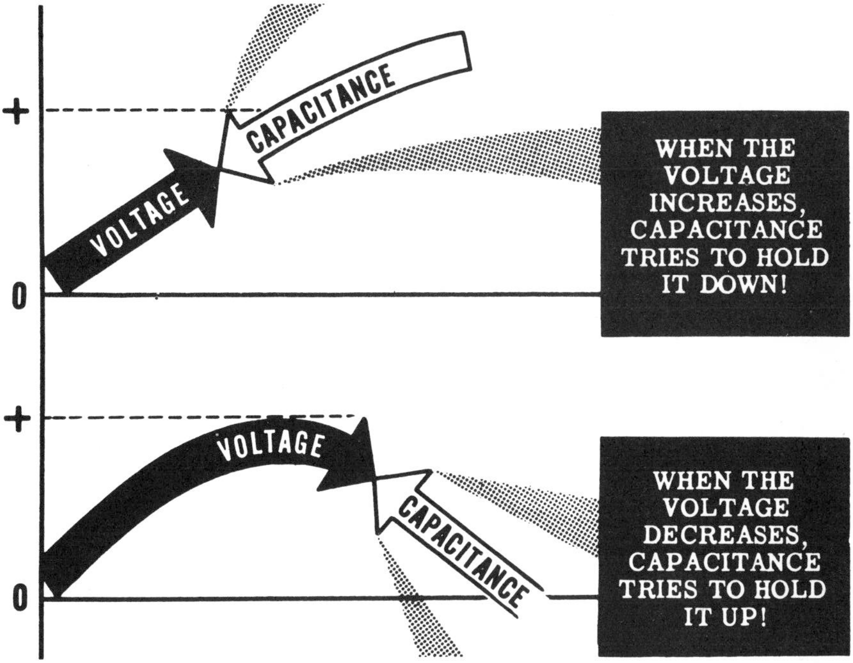

WHEN THE VOLTAGE INCREASES, CAPACITANCE TRIES TO HOLD IT DOWN!

WHEN THE VOLTAGE DECREASES, CAPACITANCE TRIES TO HOLD IT UP!

Because DC voltage usually varies only when it is turned on and off, capacitance affects DC circuits only at these times. In AC circuits, however, the voltage is continuously changing, so that the effect of capacitance is continuous. The amount of capacitance present in a circuit depends on the physical construction of the circuit and the electrical devices used. The capacitance may be so small that its effect on circuit voltage is negligible.

Electrical devices which are used to add capacitance to a circuit are called "capacitors," and the circuit symbol used to indicate a capacitor is shown below. Another term frequently used instead of capacitor is "condenser." You will often find the words "capacitor" and "condenser" used interchangeably, but they mean the same thing.

Symbols for condensers and capacitors

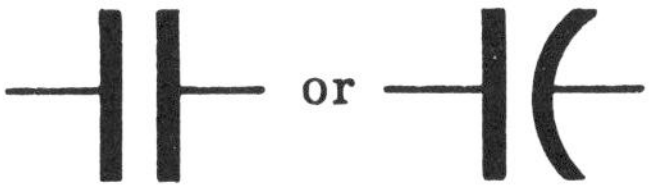

Capacitance (continued)

Capacitance exists in an electric circuit because certain parts of the circuit are able to store electric charges. Consider two flat metal plates placed parallel to each other, but not touching. You have already found out —while working with static electricity—that these plates can be charged either positively or negatively, depending on the charge which you transfer to them. If charged negatively, a plate will take extra electrons, but if charged positively it will give up some of its electrons. Thus the plates may have either an excess or lack of electrons.

The plates may be charged independently with either plate being charged positively, negatively, or having no charge. Thus they may both have no charge, one plate only may be charged, both plates may have the same type of charge, or the two plates may have opposite charges.

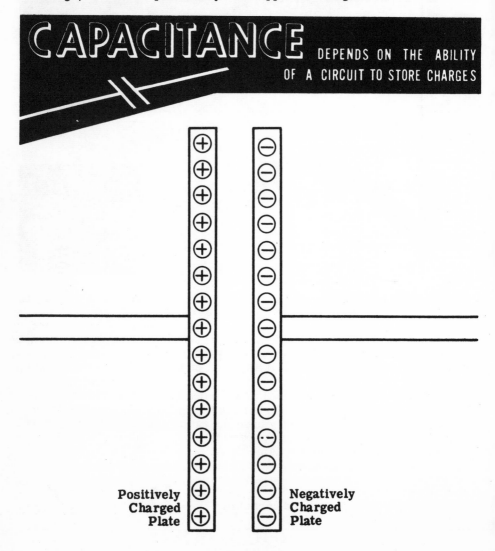

CAPACITANCE DEPENDS ON THE ABILITY OF A CIRCUIT TO STORE CHARGES

Positively Charged Plate

Negatively Charged Plate

Capacitance (continued)

In order to charge the plates, an electrical force is required. The greater the charge to be placed on each plate, the greater the electrical force required. For example, to charge a plate negatively, you must force extra electrons onto it from a source of negative charge. The first few extra electrons go onto the plate easily but once there, they oppose or repel any other electrons which try to follow them. As more electrons are forced onto the plate, this repelling force increases, so that a greater force is required to move additional electrons. When the negative repelling force equals the charging force, no more electrons will move onto the plate.

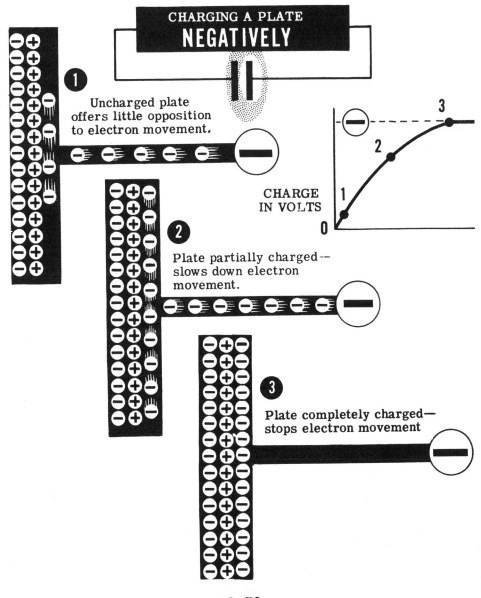

CHARGING A PLATE NEGATIVELY

1 Uncharged plate offers little opposition to electron movement.

2 Plate partially charged -- slows down electron movement.

3 Plate completely charged— stops electron movement

CHARGE IN VOLTS

Capacitance (continued)

Similarly, if electrons are removed from a plate by the attraction of a positive charge, the plate is positively charged. The first few electrons leave quite easily; but, as more electrons leave, a strong positive charge is built up on the plate. This positive charge attracts electrons and makes it more difficult to pull them away. When this positive attracting force equals the charging force, no more electrons leave the plate.

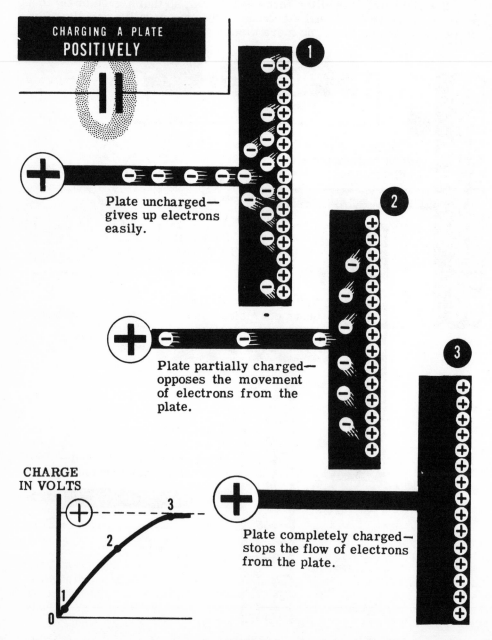

CHARGING A PLATE
POSITIVELY

1

Plate uncharged—
gives up electrons
easily.

2

Plate partially charged—
opposes the movement
of electrons from the
plate.

3

**CHARGE
IN VOLTS**

Plate completely charged—
stops the flow of electrons
from the plate.

Capacitance (continued)

To see how capacitance affects the voltage in a circuit, suppose your circuit contains a two plate capacitor, a knife switch and a dry cell as shown below. Assuming both plates are uncharged and the switch is open, then no current flows and the voltage between the two plates is zero.

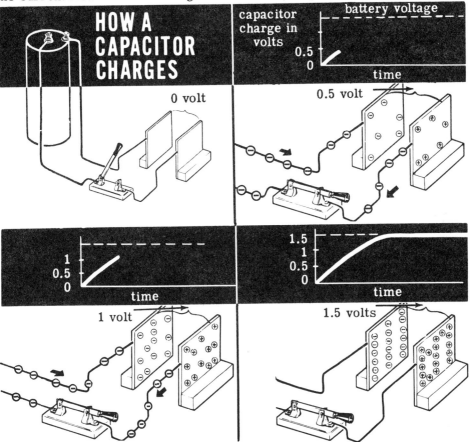

When the switch is closed, the battery furnishes electrons to the plate connected to the negative terminal and takes electrons away from the plate connected to the positive terminal. The voltage between the two plates should equal the voltage between the cell terminals, or 1.5 volts. However, this does not occur instantly because, in order for a voltage of 1.5 volts to exist between the two plates, one plate must take excess electrons to become negatively charged, while the other must give up electrons to become positively charged. As electrons move onto the plate attached to the negative terminal of the cell, a negative charge is built up which opposes the movement of more electrons onto the plate; and similarly, as electrons are taken away from the plate attached to the positive terminal, a positive charge is built up which opposes the removal of more electrons from that plate. This action on the two plates is called "capacitance" and it opposes the change in voltage (from zero to 1.5 volts). It delays the change in voltage for a limited amount of time but it does not prevent the change.

Capacitance (continued)

When the switch is opened the plates remain charged, since there is no path between the two plates through which they can discharge. As long as no discharge path is provided, the voltage between the plates will remain at 1.5 volts and, if the switch is again closed, there will be no effect on the circuit since the capacitor is already charged.

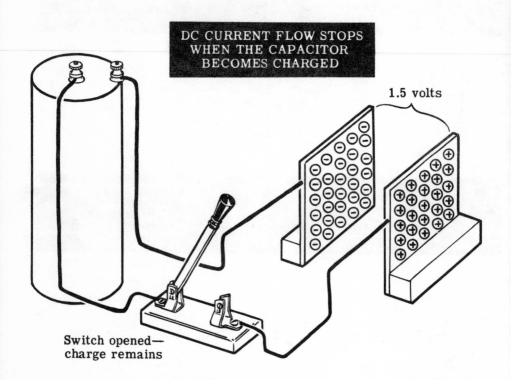

DC CURRENT FLOW STOPS WHEN THE CAPACITOR BECOMES CHARGED

1.5 volts

Switch opened—
charge remains

With a DC voltage source then, current will flow in a capacitive circuit only long enough to charge the capacitor (often called a "condenser"). When the DC circuit switch is closed, an ammeter connected to read circuit current would show that a very large current flows at first, since the condenser plates are uncharged. Then as the plates gain polarity and oppose additional charge, the charging current decreases until it reaches zero—at the moment the charge on the plates equals the voltage of the DC voltage source.

This current which charges a capacitor flows only for the first moment after the switch is closed. After this momentary flow the current stops, since the plates of the capacitor are separated by an insulator which does not allow electrons to pass through it. Thus capacitors or condensers will not allow DC current to flow continuously through a circuit.

Capacitance (continued)

While a capacitor blocks the flow of DC current it affects an AC circuit differently, allowing AC current to flow through the circuit. To see how this works, consider what happens in the DC circuit if a double-throw switch is used with the dry cell so that the charge to each plate is reversed as the switch is closed—first in one position and then in the other.

When the switch is first closed the condenser charges, with each plate being charged in the same polarity as that of the cell terminal to which it is connected.

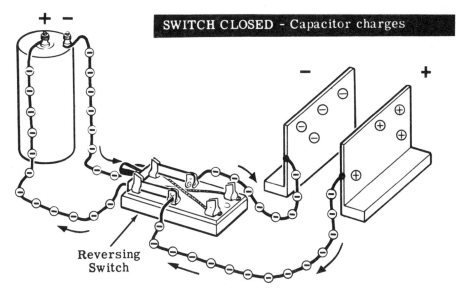

SWITCH CLOSED - Capacitor charges

Reversing
Switch

Whenever the switch is opened, the condenser retains the charges on its plates equal to the cell voltage.

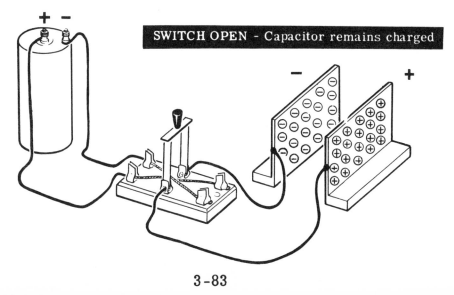

SWITCH OPEN - Capacitor remains charged

Capacitance (continued)

If the switch is then closed in its original position no current flows, since the condenser is charged in that polarity. However, if the switch is closed in the opposite direction, the condenser plates are connected to cell terminals opposite in polarity to their charges. The positively charged plate then is connected to the negative cell terminal and will take electrons from the cell—first to neutralize the positive charge, then to become charged negatively until the condenser charge is in the same polarity and of equal voltage to that of the cell. The negatively charged plate gives up electrons to the cell, since it must take on a positive charge equal to that of the cell terminal to which it is connected.

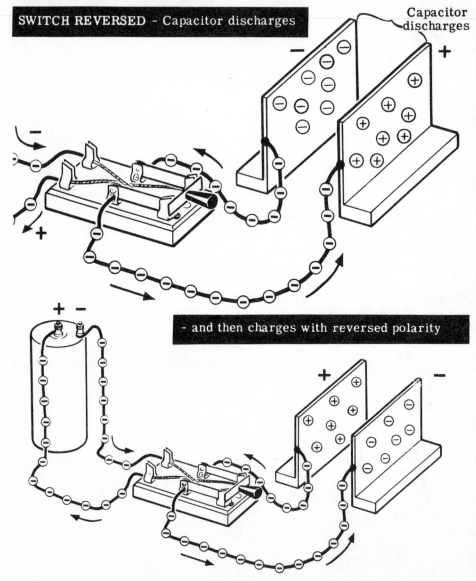

SWITCH REVERSED - Capacitor discharges

Capacitor discharges

- and then charges with reversed polarity

Capacitance (continued)

If a zero-center ammeter which can read current flow in both directions is inserted in series with one of the capacitor plates, it will indicate a current flow each time the plate is charged. When the reversing switch is first closed, it shows a current flow in the direction of the original charge. Then, when the cell polarity is reversed, it shows a current flow in the opposite direction as the plate first discharges, then charges in the opposite polarity. The meter shows that current flows only momentarily, however, each time the cell polarity is reversed.

**CHARGE AND DISCHARGE CURRENT OF A
CAPACITOR AS THE SOURCE VOLTAGE REVERSES**

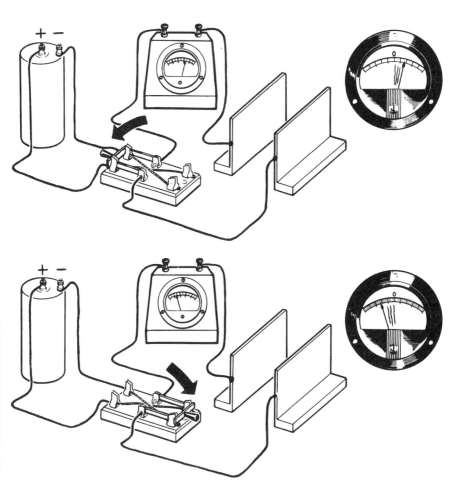

Suppose you switch the cell polarity fast enough so that at the instant the condenser plates become charged in one polarity, the cell polarity is reversed. The meter needle now moves continuously—first showing a current flow in one direction, then in the opposite direction. While no electrons move through the air from one plate to the other, the meter shows that current is continuously flowing to and from the condenser plates.

Capacitance (continued)

If a source of AC voltage is used instead of the dry cell and reversing switch, the polarity of the voltage source is automatically changed each half cycle. If the frequency of the AC voltage is low enough, the ammeter will show current flow in both directions, changing each half cycle as the AC polarity reverses.

The standard commercial frequency is 60 cycles so that a zero-center ammeter will not show the current flow, since the meter pointer cannot move fast enough. Even though it did, you would not be able to see the movement due to its speed. However, an AC ammeter inserted in place of the zero-center ammeter shows a continuous current flow when the AC voltage source is used, indicating that in the meter and in the circuit there is a flow of AC current. Remember that this current flow represents the continuous charging and discharging of the capacitor plates, and that no actual electron movement takes place directly between the plates of the capacitor. Capacitors are considered to pass AC current, because current actually flows continuously in all parts of the circuit except the insulating material between the capacitor plates.

AC CURRENT in a capacitive circuit

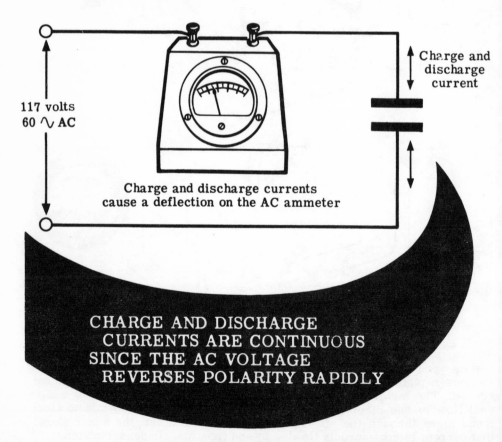

117 volts
60 ∿ AC

Charge and discharge current

Charge and discharge currents
cause a deflection on the AC ammeter

CHARGE AND DISCHARGE
CURRENTS ARE CONTINUOUS
SINCE THE AC VOLTAGE
REVERSES POLARITY RAPIDLY

CAPACITANCE IN AC CIRCUITS

Units of Capacitance

The action of capacitance in a circuit is to store a charge and to increase its charge if the voltage rises, or discharge if the voltage falls. Every circuit has some capacitance, with the amount depending on the ability of the circuit to store a charge.

The basic unit of capacitance is the farad, but the storage capacity of a farad is much too great to use as the unit of capacitance for practical electrical circuits. Because of this, the units normally used are the microfarad (equal to one-millionth of a farad) and the micromicrofarad (equal to one-millionth-millionth of a farad). Since electrical formulas use capacitance stated in farads, it is necessary that you are able to change the various units of capacitance to other units. Again the method of changing units is exactly like that used for changing units of voltage, current, ohms, etc. To change to larger units, the decimal point moves to the left; while to change to smaller units, the decimal is moved to the right.

CHANGING UNITS OF CAPACITANCE

MICROFARADS TO FARADS
Move the decimal point 6 places to the left
120 mfd equals 0.000120 farad
FARADS TO MICROFARAD
Move the decimal point 6 places to the right
8 farads equals 8,000,000 mfd

MICROMICROFARADS TO FARADS
Move the decimal point 12 places to the left
1500 mmf equals 0.000000001500 farad
FARADS TO MICROMICROFARADS
Move the decimal point 12 places to the right
2 farads equals 2,000,000,000,000 mmf

MICROMICROFARADS TO MICROFARADS
Move the decimal point 6 places to the left
250 mmf equals 0.000250 mfd
MICROFARADS TO MICROMICROFARADS
Move the decimal point 6 places to the right
2 mfd equals 2,000,000 mmf

In electrical formulas the letter C is used to denote capacitance in farads. The circuit symbols for capacitance are shown below. These symbols are also used to indicate capacitors, both fixed and variable.

CAPACITOR SYMBOLS

Fixed Capacitors   Variable Capacitors

Demonstration—Current Flow in a DC Capacitive Circuit

In circuits containing only capacitance, both the charge and discharge of a capacitor occur in a very short period of time. To show the circuit current flow during the charge and discharge of a capacitor, the instructor connects two 45-volt batteries in series to form a 90-volt battery. Next he connects the leads from this battery to two of the end terminals of a double-pole, double-throw switch. With the switch open, he then connects the 0-1 ma. zero-center milliammeter and the 1-mfd capacitor in series with the resistor to the switch as shown. Finally, he connects the other two end terminals together with a length of wire. The purpose of the 91,000-ohm resistor is to limit large current surges which may damage the meter. When the instructor moves the switch to the shorted terminals, you see that there is no current flow since the capacitor is initially uncharged. Then, when he moves the switch to the battery terminals, you see that the meter pointer momentarily registers a current flow, but drops quickly to zero again as the capacitor becomes charged.

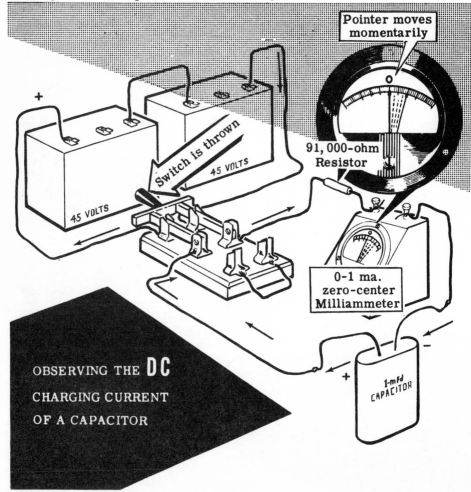

OBSERVING THE **DC** CHARGING CURRENT OF A CAPACITOR

Demonstration—Current Flow in a DC Capacitive Circuit (continued)

If the instructor opens the switch and then moves it to the shorted terminals, the meter pointer indicates a momentary current flow in the opposite direction when the switch is closed, indicating the discharge of the condenser.

The instructor then charges the capacitor as before, and you notice the instantaneous current flow. He then opens the switch and returns it to its initial position. You notice no current flow, since the capacitor is already charged. When he moves the switch to the shorted terminals, the current flow in the opposite direction again shows the discharge of the condenser.

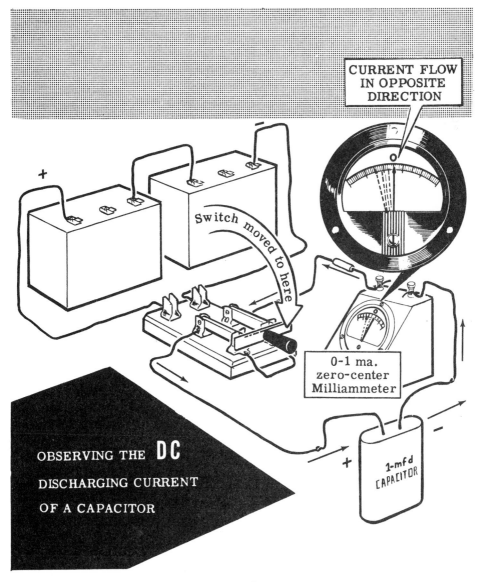

CURRENT FLOW IN OPPOSITE DIRECTION

Switch moved to here

0-1 ma. zero-center Milliammeter

1-mfd CAPACITOR

OBSERVING THE **DC** DISCHARGING CURRENT OF A CAPACITOR

Demonstration—Current Flow in a DC Capacitive Circuit (continued)

Next the instructor connects the battery to the capacitor and switch in series. The capacitor is charged by closing the switch. He then opens the switch and shorts across the capacitor terminals with a screwdriver blade, making certain to hold the screwdriver only by means of the insulated handle. Notice that the capacitor discharge causes a strong arc. If you were to discharge the capacitor by touching the two terminals with your hands, the resulting electric shock—while not dangerous in itself—might cause a serious accident by making you jump.

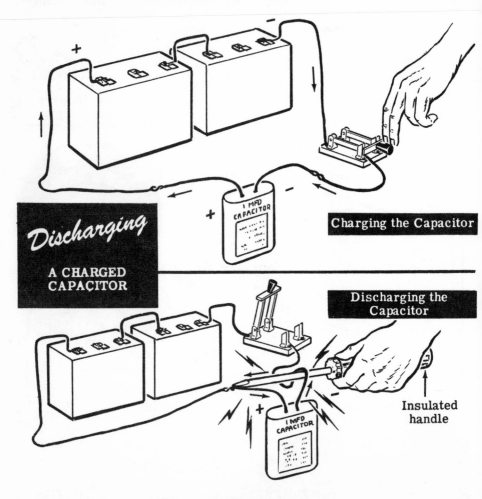

As the instructor repeatedly charges and discharges the capacitor, you see that the resulting arc is the same each time. This shows that the charge left in a capacitor when the circuit voltage is removed is always maximum in a DC circuit. CAUTION: Never discharge a capacitor while it is connected to the circuit voltage, whether the voltage source is a battery or AC power line.

CAPACITANCE IN AC CIRCUITS

Demonstration—Current Flow in an AC Capacitive Circuit

After disconnecting the DC circuit, the instructor connects the capacitor to show that AC current flows continuously in an AC capacitive circuit. One lead of the line cord is connected to a terminal of the capacitor through the switch and fuses, while the other line cord lead is connected to the remaining capacitor terminal through the 0-50 ma. AC milliammeter. When the transformer is plugged into the AC power line outlet, and the switch is closed, you see that a continuous flow of current is indicated on the milliammeter.

The milliammeter shows that approximately 22 ma. of AC current is flowing continuously. This continuous flow of circuit current is possible since the capacitor is continuously charging and discharging as the AC voltage reverses its polarity. After the instructor opens the switch, he shorts out the terminals of the capacitor with a screwdriver. Again you see that the capacitor retains a charge when the voltage is removed from the circuit. However, as the power is applied and removed several times in succession and the capacitor is discharged each time, you see that the sparks vary in size and intensity. This occurs because the amount of charge retained by the capacitor when used in an AC circuit is not always the same, since the circuit voltage may be removed while the capacitor is discharging or not yet charged.

OBSERVING **AC CURRENT FLOW..**

. . . . THROUGH A CAPACITOR

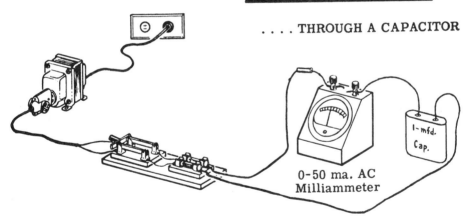

0-50 ma. AC
Milliammeter

To prove that capacitors appear to block DC but permit AC to pass, the instructor sets up the circuit shown to the right. When DC is applied the lamp will not glow and a DC voltmeter across the lamp will read zero volts. When AC is applied the lamp will glow and an AC voltmeter across the lamp will give a reading.

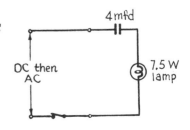

4 mfd

DC then AC

7.5 W lamp

CAPACITANCE IN AC CIRCUITS

Review of Capacitance in AC Circuits

You have found out about capacitance and have seen how it affects the flow of current in electric circuits. Now you are ready to perform an experiment on capacitance to find out more about it and its effects. Before performing the experiment, suppose you recall what you have found out about capacitance.

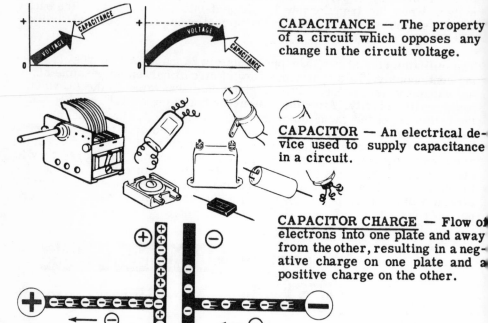

CAPACITANCE — The property of a circuit which opposes any change in the circuit voltage.

CAPACITOR — An electrical device used to supply capacitance in a circuit.

CAPACITOR CHARGE — Flow of electrons into one plate and away from the other, resulting in a negative charge on one plate and a positive charge on the other.

Insulated handle

CAPACITOR DISCHARGE — Flow of electrons from the negatively charged plate of a capacitor to the positively charged plate, eliminating the charges on the plate.

FARAD — Basic unit of capacitance used in electrical formulas.

$$1 \text{ mfd} = \frac{1}{1,000,000} \text{ farad}$$

PRACTICAL UNITS OF CAPACITANCE — Microfarad (one-millionth farad) and micromicrofarad (one-millionth-millionth of a farad).

$$1 \text{ mmf} = \frac{1}{1,000,000,000,000} \text{ farad}$$

Capacitors

Basically, capacitors consist of two plates which can be charged—separated by an insulating material called the "dielectric." While early condensers were made with solid metal plates, newer types of condensers use metal foil, particularly aluminum foil, for the plates. Dielectric materials used include air, mica, paper, plastics, ceramics, and oil.

Capacitors CONSIST OF *Two Plates* AND THE *Dielectric*

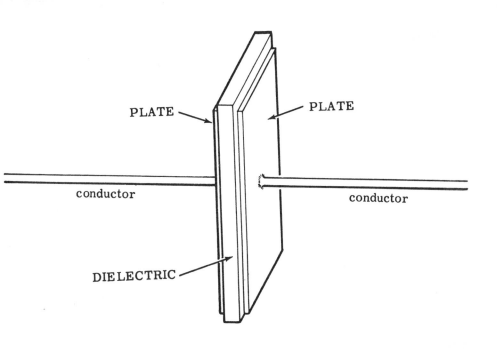

Plates are made of solid metal or metal foil.

Dielectric materials include: air, mica, paper, plastics, ceramics, and oil.

Three basic factors influence the capacity of a capacitor or condenser—the area of the plates, the distance between the plates (thickness of the dielectric) and the material used for the dielectric.

Factors Which Affect Capacitance

Plate area is a very important factor in determining the amount of capacitance, since the capacitance varies directly with the area of the plates. A large plate area has room for more excess electrons than a small area, and thus it can hold a greater charge. Similarly, the large plate area has more electrons to give up and will hold a much larger positive charge than a small plate area. Thus an increase in plate area increases capacitance, and a decrease in plate area decreases capacitance.

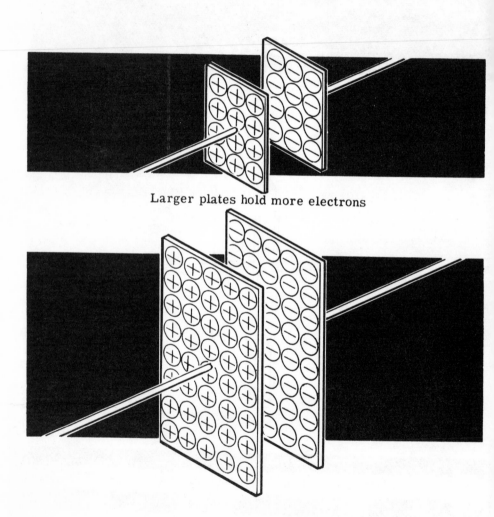

Larger plates hold more electrons

INCREASED PLATE AREA INCREASES *Capacitance*

Factors Which Affect Capacitance (continued)

The effect two charged bodies have on each other depends on the distance between the two. Since the action of capacitance depends on the two plates and the difference in their charges, the amount of capacitance changes when the distance between the plates changes. The capacitance between two plates increases as the plates are brought closer together and decreases as the plates are moved apart. This occurs because the closer the plates are to each other, the greater the effect a charge on one plate will have on the charge of the other plate.

When an excess of electrons appears on one plate of a condenser, electrons are forced off the opposite plate, inducing a positive charge on this plate. Similarly, a positively charged plate induces a negative charge on the opposite plate. The closer the plates are to each other, the stronger the force between them, and this force increases the capacitance of a circuit.

INCREASING THE DISTANCE BETWEEN THE PLATES

Decreases Capacitance

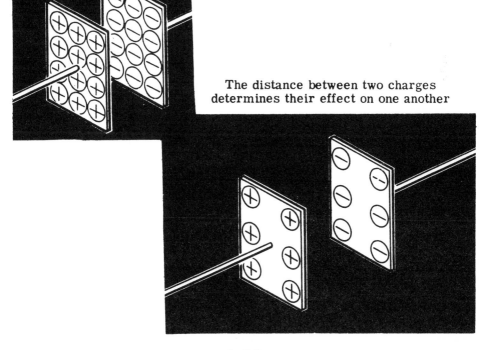

The distance between two charges determines their effect on one another

Factors Which Affect Capacitance (continued)

CHANGING THE *Dielectric* MATERIAL

CHANGES THE CAPACITANCE

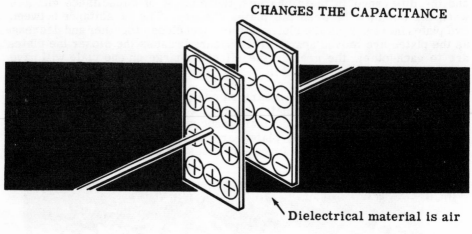

Dielectrical material is air

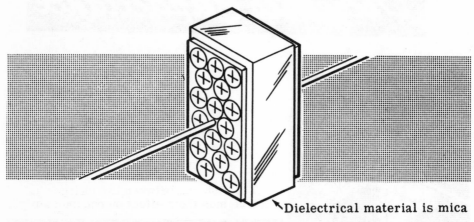

Dielectrical material is mica

Mica dielectric increases the capacitance.

Using the same plates fixed a certain distance apart, the capacitance will change if different insulating materials are used for the dielectric. The effect of different materials is compared to that of air—that is, if the condenser has a given capacitance when air is used as the dielectric, other materials used instead of air will multiply the capacitance by a certain amount called the "dielectric constant." For example, some types of oiled paper have a dielectric constant of 3 and, if this waxed paper is placed between the plates, the capacitance will be 3 times greater than air used as the dielectric. Different materials have different dielectric constants, and thus will change the capacitance when they are placed between the plates to act as the dielectric.

Capacitors in Series and Parallel

When you connect capacitors in series or in parallel, the effect on the total capacitance is opposite to that for similarly connected resistors.

Connecting resistors in series increases the total resistance because it lengthens the resistance path through which current flows, while connecting capacitances in series decreases the total capacitance since it effectively increases the spacing between the plates. To find the total capacitance of series-connected capacitors, a formula is used similar to the formula for parallel resistances.

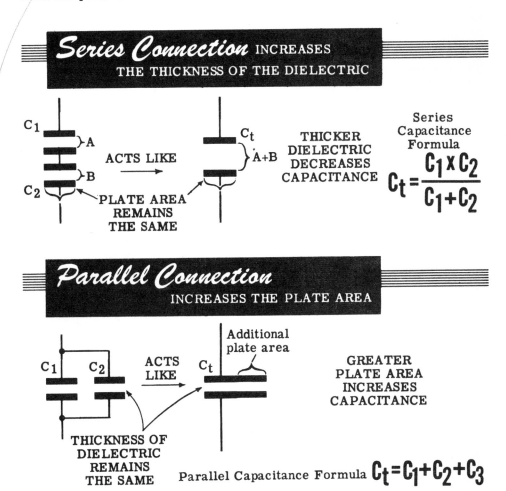

Series Connection INCREASES THE THICKNESS OF THE DIELECTRIC

C_1

} A

ACTS LIKE →

} B

C_2

PLATE AREA REMAINS THE SAME

C_t

} A+B

THICKER DIELECTRIC DECREASES CAPACITANCE

Series Capacitance Formula

$$C_t = \frac{C_1 \times C_2}{C_1 + C_2}$$

Parallel Connection INCREASES THE PLATE AREA

C_1 C_2

ACTS LIKE →

C_t

Additional plate area

GREATER PLATE AREA INCREASES CAPACITANCE

THICKNESS OF DIELECTRIC REMAINS THE SAME

Parallel Capacitance Formula $C_t = C_1 + C_2 + C_3$

When resistors are connected in parallel, the total resistance decreases since the cross section through which current can flow increases. The reverse is true of parallel-connected capacitors. The total capacitance increases, since the plate area receiving a charge increases. The total capacitance for parallel-connected capacitors is found by adding the values of the various capacitors connected in parallel.

Types of Capacitors

Many kinds of capacitors are used in electricity and electronics. In order to choose the best type for a particular job, you should know how they are made and operate. You also should be familiar with the symbols used to indicate certain special types of capacitors. Condensers (capacitors) are generally classified according to their dielectric material.

The most basic type of capacitor (which may be either fixed or variable) is the air condenser, constructed of metal plates with air spaces between them. A similar type of condenser is the vacuum condenser, which consists of two plates separated by a vacuum—the vacuum being the dielectric. Because the plates must be rather widely spaced apart to prevent arcing, the capacitance of air and vacuum condensers is low, usually between 1 mmf and 500 mmf.

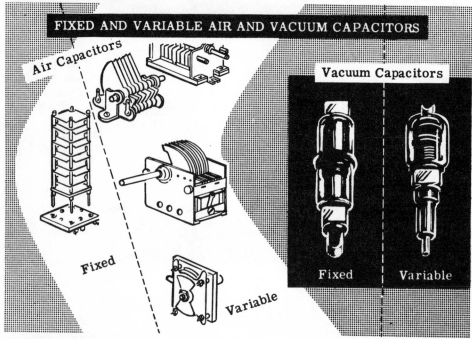

FIXED AND VARIABLE AIR AND VACUUM CAPACITORS

Air Capacitors

Vacuum Capacitors

Fixed

Variable

Fixed   Variable

A special type of mica condenser, which is variable and usually has a maximum value of less than 500 mmf, consists of two plates with a sheet of mica between them. A screw adjustment is used to force the plates together, and adjustment of this screw varies the capacitance of the condenser. Several layers of plates and mica are used in larger condensers of this type. This kind of condenser is sometimes built onto a large variable air condenser, to be used in parallel with the larger variable condenser and provide a finer adjustment of capacitance.

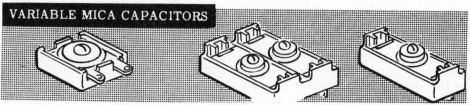

VARIABLE MICA CAPACITORS

Types of Capacitors (continued)

Fixed mica capacitors consist of thin metal foil plates separated by sheet mica and molded into a plastic cover. These capacitors are made in a capacity range between 10 mmf and 0.01 mfd. Various types of terminals are used to connect mica capacitors into circuits, and these terminals are molded into the plastic with the capacitor plates and dielectric. By molding the capacitor parts into a plastic case, corrosion and damage to the plates and dielectric are prevented in addition to making the capacitor mechanically strong.

FIXED MICA CAPACITORS

The voltage applied across the plates of a capacitor is determined by the thickness of the dielectric material which acts as an insulator between the two plates. Capacitors of exactly the same capacitance may have different voltage rating due to a difference in the thickness of the dielectric. If the dielectric thickness is increased the plates will be further apart, reducing the capacitance so that the plate areas must be increased to make up for this loss. Thus capacitors of higher voltage ratings are larger in physical size, since the plates are both larger and further apart. This is true of all types of capacitors regardless of the dielectric used. Shown below are typical mica capacitors having various voltage ratings but the same amount of capacitance.

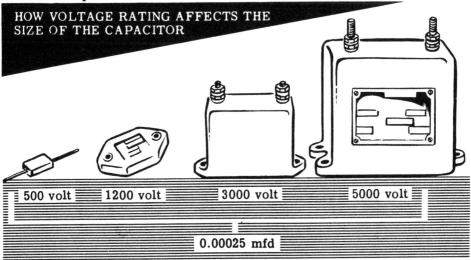

HOW VOLTAGE RATING AFFECTS THE
SIZE OF THE CAPACITOR

500 volt   1200 volt   3000 volt   5000 volt

0.00025 mfd

Types of Capacitors (continued)

Paper capacitors use strips of metal foil as plates, separated by strips of waxed paper. Paper capacitors range in value from 250 mmf to 1 mfd for most uses, although larger paper capacitors are made for special applications. Since very long strips of paper are required to obtain a usable capacitance, the strips of foil and waxed paper are rolled together to form a cartridge. This cartridge, including leads attached to the plates, is sealed in wax to prevent moisture leakage and corrosion of the plates. Many different kinds of outer covering are used for paper capacitors, the simplest being a tubular cardboard.

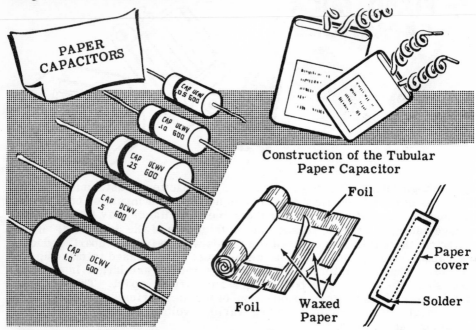

Construction of the Tubular
Paper Capacitor

Some types of paper capacitors are encased in a mold of very hard plastic. Capacitors which are so constructed are very rugged and may be used over a much wider temperature range than the cardboard case type, since the wax used in the tubular cardboard type melts at high temperatures and escapes through the open ends of the cardboard case.

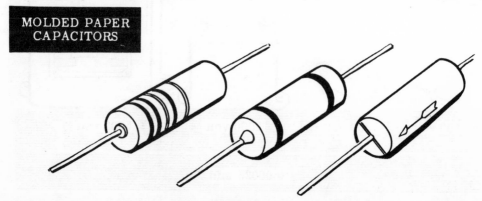

Types of Capacitors (continued)

Bathtub style capacitors are paper capacitor cartridges hermetically sealed in a metal container. The metal container is sometimes used as one terminal and, if not, it acts as a shield against electrical interference. Also, quite often a single terminal is the common terminal used for several different capacitors sealed in one bathtub case.

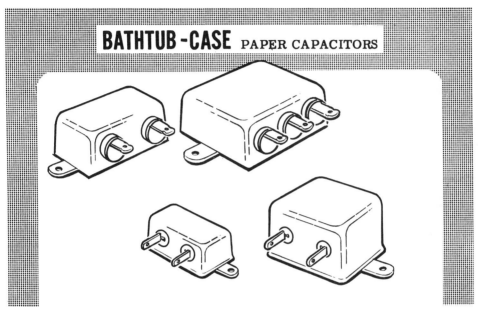

BATHTUB-CASE PAPER CAPACITORS

Capacitors used in automobile ignition systems are paper capacitor cartridges and are metal-cased, with the case serving as both a shield and terminal connection. Metal cases are necessary because automobile capacitors must be exceptionally rugged and able to withstand the effects of mechanical shock and the weather.

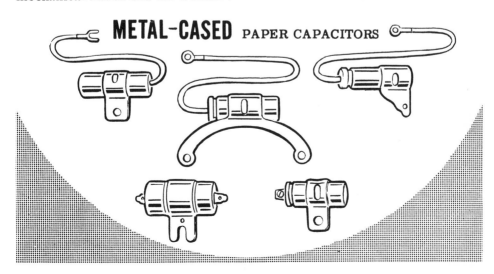

METAL-CASED PAPER CAPACITORS

Types of Capacitors (continued)

Paper capacitors used for high voltage circuits (600 volts and higher) are impregnated with oil and oil-filled. The metal container is hermetically sealed and various types of terminal connections are used.

OIL-FILLED HIGH VOLTAGE PAPER CAPACITORS

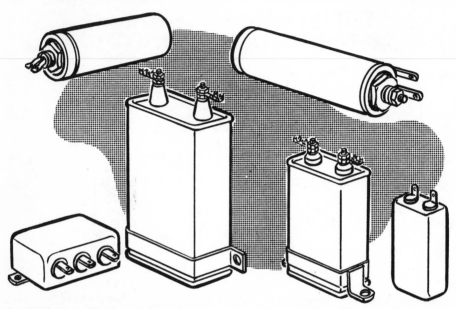

A recently developed type of extremely small capacitors—both fixed and variable—use ceramic as the dielectric and a film deposit of silver for the plates. Ceramic capacitors usually range in value between 1 mmf and 0.01 mfd. They are constructed in various shapes, the most common being disk and tubular shapes. Variable ceramic capacitors have one fixed plate of silver film and a movable metal plate which is silver-plated. Although ceramic capacitors have a dielectric which will insulate against voltages above 2,000 volts, they are quite small and take up little space, so that they are used in many special circuits for voltages of 10,000 volts or more.

CERAMIC CAPACITORS

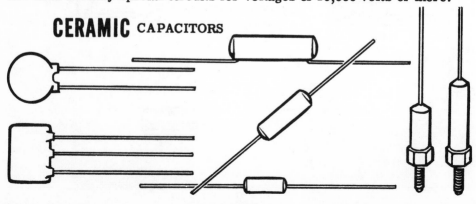

Types of Capacitors (continued)

For values of capacitance greater than 1 mfd, the physical size of a paper or a mica capacitor becomes excessive. Electrolytic capacitors are used for such values of capacitance, ranging from 1 to 1,000 mfd. Unlike other types of capacitors the electrolytic capacitor is polarized and, if connected in the wrong polarity, it will break down and act as a short circuit. A special type of electrolytic capacitor is made which compensates for changing polarity, and may be used on AC.

Electrolytic capacitors are constructed in a wide variety of shapes and physical sizes, using either cardboard or metal cases and various types of terminal connections. Remember that unless an electrolytic is designed for use on AC, such as a motor-starting capacitor, you must always be careful to connect it only in a DC circuit and to observe the correct polarity.

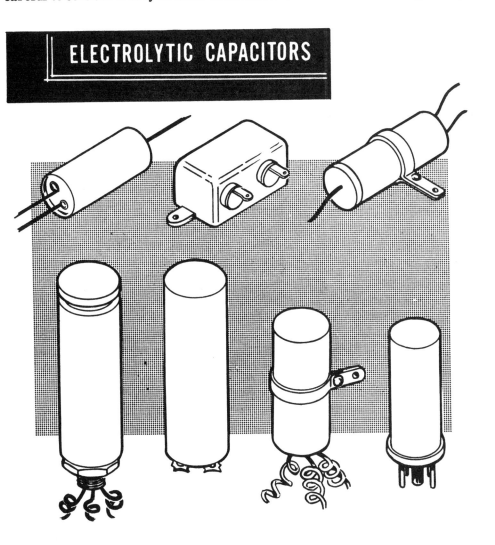

ELECTROLYTIC CAPACITORS

Capacitor Color Code

The capacitance value and voltage rating of most capacitors is printed or stamped on the body of the capacitor, together with the polarity in the case of electrolytics. Voltage ratings marked on the body of a capacitor usually refer to the maximum DC voltage which can be applied across the terminals without a breakdown of the dielectric insulation. Many capacitors are marked with a color code similar to the resistor color code, and the corresponding colors and numbers are the same for the two codes. Suppose you review the colors and numbers which are used.

CAPACITANCE COLOR CODE

Color	No.	Tolerance	Voltage Rating	Color	No.	Tolerance	Voltage Rating
Black	0		–	Violet	7	–	700
Brown	1	–	100	Gray	8	–	800
Red	2	–	200	White	9	–	900
Orange	3	–	300	Gold	–	5%	1,000
Yellow	4	–	400	Silver	–	10%	2,000
Green	5	–	500	No Color	–	20%	–
Blue	6	–	600				

The order in which these colors are used by the different manufacturers varies. The simplest color code marking uses three dots of color which give the value of capacitance in mmf. The first two dots represent the first two numbers and the last dot the number of zeros to be added. All color coded values are in mmf and must be changed to mfd if the answer in mfd is desired. If no arrows are present, the capacitor is placed in such a position that the trademark can be read correctly; and the three dots of color are read from LEFT to RIGHT. When each dot is placed on a small arrow, they are read in the direction of the arrows. If the dots are red, green and brown, reading in the proper direction the capacitance is 250 mmf or 0.00025 mfd as shown below. If no tolerance and voltage ratings are indicated, they are assumed to be ± 20% at 500 volts.

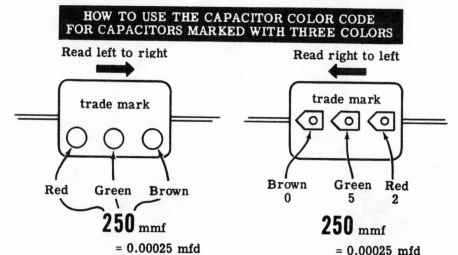

HOW TO USE THE CAPACITOR COLOR CODE FOR CAPACITORS MARKED WITH THREE COLORS

Read left to right

trade mark

Red   Green   Brown

250 mmf

= 0.00025 mfd

Read right to left

trade mark

Brown   Green   Red
0   5   2

250 mmf

= 0.00025 mfd

Capacitor Color Code (continued)

Capacitors which are marked with six dots of color are coded for percentage of accuracy (tolerance) and voltage rating, in addition to the capacitance value. The top row of dots is read from LEFT to RIGHT, and the bottom row is read from RIGHT to LEFT. In this type of marking, 3 digits are obtained from the top row of dots; and from the bottom row from RIGHT to LEFT in order are read the number of zeros, the percentage tolerance and the voltage rating.

HOW TO USE CAPACITOR COLOR CODE FOR CAPACITORS MARKED WITH SIX COLORS

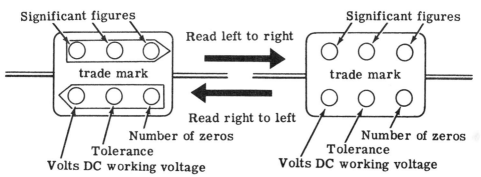

Suppose the six dots read in the correct order are brown, orange, green, red, silver and blue. The capacitor then has a capacitance of 13,500 mmf, a tolerance of 10 percent and a voltage rating of 600 volts.

Color code marking is not only used on mica or ceramic capacitors, but is also used with molded tubular paper capacitors. The marking then is done with bands of color which are read from the band nearest one end of the capacitor in order toward the center. The colors are read in the same manner as the six-dot system with the first 3 bands denoting digits, the fourth band giving the number of zeros, the fifth band the tolerance and the sixth band the voltage rating.

BAND MARKING OF MOLDED PAPER CAPACITORS

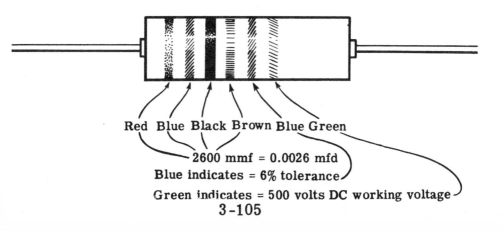

Red Blue Black Brown Blue Green

2600 mmf = 0.0026 mfd
Blue indicates = 6% tolerance
Green indicates = 500 volts DC working voltage

Capacitive Time Constant

When a voltage is applied across the terminals of a circuit containing capacitance, the voltage across the capacitance does not instantaneously equal the voltage applied to the terminals. You have already found that it takes time for the plates of a capacitor to reach their full charge, and that the voltage between the plates rises to equal the applied voltage in a curve similar to the current curve of an inductive circuit. The greater the circuit resistance, the longer the time required for the capacitor to reach its maximum voltage since the circuit resistance opposes the flow of current required to charge the capacitor.

The time required for the capacitor to become fully charged depends on the product of circuit resistance and capacitance. This product RC— resistance times capacitance—is the "time constant" of a capacitive circuit. The RC time constant gives the time in seconds required for the voltage across the capacitor to reach 63.2 percent of its maximum value. Similarly, the RC time constant equals the time in seconds required for a discharging capacitor to lose 63.2 percent of its full charge.

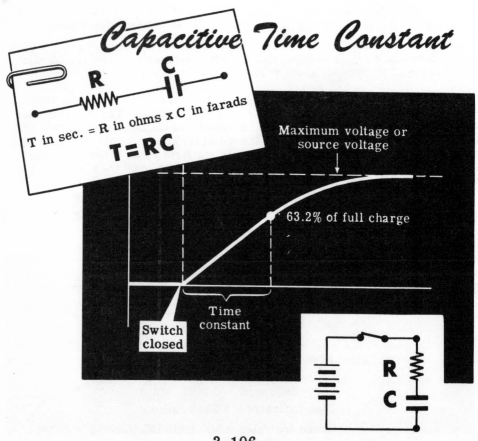

Capacitive Reactance

Capacitive reactance is the opposition to current flow offered by the capacitance of a circuit. When a DC source is used, current flows only to charge or discharge the capacitor. Since there is no continuous flow of DC current in a capacitive circuit, the capacitive reactance to DC is considered infinite. AC continuously varies in value and polarity; therefore the capacitor is continuously charging and discharging, resulting in a continuous circuit current flow and a finite value of capacitive reactance.

The charge and discharge currents of a capacitor start at a maximum value and fall to zero as the capacitor becomes either fully charged or discharged. In the case of a charging capacitor, the uncharged plates offer little opposition to the charging current at first, but as they become charged they offer more and more opposition, reducing the current flow. Similarly, the discharge current is high at beginning of the discharge since the voltage of the charged capacitor is high but, as the capacitor discharges, its charge voltage drops resulting in less current flow. Since the charging and discharging currents are highest at the beginning of the charge and discharge of a capacitor, the average current is higher if the polarity is reversed rapidly, keeping the current flowing at high values.

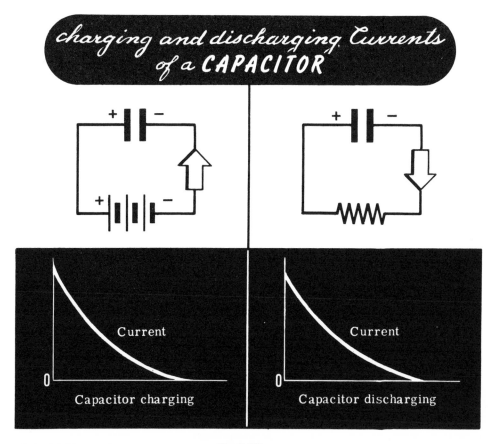

charging and discharging Currents of a CAPACITOR

Current

0

Capacitor charging

Current

0

Capacitor discharging

Capacitive Reactance (continued)

For a given value of capacitance the amount of current flow in an AC circuit depends on the frequency of the AC voltage. The higher the frequency,
the greater the current flow since the charging current in each direction
will be reversed before it has time to drop to a low value. If the source
voltage is low in frequency, the current will drop to a low value before the
polarity reverses, resulting in a lower average value of current flow.

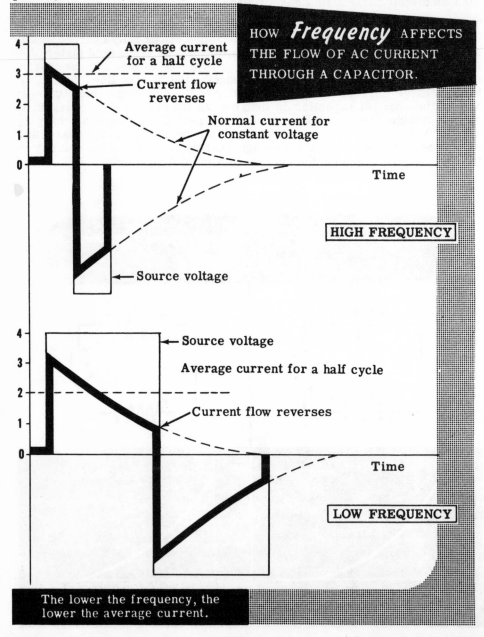

HOW *Frequency* AFFECTS THE FLOW OF AC CURRENT THROUGH A CAPACITOR.

Average current for a half cycle

Current flow reverses

Normal current for constant voltage

Time

HIGH FREQUENCY

Source voltage

Source voltage

Average current for a half cycle

Current flow reverses

Time

LOW FREQUENCY

The lower the frequency, the lower the average current.

Capacitive Reactance (continued)

Comparing the charge current curves for different values of capacitance, you see that the larger the capacitance the longer the current remains at a high value. Thus, if the frequency is the same, a greater average current will flow through a larger capacitance than a small capacitance. This holds true only if the circuit resistances are equal, however, because the charge curve of a capacitance depends on the RC time constant of the circuit.

HOW CAPACITANCE VALUES AFFECT CAPACITIVE *Reactance*

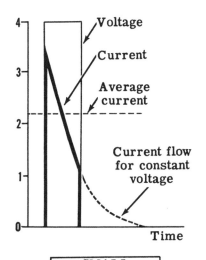

SMALL CAPACITANCE
Low average current high reactance

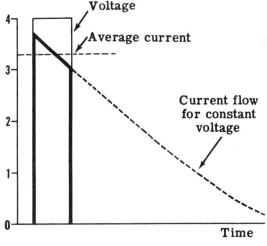

LARGE CAPACITANCE
High average current low reactance

The smaller the capacitance— the lower the average current.

The current flow in a capacitive circuit, assuming that there is no change in the resistance, increases with an increase in either frequency or capacitance. Then capacitive reactance—the opposition to current flow through a capacitance—must decrease when the frequency or capacitance increases. The formula used to obtain capacitive reactance is $X_C = \dfrac{1}{2\pi f C}$ In this formula X_C is capacitive reactance, f is frequency in cycles, C is capacitance in farads and 2π is a constant number (6.28). Since X_C represents opposition or resistance to current flow, it is expressed in ohms.

Capacitive Reactance (continued)

The phase relationship between current and voltage waves in a capacitive circuit is exactly the opposite to that of an inductive circuit. In a purely inductive circuit the current wave lags the voltage by 90 degrees, while in a purely capacitive circuit the current wave leads the voltage by 90 degrees.

In a theoretical circuit of pure capacitance and no resistance, the voltage across the capacitance exists only after current flows to charge the plates. At the moment a capacitance starts to charge, the voltage across its plates is zero and the current flow is maximum. As the capacitance charges, the current flow drops toward zero while the voltage rises to its maximum value. When the capacitance reaches full charge, the current is zero and the voltage is maximum. In discharging, the current starts at zero and rises to a maximum in the opposite direction, while the voltage falls from maximum to zero. In comparing the voltage and current waves, you can see that the current wave leads the voltage by 90 degrees or, in opposite terms, the voltage wave lags the current by 90 degrees.

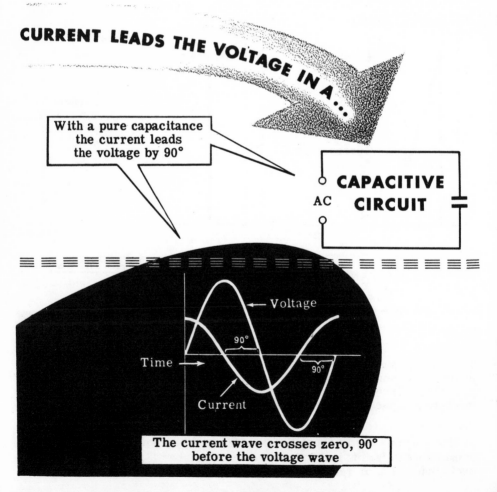

CURRENT LEADS THE VOLTAGE IN A...

With a pure capacitance the current leads the voltage by 90°

CAPACITIVE CIRCUIT

AC

Voltage

90°

Time →

90°

Current

The current wave crosses zero, 90° before the voltage wave

Capacitive Reactance (continued)

Resistance affects capacitive circuits similarly to the way it affects inductive circuits. Remember, in an inductive circuit containing both inductance and resistance, the current wave lags the voltage wave by an angle between zero degrees and 90 degrees, depending on the ratio of inductive reactance to the resistance. For a purely capacitive circuit, current leads the voltage by 90 degrees; but, with both resistance and capacitance in a circuit, the amount of lead—"phase angle"—depends on the ratio between the capacitive reactance and the resistance.

If the capacitive reactance and resistance are equal, they will have an equal effect on the angle of lead resulting in a "phase angle" of 45 degrees leading. As shown below, the current wave then leads the voltage wave by 45 degrees.

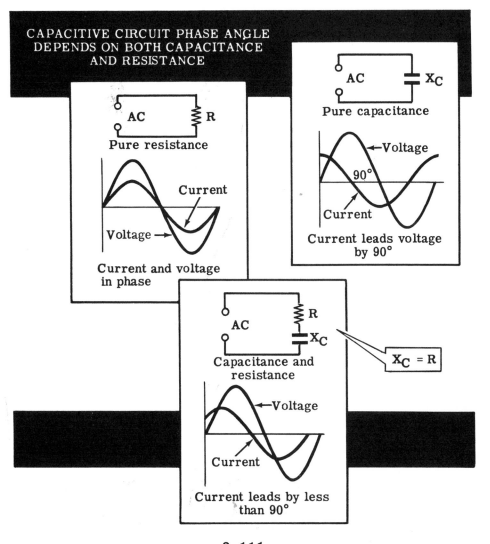

CAPACITIVE CIRCUIT PHASE ANGLE
DEPENDS ON BOTH CAPACITANCE
AND RESISTANCE

AC X_C
Pure capacitance

AC   R
Pure resistance

Current
Voltage →
Current and voltage
in phase

←Voltage
90°
Current
Current leads voltage
by 90°

AC   R
X_C
Capacitance and
resistance

$X_C = R$

←Voltage
Current
Current leads by less
than 90°

Power in a Capacitive Circuit

In a capacitive circuit as in an inductive circuit, the true power used is less than the apparent power of the circuit. Current leads the voltage in a capacitive circuit. The power waveform again is obtained by multiplying the corresponding values of voltage and current to obtain the instantaneous values of power. The power wave of an AC circuit consisting of pure capacitance is shown below and, like the power wave of a purely inductive circuit, its axis is the same as that of the voltage and current, while its frequency is twice that of the voltage and current. For this circuit the phase angle between the current wave and voltage wave is 90 degrees, and the negative power equals the positive power. The formula for power factor for a capacitive circuit is the same as that used for an inductive circuit.

When resistance is added to a capacitive circuit the phase angle decreases, and the positive power becomes greater than the negative power. Because the voltage and current are out of phase, power in watts does not equal apparent power, and power factor is between zero and 100 percent.

POWER WAVE

OF A CIRCUIT CONTAINING ONLY **CAPACITANCE**

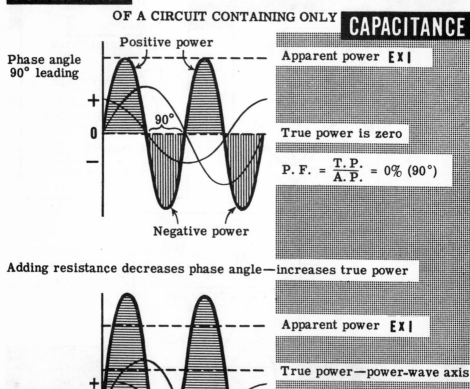

Phase angle 90° leading

Positive power

90°

Negative power

Apparent power $E \times I$

True power is zero

$$P.F. = \frac{T.P.}{A.P.} = 0\% \ (90°)$$

Adding resistance decreases phase angle—increases true power

Apparent power $E \times I$

True power—power-wave axis

$$P.F. = \frac{T.P.}{A.P.} = 70\% \ (45°)$$

CAPACITORS AND CAPACITIVE REACTANCE

Demonstration—RC Time Constant

In an RC circuit the charging current for the capacitor is limited by the resistance, and the voltage across the capacitor builds up slowly at a rate determined by the RC time constant. If a voltmeter is used to measure the voltage across a capacitor to show the rise in voltage as the capacitor charges, the plates of the capacitor are connected together through the resistance of the voltmeter. This prevents the capacitor from reaching full charge and, since the meter completes the circuit across the capacitor, it will not show the rise in voltage across the capacitor.

A VOLTMETER CONNECTED ACROSS A CAPACITOR
ACTS AS A RESISTOR

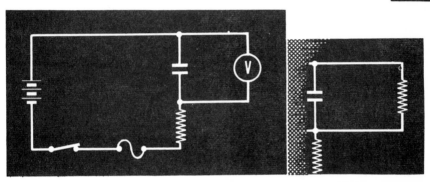

To show how voltage builds up across a capacitor, a device which will indicate voltage but will not connect the capacitor plates together is needed. A neon lamp may be used for this purpose, since it is an open circuit until the voltage across its terminals reaches a predetermined value. The lamp does not accurately measure voltage, nor show the actual building up of the voltage as the capacitor charges. However, if connected across a capacitor which is being charged, it does show that the build-up of voltage across a capacitance is delayed, since the neon lamp does not light immediately when the charging voltage is applied to the capacitor circuit. The lamp lights only after the voltage between the capacitor plates reaches the starting voltage of the lamp.

A NEON LAMP IS AN OPEN CIRCUIT
UNTIL ITS STARTING VOLTAGE IS REACHED

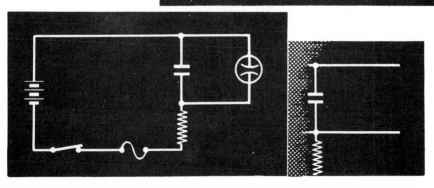

Demonstration—RC Time Constant (continued)

To show how a neon lamp may be used to indicate the time delay in the rise of voltage across a capacitor, the instructor connects a 1-mfd capacitor in series with a 2-megohm resistor. A neon lamp socket is connected across the capacitor and a neon lamp is inserted in the socket, completing the circuit except for a source of voltage. The unconnected end of the resistor is connected to the negative terminal of a 90-volt battery—two 45-volt dry cell batteries in series.

When the instructor closes the switch, you observe that after a momentary delay the neon lamp flashes, indicating that the voltage across the capacitor terminals has reached the starting voltage of the lamp. Notice that the neon lamp continues to flash at intervals of about one second. Each time that the capacitor charges to a voltage equal to the starting voltage of the lamp, the lamp lights—providing a path for current flow between the capacitor plates and discharging the charge which has been built up. When the capacitor discharges through the lighted lamp, its voltage drops to a value which is too low to operate the lamp, the lamp ceases to conduct and again becomes an open circuit. The capacitor then begins to charge again. You see that the lamp lights repeatedly, since each time that the voltage across the capacitor reaches the lamp's starting voltage, the lamp lights, discharging the capacitor.

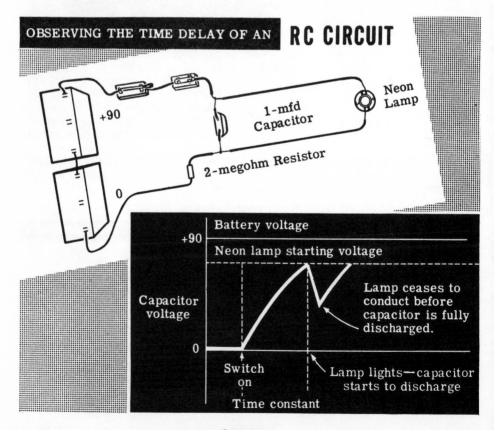

OBSERVING THE TIME DELAY OF AN **RC CIRCUIT**

Demonstration—RC Time Constant (continued)

In order to demonstrate the effect of resistance on the time required for the capacitor to charge, additional resistors are added in series with the 2-megohm resistor. Observe that, when the resistance is doubled, the time required for the capacitor to charge is also doubled.

You already know that the RC time constant gives the time in seconds required for the voltage of a charging capacitor to reach 63.2 percent of the voltage applied to the circuit. The starting voltage of the neon lamp is between 65 and 70 volts, or about 75 percent of the total battery voltage used. However, there is a difference between the computed time constant and the observed time constant. If the circuit resistance is 4 megohms, according to the computed time constant the neon lamp should flash 15 times per minute (4 megs x 1 mfd = 4 sec); but you actually see about 30 flashes per minute. The reason for this is that the lamp does not light at exactly 63.2 percent of charge because the capacitor does not fully discharge each time the lamp flashes. As various values of resistance are used, compare the time required to light the lamp with the computed time constant of the circuit.

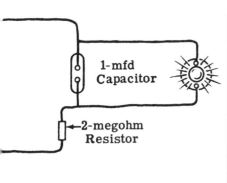
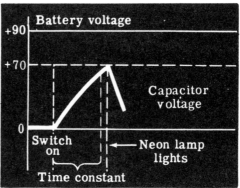

A CHANGE IN RESISTANCE CHANGES THE RC TIME CONSTANT

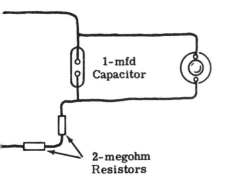
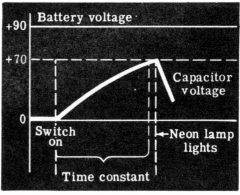

3-115

Demonstration—RC Time Constant (continued)

Next, all of the resistors are removed except the single 2-megohm resistor, and various values of capacitance are used. Notice that changes in the value of capacitance have the same effect on the circuit time constant as changes of resistance. When low values of capacitance are used, the time constant is shorter and the flashes occur so rapidly that the light appears to be steady rather than flashing.

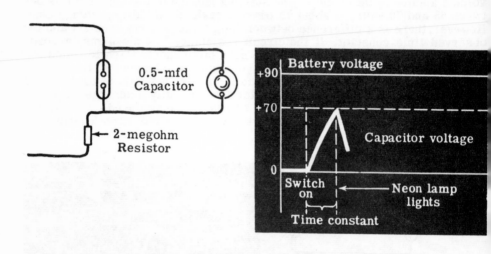

A CHANGE IN CAPACITANCE CHANGES THE RC TIME CONSTANT

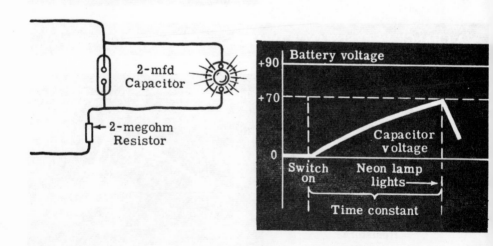

Demonstration—RC Time Constant (continued)

Current flow in charging a capacitor is next demonstrated. A 0-1 ma. zero-center milliammeter, a 200,000-ohm resistor and a 4-mfd capacitor are series-connected in the circuit shown below.

At the moment the switch is closed, you see that the meter indicates a large current flow and, as the capacitor charges, the meter reading falls toward zero. Observe that once the current reaches zero (indicating a full charge on the capacitor plates) opening and closing the switch causes no further current flow. The instructor then opens the switch and discharges the capacitor by shorting its terminals with the screwdriver. Now, when the switch is closed, the meter will indicate a charging current.

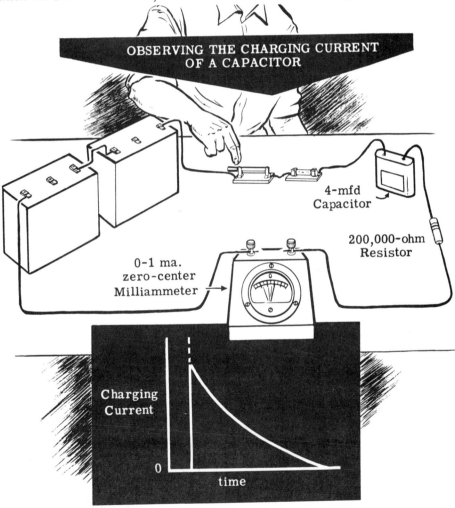

OBSERVING THE CHARGING CURRENT OF A CAPACITOR

4-mfd Capacitor

200,000-ohm Resistor

0-1 ma. zero-center Milliammeter

Charging Current

0

time

Substituting capacitors having various values, the instructor shows that the current flow lasts longer when charging larger capacitors. Notice that, for small values of capacitance, the time required to charge them is so short that it is difficult to read the current indicated on the meter.

CAPACITORS AND CAPACITIVE REACTANCE

Demonstration—Capacitive Reactance

You have already found out that AC current can flow through a capacitive circuit and that the opposition to current flow in such a circuit depends on the capacitance, provided the frequency remains constant. Using the 117-volt AC power line connected through the step-down autotransformer as a voltage source (thus obtaining a constant voltage of 60 volts and a 60-cycle frequency), the instructor connects the 0-50 ma. AC milliammeter in series with the parallel-connected 1-mfd and 0.5-mfd paper capacitors. When the transformer is plugged in and the switch is closed, you see that a current flow is indicated on the AC milliammeter.

To show the effect of changing the value of capacitance on the opposition offered to the flow of AC current, the instructor replaces the 1.5-mfd capacitor with first a 1-mfd and then a 0.5-mfd capacitor. Notice that each time the capacitor is changed, he first opens the switch and then discharges the capacitor with a screwdriver. You see that increasing the value of capacitance increases the current flow, showing that the opposition or capacitive reactance decreases whenever the capacitance increases.

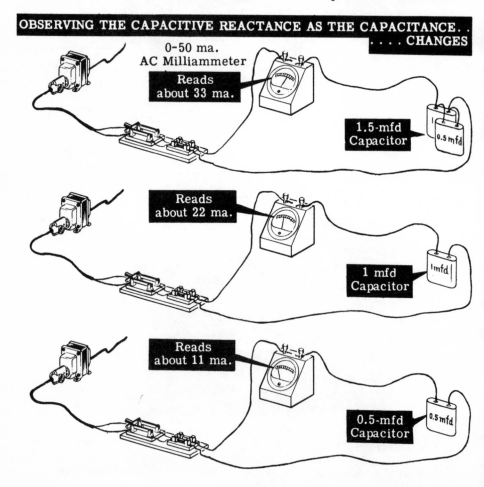

OBSERVING THE CAPACITIVE REACTANCE AS THE CAPACITANCE. . . . . . CHANGES

0-50 ma.
AC Milliammeter

Reads about 33 ma.

1.5-mfd Capacitor — 0.5 mfd

Reads about 22 ma.

1 mfd Capacitor — 1mfd

Reads about 11 ma.

0.5-mfd Capacitor — 0.5 mfd

Review of Capacitors and Capacitive Reactance

Before performing the experiment on capacitive circuit time constants, you should review some of the facts you have found out concerning capacitors, capacitive reactance and RC time constant.

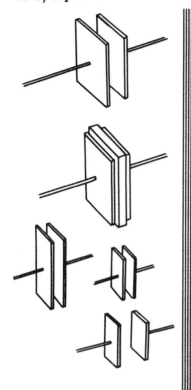

CAPACITOR PLATES — Metallic or metallized plates which can be charged.

DIELECTRIC — Insulating material between the plates of a capacitor.

FACTORS OF CAPACITANCE — Plate area, the distance between the plates and the dielectric material determine capacitance.

$T = RC$

CAPACITIVE TIME CONSTANT — The product of RC which gives the time in seconds required for a capacitance to reach 63.2 percent of full charge.

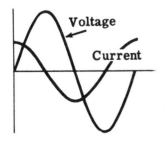

CAPACITIVE REACTANCE — The action of capacitance in opposing the flow of AC current and in causing the current to lead the voltage.

INDEX TO VOL. 3

(Note: A cumulative index covering all five volumes in this series will be found at the end of Volume 5.)

basic
electricity

by VAN VALKENBURGH,
NOOGER & NEVILLE, INC.

VOL. 4

HAYDEN BOOK COMPANY, INC.
Rochelle Park, New Jersey

PREFACE

The texts of the entire Basic Electricity and Basic Electronics courses, as currently taught at Navy specialty schools, have now been released by the Navy for civilian use. This educational program has been an unqualified success. Since April, 1953, when it was first installed, over 25,000 Navy trainees have benefited by this instruction and the results have been outstanding.

The unique simplification of an ordinarily complex subject, the exceptional clarity of illustrations and text, and the plan of presenting one basic concept at a time, without involving complicated mathematics, all combine in making this course a better and quicker way to teach and learn basic electricity and electronics. The Basic Electronics portion of this course will be available as a separate series of volumes.

In releasing this material to the general public, the Navy hopes to provide the means for creating a nation-wide pool of pre-trained technicians, upon whom the Armed Forces could call in time of national emergency, without the need for precious weeks and months of schooling.

Perhaps of greater importance is the Navy's hope that through the release of this course, a direct contribution will be made toward increasing the technical knowledge of men and women throughout the country, as a step in making and keeping America strong.

Van Valkenburgh, Nooger and Neville, Inc.

New York, N. Y.
October, 1954

TABLE OF CONTENTS

Vol. 4 — Basic Electricity

AC Series Circuit Combinations

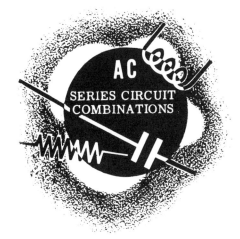

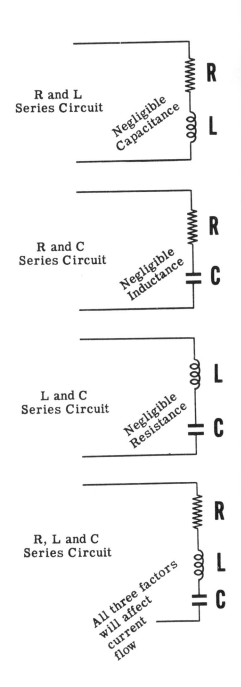

R and L
Series Circuit

Negligible Capacitance

R and C
Series Circuit

Negligible Inductance

L and C
Series Circuit

Negligible Resistance

R, L and C
Series Circuit

All three factors will affect current flow

Various combinations of R, L and C may be used to form AC series circuits. If two factors are negligible, the circuit may consist of only R, only L or only C. However if only one factor is negligible, as is the case in many AC series circuits, it may consist of R and L, R and C, or L and C. If no factors are negligible the circuit consists of R, L and C, and all three factors will affect the current flow.

You have found out how R, L and C individually affect AC current flow, phase angle and power in AC circuits containing only one of these factors. Now you will find out how the various combinations of R, L and C affect AC series circuits consisting of any two, or of all three, of these factors.

Every electric circuit contains a certain amount of resistance (R), inductance (L) and capacitance (C). Inductance and capacitance cause inductive and capacitive reactance (X_L and X_C), which oppose the flow of AC current in a circuit, so that AC circuits contain three factors which oppose current flow: R, X_L and X_C. For a given circuit any of these factors may be so negligible that it can be disregarded.

IMPEDANCE IN AC SERIES CIRCUITS

R and L Series Circuit Impedance

When resistance and inductance are connected in series, the total opposition is not found by adding these two values directly. Inductive reactance causes current to lag the voltage by 90 degrees, while for pure resistance the voltage and current are in phase. Thus the effect of inductive reactance as opposed to the effect of resistance is shown by drawing the two values at right angles to one another.

For example, suppose your series circuit consists of 200 ohms of resistance in series with 200 ohms of inductive reactance at the frequency of the AC voltage source. The total opposition to current flow is not 400 ohms; it is approximately 283 ohms. This value of total opposition, called "impedance," is obtained by a method called "vector addition." A vector is a straight line with an arrow at one end depicting direction, the length of the line depicting magnitude.

To add 200 ohms of resistance and 200 ohms of inductive reactance, a horizontal line is drawn to represent the 200 ohms of resistance. The end of this line, which is to the left, is the reference point, and the right end of the line is marked with an arrow to indicate its direction. To represent the inductive reactance, a vertical line is drawn upward from the reference point. Since X_L and R are each 200 ohms, the horizontal and vertical lines are equal in length. These lines are called "vectors."

In a series circuit the resistance vector is usually drawn horizontally and used as a reference for other vectors in the same diagram.

REPRESENTING R AND X_L AS VECTORS

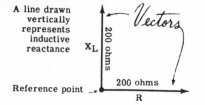

A line drawn vertically represents inductive reactance

X_L

200 ohms

Vectors

Reference point

200 ohms
R

A line drawn horizontally represents resistance

A parallelogram is completed as shown. The diagonal of this parallelogram represents the impedance Z, the total opposition to current flow of the R and L combination. Using the same scale of measure, this value is found to be 283 ohms at a phase angle of 45 degrees.

COMBINING VECTORS R AND X_L TO FIND THE IMPEDANCE

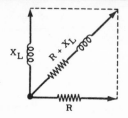

X_L $R + X_L$ R

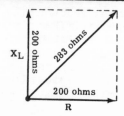

X_L 200 ohms   283 ohms   200 ohms   R

R and L Series Circuit Impedance (continued)

If the resistance and inductance values of a series circuit containing R and L are known, the impedance can be found by means of vectors. First, the inductive reactance X_L is computed by using the formula $X_L = 2\pi f L$ to obtain the value of X_L in ohms. Then the vectors representing R and X_L are drawn to scale on graph paper. A common reference point is used with the resistance vector R drawn horizontally to the right, and the inductive reactance vector X_L drawn upward, perpendicular to the resistance vector.

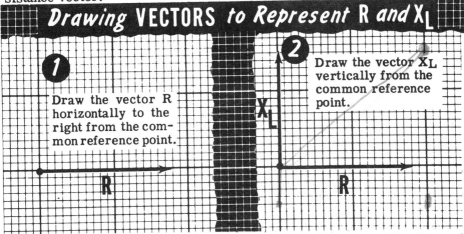

Drawing VECTORS to Represent R and X_L

1 Draw the vector R horizontally to the right from the common reference point.

2 Draw the vector X_L vertically from the common reference point.

Next the parallelogram is completed, using dotted lines, and the diagonal is drawn between the reference point and the intersection of the dotted lines. The length of the diagonal represents the value of the impedance Z in ohms.

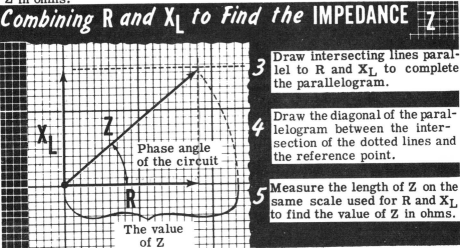

Combining R and X_L to Find the IMPEDANCE Z

Phase angle of the circuit

The value of Z

3 Draw intersecting lines parallel to R and X_L to complete the parallelogram.

4 Draw the diagonal of the parallelogram between the intersection of the dotted lines and the reference point.

5 Measure the length of Z on the same scale used for R and X_L to find the value of Z in ohms.

In addition to showing the value of the circuit impedance, the vector solution also shows the phase angle between the circuit current and voltage. The angle between the impedance vector Z and the resistance vector R is the "phase angle" of the circuit in degrees. This is the angle between the circuit voltage and current, and represents a current lag of 39 degrees.

R and L Series Circuit Impedance (continued)

A protractor is an angle-measuring device utilizing a semi-circular double scale marked off in degrees.

To measure the phase angle of a vector relative to a reference line, the horizontal edge of the protractor is lined up with the horizontal reference vector and the protractor vertical line is lined up with the vertical vector. The degree point at which the diagonal vector intersects the semi-circular scale is the phase angle of the diagonal vector. The angle is read between zero and 90 degrees, because the phase angle will never be less than zero or greater than 90 degrees.

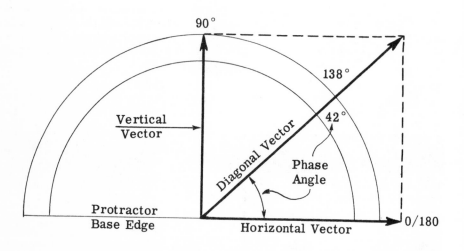

USING A PROTRACTOR TO MEASURE PHASE ANGLE

R and L Series Circuit Impedance (continued)

Ohm's law for AC circuits may also be used to find the impedance Z for a series circuit. In applying Ohm's law to an AC circuit, Z is substituted for R in the formula. Thus the impedance Z is equal to the circuit voltage E divided by the circuit current I. For example, if the circuit voltage is 117 volts and the current is 0.5 ampere, the impedance Z is 234 ohms.

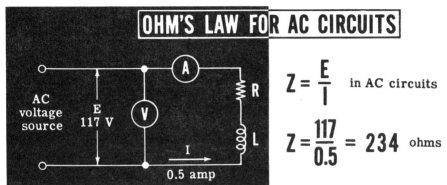

If the impedance of a circuit is found by applying Ohm's law for AC, and the value of R is known and X_L is unknown, the phase angle and the value of X_L may be determined graphically by using vectors. If the resistance in the circuit above is known to be 200 ohms, the vector solution is as follows:

1. Since the resistance is known to be 200 ohms, the resistance vector is drawn horizontally from the reference point. At the end of the resistance vector, a dotted line is drawn perpendicular to the resistance vector.

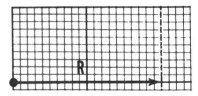

2. Using a straight edge marked to indicate the length of the impedance vector Z, find the point on the perpendicular dotted line which is exactly the length of the impedance vector from the reference point. Draw the impedance vector between that point and the zero position. The angle between the two vectors Z and R is the circuit phase angle, and the length of the dotted line between the ends of the two vectors represents X_L.

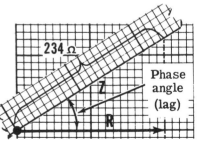

3. Complete the parallelogram by drawing a horizontal dotted line between the end of the vector Z and a vertical line drawn up from the reference point. X_L is this vertical line, and its length can be read by using the same scale. In the example shown, $X_L = 122\,\Omega$.

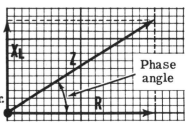

4. Measure the phase angle with a protractor.

5. Divide R/Z = Power Factor = 200/234 = .85 or 85%.

R and L Series Circuit Impedance (continued)

If the impedance and inductance are known, but the resistance is not known, both the phase angle and resistance may be found by using vectors. For example, the impedance is found to be 300 ohms by measuring the current and voltage and applying Ohm's law for AC. If the circuit inductance is 0.5 henry, the vector solution is as follows:

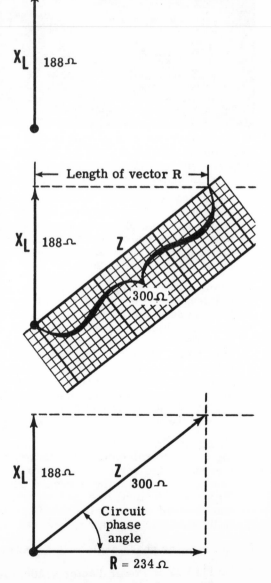

1. First the inductive reactance is computed by using the formula $X_L = 2\pi fL$. If the frequency is 60 cycles, then X_L is 188 ohms ($X_L = 6.28 \times 60 \times 0.5 = 188\,\Omega$). Draw the vector X_L vertically from the reference point. At the end of this vector, draw a horizontal dotted line perpendicular to the vector X_L.

2. Using a straight edge marked to indicate the length of the impedance vector, find the point on the horizontal dotted line which is exactly the length of the impedance from the reference point. Draw the impedance vector Z between that point and the reference point. The distance between the ends of the vectors X_L and Z represents the length of the resistance vector R.

3. Draw the vector R horizontally from the zero position and complete the parallelogram. The angle between R and Z is the phase angle of the circuit in degrees, and the length of the vector R represents the resistance in ohms.

4. Measure the phase angle with a protractor.

5. Compute the power factor. P. F. = R/Z

R and L Series Circuit Impedance (continued)

You have already learned how to calculate (by Ohm's Law) the impedance of a series circuit which is composed of a coil and a resistor, and which is connected to an AC voltage source. You will now learn how to calculate the impedance of such a circuit without the use of Ohm's Law, and without making measurements.

Assume, for this problem, that the inductive reactance X_L is 4 ohms and that the resistance is 3 ohms. The formula for finding the impedance in the circuit described is as follows:

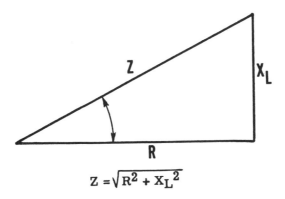

$$Z = \sqrt{R^2 + X_L^2}$$

Because you may not be familiar with the "square root" sign ($\sqrt{}$), and the "square" signs which are in position at the top right of the symbols for resistance and inductive reactance, these symbols or signs are explained below.

A simple way of showing mathematically that a number is to be multiplied once by itself, or "squared," is to place a numeral 2 at the upper right of the number in question. So that

$$3^2 = 3 \times 3 \text{ or } 9$$
$$5^2 = 5 \times 5 \text{ or } 25$$
$$4^2 = 4 \times 4 \text{ or } 16$$
$$\text{and } 12^2 = 12 \times 12 \text{ or } 144, \text{ etc.}$$

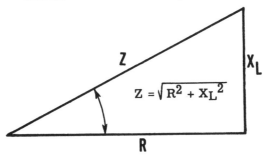

$$Z = \sqrt{R^2 + X_L^2}$$

R and L Series Circuit Impedance (continued)

The square root sign, or $\sqrt{}$, indicates that you are to break down the enclosed figure to find a number which, when multiplied by itself, results in the original enclosed figure. Consider the problem of finding the square root of 144, shown mathematically, $\sqrt{144}$. What number multiplied by itself results in 144? The answer, of course, is 12. So that

$$\sqrt{144} = 12, \text{ and } \sqrt{36} = 6,$$
$$\sqrt{25} = 5, \text{ and } \sqrt{9} = 3, \text{ etc.}$$

The formula for impedance $(Z = \sqrt{R^2 + X_L^2})$ then, indicates that you must "square" the values for R and X_L, add the two resultant figures and take the square root of the total, in order to find the impedance, Z.

As given on the previous sheet, X_L is 4 ohms and R is 3 ohms. Find the impedance.

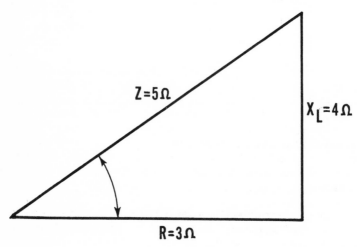

$$Z = \sqrt{R^2 + X_L^2}$$

By substitution

$$Z = \sqrt{3^2 + 4^2} = \sqrt{9 + 16} = \sqrt{25} = 5$$

More often than not, the number enclosed by the square root symbol does not permit a simple answer without decimals. In that event it is necessary to find the square root which is closest to the desired numeral within the limits outlined by the instructor. For example, the instructor may elect to accept as correct an impedance value of five ohms even though the original figure required that the square root of 30 be found. (The $\sqrt{30}$ is actually equal to 5.47.) There are, of course, methods for finding accurate square root answers but these need not be dealt with here.

IMPEDANCE IN AC SERIES CIRCUITS

Power Factor

The concept of power, particularly with regard to the calculation of power factors in AC circuits, will become a very important consideration as the circuits you work with are made more complex. In DC circuits the expended power may be determined by multiplying the voltage by the current. A similar relationship exists for finding the amount of expended power in AC circuits, but certain other factors must be considered. In AC circuits the power is equal to the product of voltage and current only when the E and I are in phase. If the voltage and current waves are not in phase, the power used by the circuit will be somewhat less than the product of E and I.

A review of the following principles (most of which you already know) will be helpful later on, in the discussion.

1. Power is defined as the rate of doing work.
2. A watt is the unit of electrical power.
3. Apparent power is the product of volts and amperes in an AC circuit.
4. True power is the amount of power actually consumed by the circuit.
5. True power is equal to apparent power if the voltage and current are in phase.
6. True power is equal to zero if the voltage and current are out of phase by 90 degrees.
7. True power is equal to the apparent power multiplied by a figure called the "cosine of the phase angle." (This term will be explained shortly.)
8. The cosine of the phase angle is called the "power factor" and is often expressed as a decimal or percentage.

The power factor is important because it converts apparent power to true power. It is this true power, the kind that actually does work in the circuit, which will interest you most.

The cosine of the phase angle, or power factor, is explained with the help of the familiar impedance triangle diagram. The resistive component forms the base. The reactive component (X) forms the right angle with the base, and the third side called the "hypotenuse" is the resultant impedance (Z). The angle formed by the R and Z sides of the impedance triangle is called by the Greek letter θ (theta). The angle θ originally refers to the phase angle difference between the voltage across the resistor and the voltage across the coil in the diagram on the next sheet.

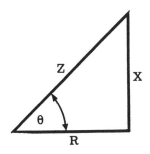

Power Factor (continued)

Theoretically, the voltage across the coil leads the current through the circuit by a phase angle of 90 degrees. E_L leads the voltage across the resistor because E_R is in phase with I.

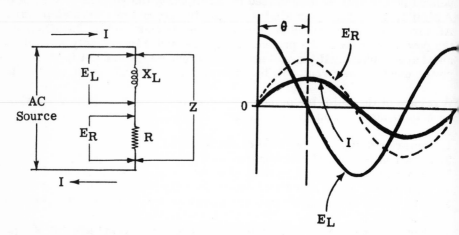

In practical circuits a phase angle of 90 degrees is an impossibility because every coil (and wire) has some resistance, however small. It is this resistance, and the resistance placed in the circuit by design, which reduces the phase angle to something less than 90 degrees. Consider the voltage triangle of the circuit above. Each of the voltages noted may also be expressed

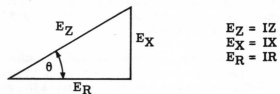

$$E_Z = IZ$$
$$E_X = IX$$
$$E_R = IR$$

as the product of the current times the resistance, reactance, or impedance, as the case may be. The term, cosine of the phase angle, refers to a ratio of E_R to E_Z and is expressed mathematically as

$$\text{Cos } \theta = \frac{E_R}{E_Z}$$

This formula is used just as well where impedance, resistance, and reactance are the prime considerations, because

$$\text{Cos } \theta = \frac{E_R}{E_Z} = \frac{IR}{IZ} = \frac{R}{Z}$$

You now know all of the factors mentioned in points 7 and 8 on the previous sheet. The formula for true power should, therefore, present no difficulties. This formula is expressed mathematically as

$$P = EI \text{ Cos } \theta \quad \text{or,} \quad \text{Cos } \theta = \frac{P}{EI} \quad \text{or,} \quad EI = \frac{P}{\text{Cos } \theta}$$

Power Factor (continued)

Suppose that you wish to find the amount of power expended (true power) in a circuit where the impedance is five ohms, the resistance is three ohms, and the inductive reactance is four ohms. The impressed voltage is ten volts AC, and the current is two amperes.

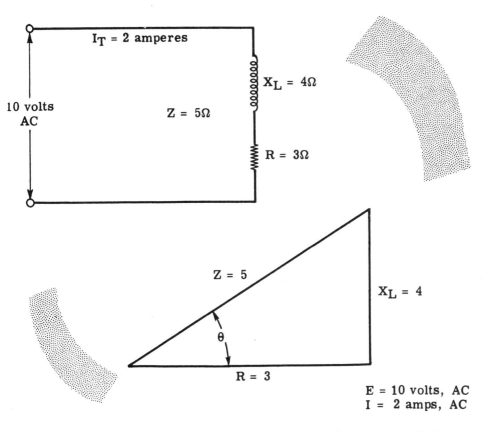

$$I_T = 2 \text{ amperes}$$

$$X_L = 4\Omega$$

10 volts AC

$$Z = 5\Omega$$

$$R = 3\Omega$$

$$Z = 5$$

$$X_L = 4$$

$$\theta$$

$$R = 3$$

E = 10 volts, AC
I = 2 amps, AC

The formula for true power is $P = EI \cos \theta$. With reference to the impedance triangle the $\cos \theta$ is equal to the ratio of R divided by Z, or

$$\cos \theta = \frac{R}{Z} = \frac{3}{5} = .60 \text{ or } 60\%$$

Substituting in the formula for true power

$$P = EI \cos \theta$$
$$P = 10 \times 2 \times .6$$
$$P = 12 \text{ watts of power expended}$$

The components in the circuit must be chosen of such size that they will be able to dissipate twelve watts of power at the very minimum, or burnout will occur.

R and L Series Circuits Impedance Variation

The impedance of a series circuit containing only resistance and inductance is determined by the vector addition of the resistance and the inductive reactance. If a given value of inductive reactance is used, the impedance varies as shown when the resistance value is changed.

How Impedance Varies

WHEN X_L IS A FIXED VALUE AND R IS VARIED

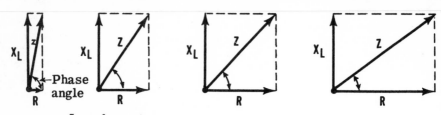

Impedance increases
and the phase angle decreases
as R increases

Similarly, if a given value of resistance is used, the impedance varies as shown when the inductive reactance is changed.

How Impedance Varies

WHEN R IS A FIXED VALUE AND X_L IS VARIED

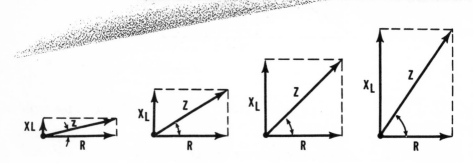

Impedance increases and the phase angle increases
as X_L increases

When the resistance equals zero the impedance is equal to X_L, and when the inductive reactance equals zero the impedance is equal to R. While the value of Z may be determined by means of a complex mathematical formula, you will use the practical methods—a vector solution or Ohm's law for AC circuits.

IMPEDANCE IN AC SERIES CIRCUITS

R and C Series Circuit Impedance

If your AC series circuit consists of resistance and capacitance in series, the total opposition to current flow (impedance) is due to two factors, resistance and capacitive reactance. The action of capacitive reactance causes the current in a capacitive circuit to lead the voltage by 90 degrees, so that the effect of capacitive reactance is at right angles to the effect of resistance. While the effects of both inductive and capacitive reactance are at right angles to the effect of resistance, their effects are exactly opposite—inductive reactance causing current to lag and capacitive reactance causing it to lead the voltage. Thus the vector X_C, representing capacitive reactance, is still drawn perpendicular to the resistance vector, but is drawn down rather than up from the zero position.

The impedance of a series circuit containing R and C is found in the same manner as the impedance of an R and L series circuit. For example, suppose that in your R and C series circuit R equals 200 ohms and X_C equals 200 ohms. To find the impedance, the resistance vector R is drawn horizontally from a reference point. Then a vector of equal length is drawn downward from the reference point at right angles to the vector R. This vector X_C represents the capacitive reactance and is equal in length to R since both R and X_C equal 200 ohms.

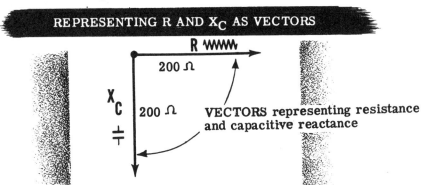

REPRESENTING R AND X_C AS VECTORS

R ⌇⌇⌇⌇
200 Ω

X_C 200 Ω   VECTORS representing resistance and capacitive reactance

To complete the vector solution, the parallelogram is completed and a diagonal drawn from the reference point. This diagonal is the vector Z and represents the impedance in ohms (283 ohms). The angle between the vectors R and Z is the phase angle of the circuit, indicating the amount in degrees that the current leads the voltage.

COMBINING VECTORS R AND X_C TO FIND THE IMPEDANCE

R ⌇⌇⌇⌇
200 Ω
283 Ω   circuit phase angle = 45°
X_C 200 Ω   Z

4-13

R and C Series Circuit Impedance (continued)

R and C series circuit impedances can be found either by using the vector solution or by application of Ohm's law. To find the impedance Z by using a vector solution, you should perform the steps outlined.

1. Compute the value of X_C by using the formula $X_C = \dfrac{1}{2\pi fC}$. In this formula 2π is a constant equal to 6.28, f is the frequency in cycles per second and C is the capacitance in farads.

2. Draw vectors R and X_C to scale on graph paper, using a common reference point for the two vectors. R is drawn horizontally to the right from the reference point and X_C is drawn downward from the reference point, perpendicular to the resistance vector R.

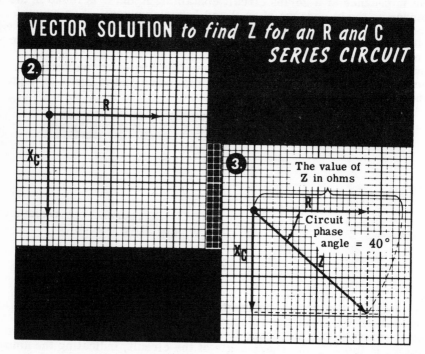

VECTOR SOLUTION *to find* Z *for an* R *and* C SERIES CIRCUIT

The value of Z in ohms

Circuit phase angle = 40°

3. Using dotted lines, a parallelogram is completed and a diagonal drawn from the reference point to the intersection of the dotted lines. The length of this diagonal represents the impedance Z as measured to the same scale as that used for R and X_C. The angle between the vectors R and Z is the phase angle between the circuit current and voltage.

4. Measure the angle in degrees with a protractor.

You can also use Ohm's law ($Z = \dfrac{E}{I}$) to find Z. After measuring the circuit current and voltage, the impedance in ohms can be found by dividing the voltage by the current. For example, if the circuit voltage is 117 volts and 0.1 ampere of current flows through an AC series circuit consisting of R and C, the impedance is 1170 ohms ($117 \div 0.1 = 1170$ ohms).

R and C Series Circuit Impedance (continued)

When the value of either R or X_C is unknown, but the value of Z is known, you can find the unknown value by vector solution.

If you find Z by applying Ohm's law to the AC circuit, and the value of R is known and X_C is unknown, the first step in finding X_C is to draw the resistance vector R to scale. Next a dotted line is drawn downward at the end of and perpendicular to the vector R. A straight edge, marked to indicate the length of the impedance vector Z, is used to find the point on the dotted line which is exactly the length of the impedance vector Z from the reference point. Draw the vector Z between that point and the reference point. Complete the parallelogram with the value of X_C being equal to the distance between the ends of the vectors R and Z. If Z and X_C are known but R is unknown, the vector X_C is first drawn to scale. A horizontal dotted line is drawn to the right, at the end of and perpendicular to the vector X_C. Then a straight edge is used as before to find the point on this dotted line which is exactly the length of the impedance vector Z from the reference point. Draw the vector Z between that point and the reference point. Complete the parallelogram, with the value of R being equal to the distance between the ends of the vectors X_C and Z.

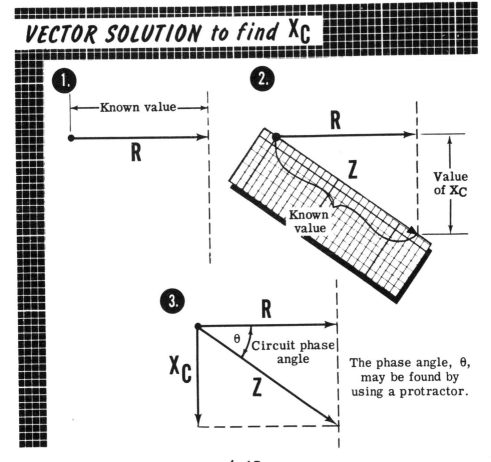

VECTOR SOLUTION to find X_C

1. Known value — R

2. R — Z — Known value — Value of X_C

3. R — θ Circuit phase angle — X_C — Z

The phase angle, θ, may be found by using a protractor.

R and C Series Circuit Impedance (continued)

The ratio of **R** to X_C determines both the amount of impedance and the phase angle in series circuits consisting only of resistance and capacitance. If the capacitive reactance is a fixed value and the resistance is varied, the impedance varies as shown. When the resistance is near zero, the phase angle is nearly 90 degrees and the impedance is almost entirely due to the capacitive reactance; but, when R is much greater than X_C, the phase angle approaches zero degrees and the impedance is affected more by R than X_C.

How Impedance Varies

WHEN X_C IS A FIXED VALUE AND R IS VARIED

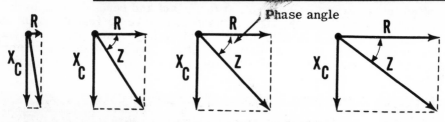

... Impedance increases and phase angle decreases as R increases

If your circuit consists of a fixed value of resistance and the capacitance is varied, the impedance varies as shown below. As the capacitive reactance is reduced toward zero, the phase angle approaches zero degrees and the impedance is almost entirely due to the resistance; but, as X_C is increased to a much greater value than R, the phase angle approaches 90 degrees and the impedance is affected more by X_C than R.

How Impedance Varies

WHEN R IS A FIXED VALUE AND X_C IS VARIED

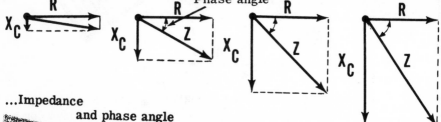

...Impedance
    and phase angle
        increases
            as X_C increases

⌐ and C Series Circuit Impedance

n AC series circuits consisting of inductance and capacitance, with only
negligible resistance, the impedance is due to inductive and capacitive
reactance only. Since inductive and capacitive reactances act in opposite directions, the total effect of the two is equal to their difference. For
such circuits, Z can be found by subtracting the smaller value from the
larger. The circuit will then act as an inductive or a capacitive reactance
(depending on which is larger) having an impedance equal to Z. For example, if X_L = 500 ohms and X_C = 300 ohms, the impedance Z is 200 ohms
and the circuit acts as an inductance having an inductive reactance of 200
ohms. If the X_L and X_C values were reversed, Z would still equal 200
ohms, but the circuit would act as a capacitance having a capacitive reactance of 200 ohms.
The relationships of the above examples are shown below. Z is drawn on
the same axis as X_L and X_C and represents the difference in their values.
The phase angle of the L and C series circuit is always 90 degrees except
when X_L = X_C, but whether it is leading or lagging depends on whether X_L
s greater or less than X_C. The phase angle is the angle between Z and
he horizontal axis.

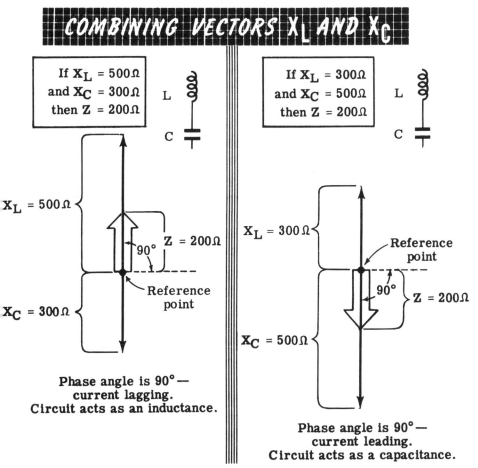

COMBINING VECTORS X_L AND X_C

If X_L = 500 Ω
and X_C = 300 Ω
then Z = 200 Ω

L

C

X_L = 500 Ω

90° Z = 200 Ω

Reference
point

X_C = 300 Ω

Phase angle is 90° —
current lagging.
Circuit acts as an inductance.

If X_L = 300 Ω
and X_C = 500 Ω
then Z = 200 Ω

L

C

X_L = 300 Ω

Reference
point

90° Z = 200 Ω

X_C = 500 Ω

Phase angle is 90° —
current leading.
Circuit acts as a capacitance.

R, L and C Series Circuit Impedance

The impedance of a series circuit consisting of resistance, capacitance and inductance in series depends on three factors: R, X_L and X_C. If the values of all three factors are known, impedance Z may be found as follows:

Combining Vectors R, X_L and X_C to find the Impedance

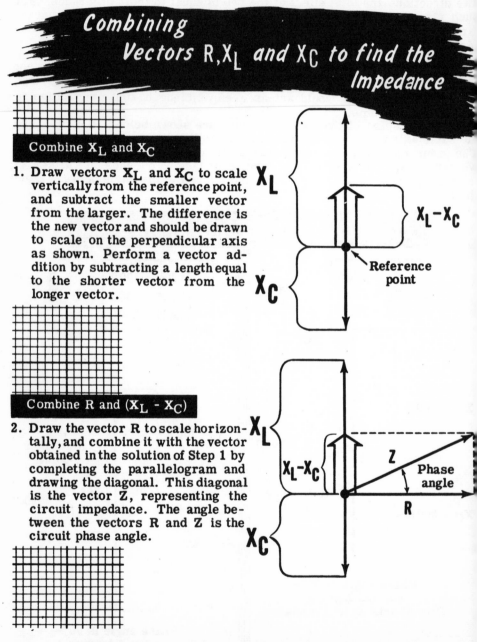

Combine X_L and X_C

1. Draw vectors X_L and X_C to scale vertically from the reference point, and subtract the smaller vector from the larger. The difference is the new vector and should be drawn to scale on the perpendicular axis as shown. Perform a vector addition by subtracting a length equal to the shorter vector from the longer vector.

X_L

X_C

$X_L - X_C$

Reference point

Combine R and (X_L - X_C)

2. Draw the vector R to scale horizontally, and combine it with the vector obtained in the solution of Step 1 by completing the parallelogram and drawing the diagonal. This diagonal is the vector Z, representing the circuit impedance. The angle between the vectors R and Z is the circuit phase angle.

X_L

$X_L - X_C$

X_C

Z

Phase angle

R

You can also find the impedance of the circuit by applying Ohm's law for AC circuits, after measuring the circuit current and voltage.

R, L and C Series Circuit Impedance (continued)

On the previous sheet you learned how to combine vectors R, X_L and X_C to find the impedance. It is a simple matter to find the phase angle between the impedance and the resistance by using a protractor. Superimpose the protractor on the vector diagram below.

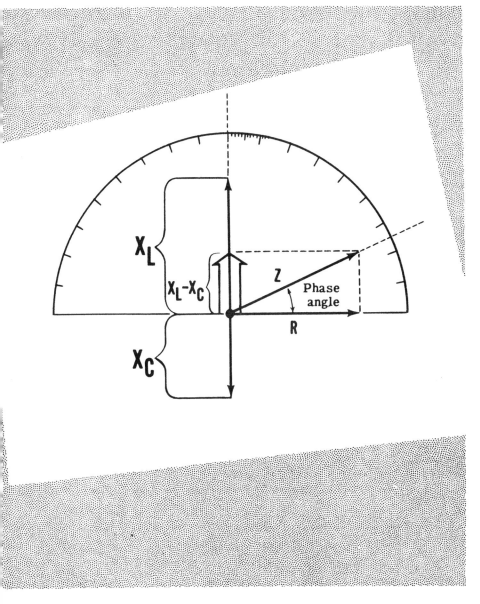

Take the angle reading at the point where the impedance line crosses the protractor scale.

R, L and C Series Circuit Impedance (continued)

The impedance of a circuit which contains R, L and C components may also be calculated by using a variation of the impedance formula $Z = \sqrt{R^2 + X^2}$. You have learned that it makes no difference if the reactive component, X is inductive or capacitive in nature; the impedance is found in the same way, using the same formula for Z. Also, when both inductive and capacitive reactance are present in a circuit it is only necessary to subtract the smaller amount of reactance, either inductive or capacitive, as the case may be, from the larger amount and then draw in the resultant diagonal vector Z. In calculating the value for impedance in a circuit containing both resistive and reactive components use the formula

$$Z = \sqrt{R^2 + X_e^2}$$

where X_e is equal to $X_L - X_C$ or vice versa, as required.

In the diagram on the previous sheet, assume that X_L is seven ohms, that X_C is three ohms, and that R is three ohms. Placing these values in the impedance formula, we find

$$Z = \sqrt{R^2 + (X_L - X_C)^2}$$

$$Z = \sqrt{3^2 + (7 - 3)^2} = \sqrt{3^2 + 4^2}$$

$$Z = \sqrt{9 + 16} = \sqrt{25}$$

$$Z = 5 \text{ ohms}$$

You will now review the method for finding the power factor and for using it to obtain true power dissipation. The apparent power is simply the voltage times the current. When this apparent power is multiplied by the cosine of the phase angle the result is the true power value. Using an impedance triangle, find the power factor and true power dissipation in a circuit which is composed of an equivalent reactance of four ohms, a resistance of three ohms, an impedance of five ohms, and which has a voltage of 2.5 volts and a current of 500 milliamps.

You have learned that the cosine of the phase angle is simply a ratio of the resistance divided by the impedance, so that

$$\text{Cosine of phase angle } \theta = \frac{R}{Z} = \frac{3}{5} = .60 \text{ or } 60\%$$

The formula for true power is

$$P = EI \cos \theta = 2.5 \times .5 \times .6$$
$$P = .75 \text{ watt}$$

Demonstration—Series Circuit Impedance

To see how series circuit impedance can be computed, by using vectors or by applying Ohm's law for AC to the circuit, you will participate in a demonstration of series circuit impedance. You will see how vector solutions are used to obtain quickly the approximate values of series circuit impedance.

You will see how the AC impedance is obtained by applying Ohm's law to various circuits and checking the computed impedances.

Using the 5-henry inductance, the 1-mfd capacitor and the 2000-ohm resistor, the instructor will demonstrate the use of vectors in finding circuit impedance for the various types of AC series circuits. Although the 5-henry filter choke used for inductance actually has a DC resistance of about 50 ohms, this value is negligible in comparison to the 2000 ohm resistor and will not be considered. To find the impedance of a circuit, the inductive and capacitive reactances must first be computed from the known inductance and capacitance values.

Finding X_L for a 5-henry inductance	Frequency = 60 cycles	Finding X_C for a 1-mfd capacitor

$$X_C = \frac{1}{2\pi f C}$$

$$X_L = 2\pi f L$$
$$X_L = 6.28 \times 60 \times 5$$
$$X_L = 1884$$

$$X_C = \frac{1}{6.28 \times 60 \times 0.000001} = \frac{1}{0.000377}$$
$$X_C = 2650$$

First the instructor uses the inductive and capacitive reactance formulas to obtain the values for X_L and X_C. To check your understanding of these formulas, find the inductive and capacitive reactances for inductances of 8 and 12 henries and capacitances of 2 and 5 mfd. Compare your answers with those obtained by others in the class.

Demonstration—Series Circuit Impedance (continued)

Using the computed values of X_L and X_C (X_L = 1884Ω and X_C = 2650Ω) and the known value of R (2000 ohms), the instructor next finds the value Z for each of the various types of series circuits by means of vector solution. (For graphical purposes, values of X_L, X_C and Z are rounded off to the nearest 50 ohms to make scale drawing possible. For example, the value used for X_L is 1900 ohms and the value used for X_C is 2650 ohms.) A protractor is used to measure phase angle in degrees.

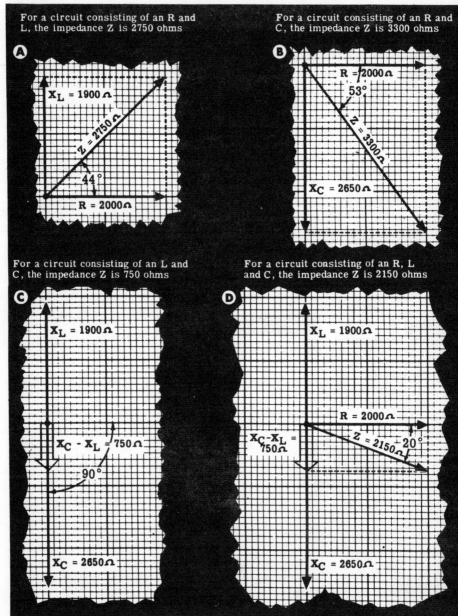

For a circuit consisting of an R and L, the impedance Z is 2750 ohms

(A) X_L = 1900 Ω; Z = 2750 Ω; 44°; R = 2000 Ω

For a circuit consisting of an R and C, the impedance Z is 3300 ohms

(B) R = 2000 Ω; 53°; Z = 3300 Ω; X_C = 2650 Ω

For a circuit consisting of an L and C, the impedance Z is 750 ohms

(C) X_L = 1900 Ω; X_C - X_L = 750 Ω; 90°; X_C = 2650 Ω

For a circuit consisting of an R, L and C, the impedance Z is 2150 ohms

(D) X_L = 1900 Ω; R = 2000 Ω; X_C-X_L = 750 Ω; Z = 2150 Ω; 20°; X_C = 2650 Ω

Demonstration—Ohm's Law for AC Circuits

To check the computed impedance values for the various types of series circuits, the instructor connects the 2000-ohm resistor, 5-henry filter choke and 1-mfd capacitor to form the various circuits in turn. Each circuit is connected to the AC power line separately, and current and voltage are measured. These values are used to compute Z by using Ohm's law ($Z = \frac{E}{I}$). The Ohm's law values are then compared to vector solutions.

The 2000-ohm resistance, 5-henry choke, a switch, a fuse and a 0-50 ma. AC milliammeter are connected in series across the AC power line through the step-down autotransformer to form a series R and L circuit. A 0-200 volt range AC voltmeter is connected across the autotransformer to measure the circuit voltage. With the switch closed, you see that the voltmeter reads approximately 60 volts and the milliammeter reads about 22 ma. The Ohm's law value of Z is about 2750 ohms (60 ÷ 0.022 ≈ 2750), and you see that the two methods of finding Z result in approximately equal values for Z. (The meter readings you observe will vary somewhat from those given due to variations in line voltage, meter accuracy and in the rating of the resistors, capacitors and chokes used. Thus the value of Z actually obtained will vary slightly in each case from the values given.)

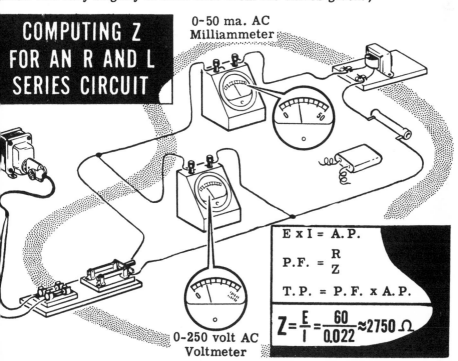

COMPUTING Z FOR AN R AND L SERIES CIRCUIT

0-50 ma. AC Milliammeter

0-250 volt AC Voltmeter

$E \times I = A.P.$

$P.F. = \dfrac{R}{Z}$

$T.P. = P.F. \times A.P.$

$Z = \dfrac{E}{I} = \dfrac{60}{0.022} \approx 2750\ \Omega$

To check the impedance of the R and C series circuit, the instructor removes the 5-henry choke from the circuit and replaces it with the 1-mfd capacitor. With the switch closed, the voltmeter reading again is about 60 volts and the milliammeter reading is about 19 ma., resulting in an Ohm's law value of approximately 3300 ohms for Z (60 ÷ 0.019 ≈ 3300).

Demonstration—Ohm's Law for AC Circuits (continued)

Next the instructor demonstrates how inductive and capacitive reactanc
oppose each other.

The 2000-ohm resistor is removed from the circuit. With the switch
closed you see that the voltage is still about 60 volts while the indicate
current is about 23 ma. The Ohm's law value of the impedance then i
approximately 2650 ohms (60 ÷ 0.023 ≈ 2650). Since only capacitance i
used in the circuit, the value of Z is equal to X_C.

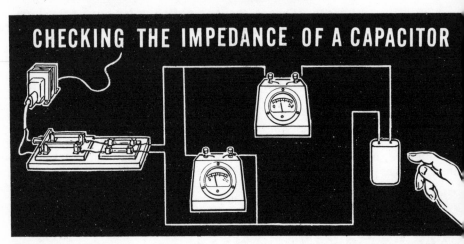

CHECKING THE IMPEDANCE OF A CAPACITOR

To construct the L and C circuit, the 5-henry filter choke is inserted
series with the 1-mfd capacitor. Close the switch only for an instar
and you see that the current flow is too high to be read on the 0-50 r
AC meter. The added inductance reactance of the filter choke has a car
celing effect on the capacitive reactance and reduces the circuit's oppos
tion to current flow.

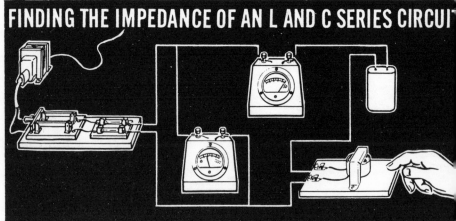

FINDING THE IMPEDANCE OF AN L AND C SERIES CIRCUI

The 2000-ohm resistor is added to the circuit in series with the 5-henr
filter choke and the 1-mfd capacitor to form an R, L and C series circu
With the switch closed, the indicated current is about 28 ma. and the vc
age is 60 volts. For the R, L and C series circuit, the Ohm's law valu
of impedance is 2150 ohms (60 ÷ 0.028 ≈ 2150).

Review of Series Circuit Impedance

Suppose you review what you have found out about impedance and the methods used to find the value of impedance.

<u>IMPEDANCE</u> — The total opposition to the flow of current in an AC circuit.

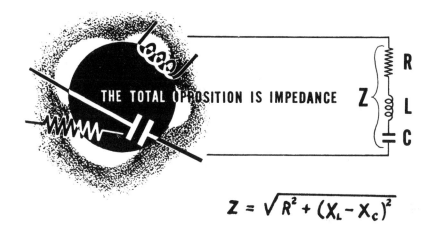

THE TOTAL OPPOSITION IS IMPEDANCE

$$Z = \sqrt{R^2 + (X_L - X_C)^2}$$

Vector solution to find impedance and use of protractor to find phase angle.

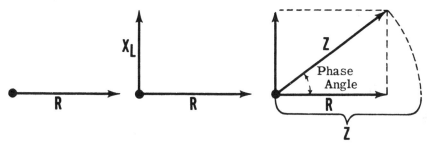

Ohm's Law for AC Circuits.

$$Z = \frac{E}{I} \quad \text{in AC circuits}$$

Formulas For Power and Power Factor

$$E_T \times I_T = A.P.$$

$$P.F. = \frac{R}{Z}$$

$$T.P. = P.F. \times A.P.$$

Current Flow in AC Series Circuits

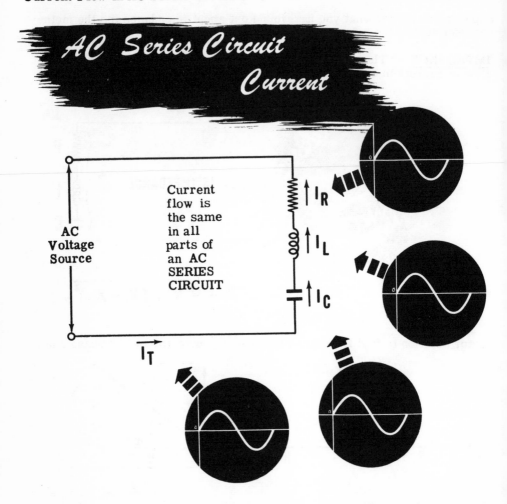

In an AC series circuit, as in a DC series circuit, there is only one path for current flow around the complete circuit. This is true regardless of the type of circuit: R and L, R and C, L and C, or R, L and C. Since there is only one path around the circuit, the current flow is exactly the same in all parts of the circuit at any time, and therefore all phase angles in a series circuit are measured with respect to the circuit current, unless otherwise mentioned.

Thus in a circuit containing R, L and C—such as the one illustrated—the current which flows into the capacitor to charge it will also flow through the resistor and the inductor. When the current flow reverses in the capacitor, it reverses simultaneously in the inductor and in the resistor. If you plot the current waveforms I_R, I_L and I_C for the resistor, inductor and capacitor in such a circuit, the three waveforms are identical in value and phase angle. The total circuit current, I_T, is also identical to these three waveforms both in value and phase angle, since $I_T = I_R = I_L = I_C$.

Voltages in AC Series Circuits

Just as the impedance of an AC series current cannot be found by adding the values of R, X_L and X_C directly, the total voltage, E_T, of an AC series circuit cannot be found by adding the individual voltages E_R, E_L and E_C across the resistance, inductance and capacitance of the circuit. They cannot be added directly because the individual voltages across R, L and C are not in phase with each other as shown below.

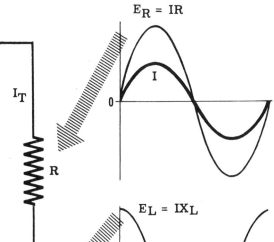

$E_R = IR$

The voltage E_R across R is in phase with the circuit current, since current and voltage are in phase in pure resistive circuits.

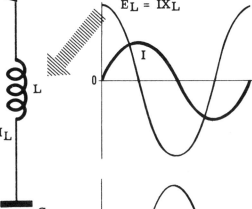

$E_L = IX_L$

The voltage E_L across L leads the circuit current by 90 degrees, since current lags the voltage by 90 degrees in purely inductive circuits. Thus E_L crosses the zero axis going in the same direction, 90 degrees before the current.

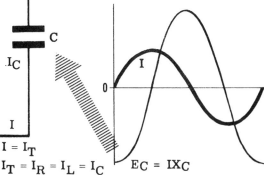

$I = I_T$

$I_T = I_R = I_L = I_C$

$E_C = IX_C$

The voltage E_C across C lags the circuit current by 90 degrees since current leads the voltage by 90 degrees in purely capacitive circuits. Thus E_C crosses the zero axis, going in the same direction, 90 degrees after the current wave.

Voltages in AC Series Circuits (continued)

To find the total voltage in a series circuit, the instantaneous values of the individual voltages for a particular moment are added together to obtain the instantaneous values of the total voltage waveform. Positive values are added directly as are negative values, and the difference between the total positive and negative values for a given moment is the instantaneous value of the total voltage waveform for that instant of time. After all possible instantaneous values have been obtained, the total voltage waveform is drawn by connecting together these instantaneous values.

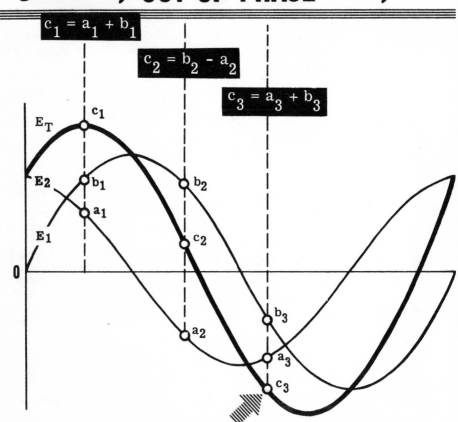

Combining OUT-OF-PHASE Voltages

$$c_1 = a_1 + b_1$$
$$c_2 = b_2 - a_2$$
$$c_3 = a_3 + b_3$$

Combined instantaneous values are the result of combining the instantaneous values of E_1 and E_2

When combining out-of-phase voltages, the maximum value of the total voltage waveform is always less than the sum of the maximum values of the individual voltages. Also, the phase angle (which is the angle between any two waveforms) of the total voltage wave differs from that of the individual voltages, and depends on the relative value and phase angles of the individual voltages.

4-28

R and L Series Circuit Voltages

Suppose you consider an **AC** series circuit having negligible capacitance. The total circuit voltage depends on the voltage E_L across the circuit inductance and the voltage E_R across the circuit resistance. E_L leads the circuit current by 90 degrees while E_R is in phase with the circuit current; thus E_L leads E_R by 90 degrees.

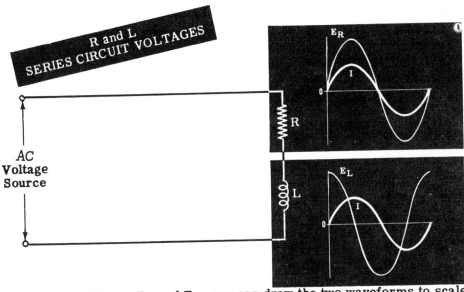

To add the voltages E_L and E_R, you can draw the two waveforms to scale and combine instantaneous values to plot the total voltage waveform. The total voltage waveform, E_T, then shows both the value and phase angle of E_T.

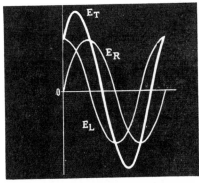

The value and phase angle of E_T also may be found by drawing vectors to represent E_L and E_R, completing the parallelogram and drawing the diagonal which represents E_T. The angle between E_R and E_T is the phase angle between total circuit voltage, E_T, and the circuit current, I_T. Use protractor to find phase angle.

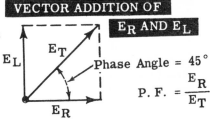

Phase Angle = 45°

$$P.F. = \frac{E_R}{E_T}$$

R and C Series Circuit Voltages

If your circuit consists of only R and C, the total voltage is found by combining E_R, the voltage across the resistance, and E_C, the voltage across the capacitance. E_R is in phase with the circuit current while E_C lags the circuit current by 90 degrees; thus E_C lags E_R by 90 degrees. The two voltages may be combined by drawing the waveforms to scale or by using vectors.

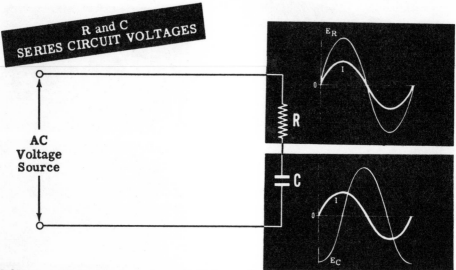

Voltage vectors for a series circuit are drawn in the same manner as resistance, reactance and impedance vectors. Following is an example of the use of Ohm's law, as it applies to each part and to the entire series circuit. Use a protractor to find the phase angle.

Ohm's Law

AND VECTOR RELATIONSHIP OF AN R AND C SERIES CIRCUIT

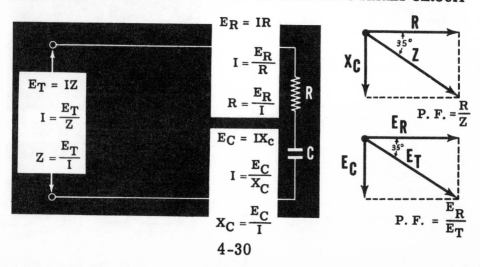

CURRENT, VOLTAGE AND RESONANCE IN AC SERIES CIRCUITS

L and C Series Circuit Voltages

To find the total voltage of an L and C series circuit, you need only find the difference between E_L and E_C since they oppose each other directly. E_L leads the circuit current by 90 degrees while E_C lags it by 90 degrees. When the voltage waveforms are drawn, the total voltage is the difference between the two individual values and is in phase with the larger of the two voltages, E_L or E_C. For such circuits, the value of the total voltage can be found by subtracting the smaller voltage from the larger.

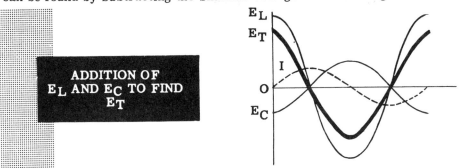

Either or both of the voltages E_L and E_C may be larger than the total circuit voltage in an AC series circuit consisting only of L and C.

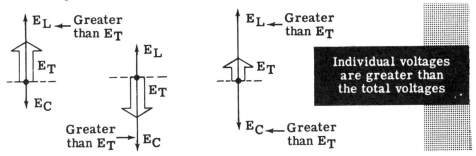

The voltage vectors and reactance vectors for the L and C circuit are similar to each other, except for the units by which they are measured. Ohm's law applies to each part and to the total circuit as outlined below.

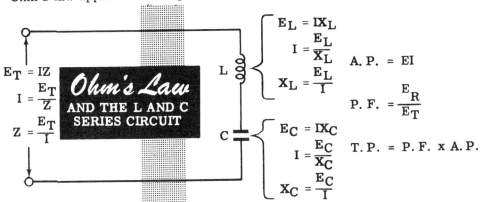

$$E_T = IZ \qquad I = \frac{E_T}{Z} \qquad Z = \frac{E_T}{I}$$

$$E_L = IX_L \qquad I = \frac{E_L}{X_L} \qquad X_L = \frac{E_L}{I}$$

$$E_C = IX_C \qquad I = \frac{E_C}{X_C} \qquad X_C = \frac{E_C}{I}$$

$$\text{A.P.} = EI$$

$$\text{P.F.} = \frac{E_R}{E_T}$$

$$\text{T.P.} = \text{P.F.} \times \text{A.P.}$$

R, L and C Series Circuit Voltages

To combine the three voltages of an R, L and C series circuit by means of vectors, two steps are required:

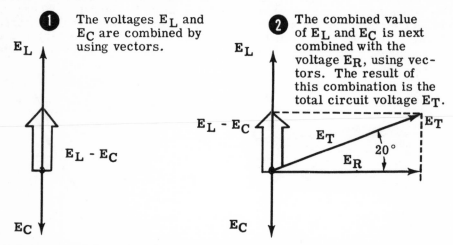

1 The voltages E_L and E_C are combined by using vectors.

2 The combined value of E_L and E_C is next combined with the voltage E_R, using vectors. The result of this combination is the total circuit voltage E_T.

You can use Ohm's law for any part of the circuit by substituting X_L or X_C for R across inductors and capacitors respectively. Then, for the total circuit, Z replaces R as it is used in the original formula.

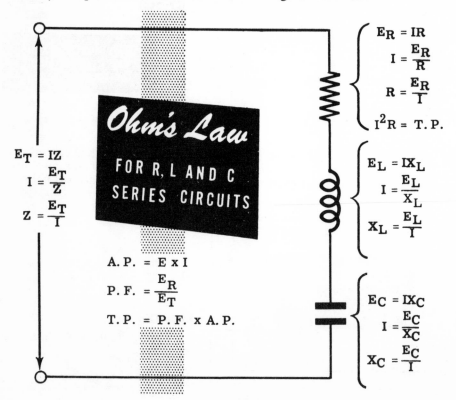

$E_R = IR$

$I = \dfrac{E_R}{R}$

$R = \dfrac{E_R}{I}$

$I^2R = T.P.$

$E_L = IX_L$

$I = \dfrac{E_L}{X_L}$

$X_L = \dfrac{E_L}{I}$

$E_C = IX_C$

$I = \dfrac{E_C}{X_C}$

$X_C = \dfrac{E_C}{I}$

$E_T = IZ$

$I = \dfrac{E_T}{Z}$

$Z = \dfrac{E_T}{I}$

Ohm's Law

FOR R, L AND C SERIES CIRCUITS

A.P. = E x I

P.F. = $\dfrac{E_R}{E_T}$

T.P. = P.F. x A.P.

Series Circuit Resonance

In any series circuit containing both L and C, the circuit current is greatest when the inductive reactance X_L equals the capacitive reactance X_C, since under those conditions the impedance is equal to R. Whenever X_L and X_C are unequal, the impedance Z is the diagonal of a vector combination of R and the difference between X_L and X_C. This diagonal is always greater than R, as shown below. When X_L and X_C are equal, Z is equal to R and is at its minimum value, allowing the greatest amount of circuit current to flow.

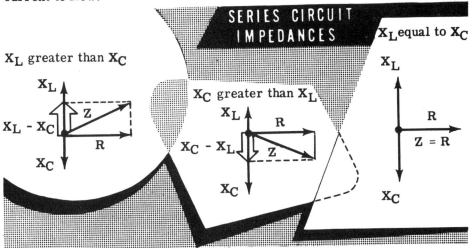

When X_L and X_C are equal the voltages across them, E_L and E_C, are also equal and the circuit is said to be "at resonance." Such a circuit is called a "series resonant circuit." Both E_L and E_C, although equal, may be greater than E_T which equals E_R. The application of Ohm's law to the series resonant circuit is shown below.

SERIES RESONANT *Circuit*

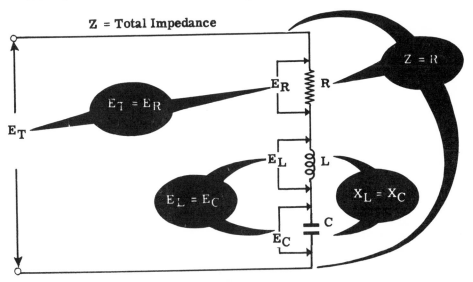

Series Circuit Resonance (continued)

If either the frequency, the inductive reactance or the capacitive reactance is varied in a series circuit consisting of R, L and C, with the other values kept constant, the circuit current variation forms a curve called the "resonance curve." This curve shows the rise in current to a maximum value at exact resonance, and the decrease in current on either side of resonance. For example, consider a 60-cycle AC series circuit having a fixed value of inductance and a variable value of capacitance, as in a radio receiver. The circuit impedance and current variations, as the capacitance is changed, are shown below in outline form. At resonance $X_L = X_C$, $E_L = E_C$, $E_T = E_R$, Z is at its minimum value and I_T is at its maximum value. Resonant frequency (f_r) is calculated by the formula $f_r = \dfrac{1}{2\pi\sqrt{LC}}$

Increasing **THE VALUE OF C DECREASES X$_C$ AND VARIES Z**

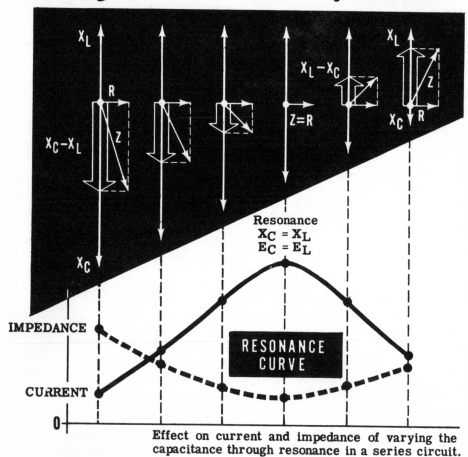

Effect on current and impedance of varying the capacitance through resonance in a series circuit.

Similar curves result if capacitance and frequency are held constant while the inductance is varied, and if the inductance and capacitance are held constant while the frequency is varied.

Series Circuits Resonance (continued)

The example described on the previous sheet may be discussed with the emphasis placed on a varying frequency of the input voltage and with the inductance and capacitance held constant.

Variation of the voltage input frequency to an R, L, and C circuit (over a suitable range) results in an output current curve which is similar to the resonance curve on the previous sheet. When operated below the resonant frequency the current output is low and the circuit impedance is high. Above resonance the same condition occurs. At the resonant frequency the output current curve is at its peak and the impedance curve is at a minimum. The graphs of current and impedance below are typical of an R, L, C series circuit when only the input signal frequency is varied.

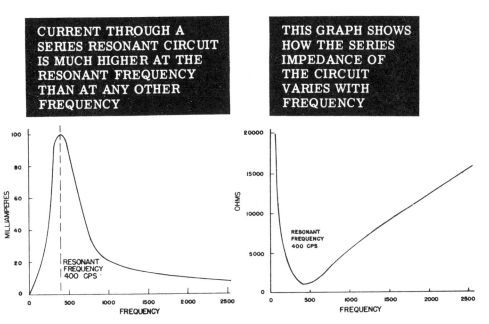

CURRENT THROUGH A SERIES RESONANT CIRCUIT IS MUCH HIGHER AT THE RESONANT FREQUENCY THAN AT ANY OTHER FREQUENCY

THIS GRAPH SHOWS HOW THE SERIES IMPEDANCE OF THE CIRCUIT VARIES WITH FREQUENCY

Further light as to the effects of reactance below and above resonance can be seen by looking at the phase angle graph below. The phase angle is clearly capacitive (negative) below resonance, and is clearly inductive (positive) above resonance. The phase angle is, of course, zero at the exact frequency of resonance.

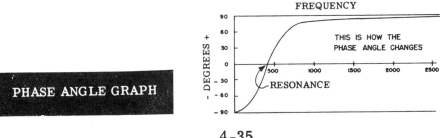

PHASE ANGLE GRAPH

THIS IS HOW THE PHASE ANGLE CHANGES

4-35

Power at Resonance in Series Circuits

You have already learned that in AC circuits the power is equal to the product of the volts and amperes only when the current and voltage are in phase. If the voltage and current are not in phase the power expended will be something less than the product of E and I. The amount by which the expended power is less than the apparent power (the E times I) is determined by the power factor of the circuit. This power factor is essentially the ratio of the resistance divided by the impedance of the circuit. It is often called the cosine of the phase angle (cos θ) which is formed by the R and Z in an impedance triangle.

In a series circuit consisting of inductance, resistance, and capacitance the condition of resonance occurs when the inductive reactance and the capacitive reactance are numerically equal and therefore completely cancel each other; see the diagram below.

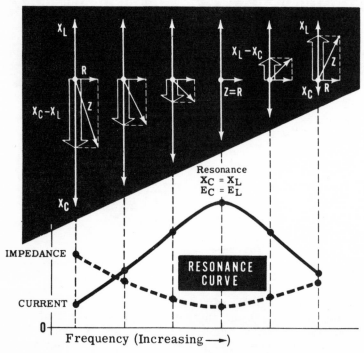

Since X_L is equal to X_C and since they oppose and therefore cancel each other out, the total impedance of the circuit (Z) must be equal to the resistance (R). Further, the phase angle θ does not exist and is therefore considered to be equal to zero.

If the impedance is equal to R then the power factor must be equal to 1, as follows:

$$Z = R$$

and

$$\cos \theta = \frac{R}{Z} = \frac{R}{R} = 1$$

Demonstration—R and L Series Circuit Voltage

To demonstrate the relationship of the various voltages in an R and L series circuit, the instructor connects a 1500-ohm resistor and a 5-henry filter choke to form an L and R series circuit. With the switch closed, individual voltage readings are taken across the choke and the resistor. Also, the total voltage across the series combination of the resistor and choke is measured. Notice that, if the measured voltages across the choke and resistor are added directly, the result is greater than the total voltage measured across the two in series.

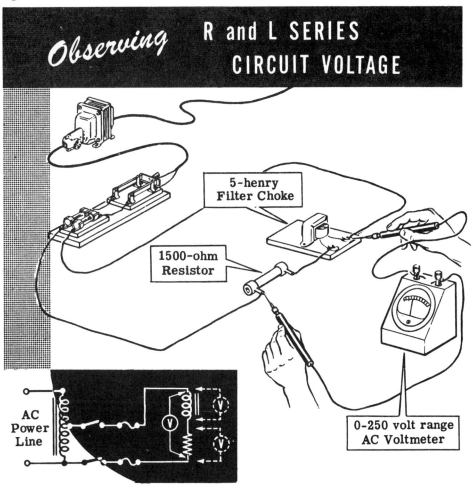

$Observing$ R and L SERIES CIRCUIT VOLTAGE

5-henry Filter Choke

1500-ohm Resistor

0-250 volt range AC Voltmeter

AC Power Line

The voltage E_L measured across the 5-henry filter choke is approximately 47.5 volts, and E_R measured across the 1500-ohm resistor is about 37.5 volts. When added directly, the voltages E_L and E_R total approximately 85 volts but the actual measured voltage across the resistor and filter choke in series is only about 60 volts. Using vectors to combine E_R and E_L, you see that the result is about 60 volts—the actual total circuit voltage as measured.

Demonstration—R and C Series Circuit Voltage

Next the instructor removes the 5-henry filter choke from the circuit, replaces it with a 1-mfd capacitor and measures the individual and total voltages of the circuit. Again you see that the sum of the voltages across the capacitor and resistor is greater than the actual measured total voltage.

Measuring the Voltage of an R and C SERIES CIRCUIT....

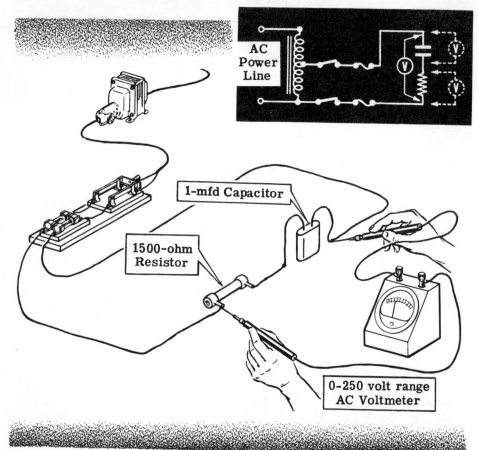

1-mfd Capacitor

1500-ohm Resistor

AC Power Line

0-250 volt range AC Voltmeter

The measured voltage across the capacitor is about 53 volts, while that across the resistor is approximately 30 volts. When added these voltages total 83 volts, but the actual measured voltage across the capacitor and resistor in series is only approximately 60 volts. Using vectors to combine the two circuit voltages, E_R and E_C, you see that the result is about 60 volts, equal to the measured voltage of the circuit. Notice that, whenever the circuit power is removed, the instructor shorts the terminals of the capacitor together to discharge it.

Demonstration—L and C Series Circuit Voltages

By replacing the 1500-ohm resistor with a 5-henry filter choke, the instructor forms an L and C series circuit having negligible resistance. With the power applied, the voltages across the filter choke and capacitor are measured individually and the total voltage is measured across the series circuit. Notice that the voltage across the inductance (filter choke) alone is greater than the measured total voltage across the circuit. Adding the voltage across the filter choke to that across the capacitor results in a much greater value than the actual measured total circuit voltage.

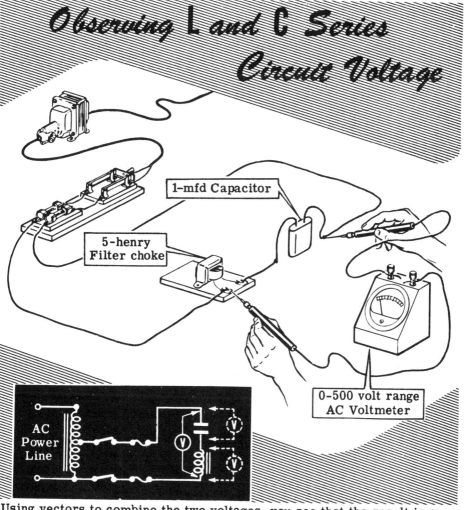

Using vectors to combine the two voltages, you see that the result is approximately equal to the measured total voltage, or about 60 volts. Although it is considered negligible, the resistance of the filter choke wire causes a slight difference in the computed and actual results. A 0-500 volt range AC meter is used instead of the 0-250 volt range meter, as the readings may exceed the 0-250 volt scale.

Demonstration—Series Resonance

To demonstrate series resonance, the instructor replaces the 1-mfd capacitor with a 0.25-mfd capacitor and inserts a 1500-ohm, 10-watt resistor in series with the 5-henry filter choke and the capacitor. This forms an R, L and C series circuit in which C will be varied to show the effect of resonance on circuit voltage and current. A 0-50 ma. AC milliammeter is connected in series with the circuit to measure the circuit current. A 0-250 volt range AC voltmeter will be used to measure circuit voltages.

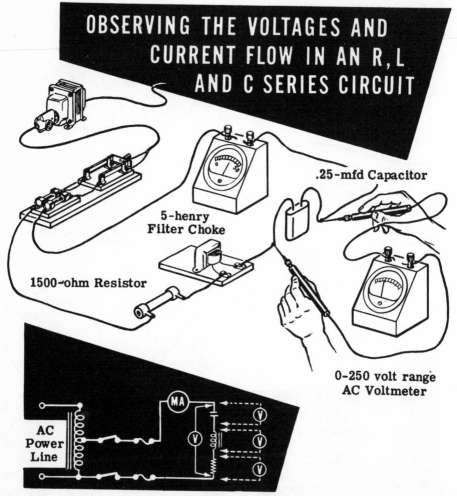

OBSERVING THE VOLTAGES AND CURRENT FLOW IN AN R, L AND C SERIES CIRCUIT

.25-mfd Capacitor

5-henry Filter Choke

1500-ohm Resistor

0-250 volt range AC Voltmeter

AC Power Line

With the switch closed, you see that the current is not large enough to be read accurately since it is less than 10 ma. As the instructor measures the various circuit voltages, you see that the voltage E_R across the resistor is less than 10 volts, the voltage E_L across the filter choke is about 13 volts and the voltage E_C across the capacitor is about 55 volts. The total voltage E_T across the entire circuit is approximately 60 volts.

Demonstration—Series Resonance (continued)

By using various parallel combinations of the 0.25-mfd, 0.5-mfd, 1-mfd and 2-mfd capacitors, the instructor varies the circuit capacitance from 0.25 mfd to 3.5 mfd in steps of 0.25 mfd. Notice that he removes the circuit power and discharges all capacitors used before removing or adding capacitors to the circuit. You see that as the capacitance is increased the current rises to a maximum value reached at the point of resonance, then decreases as the capacitance is increased further.

OBSERVING THE CIRCUIT VOLTAGES AND CURRENT CHANGE AS THE CAPACITANCE VALUE IS CHANGED

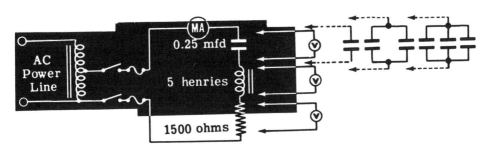

Except for the total circuit voltage E_T, the measured circuit voltages vary as the capacitance is changed. The voltage E_R across the resistor changes in the same manner as the circuit current. For capacitance values less than the resonance value, E_C is greater than E_L. Both voltages increase as the capacitance approaches the resonance point, with E_L increasing more rapidly so that at resonance E_L equals E_C. As the capacitance is increased beyond the resonance point, both E_C and E_L decrease in value. E_C decreases more rapidly, so that E_L is greater than E_C when the circuit capacitance is greater than the value required for resonance. (The maximum E_L and E_C are not equal due to the relatively high resistance. If the resistance is reduced, E_L and E_C will be equal at resonance.)

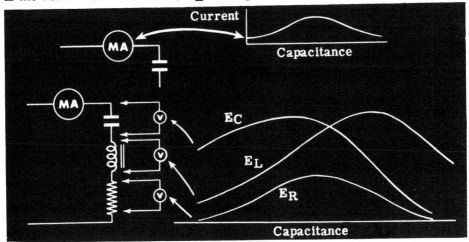

CURRENT, VOLTAGE AND RESONANCE IN AC SERIES CIRCUITS

Review of AC Series Circuit Voltages and Current

You have found that the rules for AC series circuit voltage and current are the same as those for DC circuits, except that the various circuit voltages must be added by means of vectors because of the phase difference between the individual voltages. Now review what you have found out about AC series circuit current, voltages and resonance, and how Ohm's law applies to an AC series circuit.

<u>AC SERIES CIRCUIT CURRENT</u> — The current is the same in all parts of a series circuit.

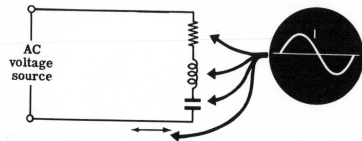

<u>AC SERIES CIRCUIT VOLTAGES</u> — E_R is in phase with the current, E_L leads the current by 90 degrees, and E_C lags the current by 90 degrees.

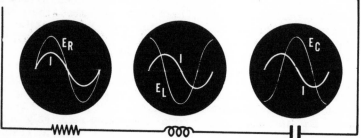

SERIES CIRCUIT RESONANCE — At resonance $X_L = X_C$, $E_L = E_C$, current is maximum and $Z = R$. P.F. = 100%.

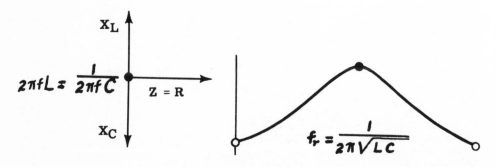

$$2\pi f L = \frac{1}{2\pi f C} \qquad\qquad f_r = \frac{1}{2\pi\sqrt{LC}}$$

AC Parallel Circuit Combinations

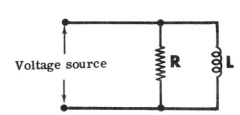

Voltage source

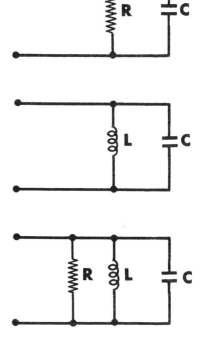

Electrical equipment is usually connected in parallel across AC power lines, forming parallel combinations of R, L and C. As in series circuits, every parallel circuit contains a certain amount of resistance, inductive reactance and capacitive reactance; but for a given circuit any of these factors may be so negligible that it can be disregarded.

The same combinations of R, L and C which are used to form the various types of series circuits may also be used to form parallel circuits. If one factor is negligible, the three possible combinations are R and L, R and C, or L and C, while a fourth type of parallel circuit contains R, L and C.

You have found out how R, L and C, individually and in various series circuit combinations, affect AC current flow, voltage, phase angle and power. Now you will find out how current, voltage, phase angle and power are affected by the various parallel combinations.

Voltages in AC Parallel Circuits

You will remember that in a parallel DC circuit the voltage across each of the parallel branches is equal. This is also true of AC parallel circuits; the voltages across each parallel branch are equal and also equal E_T, the total voltage of the parallel circuit. Not only are the voltages equal, but they are also in phase.

For example, if the various types of electrical equipment shown below—a lamp (resistance), a filter choke (inductance) and a capacitor (capacitance) —are connected in parallel, the voltage across each is exactly the same.

AC PARALLEL CIRCUIT BRANCH VOLTAGES

ARE **EQUAL** AND IN **PHASE**

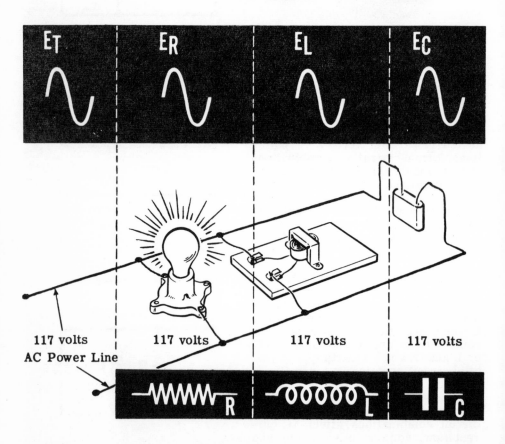

Regardless of the number of parallel branches, the value of the voltage across them is equal and in phase. All of the connections to one side of a parallel combination are considered to be one electrical point, as long as the resistance of the connecting wire may be neglected.

Currents in AC Parallel Circuits

The current flow through each individual branch is determined by the opposition offered by that branch. If your circuit consists of three branches —one a resistor, another an inductor and the third a capacitor—the current through each branch depends on the resistance or reactance of that branch. The resistor branch current I_R is in phase with the circuit voltage E_T, while the inductor branch current I_L lags the circuit voltage by 90 degrees and the capacitor branch current I_C leads the voltage by 90 degrees.

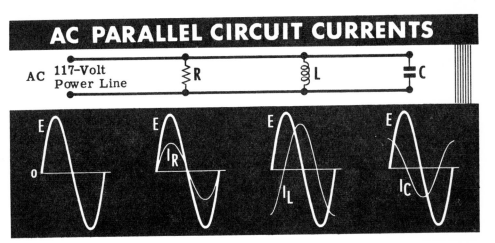

Because of the phase difference between the branch currents of an AC parallel circuit, the total current I_T cannot be found by adding the various branch currents directly—as it can for a DC parallel circuit. When the waveforms for the various circuit currents are drawn in relation to the common circuit voltage waveform, X_L and X_C again are seen to cancel each other since the waveforms for I_L and I_C are exactly opposite in polarity at all points. The resistance branch current I_R, however, is 90 degrees out of phase with both I_L and I_C and, to determine the total current flow by using vectors, I_R must be combined with the difference between I_L and I_C.

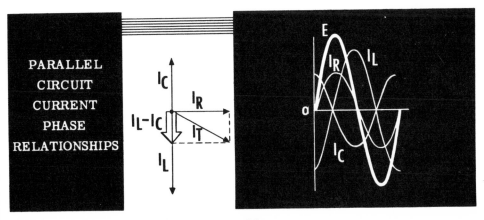

Currents in AC Parallel Circuits (continued)

To add the branch currents in an **AC** parallel circuit, the instantaneous values of current are combined, as voltages are in a series circuit, to obtain the instantaneous values of the total current waveform. After all the possible instantaneous values of current are obtained, the total current waveform is drawn by connecting together the instantaneous values.

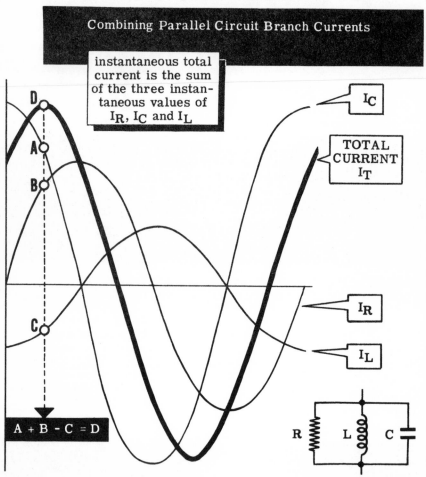

Combining Parallel Circuit Branch Currents

instantaneous total current is the sum of the three instantaneous values of I_R, I_C and I_L

I_C

TOTAL CURRENT I_T

D

A

B

C

I_R

I_L

A + B - C = D

R   L   C

The maximum value of I_T is less than the sum of the maximum values of the individual currents, and is out of phase with the various branch currents. With respect to the circuit voltage, the total current either <u>leads</u> or <u>lags</u> I_C and I_L between zero and 90 degrees, depending on whether the inductive or capacitive reactance is greater.

A graph showing the various circuit currents and the circuit voltage of an AC parallel circuit is similar to the graph of circuit current and voltages for an AC series circuit. They differ in that the different series circuit voltages are drawn with reference to total circuit current, while for parallel circuits the different currents are drawn with reference to the total circuit voltage.

R and L Parallel Circuit Currents

If your AC parallel circuit consists of a resistance and inductance connected in parallel, and the circuit capacitance is negligible, the total circuit current is a combination of I_R (the current through the resistance) and
I_L (the current through the inductance). I_R is in phase with the circuit
voltage E_T while I_L lags the voltage by 90 degrees.

PHASE RELATIONSHIPS IN AN R AND L PARALLEL CIRCUIT

IR IN PHASE   IL. LAGS 90°

To find the total current I_T, you can
draw I_R and I_L to scale and in the
proper phase relationship to each
other and combine the corresponding
instantaneous values to plot the total
current waveform. This waveform
then shows both the maximum value
and the phase angle of I_T.

VECTOR
ADDITION OF
I_R AND I_L

Phase angle 45°

COMBINING WAVEFORMS IR AND IL

You can also use an easier method to find the value and phase angle of I_T.
By drawing vectors to scale representing I_R and I_L, then combining the
vectors by completing the parallelogram and drawing the diagonal, you can
obtain both the value and phase angle of I_T. The length of the diagonal
represents the value of I_T, while the angle between I_T and I_R is the phase
angle between total circuit voltage, E_T, and the total circuit current, I_T.

R and C Parallel Circuit Currents

The total current of an AC parallel circuit which consists only of R and C is found by combining I_R (the resistance current) and I_C (the capacitance current). I_R is in phase with the circuit voltage E_T, while I_C leads the voltage by 90 degrees. To find the total current and its phase angle when I_R and I_C are known, you can draw the waveforms of I_R and I_C or their vectors

FINDING THE TOTAL CURRENT IN AN R AND C CIRCUIT. . .

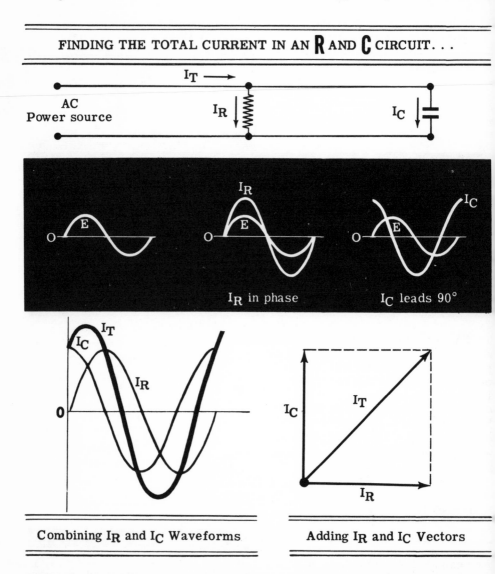

$I_T \longrightarrow$

AC
Power source

I_R

I_C

I_R in phase I_C leads 90°

Combining I_R and I_C Waveforms   Adding I_R and I_C Vectors

While the capacitance does increase the circuit current, only the resistance current consumes power, so that parallel circuits containing a capacitance branch will pass more current than is necessary to provide a given amount of power. This means that the power line wires which carry current to such circuits must be larger than if the circuit were purely resistive.

L and C Parallel Circuit Currents

When your parallel circuit consists only of L and C, the total current is equal to the difference between I_L and I_C since they are exactly opposite in phase relationship. When the waveforms for I_L and I_C are drawn, you see that all the instantaneous values of I_L and I_C are of opposite polarity. If all the corresponding combined instantaneous values are plotted to form the waveform of I_T, the maximum value of this waveform is equal to the difference between I_L and I_C. For such circuits the total current can be found by subtracting the smaller current, I_L or I_C, from the larger.

FINDING THE TOTAL CURRENT IN AN L AND C PARALLEL CIRCUIT

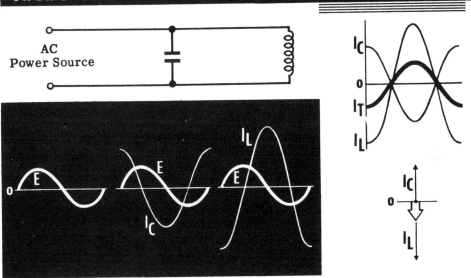

The relationships and paths of circuit currents for L and C circuits are shown below.

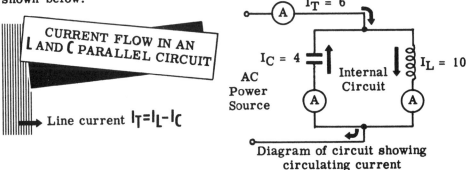

CURRENT FLOW IN AN L AND C PARALLEL CIRCUIT

Line current $I_T = I_L - I_C$

$I_T = 6$

$I_C = 4$

AC Power Source

Internal Circuit

$I_L = 10$

Diagram of circuit showing circulating current

The parallel circuit can also be considered as consisting of an internal and external circuit. Since the current flowing through the inductance is exactly opposite in polarity to that which is flowing through the capacitance at the same time, an internal circuit is formed. The amount of current flow around this internal circuit is equal to the smaller of the two currents, I_L and I_C. The amount of current flowing through the external circuit (the voltage source) is equal to the difference between I_L and I_C.

L and C Parallel Circuit Currents (continued)

The relationship between the various currents in a parallel circuit consisting of L and C is illustrated in the following example. A capacitor and an inductor are connected in parallel across a 60-cycle, 150-volt source, so that $X_L = 50$ ohms and $X_C = 75$ ohms. The currents in the circuit are:

$$I_L = \frac{E}{X_L} = \frac{150}{50} = 3A. \qquad\qquad I_C = \frac{E}{X_C} = \frac{150}{75} = 2A.$$

Since I_L and I_C are exactly opposite in phase, they have a canceling effect on each other. Therefore, the total current $I_t = I_L - I_C = 3-2 = 1A$. Due to the phase relationship of I_L and I_C, the current flow through the capacitor is always opposite in direction to the current flow through the inductor.

Using this phase relationship and the Kirchhoff's law relating to currents approaching and leaving a point in a circuit, you can see in the diagram that I_C and I_t are approaching point Z while I_L is leaving point Z. For this particular circuit, I_L must be equal to the sum of I_t and I_C.

$$I_L = I_t + I_C$$
$$3 = 1 + 2$$

Since I_L is made up partially of I_C, it can be seen that I_C must flow through the inductor. Therefore, I_C flows through the capacitor and through the inductor and then back through the capacitor. The result of the opposing phase of I_L and I_C is to form an internal circuit, whose circulating current has a value equal to the smaller of I_L and I_C, in this case I_C.

If the values of X_L and X_C were reversed, I_L would be the circulating current. The smaller current (I_L or I_C) is always the circulating current.

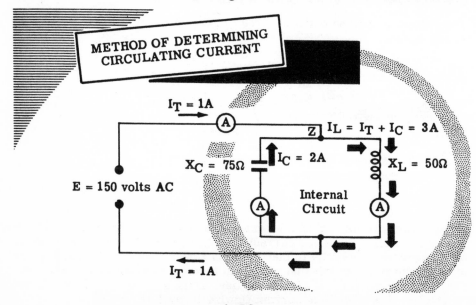

METHOD OF DETERMINING CIRCULATING CURRENT

$I_T = 1A$

Z $I_L = I_T + I_C = 3A$

$X_C = 75\Omega$ $I_C = 2A$

$X_L = 50\Omega$

$E = 150$ volts AC

Internal Circuit

$I_T = 1A$

R, L and C Parallel Circuit Currents

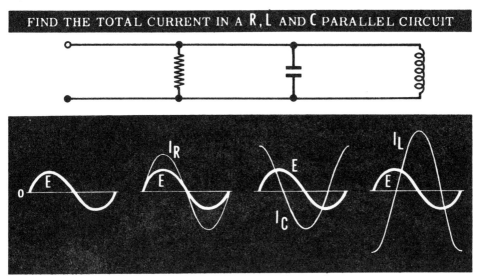

FIND THE TOTAL CURRENT IN A R, L AND C PARALLEL CIRCUIT

To combine the three branch currents of an R, L and C alternating-current parallel circuit by means of vectors requires two steps as outlined below:

1. The currents I_L and I_C are combined by using vectors. (Both the value, which may be obtained by direct subtraction, and the phase angle of this combined current are required.)

2. The combined value of I_L and I_C is then combined with I_R to obtain the total current.

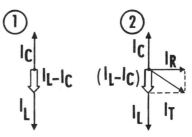

In an R, L and C circuit—as in the L and C circuit—a circulating current equal to the smaller of the two currents I_L and I_C flows through an internal circuit consisting of the inductance branch and the capacitance branch. The total current which flows through the external circuit (the voltage source) is the combination of I_R and the difference between the currents I_L and I_C.

$$I_T = \text{Vector addition of } I_R + (I_L - I_C)$$

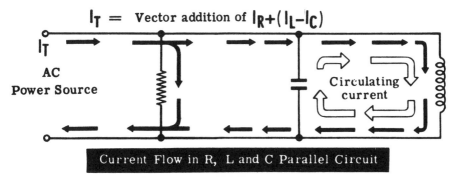

Current Flow in R, L and C Parallel Circuit

AC Parallel Circuit Impedance

The impedance of a parallel circuit can be found using complicated vector or mathematical solutions, but the most practical method is to apply Ohm's law for AC to the total circuit. Using Ohm's law for AC, the impedance Z for all AC parallel circuits is found by dividing the circuit voltage by the total current $\left(Z = \dfrac{E_T}{I_T}\right)$.

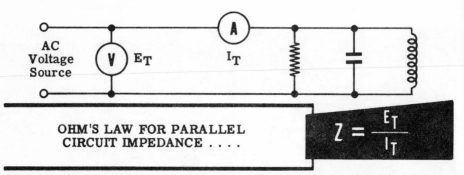

OHM'S LAW FOR PARALLEL
CIRCUIT IMPEDANCE ....

$$Z = \frac{E_T}{I_T}$$

To find the impedance of a parallel circuit the total current is first found by using vectors; then Ohm's law for AC is applied to find Z. The steps used to find Z for the various types of AC parallel circuits are outlined below.

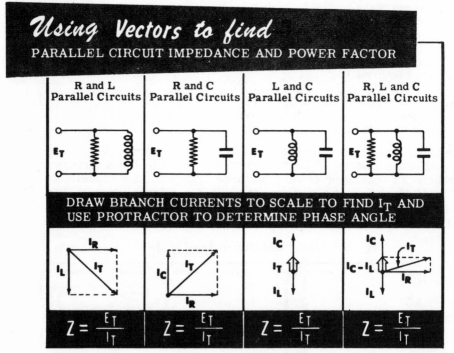

Using Vectors *to find*
PARALLEL CIRCUIT IMPEDANCE AND POWER FACTOR

R and L Parallel Circuits	R and C Parallel Circuits	L and C Parallel Circuits	R, L and C Parallel Circuits

DRAW BRANCH CURRENTS TO SCALE TO FIND I_T AND USE PROTRACTOR TO DETERMINE PHASE ANGLE

$$Z = \frac{E_T}{I_T} \qquad Z = \frac{E_T}{I_T} \qquad Z = \frac{E_T}{I_T} \qquad Z = \frac{E_T}{I_T}$$

$$\text{POWER FACTOR} = \frac{I_R}{I_T}$$

Demonstration—R and L Parallel Circuit Current and Impedance

The current flow and the practical method of obtaining the impedance of an R and L parallel circuit is demonstrated first. The instructor connects a 2500-ohm, 20-watt resistor and a 5-henry filter choke in parallel across the AC power line through a step-down autotransformer, to form an AC parallel circuit of R and L. A 0-50 ma. AC milliammeter is connected to measure the total circuit current and a 0-250 volt range AC voltmeter is used to measure circuit voltage. With the power applied to the circuit, you see that the circuit voltage is about 60 volts and the total circuit current is approximately 40 milliamperes.

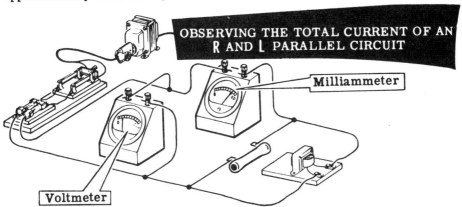

OBSERVING THE TOTAL CURRENT OF AN R AND L PARALLEL CIRCUIT

Milliammeter

Voltmeter

To measure the individual currents I_R and I_L through the resistor and the filter choke, the instructor first connects the milliammeter to measure only the resistor current, then to measure only the filter choke current. You see that the milliammeter reading for I_R is about 24 ma., and the current indicated for I_L is approximately 32 ma. The sum of these two branch currents I_R and I_L then is 56 ma. while the actual measured total circuit current is about 40 ma., showing that the branch currents must be added by means of vectors.

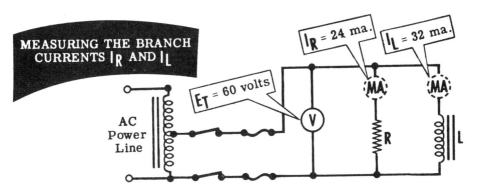

MEASURING THE BRANCH CURRENTS I_R AND I_L

$I_R = 24$ ma. $I_L = 32$ ma.

$E_T = 60$ volts

AC Power Line

The calculated value of the impedance for this R and L circuit is 1500 ohms (60 ÷ 0.040 = 1500), indicating that the parallel connection of R and L reduces circuit impedance. The total circuit impedance is less than that of either branch of the circuit, since R = 2500 Ω and $X_L = 1884 \Omega$.

Demonstration—R and C Parallel Circuit Current and Impedance

Next the instructor replaces the 5-henry filter choke with a 1-mfd capacitor and repeats the previous demonstration. The total circuit voltage and current (E_T and I_T) is measured, and then the branch currents I_R and I_C are measured through the resistor and capacitor.

You see that the total circuit current I_T is approximately 32 ma., while the measured branch currents I_R and I_C are about 24 ma. and 23 ma. respectively. Again you see that the total current is less than the sum of the branch currents, due to the phase difference between I_R and I_C. The total impedance is about 1875 ohms ($60 \div 0.032 \approx 1875$), a value less than the opposition offered by either branch alone, since $R = 2500 \,\Omega$ and $X_C = 2650 \,\Omega$.

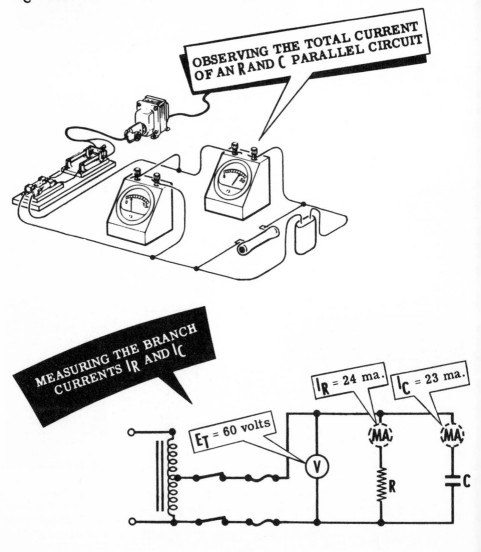

OBSERVING THE TOTAL CURRENT OF AN R AND C PARALLEL CIRCUIT

MEASURING THE BRANCH CURRENTS I_R AND I_C

I_R = 24 ma. I_C = 23 ma.

E_T = 60 volts

R   C

Demonstration—L and C Parallel Circuit Current and Impedance

To demonstrate the opposite effects of L and C in a parallel circuit, the 2500-ohm resistor is replaced by the 5-henry filter choke forming an L and C parallel circuit. Again the instructor repeats each step of the demonstration, first measuring the total circuit current, then that of each branch.

You see that the total circuit current is about 9 ma., while I_L is about 32 ma. and I_C is about 23 ma. Thus, the total current is not only less than that of either branch but is actually the difference between the currents I_L and I_C.

The total circuit impedance of the L and C circuit is 6700 ohms (60 ÷ 0.009 ≈ 6700), a value greater than the opposition of either the L or C branch of the circuit. Notice that when L and C are both present in a parallel circuit the impedance increases, which is opposite in effect to that of a series circuit where combining L and C results in a lower impedance.

Demonstration—R, L and C Parallel Circuit Current and Impedance

By connecting a 2500-ohm, 20-watt resistor in parallel with the 5-henry filter choke and the 1-mfd capacitor, the instructor forms an R, L and C parallel circuit. To check the various currents and find the total circuit impedance he measures the total circuit current, then the individual currents through the resistor, filter choke and capacitor in turn.

Observe that the total circuit current increases and that the individual currents are the same as those previously measured in each branch. You see that I_R is 24 ma., I_L is 32 ma. and I_C is 23 ma. Again you see that the sum of the individual currents is much greater than the actual measured total current of 29 ma.

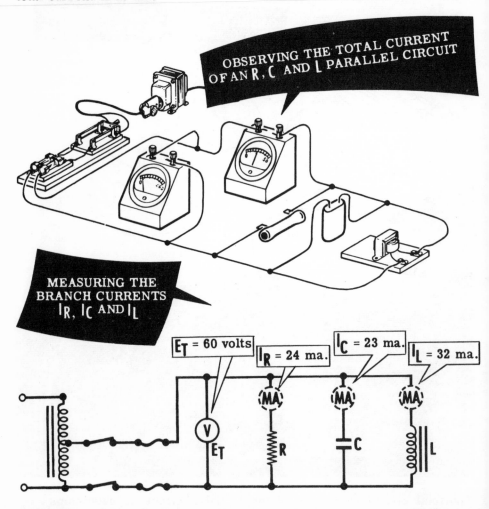

The total circuit impedance is about 2070 ohms (60 ÷ 0.029 = 2070). The total circuit current is the sum of the resistor current I_R and the combined inductance and capacitance currents I_L and I_C, added by means of vectors.

Review of AC Parallel Circuit Current and Impedance

Consider what you have found out so far about AC parallel circuits. While reviewing parallel circuit current and impedance, compare the effects of series and parallel connections of R, L and C in AC circuits.

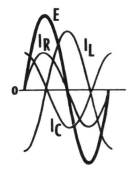

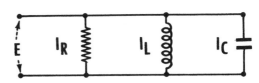

AC PARALLEL CIRCUIT CURRENT — The current divides to flow through the parallel branches. I_R is in phase with the circuit voltage, I_L lags the voltage by 90 degrees and I_C leads the voltage by 90 degrees.

$$E_T = E_R = E_L = E_C$$

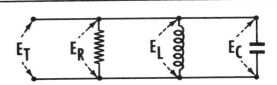

AC PARALLEL CIRCUIT VOLTAGE — The voltage across each branch of a parallel circuit is equal to, and in phase with, that of each branch and that of the total circuit.

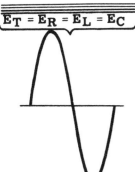

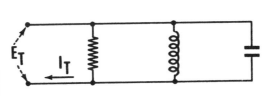

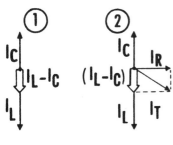

AC PARALLEL CIRCUIT IMPEDANCE AND POWER FACTOR — The impedance of an AC parallel circuit is equal to the circuit voltage divided by the total circuit current. The power factor equals the resistive current divided by the total circuit current.

$$Z = \frac{E_T}{I_T}$$

$$P.F. = \frac{I_R}{I_T}$$

Parallel Circuit Resonance

In a parallel circuit containing equal X_L and X_C, the external circuit current is equal to that flowing through the parallel resistance. If the circuit contains no parallel resistance, the external current is zero. However, within a theoretical circuit consisting only of L and C and $X_L = X_C$, a large current called the "circulating current" flows, using no current from the power line. This occurs because the corresponding instantaneous values of the currents I_L and I_C always flow in opposite directions and, if these values are equal, no external circuit current will flow. This is called "parallel resonant" circuit.

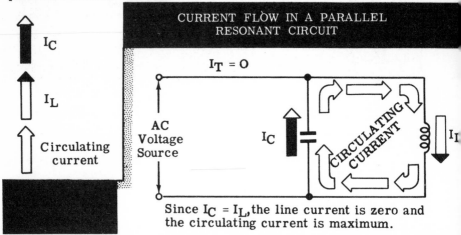

Since $I_C = I_L$, the line current is zero and the circulating current is maximum.

Because no external current flows in a resonant parallel circuit consisting only of L and C, the impedance at resonance is infinite, I_L equals I_C and the total circuit current I_T is zero. Since these effects are exactly opposite those of series resonance, parallel resonance is sometimes called "anti-resonance." Ohm's law for AC when applied to a parallel resonant circuit can be used to determine the value of the internal circulating current.

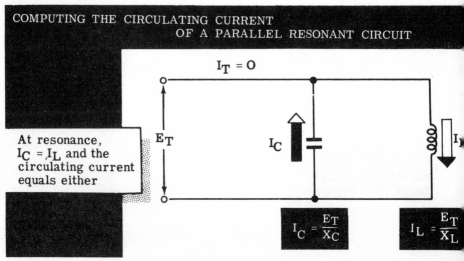

Parallel Circuit Resonance (continued)

As in the case of a series resonant circuit, if either the frequency, inductive reactance or capacitive reactance of a circuit is varied and the two other values kept constant, the circuit current variation forms a resonance curve. However, the parallel resonance curve is the opposite of a series resonance curve. The series resonance current curve increases to a maximum at resonance then decreases as resonance is passed, while the parallel resonance current curve decreases to a minimum at resonance then increases as resonance is passed.

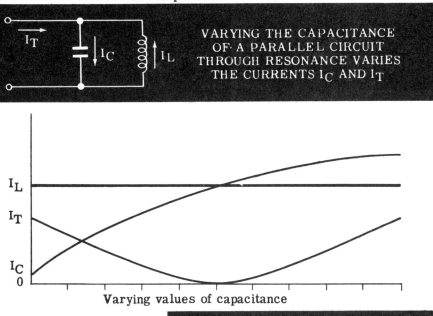

I_T is the difference between I_L and I_C

For a circuit of pure L and C the curve would be as shown above. However, all actual capacitors and inductors have some resistance which prevents the current from becoming zero.

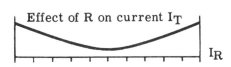

A comparison of circuit factors at resonance for series and parallel circuits, made in chart form, is shown below.

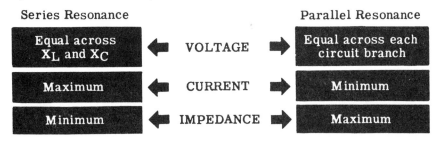

Series Resonance		Parallel Resonance
Equal across X_L and X_C	VOLTAGE	Equal across each circuit branch
Maximum	CURRENT	Minimum
Minimum	IMPEDANCE	Maximum

Demonstration—Parallel Circuit Resonance

To show how parallel resonance affects parallel circuit current, the instructor connects a 0.25-mfd capacitor and a 5-henry filter choke in parallel to form an L and C parallel circuit. A 0-50 ma. AC milliammeter and a 0-250 volt range AC voltmeter are connected to measure circuit current and voltage. This circuit is connected to the AC power line through a switch, fuses and step-down autotransformer. When the switch is closed, you observe that the circuit current is about 30 ma. and the voltage is approximately 60 volts.

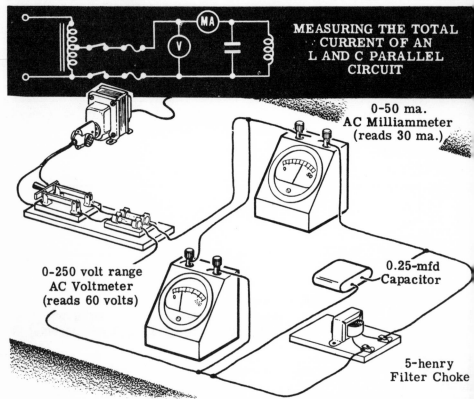

MEASURING THE TOTAL CURRENT OF AN L AND C PARALLEL CIRCUIT

0-50 ma. AC Milliammeter (reads 30 ma.)

0-250 volt range AC Voltmeter (reads 60 volts)

0.25-mfd Capacitor

5-henry Filter Choke

The total current indicated by the meter reading is actually the difference between the currents I_L and I_C through the inductive and capacitive branches of the parallel circuit. Because a meter connected in series with either of the branches would add resistance to that branch, causing inaccurate readings, the branch currents are not read. The circuit voltage remains constant in parallel circuits so that, if a fixed value of inductance is used as one branch of the circuit, the current in that branch remains constant. If the capacitance of the other branch is varied, its current varies as the capacity varies, being low for small capacitance values and high for large capacitance values. The total circuit current is the difference between the two branch currents and is zero when the two branch currents become equal. As the instructor increases the circuit capacitance, the total current will drop as the current I_C increases toward the constant value of I_L, will be zero when I_C equals I_L and then will rise as I_C becomes greater than I_L.

Demonstration—Parallel Circuit Resonance (continued)

The instructor varies the circuit capacitance in steps of 0.25 mfd from 0.25 mfd through 2.5 mfd. Observe that the current decreases from approximately 30 ma. to a minimum value less than 10 ma., then rises to a value beyond the range of the milliammeter. The current at resonance does not reach zero because the circuit branches are not purely capacitive and inductive and cannot be so in a practical parallel circuit. You also observe that the voltage does not change across either the branches or the total parallel circuit as the capacitance value is changed.

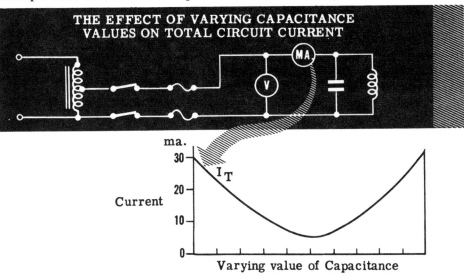

After the value of capacitance has been varied through the complete range of values, the value which indicates resonance—minimum current flow—is used to show that the circulating current exceeds the line current at resonance. The instructor again measures the line current of the parallel resonant circuit, then connects the milliammeter to measure only the current in the inductive branch. You see that the total current is less than 10 ma., yet the circulating current is approximately 30 ma.

CHECKING THE VALUE OF CIRCULATING CURRENT
IN A PARALLEL RESONANT CIRCUIT

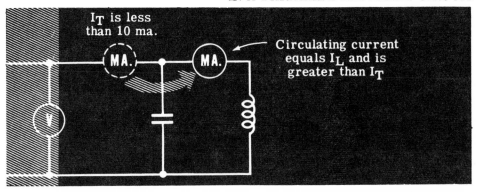

RESONANCE IN AC PARALLEL CIRCUITS

Review of Parallel Circuit Resonance

You have found that the effect of parallel circuit resonance on circuit current is exactly opposite to that of series resonance. Also, you have seen parallel resonance demonstrated, showing how it affects both line current and circulating current. Before performing the experiment on parallel resonance, suppose you review its effects on current and voltage.

PARALLEL RESONANCE LINE CURRENT
— The line current is minimum in a parallel resonant circuit.

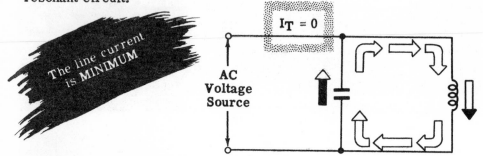

PARALLEL RESONANCE CIRCULATING
CURRENT — The circulating current is maximum in a parallel resonant circuit.

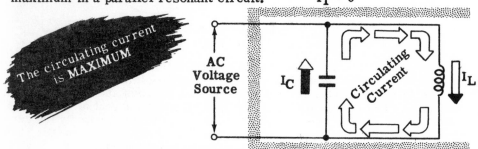

PARALLEL RESONANCE VOLTAGE — The
voltage of parallel circuit branches at resonance is the same as the voltage when the circuit is not at resonance.

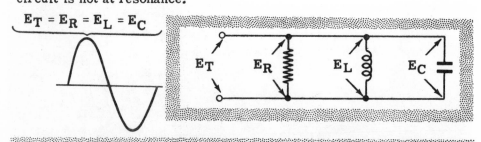

Complex AC Circuits

Many AC circuits are neither series nor parallel circuits but are a combination of these two basic circuits. Such circuits are called "series-parallel" or "complex" circuits and, as in DC circuits, they contain both parallel parts and series parts. The values and phase relationships of the voltages and currents for each particular part of a complex circuit depend on whether the part is series or parallel. Any number of series-parallel combinations form complex circuits and, regardless of the circuit variations, the step-by-step vector solution is similar to the solution of DC complex circuits. The parts of the circuit are first considered separately, then the results are combined. For example, suppose your circuit consists of the series-parallel combination shown below, with two separate series circuits connected in parallel across a 120-volt AC power line. The vector solution used to find the total circuit current, total impedance and the circuit phase angle is outlined below:

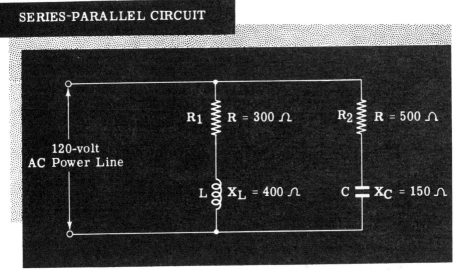

SERIES-PARALLEL CIRCUIT

R_1 R = 300 Ω R_2 R = 500 Ω

120-volt
AC Power Line

L X_L = 400 Ω   C X_C = 150 Ω

To find the values of the branch currents I_1 and I_2, the impedance of each branch is found separately by using vectors. The current values are then determined by applying Ohm's law to the branches separately.

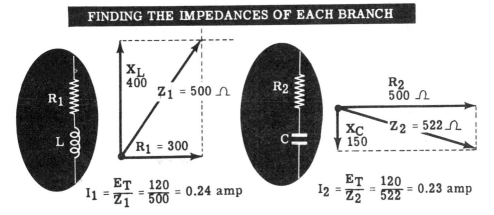

FINDING THE IMPEDANCES OF EACH BRANCH

R_1

L

X_L 400

Z_1 = 500 Ω

R_1 = 300

R_2

C

R_2 500 Ω

X_C 150

Z_2 = 522 Ω

$$I_1 = \frac{E_T}{Z_1} = \frac{120}{500} = 0.24 \text{ amp}$$

$$I_2 = \frac{E_T}{Z_2} = \frac{120}{522} = 0.23 \text{ amp}$$

Complex AC Circuits (continued)

Although you know the branch currents I_1 and I_2, the total current I_T cannot be found by adding I_1 and I_2 directly. Since they are out of phase, the instantaneous values for each branch current are not equal.

To find the phase relationship between I_1 and I_2 so that they may be added by using vectors, the voltage and current vectors for each series branch must first be drawn separately. (Since the values of I_1 and I_2 are known, the voltages across the various parts of each series branch can be found by applying Ohm's law.)

VOLTAGE AND CURRENT VECTORS FOR EACH BRANCH

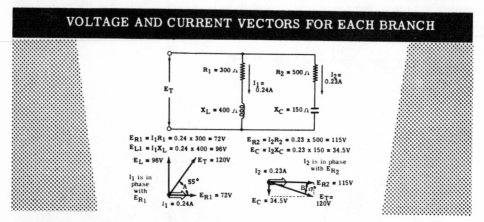

$E_{R1} = I_1R_1 = 0.24 \times 300 = 72V$

$E_{L1} = I_1X_L = 0.24 \times 400 = 96V$

$E_L = 96V$

$E_T = 120V$

I_1 is in phase with E_{R1}

$I_1 = 0.24A$

$E_{R1} = 72V$

$E_{R2} = I_2R_2 = 0.23 \times 500 = 115V$

$E_C = I_2X_C = 0.23 \times 150 = 34.5V$

$I_2 = 0.23A$

I_2 is in phase with E_{R2}

$E_{R2} = 115V$

$E_C = 34.5V$

$E_T = 120V$

The vector solutions for each separate branch, when drawn to scale, show both the values and the phase relationships between the branch currents and the total circuit voltage, E_T. To show the phase relation between I_1 and I_2, they are redrawn with respect to E_T which is drawn horizontally as the reference vector. Draw I_1 down in relation to E_T at the angle found vectorally. I_1 lags the voltage as the branch has the inductor in it. Draw I_2 up in relation to E_T, at the angle found vectorally. I_2 leads the voltage as the branch has the capacitor in it. Lay the protractor at the end of I_1 with the vertical line up and the base horizontal to the reference line E_T. Mark off an angle equal to the angle of the I_2 vector. Next lay the protractor at the end of I_2 with the vertical line down and the base horizontal to the reference line E_T. Mark off an angle equal to the angle of the I_1 vector. Complete the parallelogram by drawing a dotted line from the end of each vector to the point marked off from your protractor. From the reference point draw a line to where the two dotted lines cross. This vector represents the total current of the circuit. Measure with the protractor the angle between I_T and E_T and this will be the phase angle of the circuit.

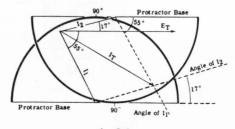

Complex AC Circuits (continued)

Series-parallel circuits may be even more complex than the one just illustrated. For example, suppose that the series-parallel circuit is connected in series with an inductance and a resistance as shown below.

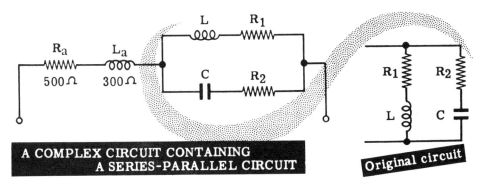

**A COMPLEX CIRCUIT CONTAINING
A SERIES-PARALLEL CIRCUIT**

Original circuit

To find the total circuit current and impedance, the vectors I_T and E_T are redrawn with I_T as the horizontal reference vector. The phase angle between these two vectors is positive, indicating that inductance more than cancels capacitance in the parallel part of the circuit. Therefore, this part of the circuit can be replaced by an R and L series circuit since the value of E_T in the parallel circuit is the result of adding the vector voltages, E_R and E_L. By completing the parallelogram, the voltages E_L and E_R across this series circuit can be determined. The resistance and inductive reactance (X_{L_e} and R_e) of this equivalent series circuit can be found by using the vector voltages and the total current, then applying Ohm's law. (Although the voltage across the parallel part of the complex circuit may not be 120 volts, the computed values of R and X_C for the equivalent circuit are the same regardless of the voltage, actual or assumed, across this part of the circuit.)

**FINDING THE EQUIVALENT SERIES CIRCUIT
OF THE SERIES-PARALLEL CIRCUIT**

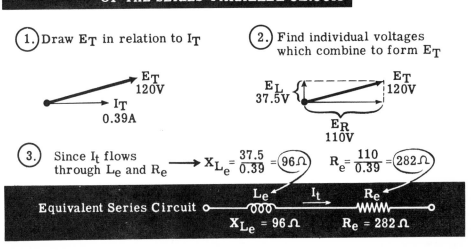

1. Draw E_T in relation to I_T

2. Find individual voltages which combine to form E_T

3. Since I_t flows through L_e and R_e $\longrightarrow$ $X_{L_e} = \dfrac{37.5}{0.39} = 96\,\Omega$ $\quad R_e = \dfrac{110}{0.39} = 282\,\Omega$

Equivalent Series Circuit $\quad X_{L_e} = 96\,\Omega \quad R_e = 282\,\Omega$

Complex AC Circuits (continued)

By replacing the parallel part of the complex circuit with the equivalent R_e and X_{L_e} values, the circuit becomes a series circuit. Combining the two values of R and the two values of X_L results in a simple R and L series circuit, which would have the same effect on total circuit current and voltage as the entire complex circuit. To find the value of total circuit impedance and current flow, the simple series circuit is then solved by using vectors.

Substituting the EQUIVALENT SERIES CIRCUIT for the SERIES-PARALLEL CIRCUIT

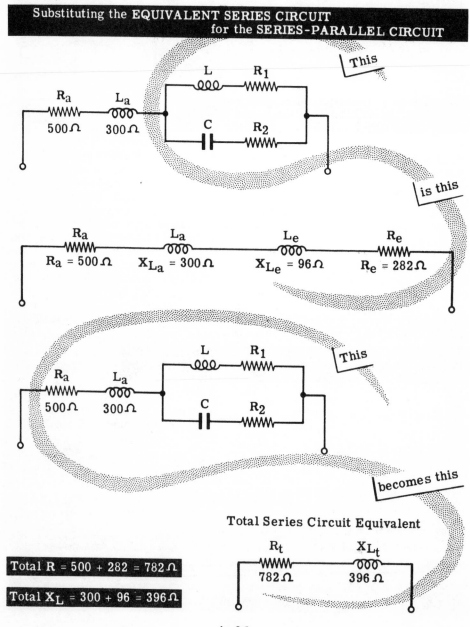

Total R = 500 + 282 = 782 Ω

Total X_L = 300 + 96 = 396 Ω

Total Series Circuit Equivalent

Demonstration of Complex Circuits

For demonstration purposes, a series-parallel circuit containing resistance, inductance and capacitance is used. The instructor will demonstrate the method of solving such circuits to find the total circuit current, the branch currents, the impedance and the equivalent series circuit. The calculated results will be checked with actual voltage and current measurements, and you will see how the values compare. Because pure inductances and pure capacitances are only theoretical, there will be a noticeable difference between the actual and calculated results. However, the measured results will show that the calculations are accurate enough for practical use in electrical circuits.

The instructor connects a 500-ohm resistor, a 1000-ohm resistor, a 1-mfd capacitor and a 5-henry filter choke to form the complex circuit shown below. Because the filter choke has a DC resistance of approximately 50 ohms, the total resistance of the R and L branch of the circuit is 1050 ohms. R_2 is rated as a 1050-ohm resistor rather than a 1000-ohm resistor.

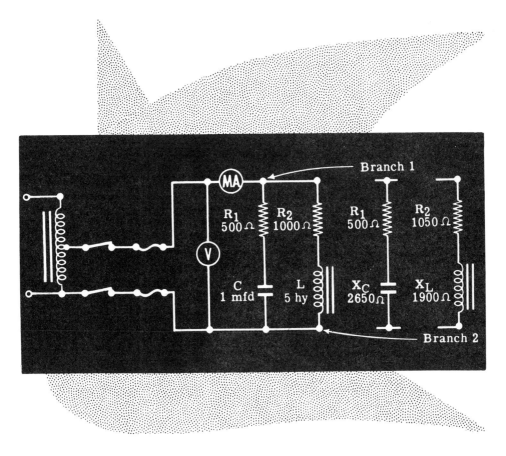

Demonstration—Vector Solution of Complex Circuits

Before applying power to the circuit, the instructor demonstrates the vector solution to find the total current, branch currents and impedance. First the values of X_L and X_C are computed, using 60 cycles as the power line frequency. Rounded off to the nearest 50 ohms, these values are 1900 ohms for X_L and 2650 ohms for X_C.

Using the known values of R_1 and R_2 together with the computed values of X_L and X_C, the impedances of each series branch are found separately by using vectors. From these values of impedance and a source voltage of 60 volts, the values of the branch currents I_1 and I_2 are found.

FIND THE BRANCH CURRENTS I_1 AND I_2

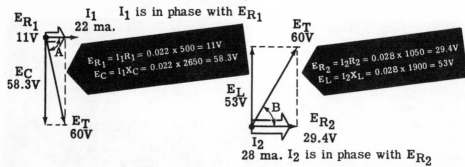

$$I_1 = \frac{E}{Z_1} = \frac{60}{2700} = 22 \text{ ma.}$$

$$I_2 = \frac{E}{Z_2} = \frac{60}{2170} = 28 \text{ ma.}$$

Next the individual voltages of each branch are drawn with respect to their corresponding branch current, to find the relationship between E_T and each of the branch currents individually.

I_1 is in phase with E_{R_1}

$$E_{R_1} = I_1 R_1 = 0.022 \times 500 = 11V$$
$$E_C = I_1 X_C = 0.022 \times 2650 = 58.3V$$

$$E_{R_2} = I_2 R_2 = 0.028 \times 1050 = 29.4V$$
$$E_L = I_2 X_L = 0.028 \times 1900 = 53V$$

I_2 is in phase with E_{R_2}

These individual relationships are drawn with reference to the common total voltage vector, E_T, and the two branch current vectors are combined to find the total circuit current. From the computed value of the total current and the given value of voltage, 60 volts, the total impedance is computed.

$$Z_T = \frac{E}{I_T} = \frac{60}{.020} = 3000 \ \Omega$$

Z_T is approximately 3000 ohms

Demonstration—Complex Circuit Currents and Impedance

To check the computed values of the total current and circuit impedance, the instructor applies power to the circuit and measures the total circuit current and voltage. You see that the measured total current and voltage are approximately the same as the computed values. From these measured values the impedance Z_T is determined and compared to the value obtained by using vectors.

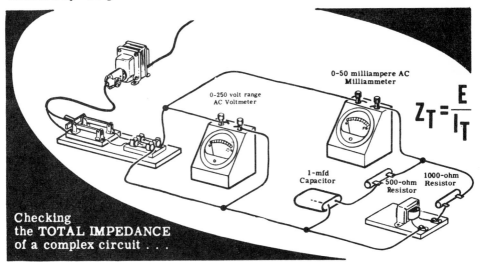

0-50 milliampere AC Milliammeter

0-250 volt range AC Voltmeter

$$Z_T = \frac{E}{I_T}$$

1-mfd Capacitor

500-ohm Resistor

1000-ohm Resistor

Checking
the **TOTAL IMPEDANCE**
of a complex circuit . . .

MEASURING THE BRANCH CURRENTS

Next the instructor connects the milliammeter to measure each branch current in turn. You see that the measured values are about the same as the computed values, and that the total circuit current is less than the sum of the two branch currents.

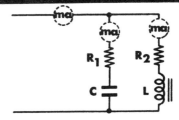

MEASURING THE CIRCUIT VOLTAGES

To check the computed values of the various voltages in the circuit, the instructor measures the voltage across each resistor, the capacitor and the inductance. You see that the sum of the voltages across each branch is greater than the total voltage and that the measured voltages are nearly equal to the computed values.

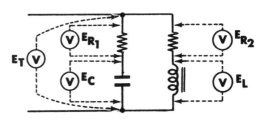

4-69

Review of AC Complex Circuits

The solution of a complex AC circuit requires a step-by-step use of vectors and Ohm's law to find unknown quantities of voltage, current and impedances. Suppose you review the vector solution of a typical complex circuit:

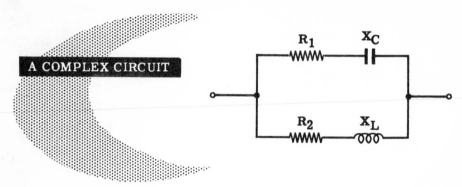

A COMPLEX CIRCUIT

1. Calculate the reactance values of circuit capacitances and/or inductances.

$$X_C = \frac{1}{2\pi fC} \qquad X_L = 2\pi fL$$

2. Using vectors, find the impedance of each series branch separately, and compute the Ohm's law values of the branch currents.

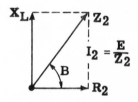

3. Compute the individual voltages of each branch and draw them with respect to their respective branch current. Complete the voltage parallelograms to find the phase relationship between each branch current and the total circuit voltage.

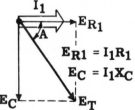

$$E_{R1} = I_1 R_1$$
$$E_C = I_1 X_C$$

$$E_{R2} = I_2 R_2$$
$$E_L = I_2 X_L$$

4. Draw the branch current vectors with respect to a common total circuit voltage vector, then combine the currents to find the total circuit current. Calculate the total impedance of the circuit.

$$Z_T = \frac{E}{I_T}$$

The Importance Of Transformers

When you studied AC circuits, you learned that alternating current as a source of power has certain advantage over direct current. The most important advantage of AC is that the voltage level can be raised or lowered by means of a transformer. You remember it is better to transmit power over long distances at a high voltage and low current level, since the IR drop due to the resistance of the transmission lines is greatly reduced.

It is not practical to generate a very high voltage directly with a generator because it is difficult to insulate a generator for more than about 14,000 volts. Therefore, to transmit AC power at a high-voltage, low-current level, the generated voltage is fed to a transformer. The transformer raises the voltage, and since power depends on both voltage and current, a higher voltage means the same amount of power will require a lower current. At the load end of the transmission line, another transformer reduces the voltage to the level necessary to operate the load equipment. For example, at Niagara Falls AC is generated at 6000 volts, stepped up by transformers to 120,000 volts and distributed over long transmission lines, stepped down at different points to 6000 volts for local distribution, and finally stepped down to 220 and 110 volts AC for lighting and local power use.

Transformers are used in all types of electronic equipment, to raise and lower AC voltages. It is important for you to become familiar with transformers, how they work, how they are connected into circuits, and precautions in using them.

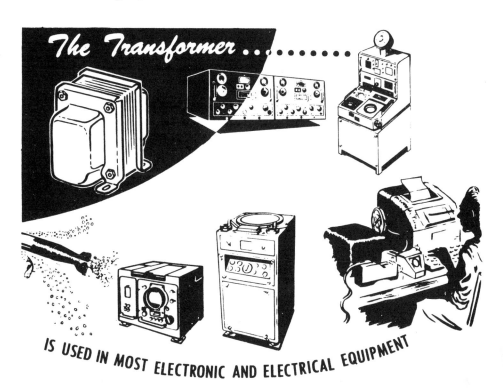

IS USED IN MOST ELECTRONIC AND ELECTRICAL EQUIPMENT

How a Transformer Works

When AC flows through a coil, an alternating magnetic field is generated around the coil. This alternating magnetic field expands outward from the center of the coil and collapses into the coil as the AC through the coil varies from zero to a maximum and back to zero again. Since the alternating magnetic field must cut through the turns of the coil an emf of self induction is induced in the coil which opposes the change in current flow

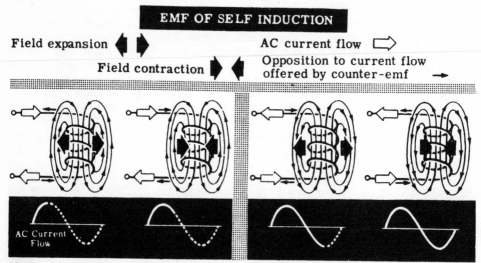

EMF OF SELF INDUCTION

Field expansion ◀ ▶   AC current flow ▭⟶

Field contraction ▶ ◀   Opposition to current flow
                                offered by counter-emf ⟶

AC Current Flow

If the alternating magnetic field generated by one coil cuts through the turns of a second coil, an emf will be generated in this second coil just as an emf is induced in a coil which is cut by its own magnetic field. The emf generated in the second coil is called the "emf of mutual induction," and the action of generating this voltage is called "transformer action." In transformer action, electrical energy is transferred from one coil (the primary) to another (the secondary) by means of a varying magnetic field.

EMF OF MUTUAL INDUCTION

Transformer Action

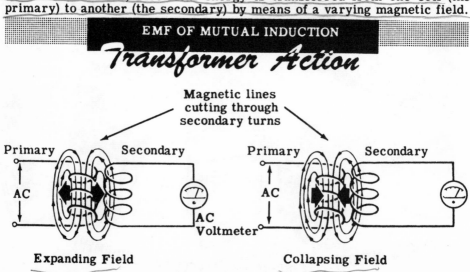

Magnetic lines
cutting through
secondary turns

Primary   Secondary   Primary   Secondary

AC   AC

                 AC
                 Voltmeter

Expanding Field   Collapsing Field

How a Transformer Works (continued)

A simple transformer consists of two coils very close together, electrically insulated from each other. The coil to which the AC is applied is called the "primary." It generates a magnetic field which cuts through the turns of the other coil, called the "secondary," and generates a voltage in it. The coils are not physically connected to each other. They are, however, magnetically coupled to each other. Thus, a transformer transfers electrical power from one coil to another by means of an alternating magnetic field.

Assuming that all the magnetic lines of force from the primary cut through all the turns of the secondary, the voltage induced in the secondary will depend on the ratio of the number of turns in the secondary to the number of turns in the primary. For example, if there are 1000 turns in the secondary and only 100 turns in the primary, the voltage induced in the secondary will be 10 times the voltage applied to the primary ($\frac{1000}{100} = 10$). Since there are more turns in the secondary than there are in the primary, the transformer is called a "step-up transformer." If, on the other hand, the secondary has 10 turns and the primary has 100 turns, the voltage induced in the secondary will be one-tenth of the voltage applied to the primary ($\frac{10}{100} = \frac{1}{10}$). Since there are less turns in the secondary than there are in the primary, the transformer is called a "step-down transformer." Transformers are rated in KVA because it is independent of power factor.

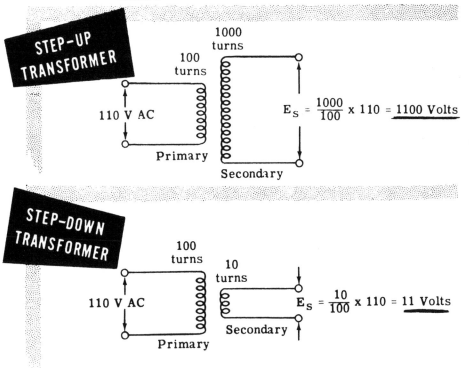

STEP-UP TRANSFORMER

1000 turns

100 turns

110 V AC

Primary

Secondary

$E_S = \frac{1000}{100} \times 110 = 1100$ Volts

STEP-DOWN TRANSFORMER

100 turns

10 turns

110 V AC

Primary

Secondary

$E_S = \frac{10}{100} \times 110 = 11$ Volts

4-73

How a Transformer Works (continued)

A transformer does not generate electrical power. It simply transfers electric power from one coil to another by magnetic induction. Although transformers are not 100 percent efficient, they are very nearly so. For practical purposes, their efficiency is considered to be 100 percent. Therefore, a transformer can be defined as a device that transfers power from its primary circuit to the secondary circuit without any loss (assuming 100 percent efficiency).

Since power equals voltage times current, if $E_p I_p$ represents the primary power and $E_S I_S$ represents the secondary power, then $E_p I_p = E_S I_S$. If the primary and secondary voltages are equal, the primary and secondary currents must also be equal. Suppose E_p is twice as large as E_S. Then, in order for $E_p I_p$ to equal $E_S I_S$, I_p must be one half of I_S. Thus a transformer which steps voltage down, steps current up. Similarly, if E_p is only half as large as E_S, I_p must be twice as large as I_S and a transformer which steps voltage up, steps current down. Transformers are classified as step-down or step-up only in relation to their effect on voltage.

PRIMARY POWER EQUALS SECONDARY POWER

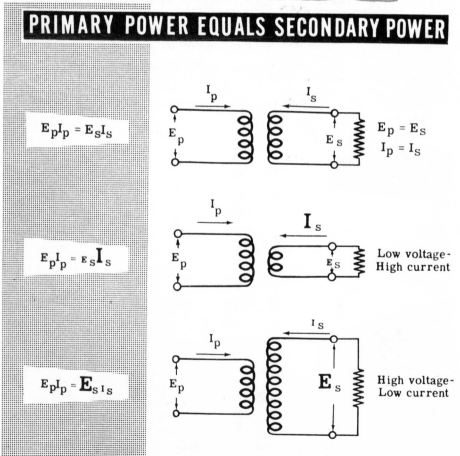

$E_p I_p = E_S I_S$ $E_p = E_S$
$I_p = I_S$

$E_p I_p = E_S I_S$ Low voltage-
High current

$E_p I_p = E_S I_S$ High voltage-
Low current

Transformer Construction

Transformers designed to operate on low frequencies have their coils, called "windings," wound on iron cores. Since iron offers little resistance to magnetic lines, nearly all the magnetic field of the primary flows through the iron core and cuts the secondary. The iron core increases the efficiency of the transformer to 98 or 99 percent, which can practically be considered 100 percent, or "no loss."

Iron cores are constructed in three main types—the open core, the closed core and the shell type. The open core is the least expensive to build— the primary and the secondary are wound on one cylindrical core. The magnetic path is partly through the core, partly through the air. The air path opposes the magnetic field, so that the magnetic interaction or "link-age" is weakened. The open core transformer is inefficient and never used for power transfer.

The closed core improves the transformer efficiency by offering more iron paths and less air path for the magnetic field, thus increasing the magnetic "linkage" or "coupling." The shell type core further increases the magnetic coupling and therefore the transformer efficiency, because it provides two parallel magnetic paths for the magnetic field. Thus maximum coupling is attained between the primary and secondary.

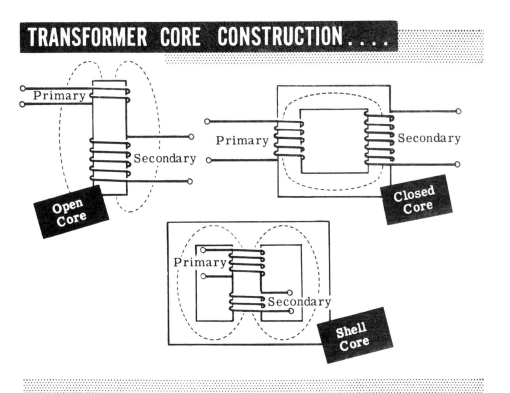

TRANSFORMER CORE CONSTRUCTION . . . .

Primary

Secondary

Open Core

Primary

Secondary

Closed Core

Primary

Secondary

Shell Core

Transformer Losses

Not all of the electrical energy from the primary coil is transferred to the secondary coil. A transformer has some losses; and the actual efficiency, although usually greater than 90 percent, is less than 100 percent. Transformer losses are generally of two types—"copper losses" and "core losses."

Copper losses represent the power loss in resistance of the wire in the windings. These are called copper losses since copper wire usually is used for the windings. Although normally the resistance of a winding is not high, current flow through the wire causes it to heat, using power. This power can be computed from the formula I^2R, where R is the coil wire resistance and I is the current through the coil.

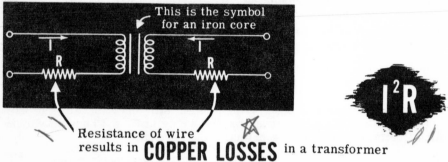

This is the symbol for an iron core

Resistance of wire results in **COPPER LOSSES** in a transformer

I^2R

Core losses are due to eddy currents and hysteresis. The magnetic field which induces current in the secondary coil also cuts through the core material, causing a current, called "eddy current," to flow through the core. This eddy current heats the core material—an indication that power is being used. If the resistance of the eddy current path is increased less current will flow, reducing the power losses. By laminating the core material, that is by using thin sheets of metal insulated by varnish—the cross-section of each current path is diminished, and the resistance to eddy current flow increases.

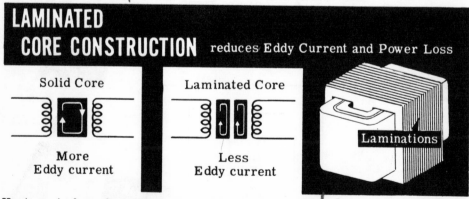

LAMINATED CORE CONSTRUCTION reduces Eddy Current and Power Loss

Solid Core

More Eddy current

Laminated Core

Less Eddy current

Laminations

Hysteresis loss depends on the core material used. Each time the AC current reverses in the primary winding, the field in the core reverses its magnetic polarity. This field reversal requires a certain amount of power, resulting in a loss called "hysteresis loss." Some materials, such as silicon steel, change polarity easily, and when these materials are used as the core material, hysteresis loss is reduced to a minimum.

The Power Supply Transformer

Transformers are designed for many different uses and frequencies. The type of transformer you will probably be most concerned with is the power supply transformer. It is used to change the 117 volt 60 cycle power frequency to whatever 60 cycle voltage is needed to operate motors, lighting circuits and electronic equipment.

The illustration shows a typical power supply transformer for electronic equipment. You see that the secondary consists of three separate windings —each secondary winding supplying a different circuit with its required voltage. The multiple secondary eliminates the need for three separate transformers, saving cost, space and weight. The iron core is shown by the standard symbol. Each secondary has three connections. The middle connection is called the "center tap," and the voltage between the center tap and either outside connection is one half the total voltage across the winding.

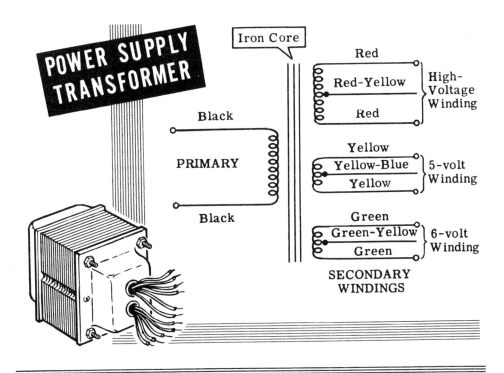

The number of turns shown in a schematic does not necessarily indicate whether the transformer is step-up or step-down. The windings are color-coded by the manufacturer, to indicate the separate secondary windings, their use and the way they are to be connected. The color-code shown is a standard one, but manufacturers may use other color-codes or may use numbers to indicate the proper connections.

Other Types of Transformers

In addition to power transformers, which operate at 60 cps (cycle per second), there are transformers designed to operate at different frequencies.

The audio transformer is designed to operate on the range of "audio" frequencies—those frequencies which are audible to the human ear—20 cps to 20,000 cps. The audio transformer has an iron core and is similar in appearance to the power transformer. In some cases, the core is made from a powdered iron compound that is molded together. This type of core gives better results at higher frequencies.

In receivers and transmitters, frequencies much higher than the audio range are used, and these frequencies are called "radio frequencies" 100,000 cps or 100 kilocycles (kc) and higher. Radio frequency (rf) transformers often use iron cores of the molded powder type because the losses from a conventional laminated core would be too great. In other cases, the coils have an air core and are wound on a non-magnetic form. The illustrations show a receiver rf transformer and a transmitter rf transformer. In the transmitter rf transformer, the windings are spaced far apart because of the high voltages used.

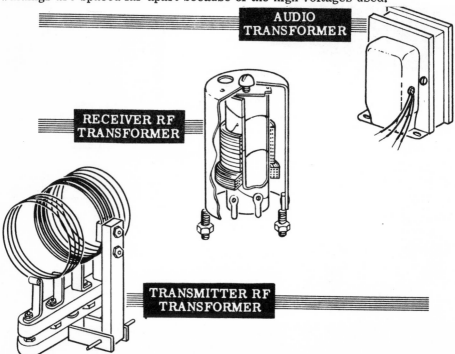

All these transformers have only one primary winding and are called "single phase" transformers. Other transformers, which operate from three AC voltages, are called "three phase" transformers. These transformers will be discussed in the section on alternators.

Autotransformers = one winding

The autotransformer differs from other transformers in that it has only one winding, rather than two or more as in ordinary transformers. Part of this winding is used for both primary and secondary, while the rest of the winding acts as either the primary or secondary exclusively, depending on whether the autotransformer is used to step down or step up the voltage.

A step-up autotransformer uses a portion of the total winding as the primary. AC current flow in this portion of the winding causes an expanding and collapsing field, which cuts across all of the coil turns and induces a higher voltage across the entire coil than that across the portion used as the primary. The end terminals of the coil then can be used as a secondary winding having a higher voltage than that of the primary section.

If the entire coil is used as the primary winding and only a portion is used for the secondary, the secondary voltage is less than that of the primary. When so connected, the autotransformer is used to step down voltage.

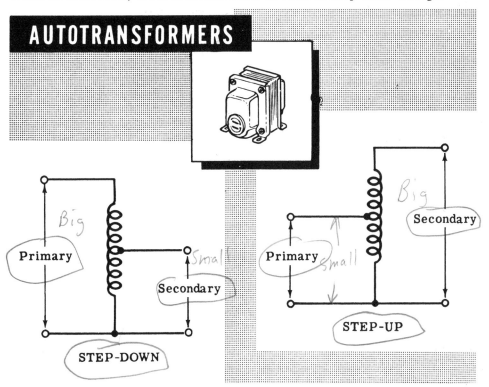

In the autotransformer, part of the winding is common to both the primary and secondary and carries both currents. Autotransformers require less wire since only one coil is used and they are less expensive than two-coil transformers. However, autotransformers do not isolate the primary and secondary circuits and are not used in most electrical and electronic circuits for this reason.

Troubleshooting

Since transformers are an essential part of the equipment you will work with, you should know how to test and locate troubles that develop in transformers. The three things that cause transformer failures are open windings, shorted windings, and grounds.

When one of the windings in a transformer develops an "open," no current can flow and the transformer will not deliver any output. The symptom of an open-circuited transformer is that the circuits which derive power from the transformer are dead. A check with an AC voltmeter across the transformer output terminals will show a reading of zero volts. A voltmeter check across the transformer input terminals shows that voltage is present. Since there is voltage at the input and no voltage at the output, you conclude that one of the windings is open. Next you check the transformer windings for continuity. After disconnecting all of the primary and secondary leads, each winding is checked for continuity, as indicated by a resistance reading taken with an ohmmeter. Continuity, (a continuous circuit) is indicated by a fairly low resistance reading, while the open winding will indicate an infinite resistance on the ohmmeter. In the majority of cases the transformer will have to be replaced, unless of course the break is accessible and can be repaired.

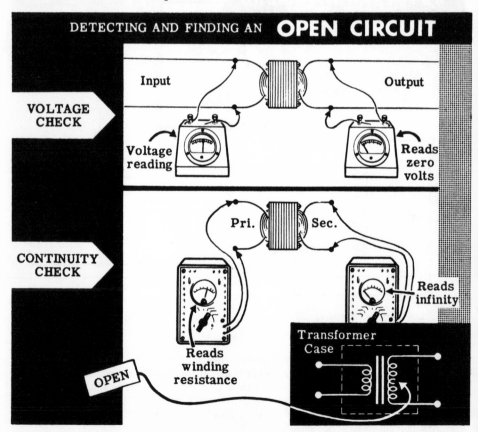

DETECTING AND FINDING AN **OPEN CIRCUIT**

VOLTAGE CHECK

Input

Output

Voltage reading

Reads zero volts

CONTINUITY CHECK

Pri.

Sec.

Reads infinity

Reads winding resistance

OPEN

Transformer Case

Troubleshooting (continued)

When a few turns of a secondary winding are shorted, the output voltage drops. The symptoms are that the transformer overheats due to the large circulating currents flowing in the shorted turns and the transformer output voltage is lower than it should be. The winding with the short gives a lower reading on the ohmmeter than normal. If the winding happens to be a low voltage winding, its normal resistance reading is so low that a few shorted turns cannot be detected by using an ordinary ohmmeter. In this case, a sure way to tell if the transformer is bad is to replace it with another transformer. If the replacement transformer operates satisfactorily it should be used and the original transformer repaired or discarded, depending upon its size and type.

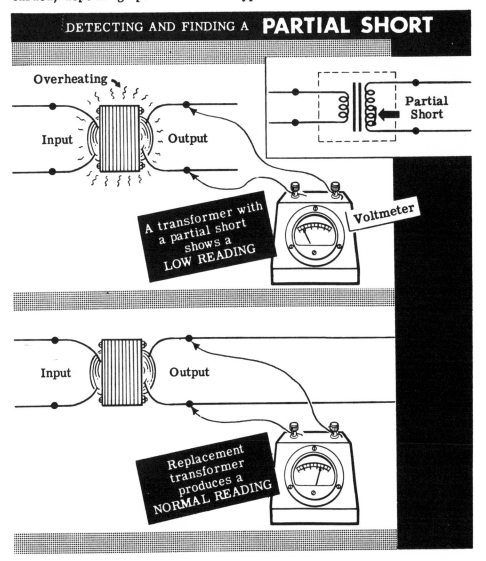

DETECTING AND FINDING A **PARTIAL SHORT**

Overheating

Input

Output

Partial Short

A transformer with a partial short shows a LOW READING

Voltmeter

Input

Output

Replacement transformer produces a NORMAL READING

Troubleshooting (continued)

Sometimes a winding has a complete short across it. Again, one of the symptoms is excessive overheating of the transformer due to the very large circulating current. The heat often melts the wax inside the transformer, which you can detect quickly by the odor. Also, there will be no voltage output across the shorted winding and the circuit across the winding will be dead. In equipment which is fused, the heavy current flow will blow the fuse before the transformer is damaged completely. If the fuse does not blow, the shorted winding may burn out. The short may be in the external circuit connected to the winding or in the winding itself. The way to isolate the short is to disconnect the external circuit from the winding. If the voltage is normal with the external circuit disconnected the short is in the external circuit. If the voltage across the winding is still zero, it means the short is in the transformer and it will have to be replaced.

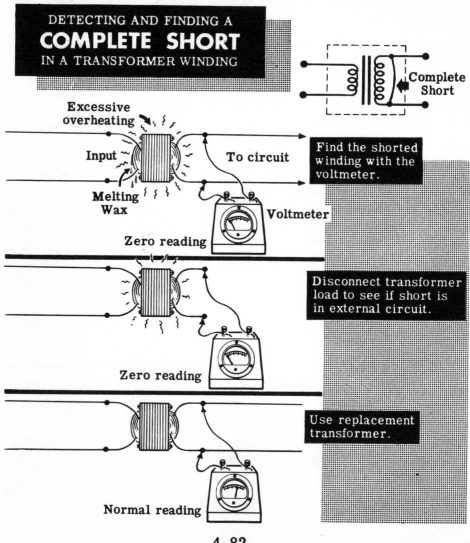

DETECTING AND FINDING A
COMPLETE SHORT
IN A TRANSFORMER WINDING

Complete Short

Excessive overheating

Input

To circuit

Melting Wax

Find the shorted winding with the voltmeter.

Voltmeter

Zero reading

Disconnect transformer load to see if short is in external circuit.

Zero reading

Use replacement transformer.

Normal reading

Troubleshooting (continued)

Sometimes the insulation at some point in the winding breaks and the wire becomes exposed. If the bare wire is at the outside of the winding, it may touch the inside of the transformer case, shorting the wire to the case and grounding the winding.

If a winding develops a ground, and a point in the external circuit connected to this winding is also grounded, part of the winding will be shorted out. The symptoms will be the same as those described for a shorted winding and the transformer will have to be replaced. You can check for a transformer ground by connecting the megger between one side of the winding in question and the transformer case, after all the transformer leads have been disconnected from the circuit. A zero or low reading on the megger shows that the winding is grounded.

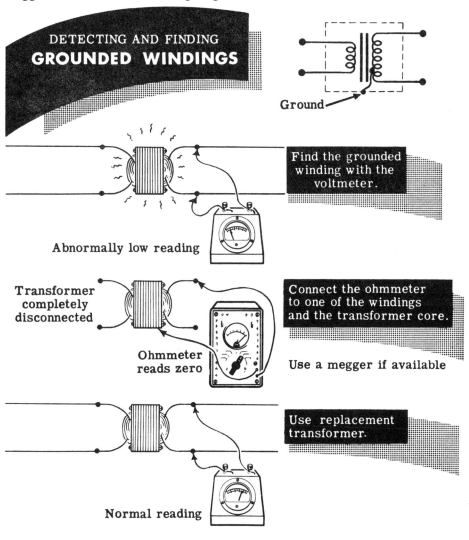

DETECTING AND FINDING
GROUNDED WINDINGS

Ground

Abnormally low reading

Find the grounded winding with the voltmeter.

Transformer completely disconnected

Ohmmeter reads zero

Connect the ohmmeter to one of the windings and the transformer core.

Use a megger if available

Normal reading

Use replacement transformer.

Demonstration—Voltage Measurements

To demonstrate power transformer action in stepping voltage up or down, the instructor uses a power transformer made up of one primary winding, and three secondary windings consisting of a step-up high voltage winding and two step-down low voltage windings, all center-tapped. See the schematic below.

The instructor carefully separates the winding leads to make certain none are touching each other or the case. Then he attaches a line cord to the primary leads. A 0-1000 volt range AC voltmeter is set up to take measurements. He plugs the line cord into the 110-volt socket and measures the AC voltage across the different transformer windings. With the voltmeter leads placed across the primary, the voltmeter reads 110 volts, the line voltage. Next, he places the voltmeter leads across the two outside high voltage leads. These leads can be identified by their red color. Notice that the voltmeter reads a very high voltage. Knowing the high voltage and the primary voltage, you can easily determine the turns ratio between the secondary high voltage winding and the primary by dividing the secondary voltage by the primary voltage.

Now the instructor measures the voltage between the high voltage center tap and first one and then the other high voltage lead. Notice that the voltage is exactly half that across the outside terminals. He repeats the above voltage measurements with the two low voltage step-down windings.

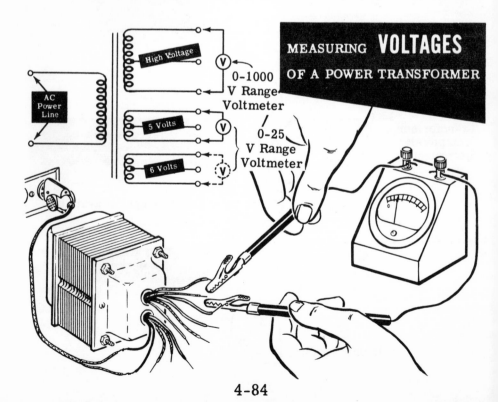

Demonstration—Resistance Measurements

Next the instructor measures the resistance of the various windings of the power transformer with an ohmmeter. (Caution: This reading must be taken with no power applied to the transformer, otherwise the ohmmeter would be damaged.) The ohmmeter leads are first placed across the primary winding, then across the entire high voltage secondary. Observe that the resistance of the high voltage winding is much higher than the resistance of the primary. This is because the high voltage winding has many more turns than the primary winding. As the instructor measures the resistance from the center tap of the high voltage winding to either end you see that resistance equals one-half that of the full winding.

Next the ohmmeter leads are placed across the two low voltage windings. Observe that the ohmmeter reads practically zero ohms for both windings. This is because these windings have few turns of comparatively large diameter wire. You could not tell if these windings were shorted by means of a resistance measurement. The only way to check the low voltage windings is to measure their output voltage with all circuits disconnected from them. If the voltage readings are normal, the windings are probably in good condition.

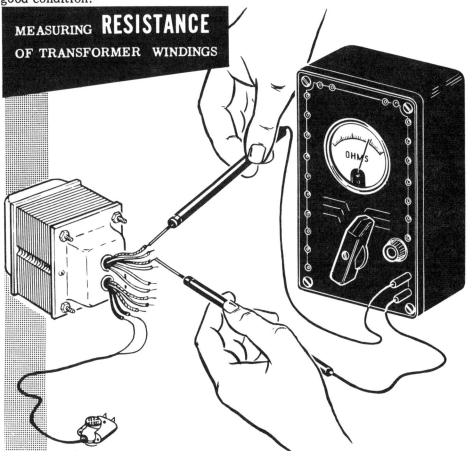

MEASURING **RESISTANCE** OF TRANSFORMER WINDINGS

ALTERNATING CURRENT CIRCUITS

Review of AC Circuits

You have learned about AC circuits, and have investigated the various factors which affect AC current flow. This review sums up all these factors, and gives you the opportunity to check yourself on each point.

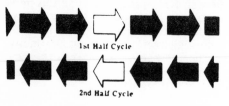

1st Half Cycle

2nd Half Cycle

ALTERNATING CURRENT — Current flow which reverses its direction at regular intervals and is constantly changing in magnitude.

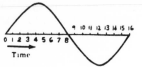

Time

SINE WAVE — A continuous curve of all the instantaneous values of an AC current or voltage.

INDUCTANCE — The property of a circuit which opposes any change in the current flow.

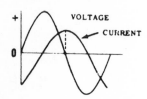

INDUCTIVE REACTANCE — The action of inductance in opposing the flow of AC current and in causing the current to lag the voltage.

CAPACITANCE — The property of a circuit which opposes any change in the circuit voltage.

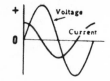

CAPACITIVE REACTANCE — The action of capacitance in opposing the flow of AC current and in causing the current to lead the voltage.

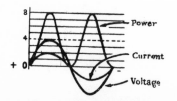

POWER — In AC circuits true power is equal to EI x cos θ, where the power factor (cos θ) is equal to the ratio of the resistance divided by the impedance ($\frac{R}{Z}$).

Review of AC Circuits (continued)

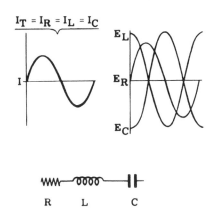

AC SERIES CIRCUIT — The current is the same in all parts of the circuit, while the voltage divides across the circuit and differs in phase.

SERIES RESONANCE — When X_L and X_C are equal, a series circuit is at resonance having minimum impedance and maximum current.

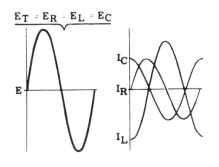

AC PARALLEL CIRCUIT — The voltage is the same across each parallel branch while the current divides to flow through the various branches, with the branch currents differing in phase and amplitude.

PARALLEL RESONANCE — When X_L and X_C are equal, a parallel circuit is at resonance, having maximum impedance and minimum line current. At resonance, the circulating current is greater than the line current.

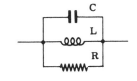

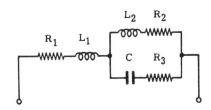

AC SERIES-PARALLEL CIRCUIT — The current divides to flow through the parallel branches while the voltage divides across series parts of the circuit. Voltage and current phase relationships for each part of the circuit depend on whether the part is made up of resistance, inductance or capacitance.

4-87

Review

Here is a review of the most important points about the transformer.

TRANSFORMER ACTION—The
method of transferring electrical
energy from one coil to another by
means of an alternating magnetic
field. The coils are not physically
connected. They are only magnetically coupled. The alternating magnetic field generated in one coil cuts
through the turns of another coil and
generates a voltage in that coil.

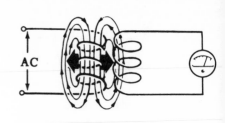

PRIMARY AND SECONDARY WIND-
INGS—The coil which generates the
alternating magnetic field is called
the "primary." The coil in which a
voltage is induced by the alternating
magnetic field is called the "secondary." The voltage induced in
the secondary depends upon the
turns ratio between the secondary
and primary.

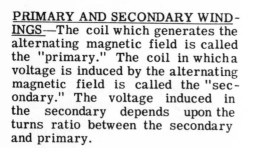

STEP-UP AND STEP-DOWN
TRANSFORMER—If there are more
turns in the secondary than in the
primary, the transformer is "step-
up," and the secondary voltage will
be higher than the primary voltage.
If there are fewer turns in the secondary than in the primary, the
transformer is "step-down," and the
secondary voltage will be lower than
the primary voltage. The ratio of
the secondary voltage to the primary
voltage is equal to the turns ratio.

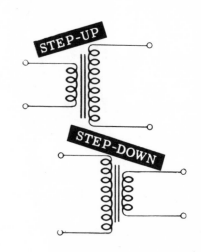

PRIMARY AND SECONDARY CUR-
RENT—The power delivered by a
transformer is equal to the power
put into the transformer, assuming
100 percent efficiency. Stating this
in terms of a formula, $E_p I_p = E_s I_s$.
From this formula it can be seen
that, if the transformer steps up the
voltage, it will reduce the current.
In other words, the transformer
changes the current in the opposite
direction to the change in voltage.

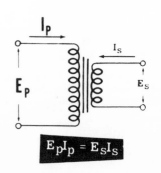

$$E_p I_p = E_s I_s$$

Review (continued)

TRANSFORMER LOSSES: Transformers designed for low frequencies are wound around iron cores to offer a low resistance path for the magnetic lines of force. This allows for a maximum amount of coupling between the primary magnetic field and the secondary winding, with the result that energy is transferred to the secondary at low loss. Transformers do suffer losses which are of three types: (1) the I^2R loss incurred by current flowing through the resistance of the windings, (2) eddy current losses caused by induction currents in the core material and (3) hysteresis losses caused by the reversal of core polarity each time the magnetic field reverses.

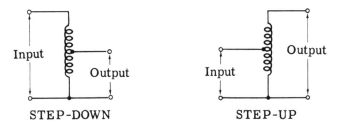

AUTOTRANSFORMERS: In addition to the two winding transformers, there are single winding transformers called "autotransformers." Electrical energy is transferred from one part of the coil to another part of the coil by magnetic induction. The voltage and currents vary in the same manner as in the two winding transformers.

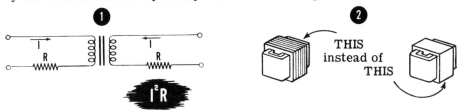

TRANSFORMER TROUBLES:

1. One of the windings can develop an open circuit.

2. Part or all of one winding can become shorted.

3. A ground can develop.

In troubleshooting a transformer, a voltmeter and ohmmeter are used to locate the trouble. If a transformer is defective, it usually must be replaced.

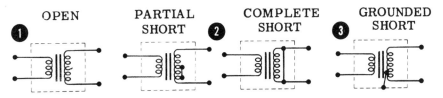

INDEX TO VOL. 4

(Note: A cumulative index covering all five volumes in this series will be found at the end of Volume 5.)

basic
electricity

by VAN VALKENBURGH,
NOOGER & NEVILLE, INC.

VOL. 5

HAYDEN BOOK COMPANY, INC.
Rochelle Park, New Jersey

PREFACE

The texts of the entire Basic Electricity and Basic Electronics courses, as currently taught at Navy specialty schools, have now been released by the Navy for civilian use. This educational program has been an unqualified success. Since April, 1953, when it was first installed, over 25,000 Navy trainees have benefited by this instruction and the results have been outstanding.

The unique simplification of an ordinarily complex subject, the exceptional clarity of illustrations and text, and the plan of presenting one basic concept at a time, without involving complicated mathematics, all combine in making this course a better and quicker way to teach and learn basic electricity and electronics. The Basic Electronics portion of this course will be available as a separate series of volumes.

In releasing this material to the general public, the Navy hopes to provide the means for creating a nation-wide pool of pre-trained technicians, upon whom the Armed Forces could call in time of national emergency, without the need for precious weeks and months of schooling.

Perhaps of greater importance is the Navy's hope that through the release of this course, a direct contribution will be made toward increasing the technical knowledge of men and women throughout the country, as a step in making and keeping America strong.

Van Valkenburgh, Nooger and Neville, Inc.

New York, N. Y.
October, 1954

TABLE OF CONTENTS

VOL. 5 — BASIC ELECTRICITY

ELEMENTARY GENERATORS

The Importance of Generators

You are all familiar with flashlights, portable radios and car lighting systems—all of which use batteries as their source of power. In these applications the current drawn from the battery is comparatively small and, therefore, a battery can supply the current for a long period of time, even without recharging. Batteries work very nicely when they supply devices which require very little current.

Many kinds of electrical equipment require large amounts of current at a high voltage in order to do their job. For example, electric lights and heavy motors require larger voltages and currents than those furnished by any practical sized battery. As a result, sources of power other than batteries are required to supply large amounts of power. These large sources of power are supplied by rotating electrical machines called "generators." Generators can supply either DC or AC power. In either case, the generator can be designed to supply very small amounts of power or else it can be designed to supply many hundreds of kilowatts of power.

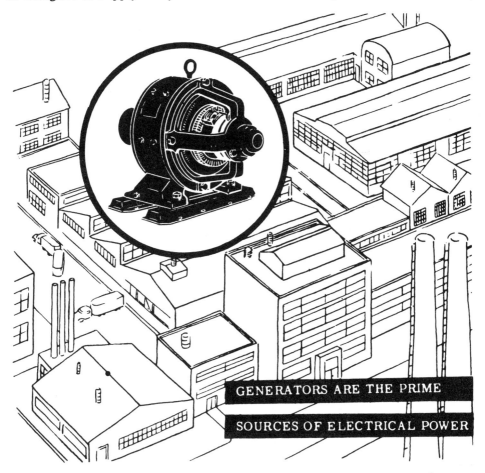

GENERATORS ARE THE PRIME

SOURCES OF ELECTRICAL POWER

The Importance of Generators (continued)

The world as we know it would be practically at a standstill without the electrical energy supplied by generators. Look about you and you will see proof of electrically generated energy in action.

Our modern lighting systems, our factories—in fact, our entire industrial life is directly or indirectly energized by the electrical power output from rotating electrical generators. A large city soon would become a "ghost town" if its generators were put out of action. The electrical generator is as important to our modern way of living as the action of the heart is to the maintenance of life in your own body.

Review of Electricity from Magnetism

You will recall that electricity can be generated by moving a wire through a magnetic field. As long as there is relative motion between the conductor and the magnetic field, electricity is generated. If there is no relative motion between the conductor and the magnetic field, electricity is not generated. The generated electricity is actually a voltage, called an "induced voltage," and the method of generating this voltage by cutting a magnetic field with a conductor is called "induction." You also know that this induced voltage will cause a current to flow if the ends of the conductor are connected through a closed circuit--in this case, the meter.

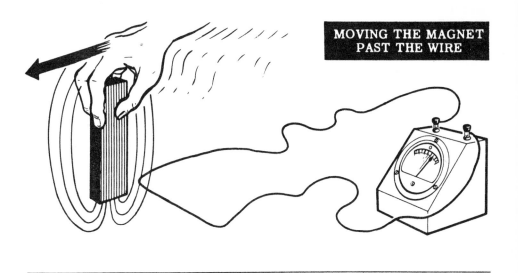

MOVING THE MAGNET PAST THE WIRE

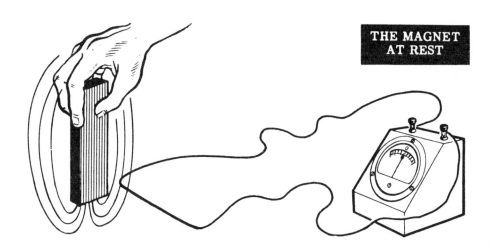

THE MAGNET AT REST

Review of Electricity from Magnetism (continued)

You know that the amount of voltage induced in the wire cutting through the magnetic field depends upon a number of factors. First, if the speed of the relative cutting action between the conductor and the magnetic field increases, the induced emf increases. Second, if the strength of the magnetic field increases, the induced emf increases. Third, if the number of turns cutting through the magnetic field is increased, the induced emf is again increased.

The polarity of this induced emf will be in such a direction that the resultant current flow will build up a field to react with the field of the magnet, and oppose the movement of the coil. This phenomenon illustrates a principle known as "Lenz's Law" which states that in all cases of electromagnetic induction, the direction of the induced emf is such that the magnetic field it sets up tends to stop the motion which produces the emf.

FACTORS WHICH DETERMINE INDUCED EMF STRENGTH

1

. . . THE SPEED OF
CONDUCTOR THROUGH
MAGNETIC FIELD

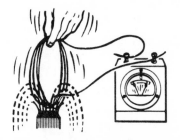

2

. . . THE STRENGTH
OF MAGNETIC FIELD

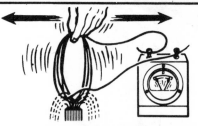

3

. . . THE NUMBER
OF TURNS

Review of Electricity from Magnetism (continued)

You also know that the direction of the generated current flow is determined by the direction of the relative motion between the magnetic field and the cutting conductor. If the relative motion is toward each other, the current flows in one direction; and, if the relative motion is away from each other, the current flows in the opposite direction.

DIRECTION OF RELATIVE MOTION DETERMINES DIRECTION OF CURRENT FLOW

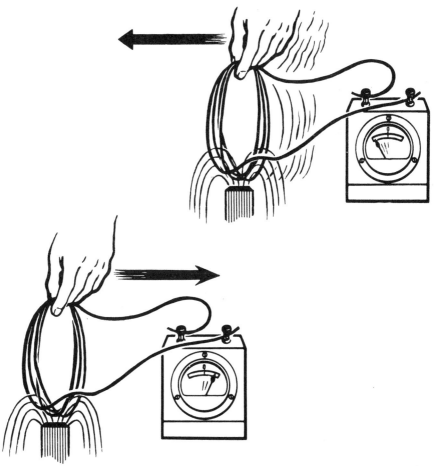

To sum up what you already know about electricity from magnetism: 1) moving a conductor through a magnetic field generates an emf which produces a current flow; 2) the faster the conductor cuts through the field, the more turns there are and the stronger the magnetic field—the greater the induced emf and the greater the current flow; and 3) reversing the direction of movement of the conductor reverses the polarity of the induced emf and, therefore, reverses the direction of current flow.

Practical Generators

You already know that you can generate electricity by having a conductor cut through a magnetic field. This is essentially the principle of operation of any generator from the smallest to the giants which produce kilowatts of power. Therefore, in order to understand the operation of practical generators, you could examine an elementary generator, made of a conductor and a magnetic field, and see how it can produce electricity in usable form. Once you know how a basic generator works, you will have no difficulty in seeing how the basic generator is built up into a practical generator.

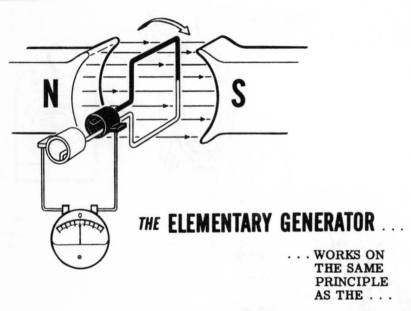

THE **ELEMENTARY GENERATOR** . . .

. . . WORKS ON
THE SAME
PRINCIPLE
AS THE . . .

. . . **PRACTICAL GENERATOR**

Elementary Generator Construction

An elementary generator consists of a loop of wire placed so that it can be rotated in a stationary magnetic field to cause an induced current in the loop. Sliding contacts are used to connect the loop to an external circuit in order to use the induced emf.

The pole pieces are the north and south poles of the magnet which supplies the magnetic field. The loop of wire which rotates through the field is called the "armature." The ends of the armature loop are connected to rings called "slip rings," which rotate with the armature. Brushes ride up against the slip rings to pick up the electricity generated in the armature and carry it to the external circuit.

THE ELEMENTARY GENERATOR

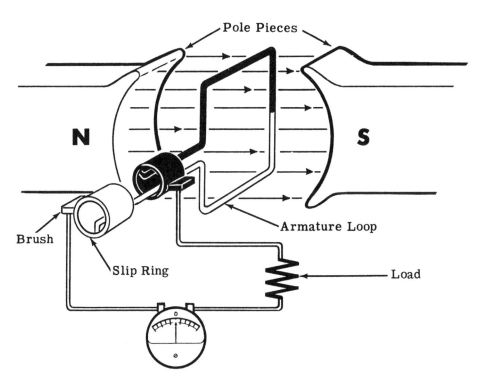

In the description of the generator action as outlined on the following sheets, visualize the loop rotating through the magnetic field. As the sides of the loop cut through the magnetic field, they generate an induced emf which causes a current to flow through the loop, slip rings, brushes, zero-center current meter and load resistor—all connected in series. The induced emf that is generated in the loop, and therefore the current that flows, depends upon the position of the loop in relation to the magnetic field. Now you are going to analyze the action of the loop as it rotates through the field.

Elementary Generator Operation

Here is the way the elementary generator works. Assume that the armature loop is rotating in a clockwise direction, and that its initial position is at A (zero degrees). In position A, the loop is perpendicular to the magnetic field and the black and white conductors of the loop are moving parallel to the magnetic field. If a conductor is moving parallel to a magnetic field, it does not cut through any lines of force and no emf can be generated in the conductor. This applies to the conductors of the loop at the instant they go through position A—no emf is induced in them and, therefore, no current flows through the circuit. The current meter registers zero.

As the loop rotates from position A to position B, the conductors are cutting through more and more lines of force until at 90 degrees (position B) they are cutting through a maximum number of lines of force. In other words, between zero and 90 degrees, the induced emf in the conductors builds up from zero to a maximum value. Observe that from zero to 90 degrees the black conductor cuts down through the field while at the same time the white conductor cuts up through the field. The induced emfs in both conductors are therefore in series-adding, and the resultant voltage across the brushes (the terminal voltage) is the sum of the two induced emfs, or double that of one conductor since the induced voltages are equal to each other. The current through the circuit will vary just as the induced emf varies—being zero at zero degrees and rising up to a maximum at 90 degrees. The current meter deflects increasingly to the right between positions A and B, indicating that the current through the load is flowing in the direction shown. The direction of current flow and polarity of the induced emf depend on the direction of the magnetic field and the direction of rotation of the armature loop. The waveform shows how the terminal voltage of the elementary generator varies from position A to position B. The simple generator drawing on the right is shown shifted in position to illustrate the relationship between the loop position and the generated waveform.

HOW THE ELEMENTARY GENERATOR WORKS

A Position
0°

B Position
90°

Generator
Terminal
Voltage

Elementary Generator Operation (continued)

As the loop continues rotating from position B (90 degrees) to position C (180 degrees), the conductors which are cutting through a maximum number of lines of force at position B cut through fewer lines, until at position C they are moving parallel to the magnetic field and no longer cut through any lines of force. The induced emf therefore will decrease from 90 to 180 degrees in the same manner as it increased from zero to 90 degrees. The current flow will similarly follow the voltage variations. The generator action at positions B and C is illustrated.

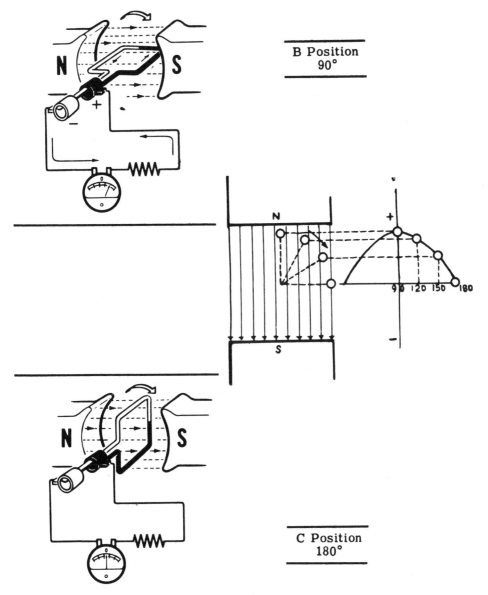

B Position
90°

C Position
180°

Elementary Generator Operation (continued)

From zero to 180 degrees the conductors of the loop have been moving in the same direction through the magnetic field and, therefore, the polarity of the induced emf has remained the same. As the loop starts rotating beyond 180 degrees back to position A, the direction of the cutting action of the conductors through the magnetic field reverses. Now the black conductor cuts up through the field, and the white conductor cuts down through the field. As a result, the polarity of the induced emf and the current flow will reverse. From positions C through D back to position A, the current flow will be in the opposite direction than from positions A through C. The generator terminal voltage will be the same as it was from A to C except for its reversed polarity. The voltage output waveform for the complete revolution of the loop is as shown.

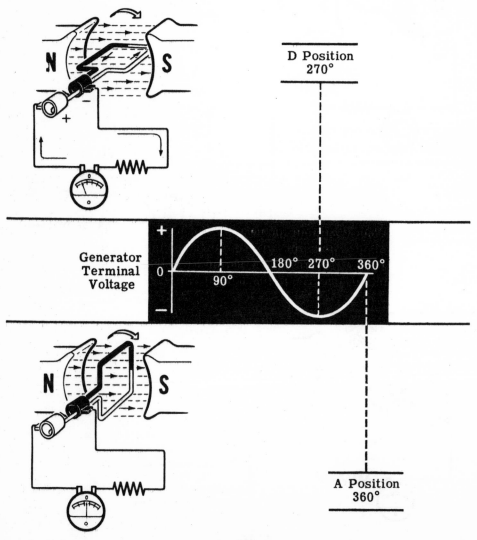

D Position
270°

Generator
Terminal
Voltage

A Position
360°

Left-Hand Rule

You have seen how an emf is generated in the coil of the elementary generator. There is a simple method for remembering the direction of the emf induced in a conductor moving through a magnetic field; it is called the "left-hand rule for generators." This rule states that if you hold the thumb, first and middle fingers of the left hand at right angles to one another with the first finger pointing in the flux direction, and the thumb pointing in the direction of motion of the conductor, the middle finger will point in the direction of the induced emf. "Direction of induced emf" means the direction in which current will flow as a result of this induced emf. You can restate the last part of the left-hand rule by saying the tip and base of the middle finger correspond to the minus and plus terminals, respectively, of the induced emf.

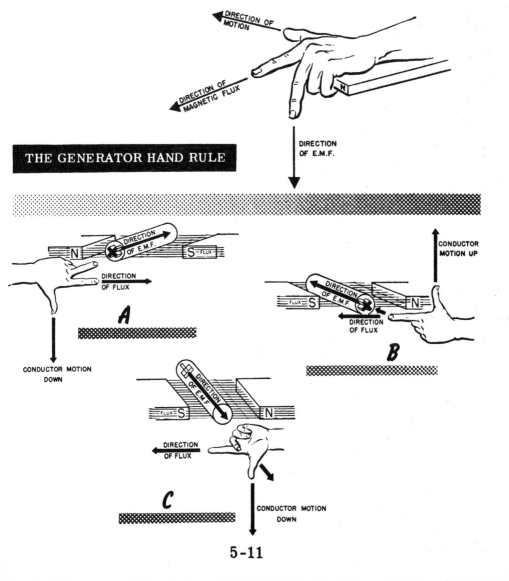

THE GENERATOR HAND RULE

Elementary Generator Output

Suppose you take a closer look at the output waveform of the elementary generator and study it for a moment.

DC voltage can be represented as a straight line whose distance above the zero reference line depends upon its value. The diagram shows the DC voltage next to the voltage waveform put out by the elementary AC generator. You see the generated waveform does not remain constant in value and direction, as does the DC curve. In fact, the generated curve varies continuously in value and is as much negative as it is positive.

The generated voltage is therefore not DC voltage, since a DC voltage is defined as a voltage which maintains the same polarity output at all times. The generated voltage is called an "alternating voltage," since it alternates periodically from plus to minus. It is commonly referred to as an AC voltage—the same type of voltage that you get from the AC wall socket. The current that flows; since it varies as the voltage varies, must also be alternating. The current is also referred to as AC current. AC current is always associated with AC voltage—an AC voltage will always cause an AC current to flow.

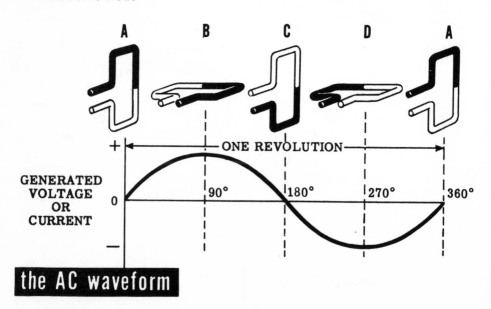

the AC waveform

Converting AC to DC by Use of the Reversing Switch

You have seen how your elementary generator has generated AC. Now you might be wondering if the AC generator can be modified to put out DC rather than AC. The answer is "Yes."

In the elementary generator, the AC voltage induced in the loop reverses its polarity each time the loop goes through zero degrees and 180 degrees. At these points, the conductors of the loop reverse their direction through the magnetic field. You know the polarity of the induced emf depends on the direction a conductor moves through a magnetic field. If the direction reverses, the polarity of the induced emf reverses. Since the loop continues rotating through the field, the conductors of the loop will always have an alternating emf induced in them. Therefore, the only way that DC can be obtained from the generator is to convert the generated AC to DC. One way to do this is to have a switch hooked up across the generator output. This switch can be so connected that it will reverse the polarity of the output voltage every time the polarity of the induced emf changes inside the generator. The switch is illustrated in the diagram. The switch must be operated manually every time the polarity of the voltage changes. If this is done, the voltage applied to the load will always have the same polarity and the current flow through the resistor will not reverse direction, although it will rise and fall in value as the loop rotates.

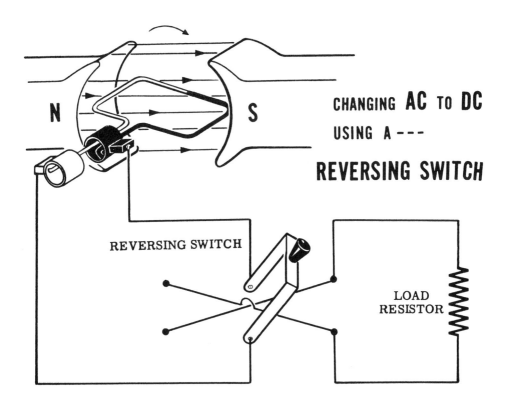

CHANGING **AC** TO **DC**
USING A - - -
REVERSING SWITCH

REVERSING SWITCH

LOAD
RESISTOR

Converting AC to DC by Use of the Reversing Switch (continued)

Consider the action of the switch as it converts the generated AC in varying DC across the load resistor. The first illustration shows the load resistor, the switch, the generator brushes, and the connecting wires. The generator terminal voltage is shown for the first half cycle, from zero to 180 degrees, when the generated voltage is positive above the zero reference line. This voltage is taken off the brushes and applied to the switch with the polarity as shown. The voltage will cause a current to flow from the negative brush through the switch and load resistor and back to the positive brush. The developed voltage waveform across the load resistor is as shown. Notice that it is exactly the same as the generator terminal voltage since the resistor is connected right across the brushes.

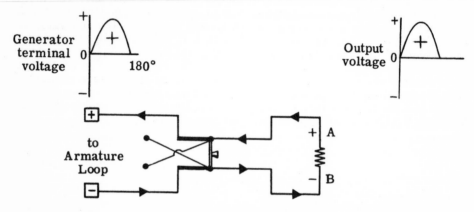

As the armature loop rotates through 180 degrees, the polarity of the generated voltage reverses. At this instant the switch is manually thrown to the other side and switches point A of the load resistor to the lower brush, which now is positive. Although the polarity of the voltage across the brushes has reversed, the polarity of the voltage across the load resistor is still the same. The action of the switch, therefore, is to reverse the polarity of the output voltage every time it changes in the generator. In this manner the AC generated in the generator is converted to varying DC outside the generator.

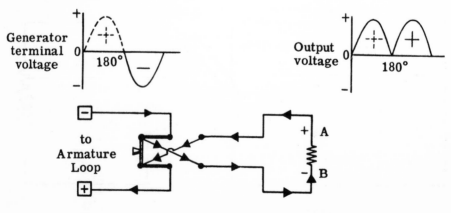

The Commutator

In order to convert the generated AC voltage into a varying DC voltage, the switch must be operated twice for every cycle. If the generator is putting out 60 cycles of AC each second, the switch must be operated 120 times per second to convert the AC to DC. It would be impossible to operate a switch manually at such a high speed. Designing a mechanical device to operate the switch also would be impractical. Although theoretically the switch will do the job, it must be replaced by something that will actually operate at this high speed.

The slip rings of the elementary generator can be changed so they actually give the same result as the impractical mechanical switch. To do this, one slip ring is eliminated and the other is split along its axis. The ends of the coil are connected one to each of the segments of the slip ring. The segments of the split ring are insulated so that there is no electrical contact between segments, the shaft, or any other part of the armature. The entire split ring is known as the "commutator," and its action in converting the AC into DC is known as "commutation."

You see the brushes are now positioned opposite each other, and the commutator segments are mounted so they are short-circuited by the brushes as the loop passes through the zero voltage points. Notice also that as the loop rotates, each conductor will be connected by means of the commutator, first to the positive brush and then to the negative brush.

When the armature loop is rotated, the commutator automatically switches each end of the loop from one brush to the other each time the loop completes a half revolution. This action is exactly like that of the reversing switch.

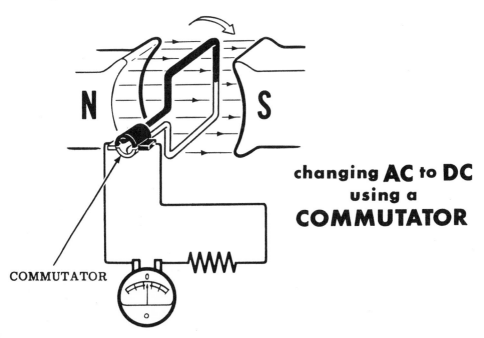

N S

changing **AC** to **DC**
using a
COMMUTATOR

COMMUTATOR

Converting AC to DC by Use of the Commutator

Suppose you analyze the action of the commutator in converting the generated AC into DC. In position A, the loop is perpendicular to the magnetic field and there will be no emf generated in the conductors of the loop. As a result, there will be no current flow. Notice that the brushes are in contact with both segments of the commutator, effectively short-circuiting the loop. This short circuit does not create any problem since there is no current flow. The moment the loop moves slightly beyond position A (zero degrees), the short circuit no longer exists. The black brush is in contact with the black segment while the white brush is in contact with the white segment.

As the loop rotates clockwise from position A to position B, the induced emf starts building up from zero until at position B (90 degrees) the induced emf is a maximum. Since the current varies with the induced emf, the current flow will also be a maximum at 90 degrees. As the loop continues rotating clockwise from position B to C, the induced emf decreases until at position C (180 degrees) it is zero once again.

The waveform shows how the terminal voltage of the generator varies from zero to 180 degrees.

COMMUTATION — CONVERTING AC TO DC

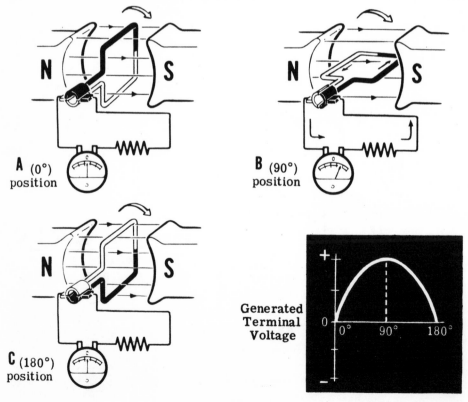

A (0°) position

B (90°) position

C (180°) position

Generated Terminal Voltage

Converting AC to DC by Use of the Commutator (continued)

Notice that in position C the black brush is slipping off the black segment and onto the white segment, while at the same time the white brush is slipping off the white segment and onto the black segment. In this way the black brush is always in contact with the conductor of the loop moving downward, and the white brush is always in contact with the conductor moving upward. Since the upward-moving conductor has a current flow toward the brush, the white brush is the negative terminal and the black brush is the positive terminal of the DC generator.

As the loop continues rotating from position C (180 degrees) through position D (270 degrees) and back to position A (360 degrees or zero degrees), the black brush is connected to the white wire which is moving down, and the white brush is connected to the black wire which is moving up. As a result, the same polarity voltage waveform is generated across the brushes from 180 to 360 degrees as was generated from zero to 180 degrees. Notice that the current flows in the same direction through the current meter, even though it reverses in direction every half cycle in the loop itself.

The voltage output then has the same polarity at all times but varies in value, rising from zero to maximum, falling to zero, then rising to maximum and falling to zero again for each complete revolution of the armature loop.

COMMUTATION—CONVERTING AC TO DC

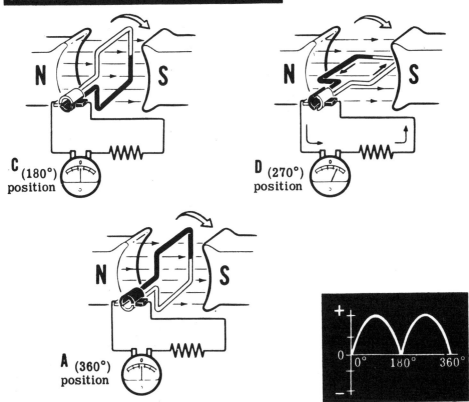

C (180°) position

D (270°) position

A (360°) position

Improving the DC Output

Before you learned about generators, the only DC voltage you were familiar with was the smooth and unvarying voltage produced, for example, by
a battery. Now you find that the DC output of an elementary DC generator
is very uneven—a pulsating DC voltage varying periodically from zero to
a maximum. Although this pulsating voltage is DC, it is not constant
enough to operate DC appliances and equipments. Therefore, the elementary DC generator must be modified so that it will put out a smooth form
of DC. This is accomplished by adding more coils of wire to the armature.

The illustration shows a generator with a two-coil armature, with the two
coils positioned at right angles to each other. Notice that the commutator
is broken up into four segments, with opposite segments connected to the
ends of a coil. In the position shown, the brushes connect to the white coil
in which a maximum voltage is generated, since it is moving at right
angles to the field. As the armature rotates clockwise, the output from the
white coil starts dropping off. After an eighth of a revolution (45 degrees)
the brushes slide over to the black commutator segments, whose coil is
just beginning to cut into the field. The output voltage starts to pick up
again, reaches a peak at 90 degrees and starts dropping off as the black
coil cuts through fewer lines of force. At 135 degrees, commutation takes
place once again and the brushes are again in contact with the white coil.
The output voltage waveform for the entire revolution is shown super-
imposed on the single coil voltage. Notice that the output never drops below point Y. The rise and fall in voltage now is limited between Y and the
maximum, rather than between zero and the maximum. This variation in
the output voltage of a DC generator is known as "generator ripple." It is
apparent that the output of the two-coil armature is much closer to constant DC than the output of the one-coil armature.

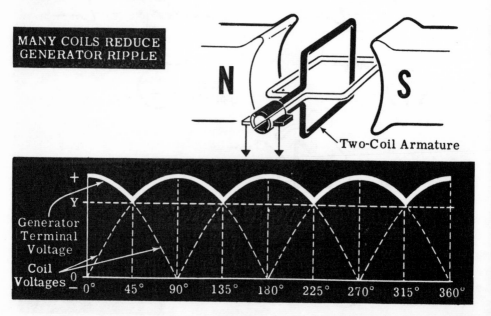

MANY COILS REDUCE GENERATOR RIPPLE

Two-Coil Armature

Improving the DC Output (continued)

Even though the output of the two-coil generator is a lot closer to being constant DC than the output of the one-coil generator, there is still too much ripple in the output to make it useful for electrical equipment. To make the output really smooth, the armature is made with a large number of coils, and the commutator is similarly divided up into a large number of segments. The coils are so arranged around the armature that at every instant there are some turns cutting through the magnetic field at right angles. As a result, the generator output contains very little ripple and is for all practical purposes a constant, or "pure," DC.

The voltage induced in a one-turn coil or loop is not very large. In order to generate a large voltage output, each coil on the armature of a commercial generator consists of many turns of wire connected in series. As a result, the output voltage is much greater than that generated in a coil having only one turn.

MANY-TURN COILS INCREASE VOLTAGE OUTPUT

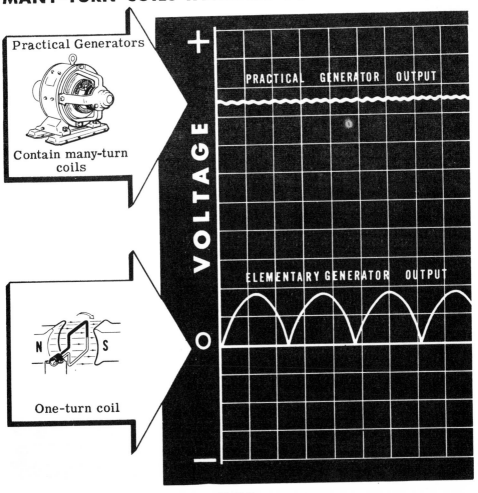

Practical Generators

Contain many-turn coils

One-turn coil

PRACTICAL GENERATOR OUTPUT

VOLTAGE

ELEMENTARY GENERATOR OUTPUT

Review

Now suppose you review what you have found out about the elementary generator and commutation:

ELEMENTARY GENERATOR — A
loop of wire rotating in a magnetic
field forms an elementary generator and is connected to an external
circuit through slip rings.

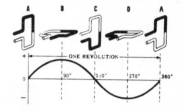

**ELEMENTARY GENERATOR OUT-
PUT** — The emf and current flow of
an elementary generator reverse in
polarity each time the armature loop
rotates 180 degrees. The voltage
output of such a generator is alternating current.

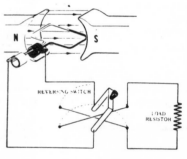

CHANGING AC TO DC — By using a
reversing switch, the AC output of
an elementary generator can be
changed to DC.

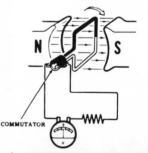

COMMUTATOR — An automatic reversing switch on the generator shaft
which switches coil connections to
the brushes each half revolution of
an elementary generator.

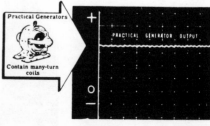

PRACTICAL GENERATOR — To
smooth out the DC taken from a generator commutator, many coils are
used in the armature and more segments are used to form the commutator. A practical generator has a
voltage output which is near maximum at all times and has only a
slight ripple variation.

DIRECT CURRENT GENERATORS

DC Generator Construction

Up until now you have learned the fundamentals of generator action and the theory of operation of elementary AC and DC generators. Now you are ready to learn about actual generators and how they are constructed. There are various components essential to the operation of a complete generator. Once you learn to recognize these components and become familiar with their function, you will find this information useful in the troubleshooting and maintenance of generators.

All generators—whether AC or DC—consist of a rotating part called a "rotor" and a stationary part called a "stator." In most DC generators the armature coil is mounted on the rotor and the field coils on the stator; while in most AC generators just the opposite is true—the field coils are on the rotor and the armature coil is on the stator.

In either case, there is relative motion between the armature and field coils so that the armature coils cut through the magnetic lines of force of the field. As a result, an emf is induced in the armature, causing a current to flow through the outside load. Since the generator supplies electrical power to a load, mechanical power must be put into the generator to cause the rotor to turn and generate electricity. The generator simply converts mechanical power into electrical power. Consequently, all generators must have machines associated with them which will supply the mechanical power necessary to turn the rotors. These machines are called "prime movers" and may be steam engines, steam turbines, electric motors, gasoline engines, etc.

Now suppose you find out about the construction of a typical DC generator and its various components. Although generator construction varies widely, the basic components and their function are the same for all types.

Let's break open a DC Generator

DC Generator Construction (continued)

The relationship of the various components making up the generator is illustrated below. In assembling the generator, the fields are mounted in the stator and one end bell (not illustrated) is bolted to the stator frame. The armature is then inserted between the field poles and the end bell, with the brush assemblies mounted last. These parts will be described in detail on the following sheets.

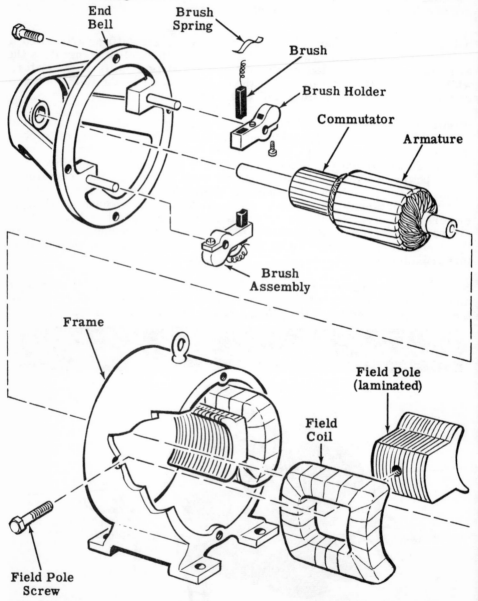

Generator assembly and disassembly varies depending on the size, type and manufacturer; but the general method is as illustrated above.

DC Generator Construction (continued)

The illustration shows a typical DC generator with the principle parts of the stator captioned. Compare each part and its function to the corresponding part used in the elementary generator.

Main Frame: The main frame is sometimes called the "yoke." It is the foundation of the machine and supports the other components. It also serves to complete the magnetic field between the pole pieces.

Pole Pieces: The pole pieces are made of many thin layers of iron or steel called laminations, joined together and bolted to the inside of the frame. These pole pieces provide a support for the field coils and are designed to produce a concentrated field. By laminating the poles, eddy currents, which you will learn about later, are reduced.

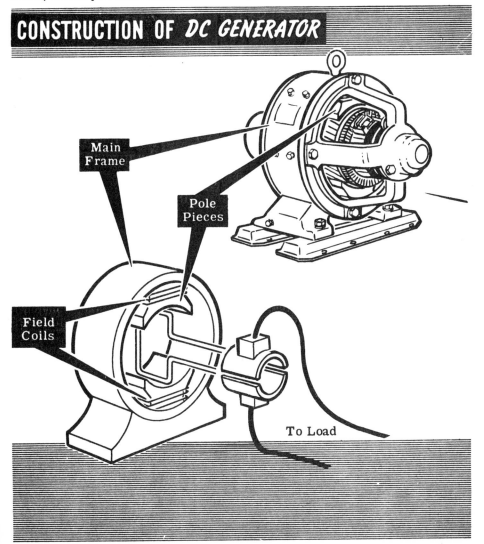

CONSTRUCTION OF *DC GENERATOR*

Main Frame

Pole Pieces

Field Coils

To Load

DC Generator Construction (continued)

Field Windings: The field windings, when mounted on the pole pieces, form electromagnets which provide the magnetic field necessary for generator action. The windings and pole pieces together are often called the "field." The windings are coils of insulated wire wound to fit closely around pole pieces. The current flowing through these coils generates the magnetic field. A generator may have only two poles, or it may have a large number of even poles. Regardless of the number of poles, alternate poles will always be of opposite polarity. Field windings can be connected either in series or in parallel (or "shunt" as the parallel connection is often called). Shunt field windings consist of many turns of fine wire, while series field windings are composed of fewer turns of fairly heavy wire.

End Bells: These are attached to the ends of the main frame and contain the bearings for the armature. The rear bell usually supports the bearing alone while the front bell also supports the brush rigging.

Brush Holder: This component is a piece of insulated material which supports the brushes and their connecting wires. The brush holders are secured to the front end bell with clamps. On some generators, the brush holders can be rotated around the shaft for adjustment.

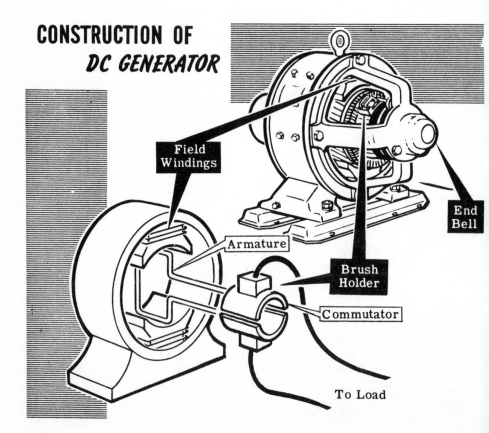

CONSTRUCTION OF DC GENERATOR

Field Windings

End Bell

Armature

Brush Holder

Commutator

To Load

DC Generator Construction (continued)

<u>Armature Assembly:</u> In practically all DC generators, the armature rotates between the poles of the stator. The armature assembly is made up of a shaft, armature core, armature windings and commutator. The armature core is laminated and is slotted to take the armature windings. The armature windings are usually wound in forms and then placed in the slots of the core. The commutator is made up of copper segments insulated from one another and from the shaft by mica. These segments are secured with retainer rings to prevent them from slipping out under the force of rotation. Small slots are provided in the ends of the segments to which the armature windings are soldered. The shaft supports the entire armature assembly and rotates in the end bell bearings.

There is a small air gap between the armature and pole pieces to prevent rubbing between the armature and pole pieces during rotation. This gap is kept to a minimum to keep the field strength at a maximum.

<u>Brushes:</u> The brushes ride on the commutator and carry the generated voltage to the load. The brushes usually are made of a high grade of carbon and are held in place by brush holders. The brushes are able to slide up and down in their holders so that they can follow irregularities in the surface of the commutator. A flexible braided conductor called a "pigtail" connects each brush to the external circuit.

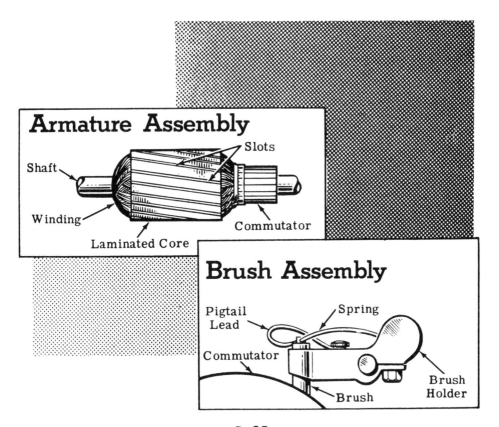

Armature Assembly

Slots
Shaft
Winding
Laminated Core
Commutator

Brush Assembly

Pigtail
Lead
Spring
Commutator
Brush
Brush
Holder

DC Generator Construction (continued)

You have learned that a current flow can be induced in a conductor when it cuts through a magnetic field. If a solid piece of metal cuts through a magnetic field instead of a single wire conductor, current also will be induced inside the solid metal piece. A large, solid piece of metal has a large cross-section and offers little resistance to current flow. As a result, a strong current called **EDDY** current flows through a solid metal conductor.

Since wire conductors used in motors and generators are always wound around metal cores, eddy currents will be induced in these metal cores just as the useful current is induced in the wires of the generator. Eddy currents flowing in the core material of rotating machinery are waste currents, since they have no useful purpose and only heat up the metal cores. Consequently, the machine operates at low efficiency. It is important that eddy currents in core material be kept down to a minimum. This is done by having the cores made up of laminations, thin plates of metal, rather than out of one solid piece. The laminations are insulated from each other, limiting the eddy current to that which can flow in the individual lamination. The diagram illustrates the effect of laminations on limiting the magnitude of eddy currents.

HOW LAMINATIONS REDUCE EDDY CURRENT

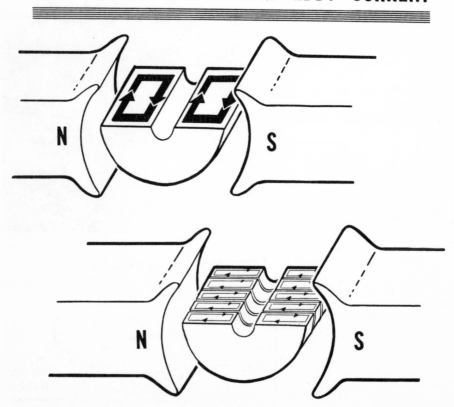

Types of Armatures

Armatures used in DC generators are divided into two general types. These are the "ring" type armature and the "drum" type armature. In the ring type armature, the insulated armature coils are wrapped around a hollow iron cylinder with taps taken off at regular intervals to form connections to the commutator segments. The ring type armature was first used in early design of rotating electrical machinery. Today the ring armature is seldom used.

The drum type armature is the standard armature construction today. The insulated coils are inserted into slots in the cylindrical armature core. The ends of the coils are then connected to each other at the front and back ends.

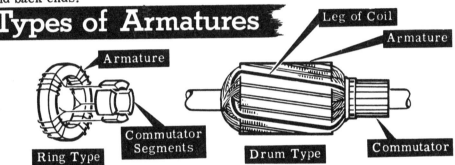

Types of Armatures

As a rule, most DC armatures use form-made coils. These coils are wound by machines with the proper number of turns and to the proper shape. The entire coil is then wrapped with tape and inserted into the armature slots as one unit. The coils are so inserted that the legs of the coil can only be under unlike poles at the same time. In a two-pole machine, the legs of each coil are situated on opposite sides of the core and therefore come under opposite poles. In a four-pole machine, the legs of the coils are placed in slots about one-quarter the distance around the armature, thus keeping opposite legs of the coil under unlike poles.

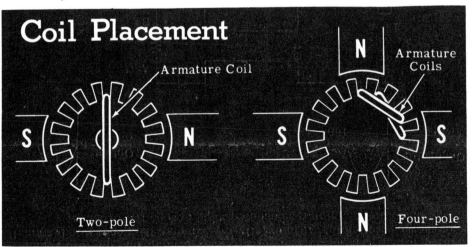

Coil Placement

Types of Armature Windings

Drum type armatures are wound with two types of windings, the "lap" winding and the "wave" winding.

The lap winding is used for high current applications and has many parallel paths within the armature. As a result, there will be a large number of field poles and an equal number of brushes.

The wave winding is used for high voltage applications. It has only two parallel current paths and can use only two brushes, regardless of the number of poles.

The only difference between the lap and wave windings is the method used to connect the winding elements. The two drawings illustrate the essential difference between a lap and wave winding. In both windings AB connects to CD which is under the next pole. In the lap winding, CD connects back to EF which is under the same pole as AB. In the wave winding, CD is connected forward to EF which is under a pole two poles away from AB. Therefore, the essential difference is that in lap winding the connections are made lapping over each other. In wave winding the connections are made forward, so that each winding passes under every pole before it comes back to its starting pole.

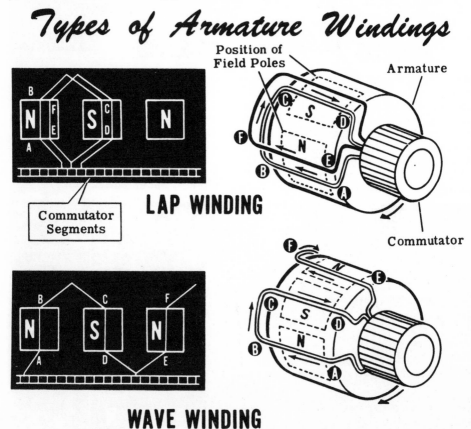

Types of Armature Windings

LAP WINDING

WAVE WINDING

Types of DC Generators

Most practical DC generators have electromagnetic fields. Permanent-magnet fields are used only in very small generators called "magnetos." To produce a constant field for use in a generator, the field coils must be connected across a DC voltage source. (AC current flow in a field coil does not produce a constant field and, therefore, an AC voltage source cannot be used.) The DC current in the field coils is called the "excitation current" and may be supplied from a separate DC voltage source, or by utilizing the DC output of the generator itself.

DC generators are classified according to the manner in which the field is supplied with excitation current. If the field is supplied with current from an external source, the generator is said to be "separately-excited." However, if some of the generator output is used to supply the field current, it is said to be "self-excited". The circuit of the generator armature and field coils determines its type and affects its performance. Various generators utilize the three basic DC circuits—series, parallel and series-parallel. Symbols, as illustrated below, are used to represent the armature and field coils in the various generator circuits.

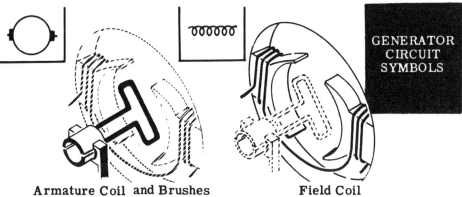

GENERATOR
CIRCUIT
SYMBOLS

Armature Coil and Brushes   Field Coil

Separately-excited DC generators have two circuits, each entirely independent of the other: the field circuit consisting of the field coils connected across a separate DC source, and the armature circuit consisting of the armature coil and the load resistance. (When two or more field coils are connected in series with one another, they are represented by a single symbol.) The two circuits of a separately-excited generator are illustrated below, showing the current flow through the various parts of the circuit.

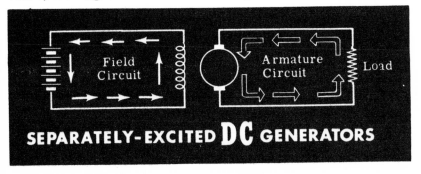

SEPARATELY-EXCITED **DC** GENERATORS

Separately-Excited DC Generators

In a separately-excited DC generator, the field is independent of the armature, since it is supplied with current from either another generator (exciter), an amplifier or a storage battery. The separately-excited field provides a very sensitive control of the power output of the generator, since the field current is independent of the load current. With a slight change in the field current, a large change in the load current will result.

The separately-excited generator is used mostly in automatic motor control systems. In these systems the field power is controlled by an amplifier and the output of the generator supplies the armature current which drives the motor. The motor is used to position a gun turret, a searchlight or any other heavy mechanism.

Separately-Excited DC Generators...

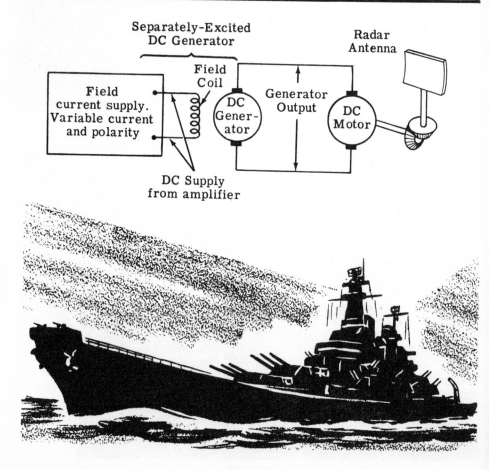

Separately-Excited
DC Generator

Radar
Antenna

Field
Coil

Field
current supply.
Variable current
and polarity

DC
Generator

Generator
Output

DC
Motor

DC Supply
from amplifier

Self-Excited DC Generators

Self-excited generators use part of the generator's output to supply excitation current to the field. These generators are classified according to the type of field connection used.

In a "series" generator, the field coils are connected in series with the armature, so that the whole armature current flows through both the field and the load. If the generator is not connected across a load, the circuit is incomplete and no current will flow to excite the field. The series field contains relatively few turns of wire.

"Shunt" generator field coils are connected across the armature circuit, forming a parallel or "shunt" circuit. Only a small part of the armature current flows through the field coils, the rest flowing through the load. Since the shunt field and the armature form a closed circuit independent of the load, the generator is excited even under "no load" conditions—with no load connected across the armature. The shunt field contains many turns of fine wire.

A "compound" generator has both a series and a shunt field, forming a series-parallel circuit. Two coils are mounted on each pole piece, one coil series-connected and the other shunt-connected. The shunt field coils are excited by only a part of the armature current, while the entire load current flows through the series field. Therefore, as the load current increases, the strength of the series field is increased.

Self-excited DC Generators..

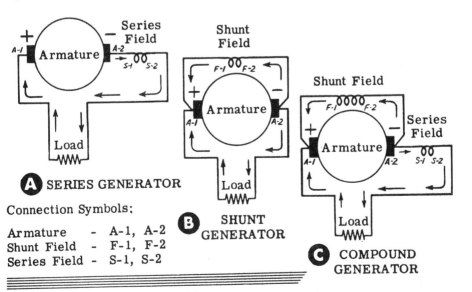

A SERIES GENERATOR

Connection Symbols:

Armature   - A-1, A-2
Shunt Field - F-1, F-2
Series Field - S-1, S-2

B SHUNT GENERATOR

C COMPOUND GENERATOR

Self-Excited DC Generators (continued)

Shunt field coils, which connect directly across the generator output voltage, are constructed of many turns of small wire so that the coil resistance will be great enough to limit the current flow to a low value. Since the shunt field current is not used to supply the load, it is necessary to keep it to as low a value as possible.

If the shunt field of a compound generator is connected across both the series field and the armature, the field is called a "long shunt" field. If the shunt field is connected just across the armature, the field is called a "short shunt" field. The characteristics of both types of shunt connections are practically the same.

Series field coils are constructed of fewer turns of heavier wire and depend on the large current flow to the load resistance for their magnetic field strength. They must have a low resistance since they are in series with the load and act as a resistor to drop the voltage output of the generator. A comparison of the connections used for the various generator circuits is outlined below:

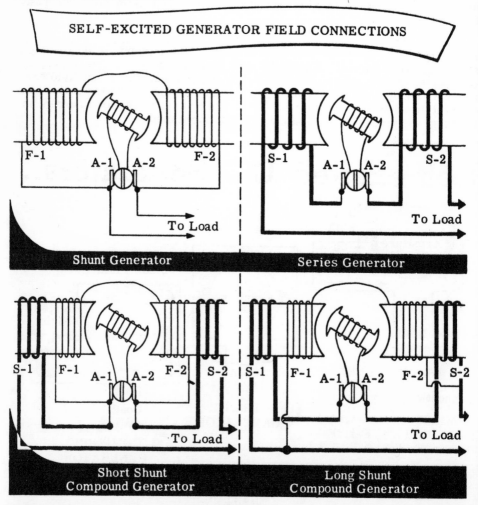

SELF-EXCITED GENERATOR FIELD CONNECTIONS

F-1   A-1 A-2   F-2

To Load

Shunt Generator

S-1   A-1 A-2   S-2

To Load

Series Generator

S-1 F-1 A-1 A-2 F-2 S-2

To Load

Short Shunt
Compound Generator

S-1 F-1 A-1 A-2 F-2 S-2

To Load

Long Shunt
Compound Generator

Self-Excited DC Generators (continued)

Almost all of the DC generators used for lighting and power are the self-excited type, in which armature current is used to excite the field. However, if the original field excitation depends upon this armature current, and no current is induced in the armature coil unless it moves through a magnetic field, you may wonder how the generator output can build up. In other words, if there is no field to start with (since no current is flowing through the field), how can the generator produce an emf?

Actually the field poles retain a certain amount of magnetism called the "residual magnetism," from a previous generator run, due to the magnetism characteristics of their steel structure. When the generator starts turning, an original field does exist which, although very weak, will still induce an emf in the armature. This induced emf forces current through the field coils, reinforcing the original magnetic field and strengthening the total magnetism. This increased flux in turn generates a greater emf which again increases the current through the field coils. This action increases until the machine attains its normal field strength. All self-excited generators build up in this manner. The build-up time normally is 20 to 30 seconds. The graph shows how generator voltage and field current build up in a shunt generator.

Remember, the output of a generator is electrical power. A generator always has to be turned by some mechanical means—the prime mover. "Build up" in a generator does not refer to its mechanical rotation, it refers to its electrical output.

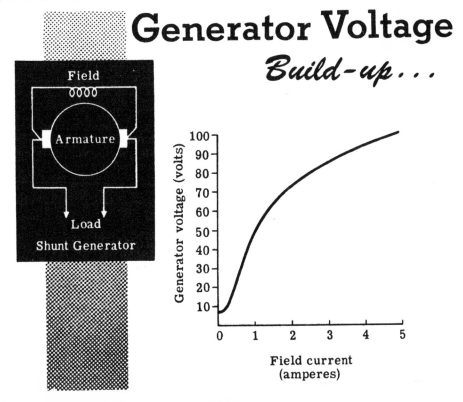

Generator Voltage
Build-up...

Field — Armature — Load — Shunt Generator

Self-Excited DC Generators (continued)

Sometimes generators will not build up. When this happens, one of several things may be wrong.

There may be too little or no residual magnetism. To provide the initial field necessary, the generator must be excited by an external DC source. This is called "flashing the field." When flashing the field, it is important to have the externally produced field of the same polarity as the residual magnetism. If these polarities are opposed, the initial field will be further weakened and the generator will still not build up.

The generator will not build up if the shunt field connections have been reversed. By reversing them again, the generator will build up properly.

Often a rheostat is connected in series with the shunt field, to control the field current. If this rheostat adds too much resistance to the circuit at first, the field current will be too small for a proper build-up.

Finally, if the field coil circuit has become "open," so the circuit is not complete, the generator will not build up. The break or open must be found and repaired.

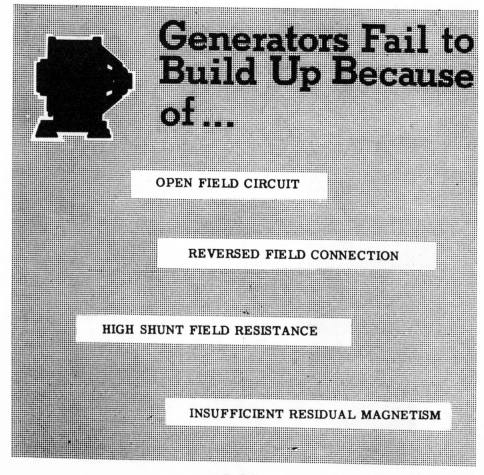

Generators Fail to Build Up Because of ...

OPEN FIELD CIRCUIT

REVERSED FIELD CONNECTION

HIGH SHUNT FIELD RESISTANCE

INSUFFICIENT RESIDUAL MAGNETISM

The Series Generator

In the series generator, the armature, the field coils and the external circuit are all in series. This means that the same current which flows through the armature and external circuit also flows through the field coils. Since the field current, which is also the load current, is large, the required strength of magnetic flux is obtained with a relatively small number of turns in the field windings.

The illustration shows the schematic of a typical DC series generator. With no load, no current can flow and therefore very little emf will be induced in the armature—the amount depending upon the strength of the residual magnetism. If a load is connected, current will flow, the field strength will build up and, consequently, the terminal voltage will increase. As the load draws more current from the generator, this additional current increases the field strength, generating more voltage in the armature winding. A point is soon reached (A) where further increase in load current does not result in greater voltage, because the magnetic field has reached the saturation point.

Beyond point A, increasing the load current decreases voltage output due to the increasing voltage drop across the resistance of the field and armature. The series generator always is operated beyond this point of rapidly dropping terminal voltage (between A and B), so that the load current will remain nearly constant with changes in load resistance. This is illustrated by the voltage graph. For this reason, series generators are called "constant current generators."

Series generators formerly were used as constant current generators to operate arc lamps. At the present time, they are not widely used.

The Series Generator

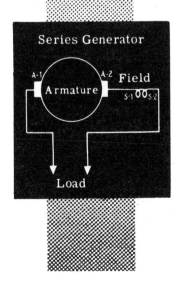

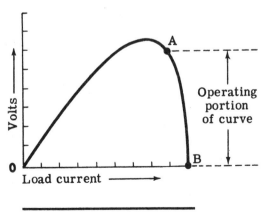

CHARACTERISTIC CURVE

The Shunt Generator

The shunt generator has its field winding connected in shunt (or parallel) with the armature. Therefore the current through the field coils is determined by the terminal voltage and the resistance of the field. The shunt field windings have a large number of turns, and therefore require a relatively small current to produce the necessary field flux.

When a shunt generator is started, the buildup time for rated terminal voltage at the brushes is very rapid since field current flows even though the external circuit is open. As the load draws more current from the armature, the terminal voltage decreases because the increased armature drop subtracts from the generated voltage. The illustration shows the schematic diagram and characteristic curve for the shunt generator. Observe that over the normal operating region of no load to full load (A-B), the drop in terminal voltage, as the load current increases, is relatively small. As a result, the shunt generator is used where a practically constant voltage is desired, regardless of load changes. If the load current drawn from the generator increases beyond point B, the terminal voltage starts dropping off sharply. The generator is never run beyond point B. The terminal voltage of a shunt generator can be controlled by varying the resistance of a rheostat in series with the field coils.

The Shunt Generator

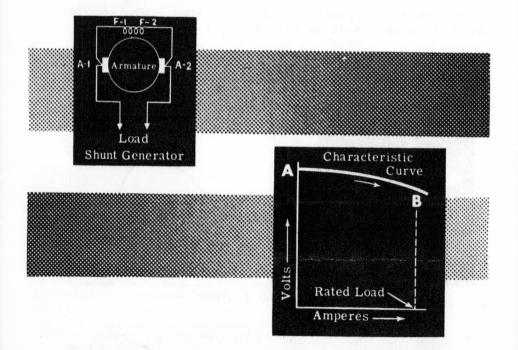

The Compound Generator

A compound generator is a combined series and shunt generator. There are two sets of field coils—one in series with the armature and one in parallel with the armature. One shunt coil and one series coil are always mounted on a common pole piece, and sometimes enclosed in a common covering.

If the series field is connected so that its field aids the shunt field, the generator is called "cumulatively" compound. If the series field opposes the shunt field, the generator is called "differentially" compound. Also, as explained before, the fields may be connected "short shunt" or "long shunt," depending on whether the shunt field is in parallel with both the series field and the armature, or just the armature. The operating characteristics for both types of shunt connections are practically the same.

Compound Generators

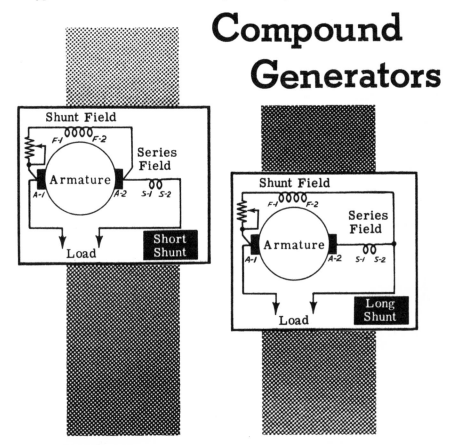

Compound generators were designed to overcome the drop in terminal voltage which occurs in a shunt generator when the load is increased. This voltage drop is undesirable where constant voltage loads, such as lighting systems, are used. By adding the series field, which increases the strength of the total magnetic field when the load current is increased, the voltage drop due to the added current flowing through the armature resistance is overcome, and constant voltage output is practically attained.

The Compound Generator (continued)

The voltage characteristics of the cumulative compound generator depend on the ratio of the turns in the shunt and series field windings. If the series windings are so proportioned that the terminal voltage is practically constant at all loads within its range, it is "flat-compounded." Usually in these machines the full-load voltage is the same as the no-load voltage, and the voltage at intermediate points is somewhat higher. Flat-compounded generators are used to provide a constant voltage to loads a short distance away from the generator. An "overcompounded" generator has its series turns so selected that the full-load voltage is greater than the no-load voltage. These generators are used where the load is some distance away. The increase in terminal voltage compensates for the drop in the long feeder lines, thus maintaining a constant voltage at the load. When the rated voltage is less than the no-load voltage, the machine is said to be "undercompounded." These generators are seldom used. Most cumulative compound generators are overcompounded. The degree of compounding is regulated by placing a low resistance shunt called a "diverter" across the series field terminal as shown. The terminal voltage can be controlled by varying the field rheostat in series with the shunt field. In a differentially compounded generator the shunt and series fields are in opposition. Therefore the difference, or resultant field, becomes weaker and the terminal voltage drops very rapidly with increase in load current.

The characteristic curves for the four types of compound generators are illustrated.

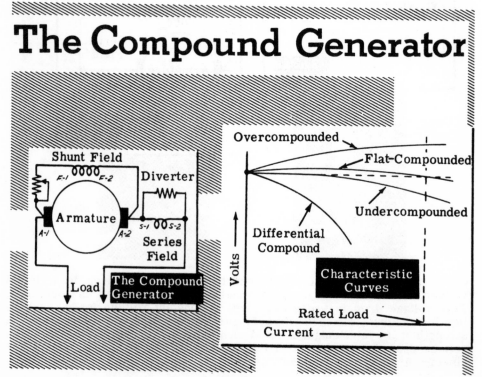

The Compound Generator

Commutation

When you studied the elementary DC generator, you learned that the
brushes are positioned so that they short-circuit the armature coil when
it is not cutting through the magnetic field. At this instant no current
flows and there is no sparking at the brushes (which are in the act of slipping from one segment of the commutator to the next.)

Proper Commutation

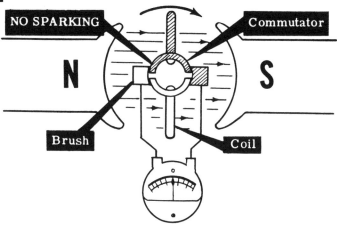

If the brushes are moved a few degrees, they short-circuit the coil when it
is cutting through the field. As a result, a voltage will be induced in the
short-circuited coil, and a short-circuit current will flow to cause sparking
at the brushes. This condition is undesirable since the short circuit current may seriously damage the coils and burn the commutator. This situation can be remedied by rotating both brushes so that commutation takes
place when the coil is moving at right angles to the field.

DC generators operate efficiently when the plane of the coil is at right
angles to the field at the instant the brushes short the coil. This plane
which is at right angles to the field is known as the "plane of commutation" or "neutral plane." The brushes will short-circuit the coil when no
current is flowing through it.

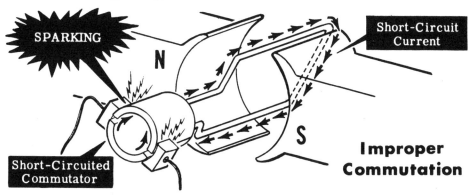

Armature Reaction

You know that for proper commutation, the coil short-circuited by the brushes should be in the neutral plane. Suppose you consider the operation of a simple two-pole DC generator. The armature is shown in a simplified view with the cross section of its coil represented as little circles. When the armature rotates clockwise, the sides of the coil to the left will have current flowing out of the paper and the sides of the coil to the right will have current flowing into the paper. The field generated around each side of the coil is also shown.

Now you have two fields in existence—the main field and the field around each coil side. The diagram shows how the armature field distorts the main field and how the neutral plane is shifted in the direction of rotation. If the brushes remain in the old neutral plane, they will be short-circuiting coils which have voltage induced in them. Consequently, there will be arcing between the brushes and commutator.

To prevent this, the brushes must be shifted to the new neutral plane. The reaction of the armature in displacing the neutral plane is known as "armature reaction."

Armature Reaction

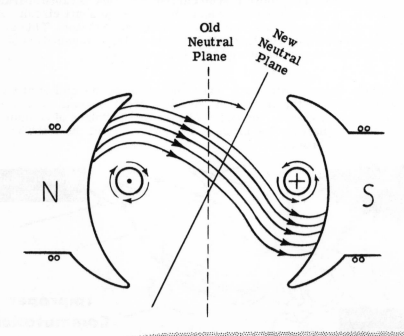

Compensating Windings and Interpoles

Shifting the brushes to the advanced position of the neutral plane does not completely solve the problems of armature reaction. The effect of armature reaction varies with the load current. Therefore, every time the load current varies, the neutral plane shifts, meaning the brush position will have to be changed.

In small machines the effects of armature reaction are minimized by mechanically shifting the position of the brushes. In larger machines more elaborate means are taken to eliminate armature reaction, such as using compensating windings or interpoles. The compensating windings consist of a series of coils embedded in slots in the pole faces. The coils are connected in series with the armature so that the field they generate will just cancel the effects of armature reaction, for all values of armature current. As a result the neutral plane remains stationary and, once the brushes have been set correctly, they do not have to be moved again.

Another way to minimize the effects of armature reaction is to place small auxiliary poles called "interpoles" between the main field poles. The interpoles have a few turns of large wire connected in series with the armature. The field generated by the interpoles just cancels the armature reaction for all values of load current and improves commutation.

Correcting **Armature Reaction**

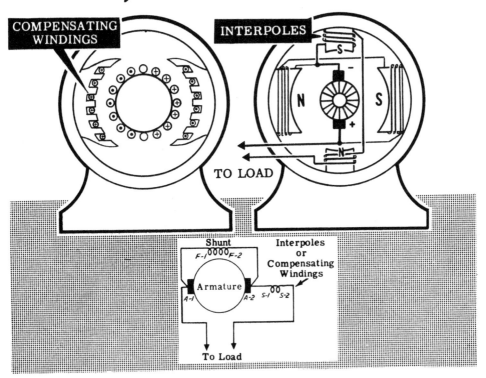

5-41

Review of DC Generators

GENERATOR CLASSIFICATION—
DC generators are classified according to the method of field excitation used. Separately-excited generators use an outside source of DC current to magnetize the fields. Self-excited generators use the output of the generator itself to excite the field.

Self-excited generators are further divided into classifications, depending on the field winding connections.

SERIES GENERATOR — The field has few turns of heavy wire and connects in series with the armature. It is operated on the constant current part of its voltage output curve to provide a constant current output.

SHUNT GENERATOR — The field has many turns of small wire and connects directly across the armature. The output voltage drops as the load current increases.

COMPOUND GENERATOR — The field has two sets of windings—a shunt field and a series field. The combined effect of the two fields makes the output voltage nearly constant regardless of the load current.

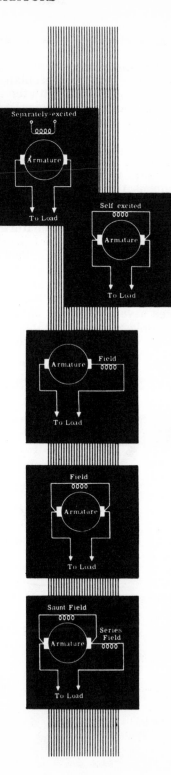

Review of DC Generators (continued)

PROPER COMMUTATION — The brushes of a DC generator should short out the commutator segments of the armature loop in which no emf is being generated at the moment of commutation. At this moment, the generating conductors of the loop are moving parallel to the lines of force in the field.

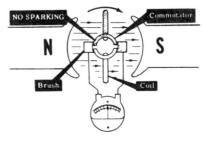

COMMUTATOR SPARKING — If the brushes short out the commutator segments whose armature conductors are not moving parallel to the lines of force in the field, the generated emf is short-circuited, causing arcing at the brushes. Shifting the brushes reduces this arcing.

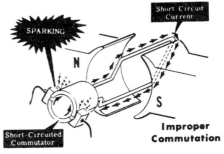

Improper Commutation

ARMATURE REACTION — Current flow in the armature coil generates a magnetic field at right angles to that of the generator field poles. The resultant total field shifts the neutral plane.

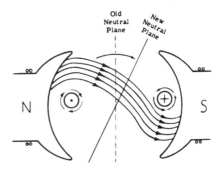

COMPENSATING WINDINGS — Windings placed in the field pole faces, carrying the same current as the armature coil but in the opposite directions, counteract the armature field.

INTERPOLES — Small poles mounted between the main field windings, to generate a field exactly opposite to that of the armature coil.

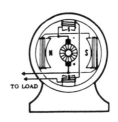

Converting Electrical Power to Mechanical Power

DC motors and DC generators have essentially the same components and are very similar in outward appearance. They differ only in the way they are used. In a generator, mechanical power turns the armature and the moving armature generates electrical power. In a motor, electrical power forces the armature to turn and the moving armature, through a mechanical system of belts or gears, turns a mechanical load.

A DC generator converts mechanical energy to electrical energy. A DC motor converts electrical energy into mechanical energy.

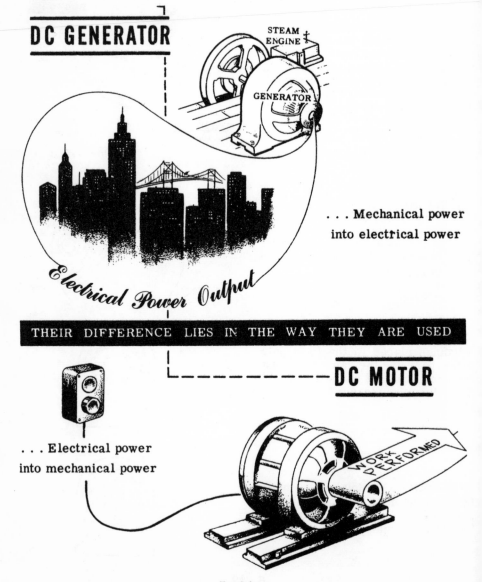

DC GENERATOR

STEAM ENGINE

GENERATOR

. . . Mechanical power into electrical power

Electrical Power Output

THEIR DIFFERENCE LIES IN THE WAY THEY ARE USED

DC MOTOR

. . . Electrical power into mechanical power

WORK PERFORMED

Converting Electrical Power to Mechanical Energy (continued)

How a DC motor works is not completely new to you. In studying meters you learned that a galvanometer has a coil suspended between the poles of a horseshoe magnet. When a current flows through the coil, the coil itself acts as a magnet, and the coil is moved by the force between the two magnetic fields. This is the principle of operation for all DC motors, from the smallest to the largest. Therefore, to understand practical motors, you can start with the most elementary—a single turn coil suspended between the poles of a magnet.

Fleming and Lenz

Fleming discovered the method for determining the direction of rotation of a motor if the direction of the current is known. The importance of this information cannot be overestimated, as you will see when you learn more about the principles which govern the operation of the numerous motors and generators in use today.

Fleming found that there is a definite relation between the direction of the magnetic field, the direction of current in the conductor, and the direction in which the conductor tends to move. This relationship is called Fleming's Right Hand Rule for Motors.

If the thumb, index finger, and third finger of the right hand are extended at right angles to each other, and if the hand is so placed that the index finger points in the direction taken by the flux lines of the magnetic field, then the thumb will point out the direction of motion of the conductor and the third finger will point in the direction taken by the current through the conductor. Obviously, if the direction of the magnetic field is not known but the motion of the conductor and the direction of the current through the conductor are known, the index finger must point in the direction of the magnetic field, provided the right hand is placed in the proper position.

The diagram below illustrates Fleming's Right Hand Rule for Motors. If you use this rule, you can always determine the direction of rotation of motors, provided you know the direction of the current.

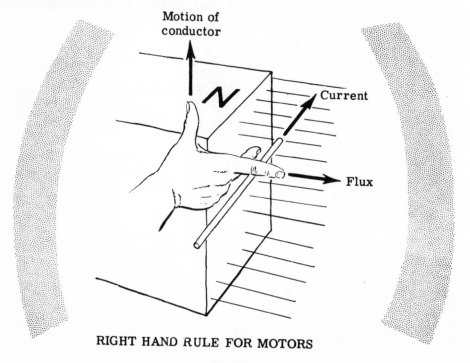

RIGHT HAND RULE FOR MOTORS

Fleming and Lenz (continued)

You have learned about the laws which were discovered by Fleming. Lenz's Law is the next basic law with which you will come in contact. An understanding of this law will be a tremendous help in your understanding of the whole field of motors and generators.

A conductor which carries a current is surrounded by a magnetic field. This is true even if the current is the result of an induced emf. Figure 1 below shows a conductor at rest in a magnetic field. No emf is induced and no current flows because the conductor is stationary. In Figure 2 the conductor is pushed downward. The result is an induced emf which produces a current flow in the conductor. Since a magnetic field surrounds every conductor which carries a current, the conductor will have a magnetic field of its own because of the induced emf and resulting current flow. This magnetic field will be set up in the direction indicated in Figure 3. Two magnetic fields now exist; one from the current through the conductor and the other from the magnet.

Since magnetic fields never cross, the lines of the two fields either crowd together or cancel each other out, producing either strong or weak resultant fields, respectively. In Figure 4 the two magnetic fields are opposing, and therefore cancel each other out. The result is a weak magnetic field above the conductor. Figure 5 shows that the magnetic fields below the wire are in the same direction and therefore additive.

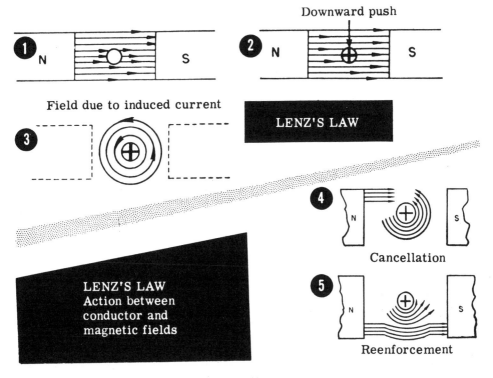

Downward push

Field due to induced current

LENZ'S LAW

Cancellation

LENZ'S LAW
Action between
conductor and
magnetic fields

Reenforcement

Fleming and Lenz (continued)

The field of the magnet is, then, distorted by the field which surrounds the
current-carrying wire. A weak resultant field exists above the wire, and
a strong resultant field exists below the wire. Remember that flux lines
tend to push each other apart. The diagram below shows that the flux lines
under the conductor, in pushing each other apart, tend to push the conductor up, whereas those above the conductor tend to push each other down.
Since, however, there are more flux lines below the conductor than there
are above, the upward push is greater, and the conductor tends to move in
the upward direction.

DOWNWARD PUSH

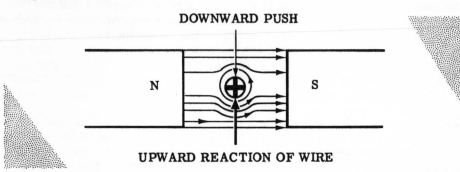

UPWARD REACTION OF WIRE

Before going on, it is well to summarize the above information, as follows:

1. The "straight" magnetic field which exists between the poles of the magnet is distorted by the circular magnetic field which surrounds the
   current-carrying conductor.

2. A downward force is applied by a push on the conductor.

3. An upward force results from the distorted field.

These facts tell you that if you push a conductor, moving it across a magnetic field, an emf is induced in the conductor. This emf causes current
to flow through the conductor, setting up a new magnetic field which tries
to move the conductor back against the push. This, in effect, is a general
statement of Lenz's Law. Lenz found that in all cases of electromagnetic
induction, the direction of the induced emf is such that the magnetic field
set up by the resulting current tends to stop the motion which is producing
the emf.

The induced emf just described actually opposes the applied line voltage.
The induced emf which develops in the rotating armature of a motor is
called a counter emf. This counter emf is of tremendous importance in
motor operation. Motor armature resistances are usually extremely low;
frequently less than one ohm. If the usual 110- or 220-volt line source is
applied to an armature, huge currents flow and burn-out occurs almost immediately. However, since the counter emf (cemf) always opposes the
line voltage source, an automatic current-limiter is always present to cut
armature current to safe limits.

DC Motor Principles

The elementary DC motor is constructed similarly to the elementary DC generator. It consists of a loop of wire that turns between the poles of a magnet. The ends of the loop connect to commutator segments which in turn make contact with the brushes. The brushes have connecting wires going to a source of DC voltage.

Keep in mind the action of the meter movement, and compare it to that of the elementary DC motor. With the loop in position 1, the current flowing through the loop makes the top of the loop a north pole and the underside a south pole, according to the left-hand rule. The magnetic poles of the loop will be attracted by the corresponding opposite poles of the field. As a result, the loop will rotate clockwise, bringing the unlike poles together. When the loop has rotated through 90 degrees to position 2, commutation takes place, and the current through the loop reverses in direction. As a result, the magnetic field generated by the loop reverses. Now like poles face each other, which means they will repel each other, and the loop continues rotating in an attempt to bring unlike poles together. Rotating 180 degrees past position 2, the loop finds itself in position 3. Now the situation is the same as when the loop was back in position 2. Commutation takes place once again and the loop continues rotating. This is the fundamental action of the DC motor.

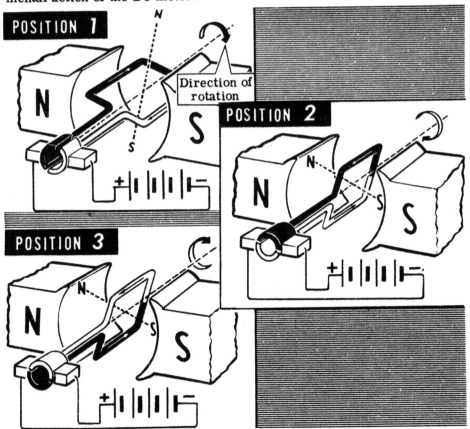

Commutator Action in a DC Motor

It is obvious that the commutator plays a very important part in the operation of the DC motor. The commutator causes the current through the
loop to reverse at the instant unlike poles are facing each other. This
causes a reversal in the polarity of the field; repulsion exists instead of
attraction, and the loop continues rotating.

In a multi-coil armature, the armature winding acts like a coil whose axis
is perpendicular to the main magnetic field and has the polarity shown below. The north pole of the armature field is attracted to the south pole of
the main field. This attraction exerts a turning force on the armature,
which moves in a clockwise direction. Thus a smooth and continuous
torque or turning force is maintained on the armature due to the large
number of coils. Since there are so many coils close to one another, a resultant armature field is produced that appears to be stationary.

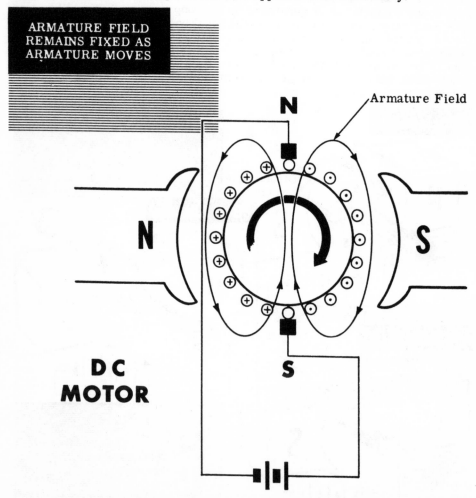

Armature Reaction

Since the motor armature has current flowing through it, a magnetic field will be generated around the armature coils as a result of this current. This armature field will distort the main magnetic field—the motor has "armature reaction" just as the generator. However, the direction of distortion due to armature reaction in a motor is just the opposite of that in a generator. In a motor, armature reaction shifts the neutral commutating plane against the direction of rotation.

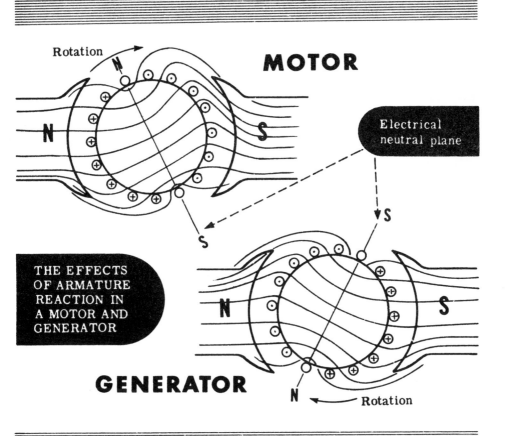

MOTOR

Electrical neutral plane

THE EFFECTS OF ARMATURE REACTION IN A MOTOR AND GENERATOR

GENERATOR

To compensate for armature reaction in a motor, the brushes can be shifted backwards until sparking is at a minimum. At this point, the coil being short-circuited by the brushes is in the neutral plane and no emf is induced in it. Also, armature reaction can be corrected by means of compensating windings and interpoles, just as in a generator, so that the neutral plane is always exactly between the main poles and the brushes do not have to be moved once they are properly adjusted.

Reversing the Direction of Motor Rotation

The direction of rotation of a motor depends upon the direction of the field and the direction of current flow in the armature. Current flowing through a conductor will set up a magnetic field about this conductor. The direction of this magnetic field is determined by the direction of current flow. If the conductor is placed in a magnetic field, force will be exerted on the conductor due to the interaction of its magnetic field with the main magnetic field. This force causes the armature to rotate in a certain direction between the field poles. In a motor, the relation between the direction of the magnetic field, the direction of current in the conductor, and the direction in which the conductor tends to move is expressed in the right-hand rule for motor action, which states: Place your right hand in such a position that the lines of force from the north pole enter the palm of the hand. Let the extended fingers point in the direction of current flow in the conductor; then the thumb, placed at right angles to the fingers, points in the direction of motion of the conductor.

If either the direction of the field or the direction of current flow through the armature is reversed, the rotation of the motor will reverse. However, if both of the above two factors are reversed at the same time, the motor will continue rotating in the same direction.

Ordinarily a motor is set up to do a particular job which requires a fixed direction of rotation. However, there are times when you may find it necessary to change the direction of rotation. Remember that you must reverse the connections of either the armature or the field, but not both.

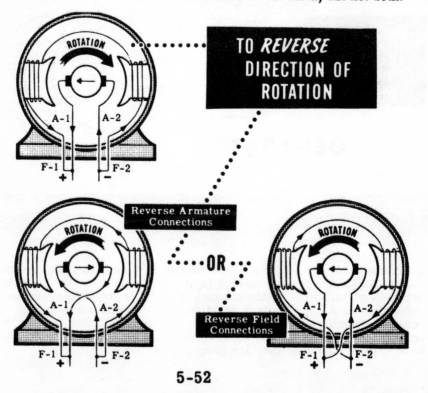

DIRECT CURRENT MOTORS

Counter Electromotive Force

In a DC motor, as the armature rotates the armature coils cut the magnetic field, inducing a voltage or electromotive force in these coils. Since this induced voltage opposes the applied terminal voltage, it is called the "counter electromotive force," or "counter-emf." This counter-emf depends on the same factors as the generated emf in the generator—the speed and direction of rotation, and the field strength. The stronger the field and the faster the rotating speed, the larger will be the counter-emf. However, the counter-emf will always be less than the applied voltage because of the internal voltage drop due to the resistance of the armature coils. The illustration represents the counter-emf as a battery opposing the applied voltage, with the total armature resistance shown symbolically as a single resistor.

VOLTAGE SOURCE = ARMATURE DROP + COUNTER-EMF

$$E_a = I_a R_a + E_c$$

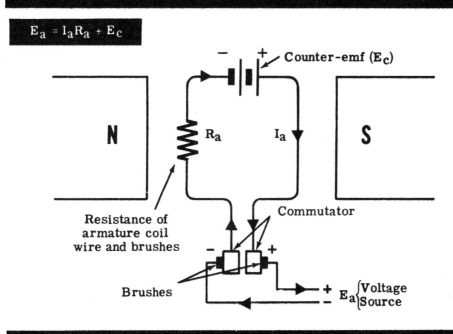

What actually moves the armature current through the armature coils is the difference between the voltage applied to the motor (E_a) minus the counter-emf (E_c). Thus $E_a - E_c$ is the actual voltage effective in the armature and it is this effective voltage which determines the value of the armature current. Since generally $I = \dfrac{E}{R}$ from Ohm's law, in the case of the DC motor, $I_a = \dfrac{E_a - E_c}{R_a}$. Also, since according to Kirchhoff's Second Law, the sum of the voltage drops around any closed circuit must equal the sum of the applied voltages, then $E_a = E_c + I_a R_a$.

Counter Electromotive Force (continued)

The internal resistance of the armature of a DC motor is very low, usually less than one ohm. If this resistance were all that limited the armature current, this current would be very high. For example, if the armature resistance is 1.0 ohm and the applied line voltage is 230 volts, the resulting armature current, according to Ohm's law, would be: $I_a = \dfrac{E_t}{R_a} = \dfrac{230}{1.0} = 230$ amps. This excessive current would completely burn out the armature.

However, the counter-emf is in opposition to the applied voltage and limits the value of armature current that can flow. If the counter-emf is 220 volts, then the effective voltage acting on the armature is the difference between the terminal voltage and the counter-emf: 230 - 220 = 10 volts. The armature current is then only 10 amps: $I_a = \dfrac{E_t - E_c}{R_a} = \dfrac{10}{1} = 10$ amps.

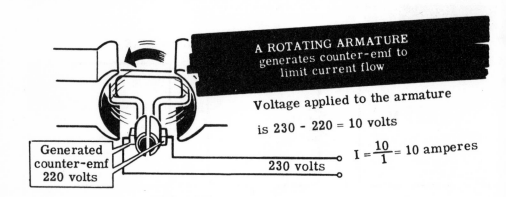

A ROTATING ARMATURE generates counter-emf to limit current flow

Voltage applied to the armature

is 230 - 220 = 10 volts

$I = \dfrac{10}{1} = 10$ amperes

Generated counter-emf 220 volts

230 volts

When the motor is just starting and the counter-emf is too small to limit the current effectively, a temporary resistance called the "starting resistance" must be put in series with the armature, to keep the current flow within safe limits. As the motor speeds up, the counter-emf increases and the resistance can be gradually reduced, allowing a further increase in speed and counter-emf. At normal speed, the starting resistance is completely shorted out of the circuit.

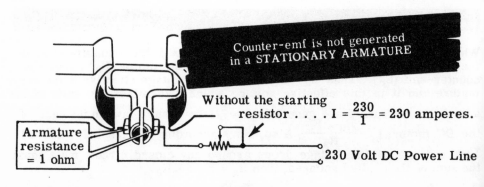

Counter-emf is not generated in a STATIONARY ARMATURE

Without the starting resistor . . . . $I = \dfrac{230}{1} = 230$ amperes.

Armature resistance = 1 ohm

230 Volt DC Power Line

Speed Depends On Load

The torque a motor develops, to turn a certain load, depends on the amount of armature current drawn from the line. The heavier the load, the more torque required, and the greater the armature current must be. The lighter the load, the less torque required, and the smaller the armature current must be.

The armature voltage drop (I_aR_a) and the counter-emf (E_c) must always add to equal the applied terminal voltage (E_t)—$E_t = I_aR_a + E_c$. Since the terminal voltage (E_t) is constant, the sum of the voltage drop and the counter-emf ($I_aR_a + E_c$) must be constant too. If a heavier load is put on the motor, it slows down. This reduces the counter-emf, which is dependent on the speed. Since $E_c + I_aR_a$ is constant, and E_c is less, then I_aR_a must be more. The armature resistance is not changed, so the current must have increased. This means the torque developed is greater, and the motor is able to turn the heavier load at a slower speed. Therefore, you see the speed of a DC motor depends upon the load it is driving.

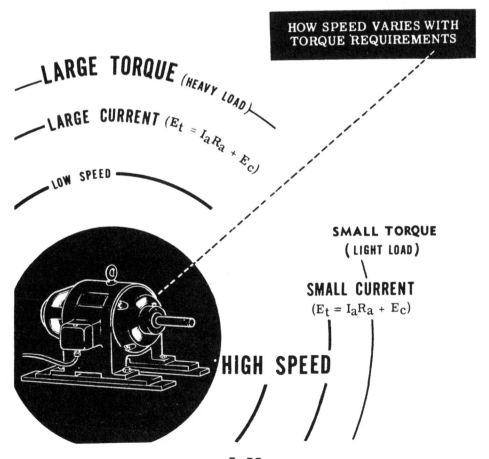

HOW SPEED VARIES WITH TORQUE REQUIREMENTS

LARGE TORQUE (HEAVY LOAD)

LARGE CURRENT ($E_t = I_aR_a + E_c$)

LOW SPEED

SMALL TORQUE (LIGHT LOAD)

SMALL CURRENT ($E_t = I_aR_a + E_c$)

HIGH SPEED

Changing Motor Speed

The speed of a DC motor depends on the strength of the magnetic field and the value of the applied voltage, as well as the load. If the strength of the field is decreased, the motor must speed up to maintain the proper amount of counter-emf. If the field circuit should become open, only the residual magnetism is left and the motor speed increases dangerously, trying to maintain the counter-emf necessary to oppose the applied voltage. With a light load or no load, an open field circuit can cause the motor to turn so fast it will tear itself apart—the commutator segments and other parts will fly out and may cause serious injury to personnel. Always be sure the field circuit is closed before running a DC motor, and always be sure the starting resistance is set to maximum before terminal voltage is applied.

The motor speed may be controlled by controlling the field strength with a field rheostat, or by controlling the voltage applied to the armature with an armature rheostat. Increasing the resistance in the armature circuit has the same effect as decreasing the voltage supply to the motor, which is to decrease the speed. This method is seldom used because a very large rheostat is necessary and also because the starting torque is lowered. Increasing the resistance in the field circuit decreases the field current and therefore the field strength. A decreased field strength means the motor must turn faster to maintain the same counter-emf.

To summarize, the speed of rotation of a DC motor depends on the field strength and the armature voltage.

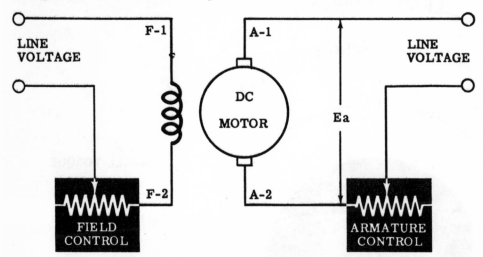

Shunt Motors

In a shunt connected motor, the field is connected directly across the line and therefore is independent of variations in load and armature current. The developed torque varies with the armature current. If the load on the motor increases, the motor slows down, reducing the counter-emf which depends on the speed as well as the constant field strength. The reduced counter-emf allows the armature current to increase, thereby furnishing the heavier torque needed to drive the increased load. If the load is decreased, the motor speeds up, increasing the counter-emf and thereby decreasing the armature current and the developed torque. Whenever the load changes, the speed changes until the motor is again in electrical balance—that is, until $E_c + I_a R_a = E_t$ again. In a shunt motor, the variation of speed from no-load to normal or "full" load is only about 10 percent of the no-load speed. For this reason, shunt motors are considered constant speed motors.

When a shunt motor is started, a starting resistance must be connected in series with the armature to limit the armature current until the speed builds up the necessary counter-emf. Since the starting current is small, due to this added resistance, the starting torque will be small. Shunt motors are usually used where constant speed under varying load is desired, and where it is possible for the motor to start under light or no load conditions.

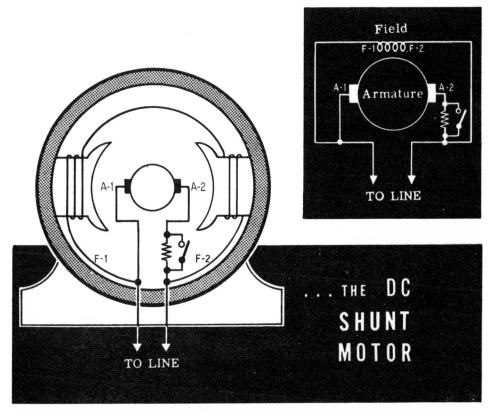

Series Motors

Since DC motors are electrically the same as DC generators, they are both classified according to their field connections.

The series motor has its field connected in series with the armature and the load, as shown. The field coil consists of a few turns of heavy wire, since the entire armature current flows through it. If the load increases, the motor slows down and the counter-emf decreases, which allows the current to increase and supply the heavier torque needed. The series motor runs very slowly with heavy loads and very rapidly with light loads. If the load is completely removed, the motor will speed dangerously and fly apart, since the current required is very small and the field very weak, so that the motor cannot turn fast enough to generate the amount of counter-emf needed to restore the balance. Series motors must never be run under no-load conditions, and they are seldom used with belt drives where the load can be removed.

Also, you can see that series motors are variable speed motors—that is, their speed changes a great deal when the load is changed. For this reason series motors are seldom used where a constant operating speed is needed, and are never used where the load is intermittent—where the load changes frequently or is put on and taken off while the motor is running.

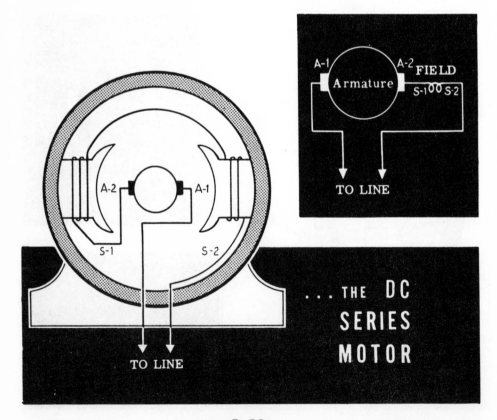

... THE DC SERIES MOTOR

Series Motors (continued)

The torque—the turning force—developed by any DC motor depends on the armature current and the field strength. In the series motor, the field strength itself depends on the armature current, so that the amount of torque developed depends doubly on the amount of armature current flowing. When the motor speed is low, the counter-emf is, of course, low and the armature current is high. This means the torque will be very high when the motor speed is low or zero, such as when the motor is starting. The series motor is said to have a high starting torque.

There are special jobs which require a heavy starting torque and the high rate of acceleration this heavy torque allows. Such applications are cranes, electric hoists and electrically powered trains and trolleys. The motors used in these machines are always series motors, because the loads here are very heavy at start and then become lighter once the machine is in motion.

THE DC
SERIES MOTOR

TREMENDOUS STARTING TORQUE

RAPID ACCELERATION

HEAVY LOAD - High Torque
Low Speed

LIGHT LOAD - Low Torque
High Speed

Compound Motors

A compound motor is a combination series and shunt motor. The field consists of two separate sets of coils. One set, whose coils are wound with many turns of fine wire, is connected across the armature as a shunt field. The other set, whose coils are wound with few turns of heavy wire, is connected in series with the armature as a series field.

The characteristics of the compound motor combine the features of the series and shunt motors. Cumulatively compound motors, whose series and shunt fields are connected to aid each other, are the most common. In a cumulatively compound motor, an increase in load decreases the speed and greatly increases the developed torque. The starting torque is also large. The cumulative compound motor is a fairly constant speed motor with excellent pulling power on heavy loads and good starting torque.

In a differentially compound motor, the series field opposes the shunt field and the total field is weakened when the load increases. This allows the speed to increase with increased load, up to a safe operating point. The starting torque is very low, and the differentially compound motor is rarely used.

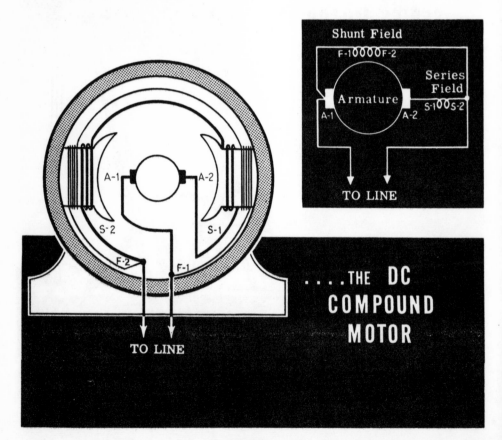

....THE DC COMPOUND MOTOR

Comparison of DC Motor Characteristics

The operating characteristics of the different types of DC motors can be summarized by drawing a graph which shows how the speed varies with the torque or load on the motor. The graph contains four curves. Notice that the speed of the shunt motor varies the least as the torque requirements of the load increase. On the other hand, the series motor speed greatly drops as the torque requirements increase. The cumulatively wound compound motor has speed characteristics between the series and shunt machines. Observe that the more heavily compounded (the greater percentage of series turns compared to shunt turns), the more the motor acts like a series motor.

The second graph shows how the developed torque varies with armature current for the different motors of the same horsepower rating. The torque curve for the shunt motor is a straight line because the field remains constant, and the torque varies directly with the armature current. The curves for the series and compound motors show that above the full load or normal operating current, the developed torque is much greater than for the shunt motor. Below the full load current, the field strength of the series and compound machines have not reached their full value and, therefore, the developed torque is less than in the shunt machine.

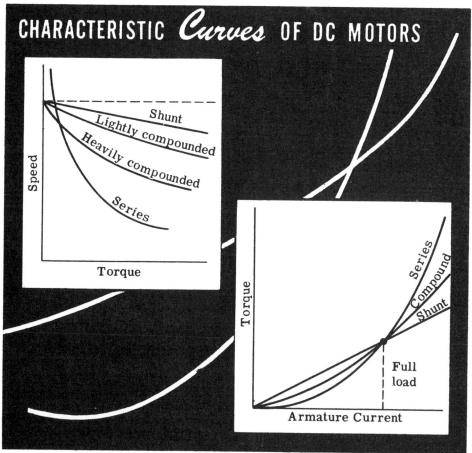

Review of DC Motors

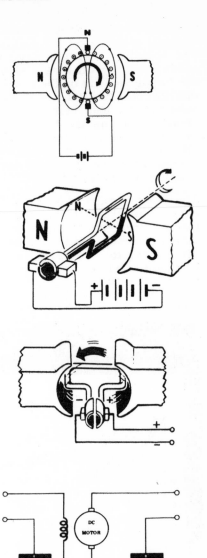

DC MOTOR PRINCIPLE — Current flow through the armature coil causes the armature to act as a magnet. The armature poles are attracted to field poles of opposite polarity, causing the armature to rotate.

DC MOTOR COMMUTATION — The commutator reverses the armature current at the moment when unlike poles of the armature and field are facing each other, reversing the polarity of the armature field. Like poles of the armature and field then repel each other causing continuous armature rotation.

DC MOTOR COUNTER ELECTROMOTIVE FORCE — The rotating armature coil of a DC motor generates an electromotive force which opposes the applied voltage. This generated counter-emf limits the flow of armature current.

DC MOTOR SPEED CONTROLS — The speed of a DC motor can be varied with a variable resistance connected either in series with the field coil or in series with the armature coil. Increasing shunt field circuit resistance increases motor speed, while increasing the armature circuit resistance decreases motor speed.

ARMATURE REACTION — The armature field causes distortion of the main field in a motor, causing the neutral plane to be shifted in the direction opposite to that of armature rotation. Interpoles, compensating windings, and slotted pole pieces are used to minimize the effect of armature reaction on motor operation.

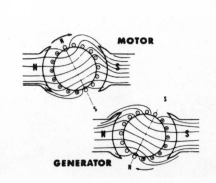

Review of DC Motors (continued)

<u>SERIES MOTORS</u> — The field windings are connected in series with the armature coil and the field strength varies with changes in armature current. When its speed is reduced by a load, the series motor develops greater torque, and its starting torque is greater than that of other types of DC motors.

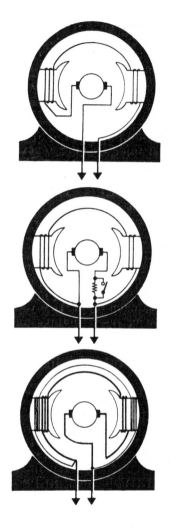

<u>SHUNT MOTORS</u> — The field windings are connected in parallel across the armature coil and the field strength is independent of the armature current. Shunt motor speed varies only slightly with changes in load and the starting torque is less than that of other types of DC motors.

<u>COMPOUND MOTORS</u> — One set of field windings is connected in series with the armature, and one set is parallel-connected. The speed and load characteristics can be changed by connecting the two sets of fields to either aid or oppose each other.

<u>MOTOR REVERSAL</u> — The direction of rotation of a DC motor can be reversed by reversing the field connections or by reversing the armature connections.

DC Starters and Controllers

In studying DC motors, you learned that the armature resistance is very low—usually less than one ohm. If this resistance were the only opposition to current flow, the armature current would be excessively high. When the motor is running, the counter-emf generated in the rotating armature opposes the line voltage and limits the size of the armature current. However, when the motor is just starting, the counter-emf is zero or very low, and the starting current would be very high if it was not limited in some way. To prevent this high starting current, which would damage the armature windings and commutator, a resistance called the "starting resistor" is put in series with the armature at starting. As the speed and the counter-emf increases, the starting resistor is gradually shorted out of the circuit.

The complete starting resistor assembly is called a "DC starter." In addition to limiting the value of the starting current, the DC starter usually includes provisions to protect the motor in case the field circuits become open or in case the line voltage becomes too low. Also, the starting resistance is automatically reconnected into the circuit each time the motor stops. When the DC starter is constructed so it can also control the operating speed of the motor, it is called a "controller."

There are various types of starters, some manually controlled and some automatic. Usually the starting current is limited to about 150 percent of normal full-load current. There are some small DC motors whose armatures contain many turns of fine wire, offering enough resistance to the current flow so that a starter is not required. However, all large DC motors require some type of starter or controller.

A DC Starter......

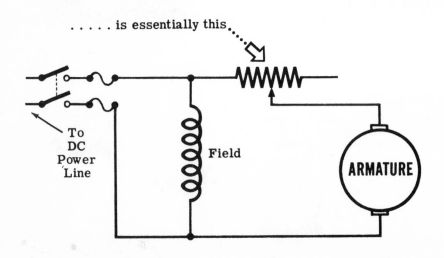

. . . . . is essentially this . . . . .

Simple Elementary Starter

Manual starters are classified by the number of connections that are made to it from the motor and the line. Thus, there are two-, three- and four-point starters.

An elementary starter consists of a resistance with taps on it. This resistance can be progressively shorted out by a knife switch whose contacts connect to the taps on the resistor. When the motor is first started, the switch contacts the end of the resistor so that all of the resistance is in series with the armature. As the motor comes up to speed, the blade is slowly closed—shorting out more and more of the resistance until, when the switch is completely closed, all of the resistance is shorted out.

The disadvantage of the elementary starter is that if the operator forgets to open the starting switch when the main switch is opened to stop the motor, the armature will have no limiting resistance connected to it when the motor is started again. Also, the elementary starter does not protect the motor from excessive speed if a break in the field circuit occurs.

The simple elementary starter has little application outside of experimental motors in the laboratory.

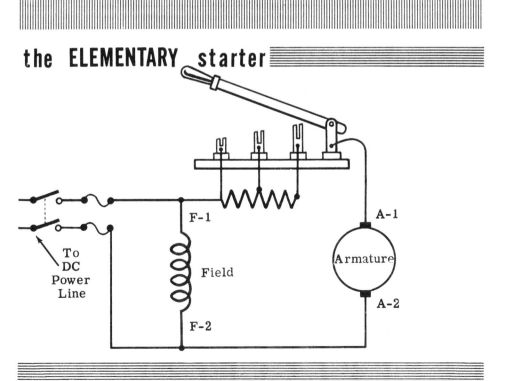

the ELEMENTARY starter

Three- and Four-Point Motor Starters

The three-point starter has three terminals, as illustrated. Point "L" goes to the line, point "A" goes to the armature, and point "F" goes to the field. When starting the motor, the arm is moved to the first contact, and the entire resistance is placed in series with the armature circuit. The field coil is connected in series with the holding coil across the line. As the motor builds up speed and the counter-emf increases, the arm is moved to each of the contacts in turn, decreasing the resistance in steps. As the arm moves across the starter, some of the resistance is also in series with the field and the holding coil. When the arm is all the way to the right, called the "run position," the armature is directly across the line, and the motor is operating at full speed. In the run position, a small piece of iron on the arm contacts the "holding coil," and is held there by the electro-magnetic attraction produced by the field current flowing through this coil. If for any reason the line voltage fails, the holding coil no longer attracts the iron, and a return spring pulls back the arm to the off position—thus disconnecting the motor from the line. This prevents the motor from starting up without any starting resistance when the line voltage is applied once again. The return spring can also be set to return the arm if the line voltage drops by a certain amount. This is called "under-voltage" protection. An open shunt field reduces the counter-emf generated by a shunt or compound motor resulting in excessive armature current and increased motor speed. Since the holding coil on a three-point starter is connected in series with the shunt field winding, the starter is released if the shunt field circuit opens for any reason.

If variable speed control is required by varying the field current, a four-point starter is used, in which the holding coil is connected across the line. Therefore, its magnetic pull is not affected by field current variations required in speed control. This type does not provide open field protection.

These starters, of the face-plate type, have a group of contacts arranged as studs on an insulated plate. The single contact of the control lever makes contact with one stud at a time, effecting starting, stopping and speed control.

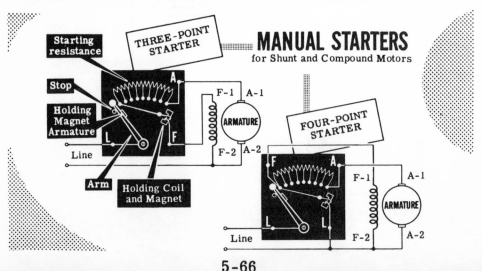

MANUAL STARTERS
for Shunt and Compound Motors

Two- and Three-Point Starters for Series Motors

Series motor starters are either the two- or three-point types. The two-point starter has two connections, one to the armature and the other to the line. The holding coil is in series with the field and armature so that when the arm is in the off position, the armature and field are disconnected from the line. By moving the arm from one point to the next, the motor is able to build up speed and counter-emf in step with the increase in armature current. When the arm is in the running position, the resistance is completely removed from the armature and field circuit. The arm is maintained in the running position by the holding coil, which is in series with the armature and therefore energized by the armature current. When the load is removed from the motor, the armature current drops, weakening the field of the holding coil. The arm is released and moves to the off position, stopping the motor. In this manner, the motor is disconnected from the line whenever the load is removed. This is called "no-load" protection.

A three-point starter can also be used with series motors. In this case, the holding coil acts as an under-voltage release. If the power line voltage is removed or drops to a low value, the holding coil releases the starter. This prevents the line voltage from being applied to the motor when the starter resistance is removed from the circuit. This type does not provide no-load protection.

Power line and motor connections for both two- and three-point starters are illustrated below.

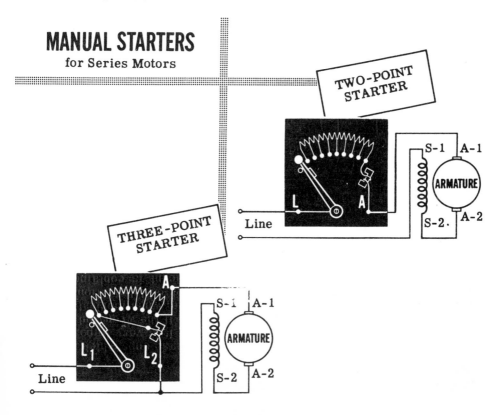

MANUAL STARTERS
for Series Motors

TWO-POINT STARTER

THREE-POINT STARTER

Generator Maintenance Precautions

When a generator is installed, it is usually used for a particular job and the installation is permanent. Once the prime mover has been coupled to the generator shaft, the only maintenance work necessary should be oil bearings, etc. If the generator leads are altered, the generator polarity may be reversed or the generator may fail to build up. For example, reversing the field of a self-excited generator will cancel the residual magnetism of the field, and the generator will not build up even when the connections are corrected. By flashing the field, residual magnetism of the proper polarity can be restored.

It should never be necessary to reverse the output polarity of a DC generator. However, if a reversed polarity is desired, the output leads of the generator should be reversed. The field connections should never be reversed. The field coils are only connected to the terminal board to make their replacement easier, in case they have been damaged. Once the field wires have been properly connected in the initial installation, they should never be changed.

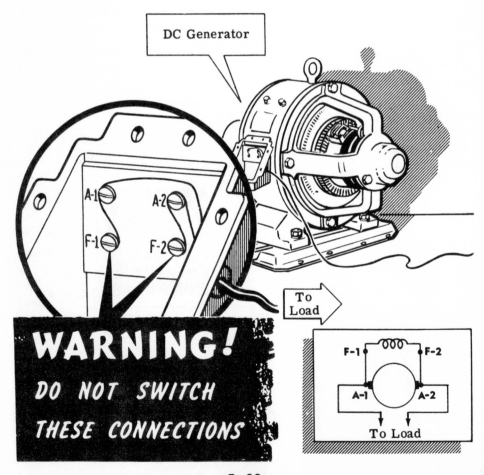

DC Generator

A-1 A-2

F-1 F-2

To Load

WARNING!
DO NOT SWITCH
THESE CONNECTIONS

F-1 F-2

A-1 A-2

To Load

Bearings

Since DC generators and motors are rotating machines, they depend upon the condition of their bearings for smooth operation. If a bearing is in good condition, the machine will run smoothly. If the bearing is in poor condition, the machine will run poorly, if at all.

Generally speaking, there are two types of bearings—friction and anti-friction. The friction bearing, or sleeve bearing, is a soft metal sleeve in which the shaft revolves. The shaft is actually separated from the metal by a thin film of lubricating oil. The shaft therefore rotates on a film of oil, and very little friction results. If there is no lubricating oil, the shaft rubs directly against the surface of the bearing sleeve, and chips of metal gradually accumulate, greatly increasing the friction in the bearing. This can ruin the bearing surfaces and cause the shaft to freeze in the bearing sleeve so that it does not turn at all. If the bearing is properly lubricated, there is no surface contact between the shaft and the surface of the sleeve bearing. As a result, there will be no wear on the bearings as long as they are properly lubricated and the oil is clean.

An anti-friction bearing is a ball bearing which uses the rolling action of steel balls to eliminate the friction. The balls are enclosed in runways called "races." The space between the balls and the races must be free of dirt or chips which cause the bearing to wear and make it unusable. Ball bearings are packed in grease, which lubricates them and keeps out foreign particles.

Some machines sometimes use bearings that do not require lubrication. These bearings, called "self-lubricating" bearings, contain a high percentage of oil which is forced out of the pores of the metal when the bearing becomes heated by rotation.

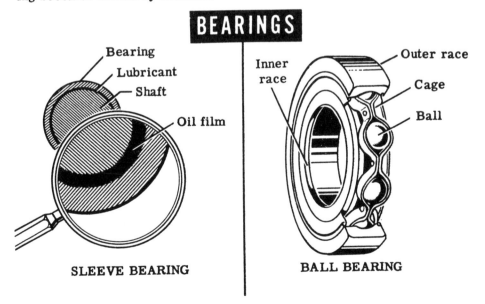

BEARINGS

Bearing
Lubricant
Shaft
Oil film

Inner race
Outer race
Cage
Ball

SLEEVE BEARING   BALL BEARING

Bearing Lubrication

Since bearings are precision-tooled, great care must be exercised in handling them, and in the greasing methods and in the type of lubricant used.

Improper greasing procedures are a frequent cause of bearing troubles in rotating equipment. An excess of grease in the bearing housing causes the grease to churn around and overheat. This results in a rapid deterioration of the grease and eventual destruction of the bearing. Grease under pressure will force its way through the bearing housing seals onto the commutator and other motor parts. Grease will eat away insulation and eventually cause short circuits and grounds.

Most large-sized motors and generators have grease cups which force the grease into the bearings when the cup is turned. It is very important that the right type of lubricant be used on bearings. If the wrong lubricant is used, it can do more harm than good. Therefore, when lubricating a rotating machine, always refer to an instruction book on lubrication in order to find out the kind to use. Often the correct lubricant is contained in the spare parts box for the particular machine.

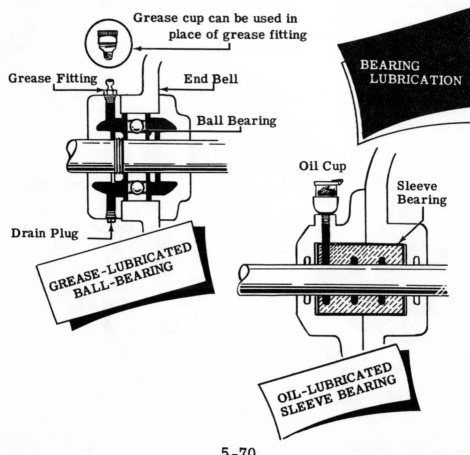

Grease cup can be used in place of grease fitting

Grease Fitting

End Bell

Ball Bearing

BEARING LUBRICATION

Oil Cup

Sleeve Bearing

Drain Plug

GREASE-LUBRICATED BALL-BEARING

OIL-LUBRICATED SLEEVE BEARING

Bearing Lubrication (continued)

Although excess lubrication causes many troubles and faults in generator or motor operation, the lack of lubrication is also serious. A bearing which is not properly lubricated will overheat immediately, causing expansion of the shaft and bearing assembly. This expansion may be sufficient to stop the shaft rotation. Lack of lubrication also results in noisy operation, due to the direct contact between the shaft and bearing.

Bearing housings should be checked periodically for overheating and noisy operation. In normal operation, the temperature of a generator or motor will rise so that the bearing housings normally heat a certain amount. If the housings overheat, do not add or change lubrication without first inspecting the bearing to make certain that lack of lubrication is the cause. Shafts may be forced out of line by a coupling unit or the lubrication may not be reaching all parts of the bearing.

Commutators and Brushes

Next to bearings, commutators and brush assemblies are the chief sources of trouble in DC rotating machinery. The continual sliding of the brushes against the commutator wears the brushes down and tends to push them out of alignment, causing trouble in the commutator and brushes. When something does go wrong in commutation, it is accompanied by excessive sparking, which aggravates the original trouble and causes additional troubles.

For satisfactory commutation of DC machines, a continuous contact must be maintained between commutator and brushes. The commutator must be mechanically true, the unit in good balance, and the brushes in good shape and well adjusted.

When correct commutation is taking place, the commutator is a dark chocolate color. This color is due to the action of the brushes in riding on the rotating commutator. The surface of the commutator is smooth. Under normal load there will be very little noticeable sparking. The mica insulation between the commutator segments is usually cut below the surface of the segments. The brushes are free to slide up and down in the brush holders and are made to bear upon the commutator with a spring adjusted to produce a pressure of one and a half to 2 pounds per square inch of brush surface. Too little pressure causes poor brush contact and unnecessary sparking, and too much pressure will cause excessive brush wear.

PROPER COMMUTATION

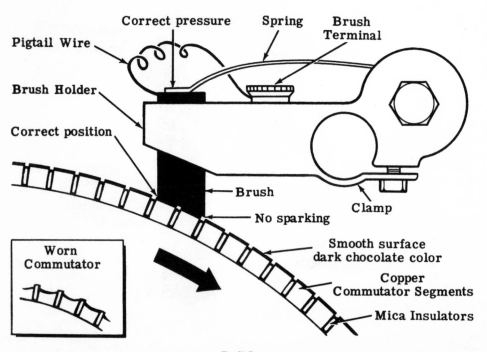

Commutators and Brushes (continued)

When there is excessive sparking at the commutator and good commutation cannot be obtained, the commutator and brush assembly should be checked and any defect found should be corrected if at all possible. The inspection procedure and the steps taken to eliminate troubles are outlined below:

1. Observe machine under actual operation to see if you can spot anything unusual such as arcing or excessive sparking, which might indicate a loose connection.

2. Turn off the machine, making sure that all power is removed before proceeding with your check.

3. Inspect all connections and make sure that none are loose.

4. Check the relative position of the brushes on the commutator. (They should be on opposite sides of the commutator.) If brushes are un-equally spaced, look for a bent brush holder and eliminate the trouble.

5. Inspect the condition of the brushes. If the brushes are worn badly, they should be replaced. When removing a brush, first lift up the spring lever to release the pressure, then remove brush. Insert new brush, making sure that brush can move freely in the holder. The end of the brush must then be fitted to the commutator by sanding it as illustrated. Adjust the brush spring pressure. Check the pigtail wire and its terminal for tightness. The pigtail wire must not touch any metal except the brush holders to which it is attached.

6. Check the commutator for dirt, pitting, irregularities, etc. Dirt can be removed with a piece of light canvas. Fine sandpaper will remove slight roughness. <u>Never</u> use emery cloth on a commutator.

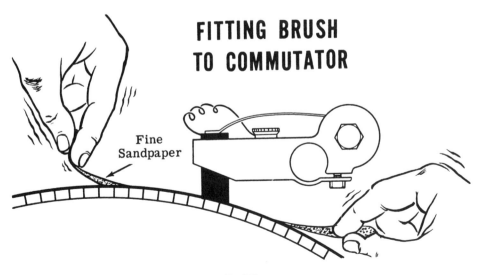

FITTING BRUSH
TO COMMUTATOR

Fine
Sandpaper

Insulation Breakdown

Under normal operation, the field and armature winding of generators and motors are completely insulated from the frame of the machine, which is bolted to the deck. A resistance measurement from the frame to the armature or the field should read infinity or several million ohms.

Sometimes, due to excessive heat generated by overloading the machine, or because of the high moisture content in the air aboard ship, the high resistance of the insulation decreases and some of the current leaks through the insulation to the frame. This leakage current adds to the "breakdown" of the insulation, and if the leakage is not found in time, the breakdown will be complete and the coil will be shorted to the frame. (Such a coil is called a "grounded" coil.) A short circuit will cause the entire winding to overheat and burn out. The armature and field windings should therefore be checked at regular intervals to detect "leaks" and "grounds" before they cause serious damage.

An ordinary ohmmeter cannot be used for insulation testing in large practical machines, since the leakage will often show itself only when a high voltage is applied to it. An ohmmeter cannot apply a high enough voltage to test adequately for breakdowns. An instrument called a "megger" is used. The megger supplies the necessary high voltage and is calibrated to read very high resistance values.

The illustration below shows how a typical insulation breakdown occurs when the insulation is broken or bruised, or becomes weakened from salt water. Each of the leakage paths shown becomes a low resistance parallel loop through which current flows to ground.

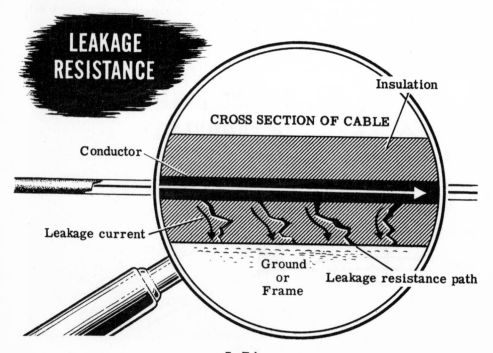

LEAKAGE RESISTANCE

CROSS SECTION OF CABLE

Insulation

Conductor

Leakage current

Ground
or
Frame

Leakage resistance path

The Megger

The megger is an instrument which is used for measuring insulation resistance, such as the resistance between windings and the frame of electric machinery, and the insulation resistance of cables, insulators and bushings. The megger consists of two parts—(1) a hand-cranked DC generator (magneto) or a high voltage "B" battery which supplies the voltage for making the measurement and (2) a special type of meter movement.

Before using the megger, the circuit is voltage checked to make sure it is de-energized because the megger must only be used on a de-energized circuit. Then both meter leads are connected to ground to ensure a good ground connection and good meter operation. Next, the megger is connected across the circuit to be tested and the hand crank is turned, generating a high voltage across the megger terminals. As a result, current flows through the circuit or insulation being tested. This current flow is measured by the meter movement as it is in an ohmmeter, but unlike the ohmmeter, the megger is calibrated to measure megohms. The normal resistance reading for a circuit insulated from ground is several hundred megohms. If the megger reads low, a ground exists, and the shorted circuit should be replaced.

A "ground" is a reference point for voltage and resistance measurements in electrical circuits. All large metal objects (such as motor housings, switch boxes, and transformer cases) that are associated with electrical equipment are directly connected to ground. A megger determines if any of the wires inside a motor or transformer have come in contact with the metal housing (have become "grounded") or are in danger of becoming so.

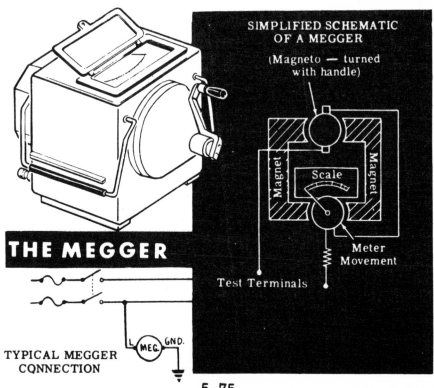

SIMPLIFIED SCHEMATIC OF A MEGGER

(Magneto — turned with handle)

Magnet

Magnet

Scale

Meter Movement

Test Terminals

THE MEGGER

L MEG. GND.

TYPICAL MEGGER CONNECTION

The Megger (continued)

Sometimes moisture in the insulation will cause the insulation resistance to be as low as one megohm. Moisture can be eliminated by drying the insulation with heaters, lamp banks, or a hot air blower. Field coils can be dried by passing a current through them.

To test a DC machine for insulation leakage and grounded coils, the leads of the megger are connected between the frame and the external terminals. The crank of the megger must be turned at a steady moderate speed. If the megger reads several megohms or more, the insulation is secure. If the megger reads less than one megohm, some of the insulation is defective somewhere and the leak must be isolated. The field leads must be disconnected from the armature and both tested separately.

The method of testing is shown. To test the field, the megger is connected between one side of the field and the frame. To test the armature, the megger is connected between the shaft and the commutator segments. If the megger reads several megohms, the insulation has its normal allowable leakage resistance. However, if the megger reads lower than this, say less than two megohms, the leakage is excessive and the insulation will eventually break down. Of course, if the megger reads zero, the insulation is broken and the coil is shorted to the frame of the machine.

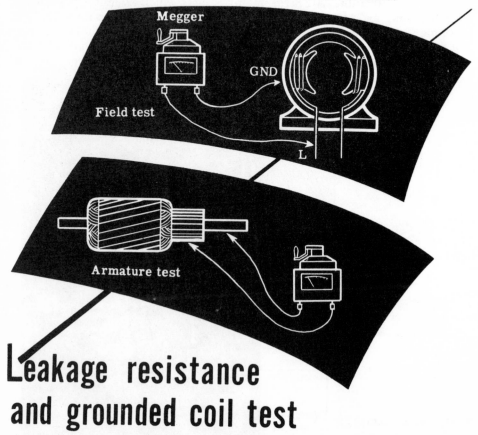

Leakage resistance and grounded coil test

Testing Field Coils

In testing for open and internally shorted field coils, an ohmmeter is used. The field coil leads are disconnected from the armature to avoid parallel circuits in testing. The ohmmeter is placed across the field leads as shown in the simplified illustration. If the ohmmeter reads infinity, there is an open circuit somewhere in the field winding. The open-circuited coil can be detected by testing each coil individually. The coil with the open circuit should be disconnected from the other coils and replaced.

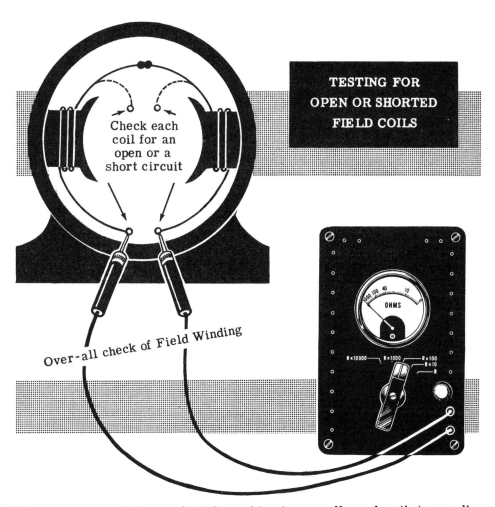

Check each coil for an open or a short circuit

TESTING FOR OPEN OR SHORTED FIELD COILS

Over-all check of Field Winding

The armature resistance of a DC machine is normally so low that an ordinary ohmmeter will not be able to measure it. The ohmmeter will read practically zero. If the armature has a few shorted turns, the ohmmeter will still read practically zero. If the armature has an open turn, the ohmmeter will also read zero due to the numerous parallel paths. Therefore special equipment is used to test armatures.

DC MACHINERY

Review of DC Generators and Motors

Now review what you have learned concerning the basic principles of **DC** motors and generators.

<u>**ELEMENTARY AC GENERATOR**</u> —
A loop of wire rotating in a magnetic field, with slip rings and brushes used to transfer the generated current to an external circuit.

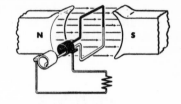

<u>**ELEMENTARY DC GENERATOR**</u> —
A loop of wire rotating in a magnetic field, with a commutator and brushes, used to transfer the generated current to an external circuit.

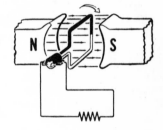

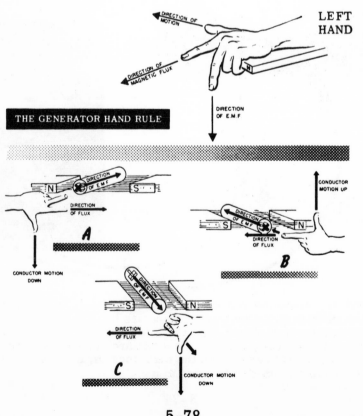

Review of DC Generators and Motors (continued)

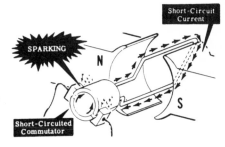

COMMUTATOR SPARKING — Sparking at the brushes occurs when the brushes short out the commutator segments of a coil which is generating an emf—a coil not in the neutral plane. Sparking is reduced by shifting the brushes, or by using interpoles or compensating windings.

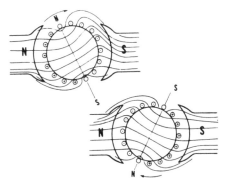

ARMATURE REACTION — The effect of the armature field in shifting the position of the main field. The armature field is caused by current flow in the armature circuit.

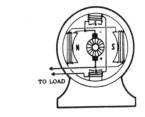

INTERPOLES — Small poles mounted between the main field windings to generate a field exactly opposite to that of the armature coil and counteract the effect of armature reaction.

SEPARATELY-EXCITED GENERATOR — Generator having a shunt field which is excited by an external source of DC voltage.

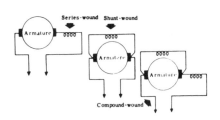

SELF-EXCITED GENERATORS — Shunt, series and compound generators connected to obtain field excitation from the generator output. Series fields are connected in series with the generator load and use the load current for field excitation while shunt fields are connected across the generator terminals in parallel with the generator load.

Review of DC Generators and Motors (continued)

DC MOTOR PRINCIPLE -- Current
flow through the armature coil causes
the armature to act like a magnet.
The poles of the armature field are
attracted to field poles of opposite polarity, causing the armature to rotate.

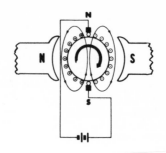

DC MOTOR COUNTER-EMF -- The
rotating armature coil of a DC motor
generates a voltage which is opposite
in polarity to that of the power line.
This generated counter-emf limits
the amount of current flow in the armature circuit.

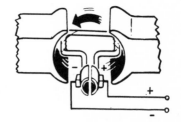

DC MOTOR SPEED CONTROL -- DC
motor speed can be varied by means
of a rheostat connected in series with
either the armature or field circuit.
Increasing the field resistance increases speed, while increasing the
armature resistance decreases speed.

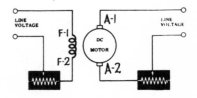

DC MOTOR CHARACTERISTICS --
DC shunt, series and compound motor
circuit connections are the same as
those of the corresponding type of DC
generator. Speed and torque versus
armature current are used as comparison characteristics for DC motors.

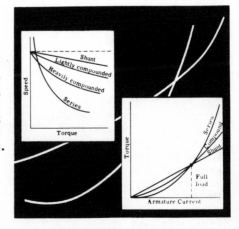

Review of DC Generators and Motors (continued)

DC MOTOR STARTER — A switching circuit containing a resistor connected in series with the armature, to reduce the armature current to a safe value at starting. As the motor speed increases, the resistor is shorted out of the circuit and the current is limited by the counter-emf of the armature.

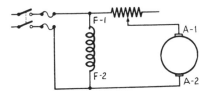

TWO-POINT STARTER — DC motor starter having only two connections, one to the DC power line and the other to the motor armature circuit. This type of starter can release automatically in case of power line failure, if a holding coil is used.

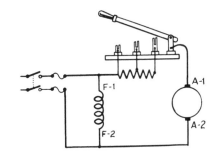

THREE-POINT STARTER — DC motor starter having three terminals —line, armature and field. A holding coil is connected in series with the motor field and releases the starter in case of power line failure or an open field circuit.

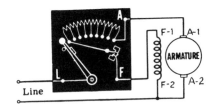

FOUR-POINT STARTER — DC motor starter having four terminals—two line terminals, field and armature. The holding coil connects directly across the line and the field winding is not in series with this coil. This starter is used when a field rheostat is used for speed control.

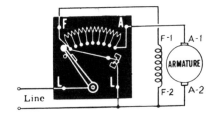

Importance of AC Generators

A large percentage of the electrical power generated is AC. As a result, the AC generator is the most important means of electrical power production. AC generators, or "alternators," vary greatly in size depending upon their power requirements. For example, the alternators used at hydroelectric plants such as Boulder Dam are tremendous in size, generating hundreds of kilowatts at voltage levels of 13,000 volts.

Regardless of their size, all electrical generators, whether DC or AC, depend upon the action of a coil cutting through a magnetic field or a magnetic field cutting through a coil. As long as there is relative motion between a conductor and a magnetic field, a voltage will be generated. That part which generates the magnetic field is called the "field," and that part in which the voltage is generated is called the "armature." In order to have relative motion take place between a conductor and a magnetic field, all generators are made up of two mechanical parts—a rotor and a stator. You know that in DC generators the armature is always the rotor.

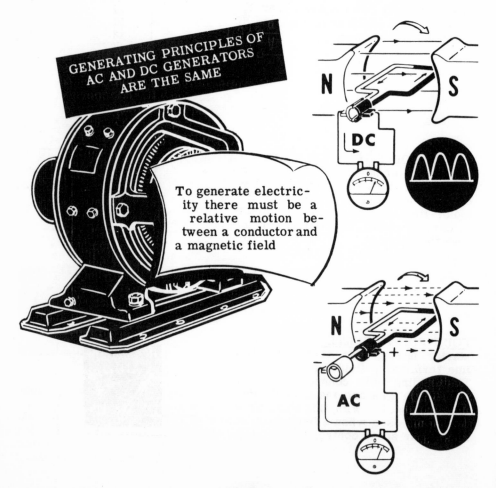

GENERATING PRINCIPLES OF AC AND DC GENERATORS ARE THE SAME

To generate electricity there must be a relative motion between a conductor and a magnetic field

Types of Alternators

There are two types of alternators—the revolving-armature type and the revolving-field type alternators. The revolving-armature type alternator is similar in construction to the DC generator in that the armature rotates through a stationary magnetic field. In the DC generator, the emf generated in the armature windings is converted into DC by means of the commutator, whereas in the alternator, the generated AC is brought to the load unchanged, by means of slip rings. The revolving-armature alternator is found only in alternators of small power rating and is not generally used.

The revolving-field type alternator has a stationary armature winding and a rotating field winding. The advantage of having a stationary armature winding is that the generated voltage can be connected directly to the load. A rotating armature would require slip rings to conduct the current from the armature to the outside. Since slip rings are exposed, arc-overs and short circuits result at high generated voltages. Therefore, high-voltage alternators are usually of the rotating field type. The voltage applied to the rotating field is low DC voltage and, therefore, the problem of arc-over at the slip rings is not encountered.

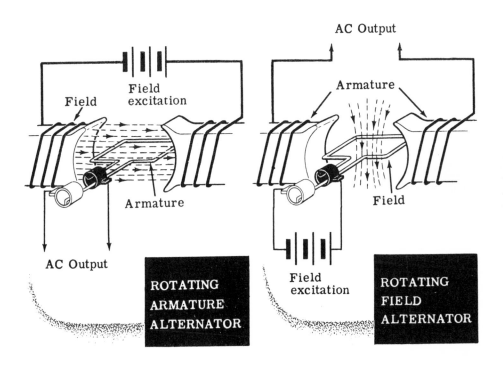

The maximum current that can be supplied by an alternator depends upon the maximum heating loss that can be sustained in the armature. This heating loss (which is an I^2R power loss) acts to heat the conductors, and if excessive, to destroy the insulation. Therefore, alternators are rated in terms of this current and in terms of the voltage output—the alternator rating is in volt-amperes, or in more practical units, kilovolt-amperes.

Alternator Construction

Alternators having high kilovolt-ampere ratings are of the turbine-driven, high-speed type. The prime mover for this type of alternator is a high-speed steam turbine which is driven by steam under high pressure. Due to the high speed of rotation, the rotor field of the turbine-driven alternator is cylindrical, small in diameter with windings firmly imbedded in slots in its face. The windings are arranged to form two or four distinct poles. Only with this type of construction can the rotor withstand the terrific centrifugal force developed at high speeds without flying apart.

In slower speed alternators which are driven by engines, water power, geared turbines and electric motors, a salient-pole rotor is used. In this type of rotor a number of separately wound pole pieces are bolted to the frame of the rotor. The field windings are either connected in series or in series groups—connected in parallel. In either case, the ends of the windings connect to slip rings mounted on the rotor shaft. Regardless of the type of rotor field used, its windings are separately excited by a DC generator called an "exciter."

The stationary armature or stator of an alternator holds the windings that are cut by the rotating magnetic field. The voltage generated in the armature as a result of this cutting action is the AC power which is applied to the load.

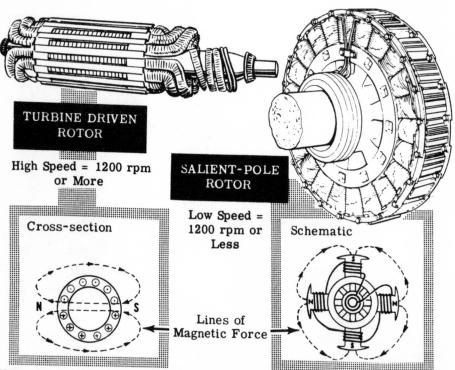

TURBINE DRIVEN ROTOR

High Speed = 1200 rpm or More

SALIENT-POLE ROTOR

Low Speed = 1200 rpm or Less

Cross-section

Schematic

Lines of Magnetic Force

The stators of all alternators are essentially the same. The stator consists of a laminated iron core with the armature windings embedded in this core. The core is secured to the stator frame.

Single-Phase Alternator

A single-phase alternator has all the armature conductors connected in series or parallel; essentially one winding across which an output voltage is generated. If you understand the principle of the single-phase, you will easily understand multi-phase alternator operation.

The schematic diagram illustrates a two-pole, single-phase alternator. The stator is two pole because the winding is wound in two distinct pole groups, both poles being wound in the same direction around the stator frame. Observe that the rotor also consists of two pole groups, adjacent poles being of opposite polarity. As the rotor turns, its poles will induce AC voltages in the stator windings. Since one rotor pole is in the same position relative to a stator pole as any other rotor pole, both the stator poles are cut by equal amounts of magnetic lines of force at any time. As a result, the voltages induced in the two poles of the stator winding have the same amplitude or value at a given instant. The two poles of the stator winding are connected to each other so that the AC voltages are in phase, or "series aiding." Assume that rotor pole 1, a south pole, induces a voltage with the polarity as shown in stator pole 1. Since rotor pole 2 is a north pole, it will induce the opposite voltage polarity in stator pole 2, in relation to the polarity of the voltage induced in stator pole 1. In order that the voltages in the two poles be series aiding, poles 1 and 2 are connected as shown. Observe that the two stator poles are connected in series so that the voltages induced in each pole add to give a total voltage that is two times the voltage in any one pole.

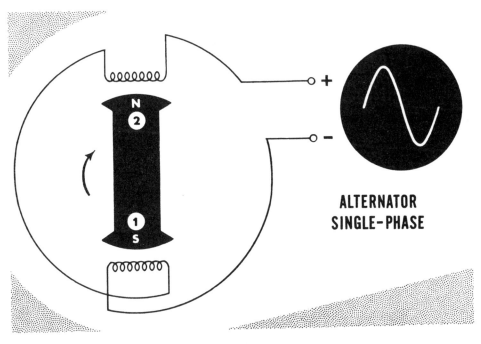

**ALTERNATOR
SINGLE-PHASE**

Two-Phase Alternator

Multi-phase or polyphase alternators have two or more single-phase windings symmetrically spaced around the stator. In a two-phase alternator there are two single-phase windings physically spaced so that the AC voltage induced in one is 90 degrees out of phase with the voltage induced in the other. The windings are electrically separate from each other. The only way to get a 90-degree phase difference is to space the two windings so that when one is being cut by maximum flux, the other is being cut by no flux.

The schematic diagram illustrates a two-pole, two-phase alternator. The stator consists of two single-phase windings completely separated from each other. Each winding is made up of a series of two windings which are in phase and connected so that their voltages add. The rotor is identical to that used in the single-phase alternator. In the first schematic, the rotor poles are opposite all the windings of phase A. Therefore, the voltage induced in phase A is maximum and the voltage induced in phase B is zero. As the rotor continues rotating, it moves away from the A windings and approaches the B windings. As a result, the voltage induced in phase A decreases from its maximum value and the voltage induced in phase B increases from zero. In the second schematic, the rotor poles are opposite the windings of phase B. Now the voltage induced in phase B is maximum, whereas the voltage induced in phase A has dropped to zero. Notice that a 90-degree rotation of the rotor corresponds to one-quarter of a cycle, or 90 degrees. The waveform picture shows the voltages induced in phase A and phase B for one cycle. The two voltages are 90 degrees out of phase.

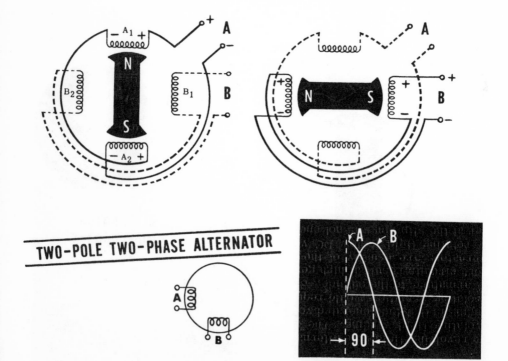

TWO-POLE TWO-PHASE ALTERNATOR

Two-Phase Alternator (continued)

If the phases of a two-phase alternator are connected so that three wires
will have to be brought to the outside instead of the original four wires
(two for each phase), the alternator is then called a "two-phase," three-
wire alternator, which is illustrated by the schematic. The schematic is
simplified in that the rotor is not shown and the entire phase, consisting of
a number of windings in series is shown as one winding. The windings are
drawn at right angles to each other to represent the 90-degree phase dis-
placement between them. The three wires make possible three different
load connections, (A) and (B) across each phase, and (C) across both
phases. The third voltage is the vector sum of both phase voltages; it is
larger in magnitude than either phase voltage and is displaced 45 degrees
from either phase. The resultant voltage is equal to the square root of two
($\sqrt{2} = 1.414$) times the phase voltage.

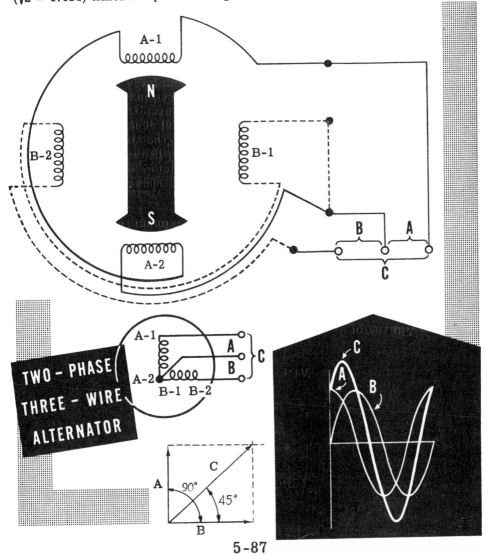

Three-Phase Alternator

The three-phase alternator, as the name implies, has three single-phase
windings spaced so that the voltage induced in any one is phase-displaced
by 120 degrees from the other two. A schematic diagram of a three-phase
stator showing all the coils becomes complex, and it is difficult to see
what is actually happening. A simplified schematic shows all the windings
of a single-phase lumped together as one winding, as illustrated. The rotor
is omitted for simplicity. The voltage waveforms generated across each
phase are drawn on a graph phase-displaced 120 degrees from each other.
The three-phase alternator as shown in this schematic is essentially
three single-phase alternators whose generated voltages are out of phase
by 120 degrees. The three phases are independent of each other.

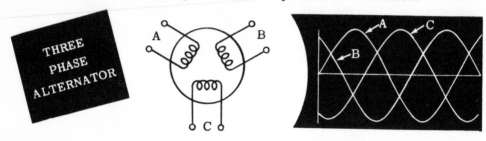

Rather than have six leads come out of the three-phase alternator, the
same leads from each phase are connected together to form a "wye," or
"star," connection. The point of connection is called the neutral, and the
voltage from this point to any one of the line leads will be the phase voltage. The total voltage or line voltage, across any two line leads is the
vector sum of the individual phase voltages. The line voltage is 1.73 times
the phase voltage. Since the windings form only one path for current flow
between phases, the line and phase currents are equal.

A three-phase stator can also be connected so that the phases are connected
end-to-end; it is now called "delta connected." In the delta connection the
line voltages are equal to the phase voltage, but the line currents will be
equal to the vector sum of the phase currents. Since the phases are 120 degrees out of phase, the line current will be 1.73 times the phase current.
Both the "wye" and the "delta" connections are used for alternators.

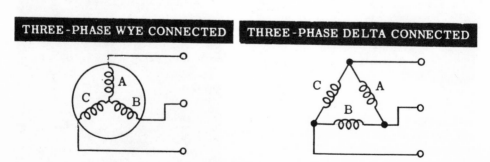

Frequency and Voltage Regulation

The frequency of the AC generated by an alternator depends upon the number of poles and the speed of the rotor. When a rotor has rotated through an angle so that two adjacent rotor poles (a north and a south) have passed one winding, the voltage induced in that one winding will have varied through a complete cycle of 360 electrical degrees. Frequency (f) can be determined from the following equation:

$$f = \frac{NP \times S}{120}$$

where

$$NP = \text{number of poles}$$
$$S = \text{speed of rotor, RPM}$$

The more poles there are, the lower the speed of rotation will be for a given frequency. A two-pole machine must rotate at four times the speed of an 8-pole machine to generate the same frequency. Put another way, if a two-pole and an eight-pole alternator are rotating at the same speed, the frequency of the AC generated by the eight-pole alternator will be four times that of the two-pole alternator.

BOTH ALTERNATORS ARE ROTATING AT SAME SPEED

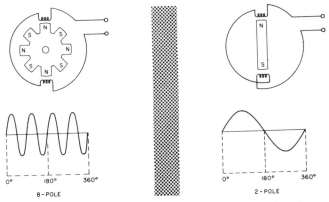

The magnitude of the voltage generated by an alternator is varied by varying the field strength (field current).

In an alternator, just as in a DC generator, the output voltage varies with the load. In addition to the IR drop, there is another voltage drop in the windings called the IX_L drop. The IX_L drop is due to the inductive reactance of the windings. Both the IR drop and the IX_L drop decrease the output voltage as the load increases. The change in voltage from no-load to full-load is called the voltage regulation of an alternator. A constant voltage output from an alternator is maintained by varying the field strength as required by changes in load.

ALTERNATORS

Three-Phase Connections

The majority of all alternators in use today are three-phase winding machines. This is because three-phase alternators are much more efficient than either two-phase or single-phase alternators.

The stator coils of three-phase alternators may be joined together in either "wye" or "delta" connections as shown below. With this type of connection only three wires come out of the alternator, and this allows convenient connection to other three-phase equipment. It is common to use three-phase transformers in connection with this type of system. Such a device may be made up of three single-phase transformers connected in the same way as for alternators. If both the primary and secondary are connected in wye, the transformer is called "wye-wye." If both windings are connected in delta, the transformer is called a "delta-delta."

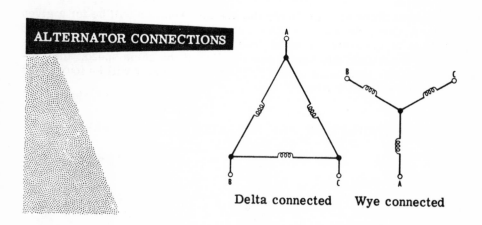

ALTERNATOR CONNECTIONS

Delta connected   Wye connected

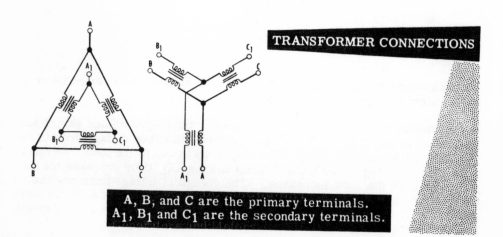

TRANSFORMER CONNECTIONS

A, B, and C are the primary terminals.
A_1, B_1 and C_1 are the secondary terminals.

Review

AC GENERATORS — An AC generator is essentially a loop rotating through a magnetic field. The cutting action of the loop through the magnetic field generates AC in the loop. This AC is removed from the loop by means of slip rings and applied to an external load.

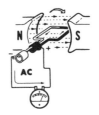

ALTERNATOR ARMATURES AND FIELDS — The armature is stationary and the field rotates. High voltages can be generated in the armature and applied to the load directly without the need of slip rings and brushes. The low DC voltage is applied to the rotor field by means of slip rings, but this does not introduce any insulation problems.

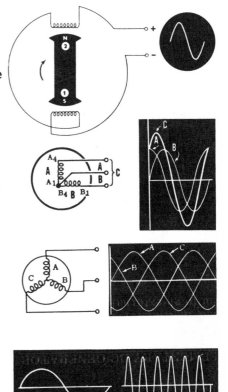

SINGLE-PHASE ALTERNATOR — A single-phase alternator has an armature which consists of a number of windings placed symmetrically around the stator and connected in series. The voltages generated in each winding add to produce the total voltage across the two output terminals.

TWO-PHASE ALTERNATOR — The two-phase alternator consists of two phases whose windings are so placed around the stator that the voltages generated in them are 90 degrees out of phase.

THREE-PHASE ALTERNATOR — In the three-phase alternator, the windings have voltages generated in them which are 120 degrees out of phase. Three-phase alternators are most often used to generate AC power.

ALTERNATOR FREQUENCY — The frequency of the AC generated by an alternator depends upon the speed of rotation and the number of pairs of rotor poles. The voltage regulation of an alternator is poorer than that of a DC generator because of the IX_L drop in the armature winding.

Types of AC Motors

Since a major part of all electrical power generated is AC, many motors are designed for AC operation. AC motors can, in most cases, duplicate the operation of DC motors and are less troublesome to operate. This is because DC machines encounter difficulties due to the action of commutation which involves brushes, brush holders, neutral planes, etc. Many types of AC motors do not even use slip rings, with the result that they give trouble-free operation over long periods of time.

AC motors are particularly well suited for constant speed applications, since the speed is determined by the frequency of the AC applied to the motor terminals. AC motors are also made that have variable speed characteristics within certain limits.

AC motors can be designed to operate from a single-phase AC line or a multi-phase AC line. Whether the motor is single-phase or multi-phase, it operates on the same principle. This principle is that the AC applied to the motor generates a rotating magnetic field, and it is this rotating magnetic field that causes the rotor of the motor to turn.

AC motors are generally classified into two types: (1) the synchronous motor and (2) the induction motor. The synchronous motor is an alternator operated as a motor, in which three-phase AC is applied to the stator and DC is applied to the rotor. The induction motor differs from the synchronous motor in that it does not have its rotor connected to any source of power. Of the two types of AC motors mentioned, the induction motor is by far the most commonly used.

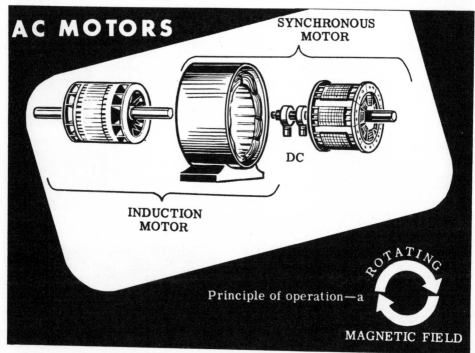

Principle of operation—a MAGNETIC FIELD

Rotating Field

Before learning how a rotating magnetic field will cause an energized rotor to turn, the thing for you to find out is how a rotating magnetic field can be produced. The schematic illustrates a three-phase stator to which three-phase AC is applied from a three phase source like the alternator you studied. The windings are connected in delta as shown. The two windings in each phase are wound in the same direction. At any instant the magnetic field generated by one particular phase depends upon the current through that phase. If the current is zero, the magnetic field is zero. If the current is a maximum, the magnetic field is a maximum. Since the currents in the three windings are 120 degrees out of phase, the magnetic fields generated will also be 120 degrees out of phase. Now, the three magnetic fields that exist at any instant will combine to produce one field, which acts upon the rotor. You will see on the following page that from one instant to the next, the magnetic fields combine to produce a magnetic field whose position shifts through a certain angle. At the end of one cycle of AC, the magnetic field will have shifted through 360 degrees, or one revolution.

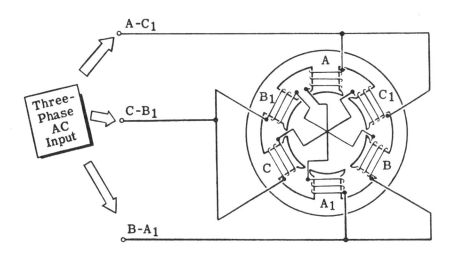

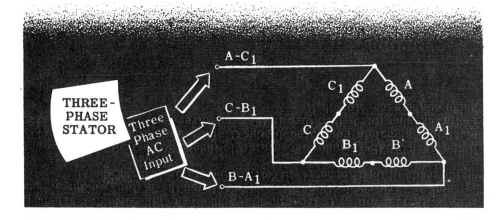

Rotating Field (continued)

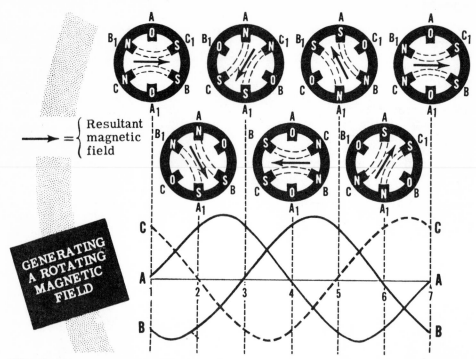

$\longrightarrow = \left\{ \begin{array}{l} \text{Resultant} \\ \text{magnetic} \\ \text{field} \end{array} \right.$

GENERATING A ROTATING MAGNETIC FIELD

The drawing shows the three current waveforms applied ·to the stator. These waveforms are 120 degrees out of phase with each other. The waveforms can represent either the three alternating magnetic fields generated by the three phases or the currents in the phases. The waveforms are lettered to correspond to their associated phase. Using the waveforms, we can combine the magnetic fields generated every 1/6 of a cycle (60 degrees) to determine the direction of the resultant magnetic field. At point 1, waveform C is positive and waveform B is negative. This means that the current flows in opposite directions through phases B and C. This establishes the magnetic polarity of phases B and C. The polarity is shown on the simplified diagram above point 1. Observe that B_1 is a north pole and B is a south pole, and C is a north pole while C_1 is a south pole. Since at point 1 there is no current flowing through phase A, its magnetic field is zero. The magnetic fields leaving poles B_1 and C will move toward the nearest south poles C_1 and B as shown. Since the magnetic fields of B and C are equal in amplitude, the resultant magnetic field will lie between the two fields and will have the direction as shown.

At point 2, 60 degrees later, the input current waveforms to phases A and B are equal and opposite, and waveform C is zero. You can see that now the resultant magnetic field has rotated through 60 degrees. At Point 3, waveform B is zero and the resultant magnetic field has rotated through another 60 degrees. From points 1 through 7 (corresponding to one cycle of AC), you can see that the resultant magnetic field rotates through one revolution for every cycle of AC supplied to the stator.

The conclusion is that, by applying three-phase AC to three windings symmetrically spaced around a stator, a rotating magnetic field is generated.

Synchronous Motor

The construction of the synchronous motor is essentially the same as the construction of the salient-pole alternator. In order to understand how the synchronous motor works, assume for the moment that the application of three-phase AC to the stator causes a rotating magnetic field to be set up around the rotor. Since the rotor is energized with DC, it acts like a bar magnet. If a bar magnet is pivoted within a magnetic field, it will turn until it lines up with the magnetic field. If the magnetic field turns, the bar magnet will turn with the field. If the rotating magnetic field is strong, it will exert a strong turning force on the bar magnet. The magnet will therefore be able to turn a load as it rotates in step with the rotating magnetic field.

THE ROTOR $TURNS$ WITH THE MAGNETIC FIELD

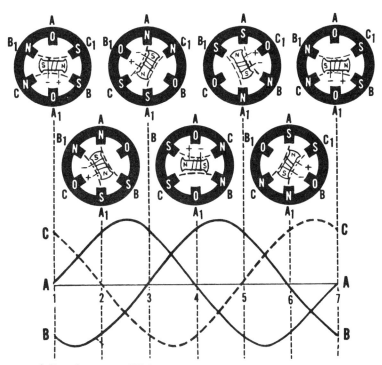

Advantages of Synchronous Motors

1. Used for constant speed
2. Used for power factor correction by over-exciting rotor field

Synchronous Motor (continued)

One of the disadvantages of a synchronous motor is that it cannot be started from a standstill by applying three-phase AC to the stator. The instant AC is applied to the stator, a high-speed rotating field appears immediately. This rotating field rushes past the rotor poles so quickly the rotor does not have a chance to get started.

The instant AC is applied to the stator of a synchronous motor, a high speed rotating magnetic field appears immediately. This rotating magnetic field rushes past the rotor poles so quickly that the rotor is repelled first in one direction and then the other. A synchronous motor in its pure form has no starting torque. Generally synchronous motors are started as squirrel cage motors; a squirrel cage winding is placed on the rotor as shown. To start the motor, the stator is energized and the DC supply to the field is not energized. The squirrel cage winding brings the rotor up to near synchronous speed; then the DC field is energized, locking the rotor in step with the rotating magnetic field.

Synchronous motors are used for loads that require constant speed from no-load to full-load.

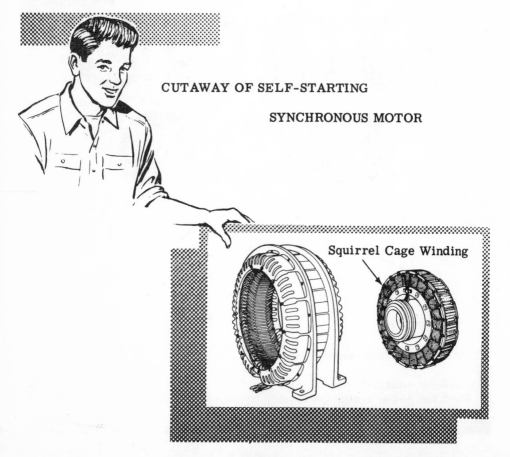

CUTAWAY OF SELF-STARTING

SYNCHRONOUS MOTOR

Squirrel Cage Winding

Induction Motors

The induction motor is the most commonly used AC motor because of its simplicity, its rugged construction and its low manufacturing cost. These characteristics of the induction motor are due to the fact that the rotor is a self-contained unit which is not connected to the external source of voltage. The induction motor derives its name from the fact that AC currents are induced in the rotor circuit by the rotating magnetic field in the stator.

The stator construction of the induction motor and the synchronous motor are almost identical but their rotors are completely different. The induction rotor is made of a laminated cylinder with slots in its surface. The windings in these slots are one of two types. The most common is called a "squirrel-cage winding." This winding is made up of heavy copper bars connected together at each end by a metal ring made of copper or brass. No insulation is required between the core and the bars because of the very low voltages generated in the rotor bars. The air gap between the rotor and stator is very small to obtain maximum field strength.

The other type of winding contains coils placed in the rotor slots. The rotor is then called a "wound rotor."

Regardless of the type of rotor used, the basic principle of operation is the same. The rotating magnetic field generated in the stator induces a magnetic field in the rotor. The two fields interact and cause the rotor to turn.

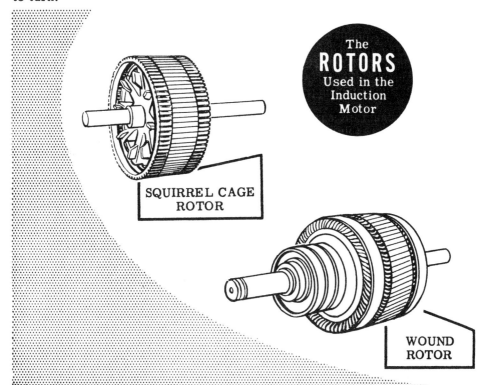

The ROTORS Used in the Induction Motor

SQUIRREL CAGE ROTOR

WOUND ROTOR

Induction Motors—How They Work

When **AC** is applied to the stator windings, a rotating magnetic field is generated. This rotating field cuts the bars of the rotor and induces a current in them. As you know from your study of meter movements and elementary motors, this induced current will generate a magnetic field around the conductors of the rotor which will try to line up with the stator field. However, since the stator field is rotating continuously, the rotor cannot line up with it but must always follow along behind it.

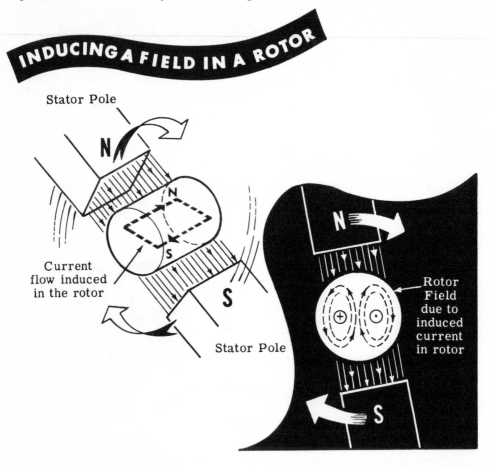

INDUCING A FIELD IN A ROTOR

Stator Pole

Current flow induced in the rotor

Stator Pole

Rotor Field due to induced current in rotor

As you know from Lenz's Law, any induced current tries to oppose the changing field which induces it. In the case of an induction motor, the change is the motion of the resultant stator field, and the force exerted on the rotor by induced current and field in the rotor is such as to try to cancel out the continuous motion of stator field—that is, the rotor will move in the same direction, as close to the moving stator field as its weight and its load will allow it.

Induction Motors—Slip

It is impossible for the squirrel-cage rotor of an induction motor to turn at the same speed as the rotating magnetic field. If the speeds were the same, no relative motion would exist between the two and no induced emf would result in the rotor. Without induced emf, a turning force would not be exerted on the rotor. The rotor must rotate at a speed less than that of the rotating magnetic field, if relative motion is to exist between the two. The percentage difference between the speed of the rotating stator field and the rotor speed is called "slip." The smaller the slip, the closer the rotor speed approaches the stator field speed.

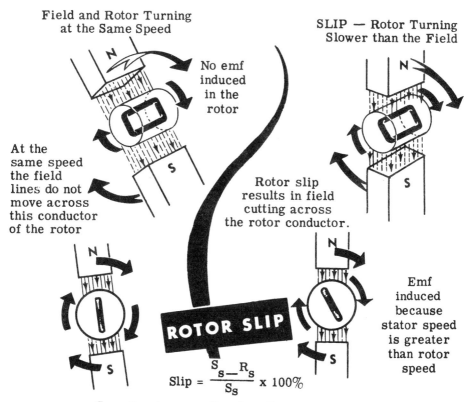

Field and Rotor Turning at the Same Speed

SLIP — Rotor Turning Slower than the Field

No emf induced in the rotor

At the same speed the field lines do not move across this conductor of the rotor

Rotor slip results in field cutting across the rotor conductor.

ROTOR SLIP

Emf induced because stator speed is greater than rotor speed

$$\text{Slip} = \frac{S_s - R_s}{S_s} \times 100\%$$

S_s = Synchronous Speed R_s = Rotor Speed

The speed of the rotor depends upon the torque requirements of the load. The bigger the load, the stronger the turning force needed to rotate the rotor. The turning force can increase only if the rotor induced emf increases and this emf can increase only if the magnetic field cuts through the rotor at a faster rate. To increase the relative speed between the field and rotor, the rotor must slow down. Therefore for heavier loads, the induction motor will turn slower than for lighter loads. Actually only a slight change in speed is necessary to produce the usual current changes required for normal changes in load. This is because the rotor windings have such a very low resistance. As a result, induction motors are called "constant speed motors."

Two Phase Induction Motors

Induction motors are designed for three-phase, two-phase, or single-phase operation. In each case the AC applied to the stator must generate a rotating field which will pull the rotor with it. You have already seen how three-phase AC, applied to a three-phase symmetrically distributed winding, will generate a rotating magnetic field.

A two-phase induction motor has its stator made up of two windings which are placed at right angles to each other around the stator. The simplified drawing illustrates a two-phase stator. The other drawing is a schematic of a two-phase induction motor. The dotted circle represents the short-circuited rotor winding.

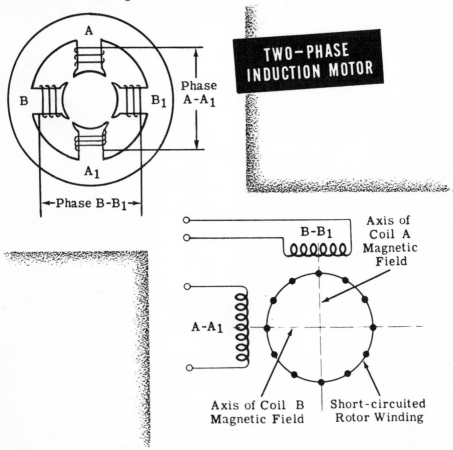

If the voltages applied to phases A-A_1 and B-B_1 are 90 degrees out of phase, the currents that will flow in the phases will be displaced by 90 degrees. Since the magnetic fields generated in the coils will be in phase with their respective currents, the magnetic fields will also be 90 degrees out of phase with each other. These two out-of-phase magnetic fields, whose coil axes are at right angles to each other will add together at every instant during their cycle to produce a resultant field which will rotate one revolution for each cycle of AC.

Two Phase Induction Motors (continued)

The diagram shows a graph of the two alternating magnetic fields which are displaced 90 degrees in phase. The waveforms are lettered to correspond to their associated phase. At position 1, the current flow and magnetic field in winding $A-A_1$ is a maximum and the current flow and magnetic field in winding $B-B_1$ is zero. The resultant magnetic field will therefore be in the direction of the winding $A-A_1$ axis. At the 45 degree point (position 2), the resultant magnetic field will lie midway between windings $A-A_1$ and $B-B_1$, since the coil currents and magnetic fields are equal in strength. At 90 degrees (position 3), the magnetic field in winding $A-A_1$ is zero and the magnetic field in winding $B-B_1$ is a maximum. Now the resultant magnetic field lies along the axis of the $B-B_1$ winding as shown. The resultant magnetic field has rotated through 90 degrees to get from position 1 to position 3.

At 135 degrees (position 4), the magnetic fields are again equal in amplitude. However, the magnetic field in winding $A-A_1$ has reversed its direction. The resultant magnetic field, therefore, lies midway between the windings and points in the direction as shown. At 180 degrees (position 5), the magnetic field is zero in winding $B-B_1$ and a maximum in winding $A-A_1$. The resultant magnetic field will, therefore, lie along the axis of winding $A-A_1$ as shown.

From 180 degrees to 360 degrees (positions 5 to 9), the resultant magnetic field rotates through another half-cycle and completes a revolution.

Thus by placing two windings at right angles to each other and by exciting these windings with voltages 90 degrees out of phase, a rotating magnetic field will result.

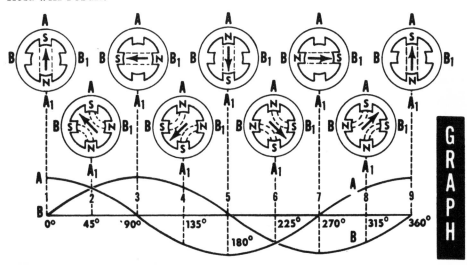

Generating a Rotating Magnetic Field

Single-Phase Motors

A single-phase induction motor has only one phase and runs on single-phase AC. This motor finds extensive use in applications which require small low-output motors. The advantage to using single-phase motors is that in small sizes they are less expensive to manufacture than other motor types. Also they eliminate the need for three-phase AC lines. Single-phase motors are used where small light-duty motors are required such as fans, refrigerators, portable drills, grinders, dish washers, etc.

Single-phase motors are divided into two groups: (1) induction motors and (2) series motors. Induction motors use the squirrel cage rotor and a suitable starting device. Series motors resemble DC machines because they have commutators and brushes.

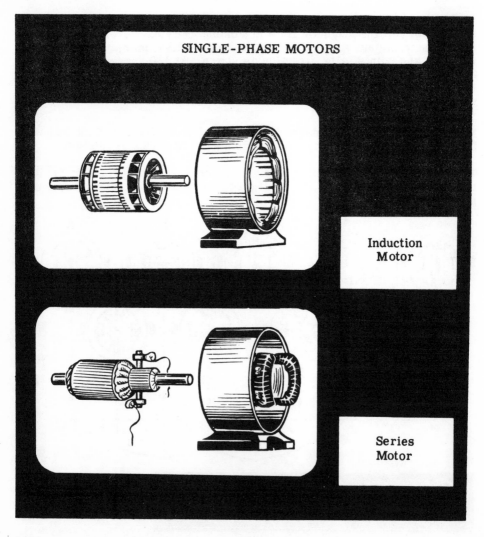

SINGLE-PHASE MOTORS

Induction
Motor

Series
Motor

Single-Phase Induction Motors

A single-phase induction motor has only one stator winding. This winding generates a field which alternates along the axis of the single winding, rather than rotating. If the rotor is stationary, the expanding and collapsing stator field induces currents in the rotor. These currents generate a rotor field exactly opposite in polarity to that of the stator. The opposition of the fields exerts a turning force on the upper and lower parts of the rotor trying to turn it 180 degrees from its position. Since these forces are exerted through the center of the rotor, the turning force is equal in each direction. As a result, the rotor does not turn.

However, if the rotor is started turning it will continue to rotate in the direction in which it is started, since the turning force in that direction is aided by the momentum of the rotor.

The rotor will increase speed until it turns nearly 180 degrees for each alternation of the stator field. Since slip is necessary to cause an induced rotor current, at maximum speed the rotor turns slightly less than 180 degrees each time the stator field reverses polarity.

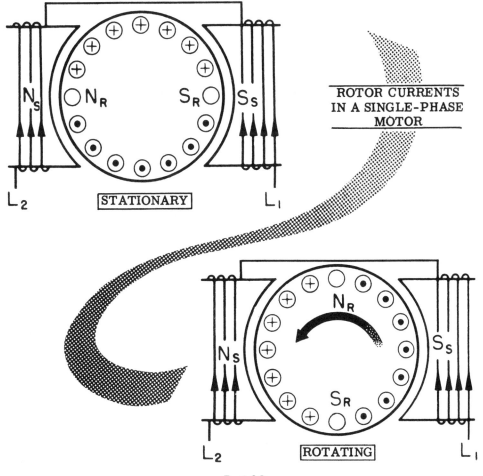

ROTOR CURRENTS
IN A SINGLE-PHASE
MOTOR

Split-Phase Induction Motors—Capacitor-Start

You have seen that once the single-phase motor is started turning it will
continue to rotate by itself. It is impractical to start a motor by turning it
over by hand, and so an electric device must be incorporated into the stator
circuit which will cause a rotating field to be generated upon starting.
Once the motor has started, this device can be switched out of the stator
as the rotor and stator together will generate their own rotating field to
keep the motor turning.

One type of induction motor which incorporates a starting device is called
a "split-phase induction motor." This motor uses combinations of inductance, capacitance and resistance to develop a rotating field.

The first type of split-phase induction motor that you will learn about is
the capacitor-start type. The diagram shows a simplified schematic of a
typical capacitor-start motor. The stator consists of the main winding and
a starting winding which is connected in parallel with the main winding and
spaced at right angles to it. The 90-degree electrical phase difference between the two windings is obtained by connecting the auxiliary winding in
series with a capacitor and starting switch. Upon starting, the switch is
closed, placing the capacitor in series with the auxiliary winding. The capacitor is of such a value that the auxiliary winding is effectively a
resistive-capacitive circuit in which the current leads the line voltage by
approximately 45 degrees. The main winding has enough resistance to
cause the current to lag the line voltage by approximately 45 degrees. The
two currents are therefore 90 degrees out of phase and so are the magnetic
fields which they generate. The effect is that the two windings act like a
two-phase stator and produce the revolving field required to start the motor.

When nearly full speed is obtained, a device cuts out the starting winding
and the motor runs as a plain single-phase induction motor. Since the
special starting winding is only a light winding, the motor does not develop
sufficient torque to start heavy loads. Split-phase motors, therefore, come
only in small sizes. Since a two-phase in-
duction motor is more efficient than a
single-phase motor, it is often desirable to
keep the auxiliary winding permanently in
the circuit so that the motor will run as a
two-phase induction motor. The starting
capacitor is usually quite large in order to
allow a large current to flow through the
auxiliary winding. The motor can thus build
up a large starting torque. When the motor
comes up to speed, it is not necessary that
the auxiliary winding continue to draw the
full starting current, and the capacitor can
be reduced. Therefore two condensers are
used in parallel for starting, and one is cut
out when the motor comes up to speed. Such
a motor is called a "capacitor-start,
capacitor-run induction motor."

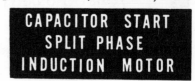

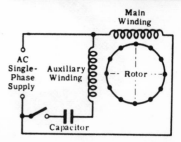

Split Phase Induction Motor—Resistance Start

Another type of split-phase induction motor is the resistance-start motor. This motor, in addition to having the regular main winding, has a starting winding which is switched in and out of the circuit just as it is in the capacitor start motor. The starting winding is positioned at right angles to the main winding. The electrical phase shift between the currents in the two windings is obtained by making the impedance of the windings unequal. The main winding has a high inductance and low resistance. The current therefore lags the voltage by a large angle. The starting winding has a comparatively low inductance and a high resistance. Here the current lags the voltage by a smaller angle. For example, suppose the current in the main winding lags the voltage by 70 degrees, and the current in the auxiliary winding lags the voltage by 40 degrees. The currents will therefore be out of phase by 30 degrees, and the magnetic fields will be out of phase by the same amount. Although the ideal angular phase difference is 90 degrees for maximum starting torque, the 30-degree phase difference will still generate a rotating field which will supply enough torque to start the motor. When the motor comes up to speed, a centrifugal switch disconnects the starting winding from the line.

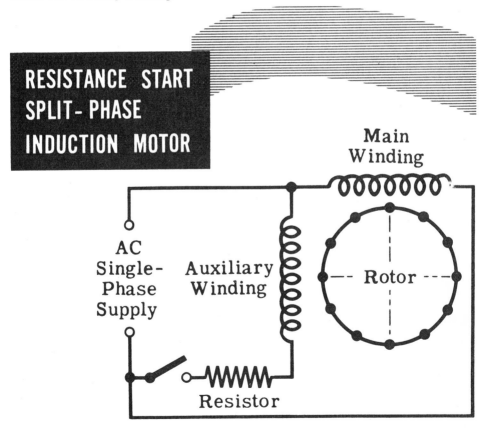

RESISTANCE START SPLIT-PHASE INDUCTION MOTOR

Main Winding

AC Single-Phase Supply

Auxiliary Winding

Rotor

Resistor

Shaded-Pole Induction Motors

The shaded-pole induction motor is a single-phase motor which uses a unique method to start the rotor turning. The effect of a moving magnetic field is produced by constructing the stator in a special way. This motor has projecting pole pieces just like DC machines. In addition, portions of the pole piece surfaces are surrounded by a copper strap called a "shading coil." The pole piece with the strap in place is shown in the illustration. The strap moves the field back and forth across the face of the pole piece in the following manner. As the alternating stator field starts increasing from zero degrees, the lines of force expand across the face of the pole piece and cut through the strap. A current is induced in the strap which generates a field to oppose the cutting action of the main field. Therefore, as the field increases to a maximum at 90 degrees, a large portion of the magnetic lines of force are concentrated in the unshaded portion of the pole. At 90 degrees the field reaches its maximum value. Since the lines of force have stopped expanding, no emf is induced in the strap and no opposing magnetic field is generated. As a result, the main field is uniformly distributed across the pole as shown. From 90 degrees to 180 degrees, the main field starts decreasing or collapsing inward. The opposition field generated in the strap opposes the collapsing field and the effect is to concentrate the lines of force in the shaded portion of the pole face as shown. Looking at the diagrams you can see that, from zero to 180 degrees, the main field has shifted across the pole face from the left to the right. From 180 degrees to 360 degrees, the main field goes through the same change as it did from zero to 180 degrees, but in the opposite direction. Since the direction of the field does not affect the way the shaded pole works, the motion of the field will be the same during the second half cycle as it was during the first half of the cycle.

The motion of the field from left to right produces a weak torque to start the motor. Due to the weak starting torque, shaded-pole motors are built in small sizes to drive small devices such as fans and relays.

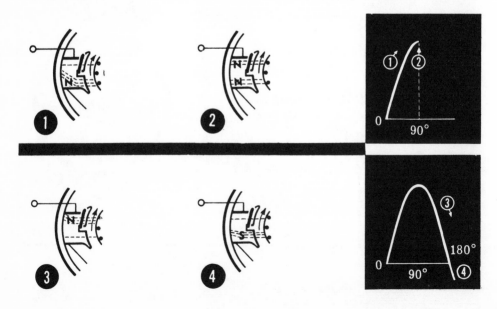

AC Series Motors

You learned that if the DC current through a series motor is reversed, the direction of rotation remains unchanged. When AC is applied to a series motor, the current through the armature and field change simultaneously and, therefore, the motor will rotate in one direction. The number of field turns in the AC series motor is less than in the DC series motor in order to decrease the reactance of the field, so that the required amount of current will flow. Cutting down the size of the field reduces the motor torque. Therefore the series AC motor is never built above fractional horsepower sizes for 60-cycle operation. The characteristics of the series AC motor are similar to those of the DC series motor. It is a varying-speed machine, with low speeds for large loads and high speeds for light loads. The starting torque is also very high. Fractional horsepower series motors are used for driving fans, electric drills and other small appliances.

Since the AC series motor has the same general characteristics as the DC series motor, a series motor has been designed which can operate both on AC and DC. This AC-DC motor is called a "universal motor" and finds wide application in small electric appliances. Universal motors operate at a lower efficiency than either the AC or DC series motor and are built in small sizes only.

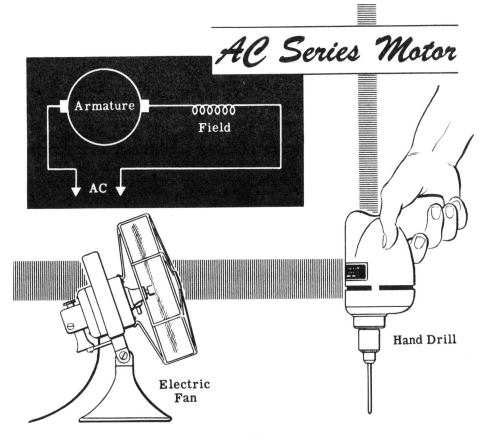

AC Series Motor

Armature

Field

AC

Hand Drill

Electric Fan

Synchro Motors and Generators

A synchro is similar to an AC motor in that it has a stator and a rotor and it requires AC in order to operate. However, an AC motor is used to turn a load, whereas synchros are used to transmit information in the form of electrical signals. Do not confuse synchros with synchronous motors— they perform completely different jobs.

A simple synchro system consists of a synchro generator (called a transmitter or G) and a synchro motor (called a receiver or M). Both the G and the M have five leads, two of which (labeled R_1 and R_2) supply the rotor with 117 volts AC from the line. The remaining leads, labeled S_1, S_2, and S_3, are connections brought out from the stator windings. The stator leads of the G connect directly to the stator leads of the M.

If the shaft of the synchro generator is turned 30 degrees clockwise, an electrical signal is generated in the G and transmitted to the synchro motor, causing its shaft to turn in the same direction and through the same angle as the generator shaft.

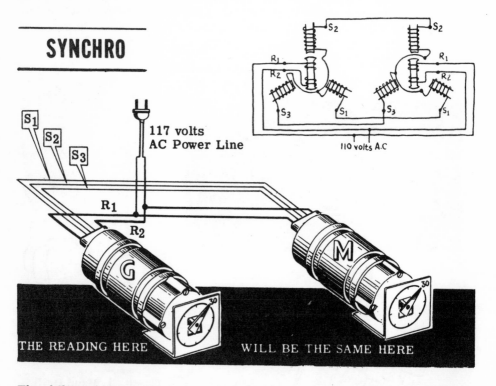

The ability of synchros to transmit electrically information about angular rotation, finds wide application—to transmit wind direction, compass bearing, gun bearing, etc. There are other types of synchros in addition to the synchro generator and motor. Synchros are identified by numbers such as 1G or 5M. The numeral indicates the size and the letter defines the type of synchro.

Demonstration—Synchros

The instructor connects the R_1 leads from both synchros to one side of the switch and the R_2 leads to the other side of the switch. Next the S leads of the motor and generator are connected together—S_1 to S_1, S_2 to S_2, S_3 to S_3.

The power cord is connected to the open DPST switch and plugged into the 117-volt AC power socket.

With the switch open, rotating the synchro generator shaft has no effect on the motor shaft.

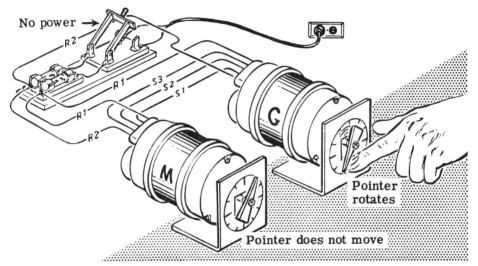

The instructor holds the generator shaft firmly and closes the power switch. Immediately the M rotor shaft turns until it is in the same position as the G rotor shaft. Now the instructor turns the generator shaft and the motor shaft duplicates its position and direction of rotation.

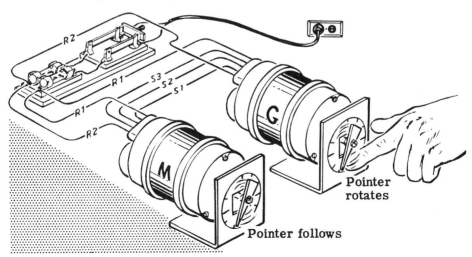

Review of AC Motors

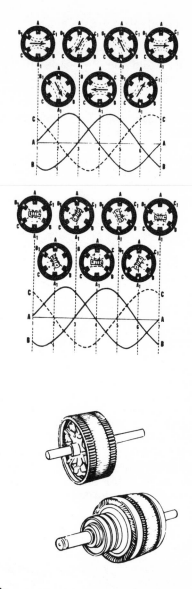

ROTATING FIELD — If three windings are placed around a stator frame,
and three phase AC is applied to the
windings, the magnetic fields generated in each of the three windings
will combine into a rotating magnetic field.

SYNCHRONOUS MOTOR — A synchronous motor uses a three-phase
stator to generate a rotating magnetic
field and an electromagnetic rotor
which is supplied with DC. The rotor
acts like a bar magnet and is attracted by the rotating stator field.
This attraction will exert a torque on
the rotor and cause it to rotate with
the field. Synchronous motors are
not self-starting and must be brought
up to near synchronous speed before
they can continue rotating by
themselves.

INDUCTION MOTOR — The induction
motor has the same stator as the synchronous motor. The rotor is different in that it does not require an
external source of power. Current is
induced in the rotor by the action of
the rotating field cutting through the
rotor conductors. This rotor current
generates a magnetic field which in-
teracts with the stator field, resulting in a torque being exerted on the
rotor causing it to rotate. The two
types of rotors used in induction
motors are the squirrel cage and
wound rotor.

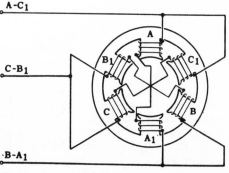

THREE-PHASE MOTORS — The magnetic fields generated in three-phase
AC motors are 120-degrees out of
phase. At any instant these fields
combine to produce one resultant field
which acts upon the rotor. The rotor
turns because the magnetic field shifts
its position through a certain angle.

5-110

Review of AC Motors (continued)

SLIP — The rotor of an induction motor rotates at less than synchronous
speed in order that the rotating field
can cut through the rotor conductors
and induce a current flow in them.
This percentage difference between
the synchronous speed and the rotor
speed is known as slip. Slip varies
very little with load changes and
therefore the induction motor is considered to be a constant speed motor.

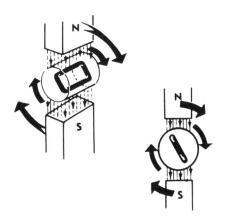

TWO-PHASE INDUCTION MOTOR —
Induction motors are designed for
three-phase, two-phase and single-
phase operation. The three-phase
stator is exactly the same as the
three-phase stator of the synchronous
motor. The two-phase stator generates a rotating field by having two
windings which are positioned at right
angles to each other. If the voltages
applied to the two windings are 90 degrees out of phase, a rotating field
will be generated.

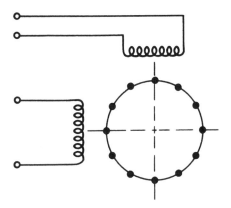

SINGLE-PHASE INDUCTION MOTOR—
A single-phase induction motor has
only one stator winding and therefore
the magnetic field generated does not
rotate. A single-phase induction motor with only one winding cannot start
rotating by itself. Once the rotor is
started rotating, it will continue to rotate and come up to speed. A field is
set up in the rotating rotor which is
90 degrees out of phase with the stator
field. The two fields together produce
a rotating field which keeps the rotor
in motion.

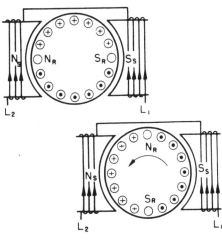

5-111

Review of AC Motors (continued)

CAPACITOR START, INDUCTION
MOTOR — In order to make a single-phase motor self-starting, a starting winding is added to the stator. If this starting winding is placed in series with a condenser across the same line as the running winding, the current in the starting winding will be out of phase with the current in the running winding. As a result, a rotating magnetic field will be generated and the rotor will rotate. Once the rotor comes up to speed, the starting winding circuit can be opened and the motor will continue running as a single-phase motor.

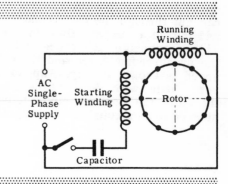

RESISTANCE START, INDUCTION
MOTOR — This motor has a starting winding in addition to the running winding. The starting winding has a different resistance than the running winding and therefore the current through the two windings will be out of phase. Since the currents are out of phase, the fields will be out of phase and a rotating field will result. When the motor comes up to speed, the starting winding is disconnected from the source of power and the motor continues turning as a single-phase induction motor.

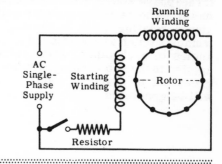

SHADED POLE INDUCTION MOTOR
— In this motor, a section of each pole face in the stator is shorted out by a metal strap. This has the effect of moving the magnetic field back and forth across the pole face. The moving magnetic field has the same effect as a rotating field and the motor is able to start up by itself.

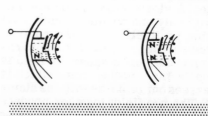

Relays

You learned in the DC motor section that a starting resistance is required
to limit the starting current of a motor to a safe value. Starting resistors
are incorporated into starting boxes which are either manual or automatic.
In the manual starting box, the starting resistance is cut out in steps by
hand. In the automatic starting box, which is called a "controller," a button
is pressed to start, stop or reverse the motor. Automatic circuits consisting of relays then take over and do the rest. Controllers are used with
AC motors as well as with DC motors.

The heart of the controller is the relay, which is an electrically operated
switch. Relays find extensive use in practically all types of electric and
electronic equipment and, therefore, their theory of operation is of interest.

The diagram on the left illustrates a very simple magnetic relay whose
essential parts are an electromagnet and a movable arm called an "armature." When current flows through the coil of the magnet, a magnetic field
is set up which attracts the iron arm of the armature to the core of the
magnet. The set of contacts on the armature and relay frame close, completing a circuit across terminals A and B. When the magnet is de-
energized, the return spring returns the armature to the open position and
the contacts open, breaking the circuit across terminals A and B. The
diagram shows only one set of contacts. However, there can be any number
of sets of contacts, depending upon the requirements of the circuit. The
relay shown on the left is called a "normally open relay" because the contacts are open when the relay is de-energized. The relay shown on the
right is a "normally closed relay" because the contacts are closed when
the relay is de-energized. When the relay is energized, the armature is
pulled to the magnet and the contacts open, breaking the circuit across
terminals A and B.

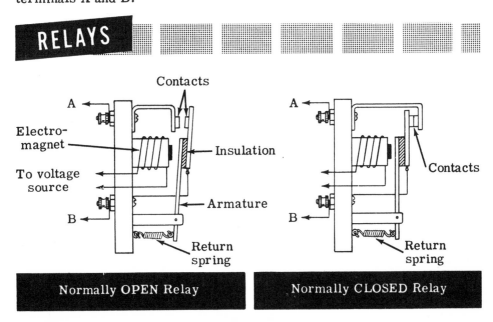

Normally OPEN Relay   Normally CLOSED Relay

Relay Circuits

Relays offer many advantages over the use of manually-operated switches. Relays make possible the control by a low voltage circuit of a high voltage (high current) circuit. For example, in the relay on the previous sheet, a high voltage circuit could be connected across terminals A and B. This circuit could be energized by applying a low voltage to the relay coil. Similarly, the high voltage circuit could be opened by removing the low voltage from the relay coil. Since the operator does not directly close or open the high voltage circuit, he is protected from high voltage shock and from a possible burn due to arcing at the switch.

Since the relay coil circuit is operated at low voltage and current, the switch for the relay circuit can be located at a point distant from the relay. By this means, an operator can turn equipment on or off from a remote location. For example, a code operator can key a transmitter located in another part of a ship, by using a code key and a relay. Whenever the operator pushes down on the key, the relay in the transmitter is energized and its contacts turn on the high voltage to the transmitter.

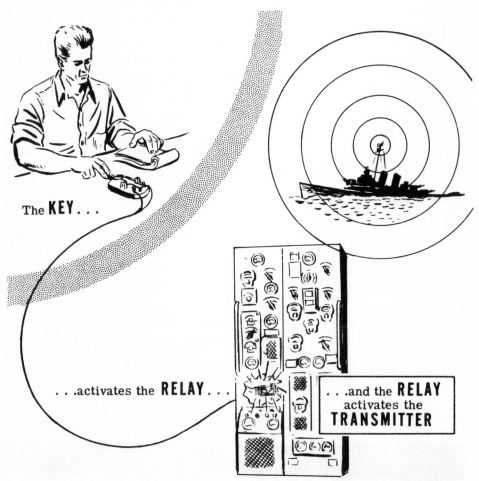

The **KEY** . . .

. . .activates the **RELAY** . . .

. . .and the **RELAY**
activates the
TRANSMITTER

Motor Controller

One application of magnetic relays is the "controller circuit." The diagram shows a simple "across-the-line" type controller used with small DC motors that require no starting resistor. There are two relays in this controller, the starting relay and the overload relay. The starting relay is a normally open relay and it has two sets of contacts in series with the motor and a set of contacts in parallel with the start button. The overload relay is a normally closed relay and it has one set of contacts, in series with the coil of the starting relay.

The diagram shows the circuit condition when the motor is stopped. When the start button is pressed, its contacts complete the circuit of the starting relay through the limiting resistor and the normally closed overload relay contacts. The starting relay coil is energized and closes its contacts. The contacts in parallel with the start button short out the start button, and when this button is released, these contacts maintain a complete circuit which keeps the starting relay coil energized. The starting relay contacts which are in series with the motor and the overload relay coil, allow current to flow through the motor, and it begins to rotate. To stop the motor, the stop button is pressed. This de-energizes the starting relay coil and its contacts open, stopping the motor. These contacts remain open until the start button is closed again.

The overload relay is designed so that normal motor current will not generate a strong enough field in its coil to open the overload relay contacts. However, if the motor draws excessive current, the field in the overload relay coil will be strong enough to pull open these contacts, which are then held open by a locking device. With the overload contacts open, the starting relay coil is de-energized and its contacts open, stopping the motor. After the cause of the overload has been removed and the motor is ready to be turned on again, the overload contacts are reset in their closed position by a manual reset button. The motor can then be started by pressing the start button.

DC MOTOR STARTER

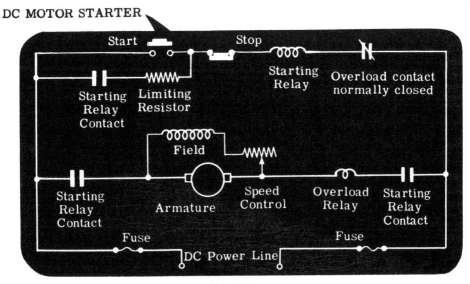

Thermal Relay

The controller illustrated on the previous sheet used two magnetic relays —one for starting and one as an overload protection for the motor. Overload protection for motors may also be obtained by using fuses and thermal relays. A fuse is simply a piece of metal with a low melting point, inserted in series with a circuit which is to be protected. When the current through the circuit exceeds the maximum safe value, the fuse metal melts, breaking the circuit. Although a fuse is simple and very inexpensive, it has the disadvantage that it is almost instantaneous in its action (when the current exceeds the maximum value, if only for an instant, the fuse blows). Therefore a fuse cannot be used to protect motors, because the starting current is many times higher than the operating current.

Thermal relays overcome this disadvantage. One type of thermal overload relay is made of two different metals which have different rates of expansion. The two metals are welded together and the unit is called a "bi-metal." When a bi-metal is heated, it will bend due to the unequal rates of expansion of the two metals. This bi-metal is placed near a heating element through which the current to the motor passes. One end of the bi-metal is fixed and the other end is free to bend when the temperature changes. When an overload current persists long enough, one end of the bi-metal bends and opens a set of normally closed contacts which are in series with the motor. The motor circuit is broken and the motor stops. The bi-metal is held open by a catch which must be manually reset to close the contacts.

Another type of thermal overload relay for motors makes use of a solder-like material which, under normal operating conditions, is solid and firmly holds a ratchet in place. When the heater coil overheats due to overload, the solder substance melts. The ratchet acting under spring tension is now free to turn and release the reset button, breaking the motor circuit. The motor can be started again by pressing the reset button.

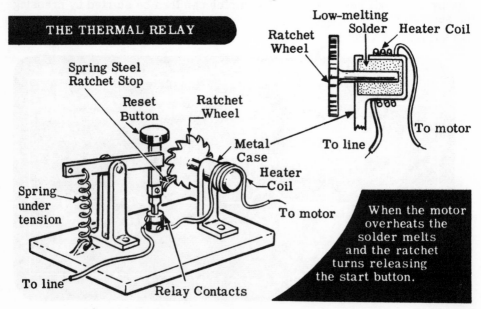

THE THERMAL RELAY

Low-melting Solder   Heater Coil
Ratchet Wheel

Spring Steel Ratchet Stop
Reset Button   Ratchet Wheel
Metal Case
To line
To motor

Spring under tension
Heater Coil
To motor

To line   Relay Contacts

When the motor overheats the solder melts and the ratchet turns releasing the start button.

Thermal Relay (continued)

One application of the thermal overload relay is in a common manually-operated, across-the-line starter used with AC motors. The illustration shows the schematic of the starter for a three-phase motor as you would find it drawn inside of the starting box cover. The line leads are connected to terminals L_1, L_2 and L_3, and the motor leads are connected to terminals T_1, T_2 and T_3. The symbols between points L_1 and T_1 represent the contacts and heating elements. The relay used in this particular starter is the solder type. When the start button is depressed, the three contacts are closed and the motor, energized with three-phase AC, rotates. If the motor is overloaded and draws excess current, the heating elements melt the solder in the relay and release the start switch. The contacts open and the motor stops. The solder quickly solidifies and the overload relay is ready to operate again.

When the stop button is pushed, it releases the start button and the contacts open, stopping the motor.

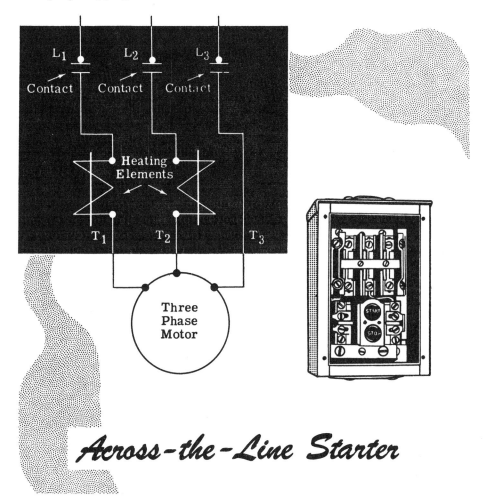

Across-the-Line Starter

Circuit Breakers

Circuit breakers are magnetic-type overload relays which are designed to protect circuits from overloads and other abnormal conditions—such as voltage failure and reversed current. Since circuit breakers are basically relays, they have many of the advantages of relays. Specifically, they are fast acting, may be remotely controlled and can be adjusted to operate on different values of current.

One type of circuit breaker which is very often encountered and has characteristics common to all types, is the open-type circuit breaker illustrated below. This circuit breaker has three sets of contacts—the main contact and two auxiliary contacts. The main contact (A) is made of thin strips of copper pressed very closely together and curved into the form of an arch. This construction allows the contacts to close in a wiping action and to fit evenly over the outer surface. The auxiliary contact (C), called an "arcing contact," has removable carbon tips fastened against long copper springs. The auxiliary contact (B) consists of a heavy copper spring with a removable copper tip.

The triggering mechanism in the circuit breaker is a magnetic coil which may be either in shunt or in series with the circuit. When the current through the coil exceeds a certain value, the coil moves a triggering bar, which permits the contacts to pull open, either by their own weight or as a result of spring action. When the breaker opens, the main contact opens first while the others are still making contact. The current, therefore, still has a path through the auxiliary contacts B and C, and the main contact (A) opens without arcing. The auxiliary contact (B) opens next, with a very small arc. The last to open is the auxiliary contact (C) where the most severe arcing occurs. The carbon tips are able to withstand the heat due to arcing and are not burned away as rapidly as the copper.

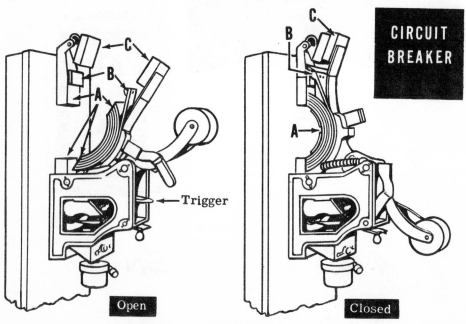

Open Closed

CIRCUIT BREAKER

Review

MAGNETIC RELAY — A magnetic relay is an electrically operated switch which consists of an electromagnet and a movable arm. When current flows through the coil, a magnetic field is set up which attracts the movable arm to the core of the magnet. This causes a set of contacts on the arm and relay frame to close, completing a circuit. When the coil is de-energized, the return spring pulls back the arm and the relay contacts open. The contacts can be normally closed or normally open.

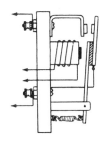

THERMAL OVERLOAD RELAY — Thermal overload relays protect a circuit from overheating. One type consists of a bi-metal strip, in which two metals having different rates of expansion are welded together. When the bi-metal is heated it bends, causing a set of contacts to open. Another type of thermal relay consists of a ratchet held in place in a container filled with solder. When the coil overheats the solder melts, releasing the ratchet which in turn releases the reset button.

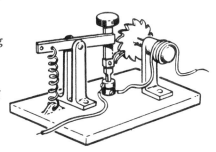

CIRCUIT BREAKER — Circuit breakers are magnetic-type overload relays which are designed to protect circuits from overloads, voltage failure or current reversal. When the current through the magnetic coil of the breaker exceeds a certain value, the triggering mechanism is released, and the contacts are pulled apart by means of a weight or spring action, thus opening the circuit.

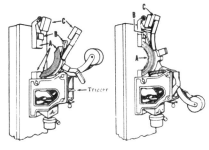

INDEX TO VOL. 5

(Note: A cumulative index covering all five volumes in this series will be found immediately following this index to Vol. 5.)

CUMULATIVE INDEX

(Note: The first number in each entry identifies the *volume* in which the information is to be found; the second number identifies the *page*.)

CUMULATIVE INDEX

CUMULATIVE INDEX